KU-782-583

Engineering Fluid Mechanics

JOHN J. BERTIN
University of Texas at Austin

Prentice-Hall, Inc., Englewood Cliffs, New Jersey 07632

Library of Congress Cataloging in Publication Data

Bertin, John J. (1938-)
  Engineering fluid mechanics.

  Includes bibliographical references and index.
  1. Fluid mechanics.   I. Title.
  TA357.B47   1984   620.1′06   83-9694
  ISBN 0-13-278812-8

Editorial/production supervision: *Raeia Maes*
Cover design: *20/20 Services Inc.* (Mark Berghash)
Manufacturing buyer: *Anthony Caruso*

© **1984 by Prentice-Hall, Inc., Englewood Cliffs, New Jersey 07632**

All rights reserved. No part of this book
may be reproduced, in any form or by any means,
without permission in writing from the publisher.

UNIVERSITY OF BRADFORD
LIBRARY
19 MAR 1985

ACCESSION No.
0278742001

CLASS No.
M 532 BER

LOCATION

Printed in the United States of America

10 9 8 7 6 5 4 3 2 1

√ ISBN   0-13-278812-8

Prentice-Hall International, Inc., *London*
Prentice-Hall of Australia Pty. Limited, *Sydney*
Editora Prentice-Hall do Brasil, Ltda., *Rio de Janeiro*
Prentice-Hall Canada Inc., *Toronto*
Prentice-Hall of India Private Limited, *New Delhi*
Prentice-Hall of Japan, Inc., *Tokyo*
Prentice-Hall of Southeast Asia Pte. Ltd., *Singapore*
Whitehall Books Limited, *Wellington, New Zealand*

Engineering
Fluid
Mechanics

*This book is dedicated to my family whose love and encouragement
provide an environment which makes this text possible.
To my parents, to my wife, Mary,
and to my children, Thomas, Randy, Elizabeth, and Michael.*

Contents

CHAPTER SIX

Dynamics of an Incompressible, Viscous Flow   216

CHAPTER SEVEN

Incompressible, Viscous Boundary Layers   256

CHAPTER ELEVEN

Computational Fluid Dynamics   410

CHAPTER TWELVE

Turbomachinery   427

APPENDIX

Conversion Factors   449

Index   453

Preface

This book is designed for use in introductory and intermediate courses in fluid mechanics for undergraduate students of mechanical engineering, of civil engineering, and of aerospace engineering. Although it is presumed that the reader has had basic courses in physics and in mathematics, including partial differential equations, problems introducing concepts involving vectors and the solution of differential equations are discussed in detail. Thus, the book is intended to be a self-contained text. The general approach taken in the book is to present a background discussion of each new topic followed by a presentation of the theory. The assumptions (and, therefore, the restrictions) incorporated into the development of the theory are carefully noted. The applications of the theory are illustrated by working example problems. Because engineers encounter some situations where English units are used and other situations where SI units are used, examples and problem exercises are divided between the two systems. An extensive compilation of conversion factors between SI units and English units are presented in the Appendix.

Fundamental concepts and fluid properties are presented in Chapter 1. The pressure field and the resultant forces in a static fluid are presented in Chapter 2. Chapter 3 is devoted to the continuity equation, i.e., the conservation of mass, and includes examples of problems that can be solved using only the continuity equation. The equations describing the conservation of linear momentum and of angular momentum are presented in Chapter 4. Problems that can be solved using only these two equations, i.e., continuity and conservation of momentum, are discussed in Chapter 4 (general applications), Chapter 5 (incompressible, inviscid flow), Chapter 6 (incompressible, viscous flow in a duct), and Chapter 7 (incompressible, viscous boundary-layer flow). Problems requiring a knowledge of the temperature field are discussed in Chapter 8 which is devoted to the energy equation and its application to heat-transfer problems and compressible flows. Chapters

9 through 12 treat specialized topics: open channel flows, the dynamics of a compressible flow field, computational fluid dynamics, and turbomachinery. Certain topics may be of special interest to one reader (type of engineer), while other topics would be more relevant to another type of engineer. Whole chapters can be by-passed without compromising the reader's understanding of other chapters. Furthermore, many chapters contain advanced material that can be omitted, if desired. The discussion of computational fluid dynamics in Chapter 11 is intended to be introductory. Basic concepts are introduced and problems solved. To best use this chapter, the reader should code some of the concepts and sample problems on a computer.

The author would like to thank his many colleagues for their help in preparing this text. Some provided suggestions; others provided photographs and illustrations; and some provided both. The author would also like to thank Professor Ronald L. Panton of the University of Texas at Austin, Professor Charles Dalton of the University of Houston, and Dr. William L. Oberkampf of the Sandia National Laboratories who read portions of the manuscript and offered suggestions for its improvement. The author would also like to thank Iraj Amirkabirian of the University of Texas at Austin who proofread the manuscript and helped prepare the solutions manual. The author is also indebted to Mrs. Liz Rich for typing the many drafts of the manuscript and Janet Brooks for preparing the figures for the manuscript.

John J. Bertin

Engineering
Fluid
Mechanics

CHAPTER ONE

Fundamental Concepts and Fluid Properties

Fluid mechanics is the science dealing with the determination of the forces acting on fluid particles and their response to those forces. The resultant flow pattern depends not only on the forces acting on the fluid particles, but on the properties of the fluid and the boundaries of the flow domain. The boundaries may be either solid surfaces or other fluids.

There are numerous, very different design applications in which the engineer must solve a fluid mechanics problem. The engineer may need to determine the velocity field, the pressure field, and/or the temperature field. To determine the forces and moments that act on an object located in a moving stream or on a vehicle moving through a fluid, we need to know the velocity and the pressure distributions as a function of space and time. With the velocity field and pressure field known, the engineer can determine the aerodynamic forces acting on an automobile, a high-rise office building, or an airplane. Such solutions are needed to determine the forces acting on offshore structures and on pipelines that transport liquids cross-country or around a processing plant. For other applications, the engineer must determine the temperature field, in addition to the velocity field and the pressure field. This is the case when the engineer is designing a heat exchanger or the thermal protection system for a reentry vehicle such as the Space Shuttle.

Because flow patterns are often very complex, it may be necessary to use both experimental investigations and theoretical analysis to obtain sufficient understanding of the resultant flow. Furthermore, it may be necessary to introduce simplifying approximations into the theoretical description of the flow to be able to obtain any solution at all. The validity of the simplifying approximations for a particular application should be verified experimentally. Thus, it is important to understand the fundamental laws that govern fluid motion so that we can relate the theoretical solutions obtained using approximate flow models with the experimental results. This becomes especially important when one must account for two orders-of-magnitude changes in geometric scale and for considerable changes in the flow conditions when extrapolating from the experimental conditions to the prototype (or design) conditions.

CONCEPT OF A FLUID

From the point of view of fluid mechanics, matter can be in one of two states, either solid or fluid. The technical distinction between these two states lie in their response to an applied shear, or tangential, stress. A solid can resist a shear stress by a static deformation; a fluid cannot. A *fluid* is a substance that deforms continuously under the action of shearing forces. An important corollary of this definition is that there can be no shear stresses acting on fluid particles if there is no relative motion within the fluid; that is, such fluid particles are not deformed. Thus, if the fluid particles are at rest or if they are all moving at the same velocity, there are no shear stresses in the fluid. This zero shear stress condition is known as the *hydrostatic stress condition.*

A fluid can be either a liquid or a gas. A liquid is composed of relatively close packed molecules with strong cohesive forces. As a result, a given mass of fluid will occupy a definite volume of space. If a liquid is poured into a container, it assumes the shape of the container up to the volume it occupies and will form a free surface in a gravitational field if unconfined from above. The upper (or free) surface is planar and perpendicular to the direction of gravity. Gas molecules are widely spaced with relatively small cohesive forces. Therefore, if a gas is placed in a closed container, it will expand until it fills the entire volume of the container. A gas has no definite volume. Thus, if it is unconfined, it forms an atmosphere that is essentially hydrostatic.

FLUID AS A CONTINUUM

When developing equations to describe the motion of a system of fluid particles, one can either define the motion of each and every molecule or one can define the average behavior of the molecules within a given elemental volume. The size of the elemental volume is important, but only in relation to the number of fluid particles contained in the volume and to the physical dimensions of the flow field. Thus, the elemental volume should be large compared with the volume occupied by a single molecule so that it contains a large number of molecules at any instant of time. Furthermore, the number of molecules within the volume will remain essentially constant even though there is a continuous flux of molecules through the boundaries. If the elemental volume is too large, there could be noticeable variation in the fluid properties determined statistically at various points in the volume.

In problems of interest to this text, our primary concern is not with the motion of individual molecules, but with the general behavior of the fluid. Thus, we are concerned with describing the fluid motion in spaces that are very large compared to molecular dimensions and that, therefore, contain a large number of molecules. The fluid in these problems may be considered to be a continuous material whose properties can be determined from a statistical average for the particles in the volume, that is, a macroscopic representation. The assumption of a continuous fluid is valid when the smallest volume of fluid that is of interest contains so many molecules that statistical averages are meaningful.

The number of molecules in a cubic meter of air at room temperature and at sea-level pressure is approximately 2.5×10^{25}. Thus, there are 2.5×10^{10} molecules in a cube 0.01 mm on a side. The mean-free path at sea level is 6.6×10^{-8} m. There are sufficient molecules in this volume for the fluid to be considered a continuum, and the fluid properties can be determined from statistical averages. However, at an altitude of 130 km, there are only 1.6×10^{17} molecules in a cube 1 m on a side. The mean-free path at this altitude is 10.2 m. Thus, at this altitude the fluid cannot be considered a continuum.

FUNDAMENTAL FLUID PROPERTIES

The motion of a given fluid in chemical equilibrium can be completely defined if one knows the pressure, temperature, and velocity as a function of space and time. The fundamental laws used to solve for fluid motion in a general problem are the following:

1. Law of conservation of mass (or the continuity equation).
2. Law of conservation of linear momentum.
3. Law of conservation of energy.

Thus, there is a system of three conservation equations (continuity, linear momentum, and energy) with three unknowns. The reader should note, as will be discussed in analyzing various flow fields, that one or another of these parameters may be assumed constant when obtaining solutions for certain flow situations. For example, in many applications temperature variations are so small that they do not affect the velocity field. Since the number of variables is reduced for such flows, the number of equations required to obtain the solution is likewise reduced. In analyzing other flow fields, additional variables, such as density, may appear in the formulation of the problem. However, since density is a function of pressure and temperature, it may be expressed in terms of the basic unknowns. Furthermore, because other fluid properties can be expressed as a function of pressure and temperature, the fluid motion can be formulated in terms of other combinations of variables (e.g., pressure, entropy, and velocity).

Temperature

We are all familiar with temperature in qualitative terms; that is, an object feels hot (or cold) to the touch. However, because of the difficulty in quantitatively defining temperature, we define the equality of temperature. Two bodies have equality of *temperature* when no change in any observable property occurs when they are in thermal contact. Furthermore, two bodies respectively equal in temperature to a third body must be equal

TABLE 1.1   U.S. STANDARD ATMOSPHERE, 1962

Altitude (km)	Pressure (mm Hg)	Temperature (K)	Density (kg/m³)	Viscosity (kg/s · m) × 10⁵	Speed of sound (m/s)
0	760.000	288.150	1.2250	1.7894	340.294
1	674.127	281.651	1.1117	1.7579	336.435
2	596.309	275.154	1.0066	1.7260	332.532
3	525.952	268.659	0.9092	1.6938	328.583
4	462.491	262.166	0.8194	1.6612	324.589
5	405.395	255.676	0.7364	1.6282	320.545
6	354.161	249.187	0.6601	1.5949	316.452
7	308.315	242.700	0.5900	1.5612	312.306
8	267.409	236.215	0.5258	1.5271	308.105
9	231.024	229.733	0.4671	1.4926	303.848
10	198.765	223.252	0.4135	1.4577	299.532
11	170.263	216.774	0.3648	1.4223	295.154
12	145.508	216.650	0.3119	1.4216	295.069
13	124.357	216.650	0.2666	1.4216	295.069
14	106.286	216.650	0.2279	1.4216	295.069
15	90.846	216.650	0.1948	1.4216	295.069
16	77.653	216.650	0.1665	1.4216	295.069
17	66.378	216.650	0.1423	1.4216	295.069
18	56.744	216.650	0.1216	1.4216	295.069
19	48.150	216.650	0.1040	1.4216	295.069
20	41.473	216.650	0.0889	1.4216	295.069
21	35.470	217.581	0.0618	1.4267	295.703
22	30.359	218.574	0.0645	1.4322	296.377
23	26.004	219.567	0.0550	1.4376	297.049
24	22.290	220.560	0.0469	1.4430	297.720
25	19.121	221.552	0.0401	1.4484	298.389
26	16.414	222.544	0.0343	1.4538	299.056
27	14.101	223.536	0.0293	1.4592	299.722
28	12.123	224.527	0.0251	1.4646	300.386
29	10.429	255.518	0.0215	1.4699	301.048
30	8.978	226.509	0.0184	1.4753	301.709

in temperature to each other. It follows that an arbitrary scale of temperature can be defined in terms of a convenient property of a standard body.

Pressure

Because of random motion due to their thermal energy, individual molecules of a fluid will continuously strike a surface that is placed in the fluid. These collisions occur even though the surface is at rest relative to the fluid. By Newton's second law, a force is exerted on the surface equal to the time rate of change of the momentum of the rebounding molecules. *Pressure* is the magnitude of this force per unit area of surface. Although the force has direction, pressure has none. Thus, pressure, which is a property of the fluid at the point in question, is a scalar quantity. Since a fluid that is at rest cannot sustain tangential forces, the force exerted by the pressure on the surface must act in the direction

TABLE 1.1 (CONTINUED)   ENGLISH UNITS

Altitude (kft)	Pressure (p/p_0)	T (°R)	Density (ρ/ρ_0)	Viscosity (μ/μ_0)	Speed of sound (ft/s)
0	1.00000	518.67	1.0000	1.00000	1116.45
5	0.83209	500.84	0.8617	0.97307	1097.10
10	0.68783	483.03	0.7386	0.94570	1077.40
15	0.56459	465.22	0.6295	0.91786	1057.36
20	0.45991	447.42	0.5332	0.88953	1036.93
25	0.37158	429.62	0.4486	0.86070	1016.10
30	0.29754	411.84	0.3747	0.83135	994.85
35	0.23596	394.06	0.3106	0.80144	973.14
40	0.18577	389.97	0.2471	0.79447	968.08
45	0.14623	389.97	0.1945	0.79447	968.08
50	0.11512	389.97	0.1531	0.79447	968.08
55	0.09063	389.97	0.1206	0.79447	968.08
60	0.07137	389.97	0.0949	0.79447	968.08
65	0.05620	389.97	0.0747	0.79447	968.08
70	0.04429	392.25	0.0586	0.79835	970.90
75	0.03496	394.97	0.0459	0.80298	974.26
80	0.02765	397.69	0.0361	0.80760	977.62
85	0.02190	400.42	0.0284	0.81219	980.95
90	0.01738	403.14	0.0224	0.81678	984.28
95	0.01381	405.85	0.0177	0.82134	987.59
100	0.01100	408.57	0.0140	0.82589	990.90

The corresponding sea-level values are:

$p_0 = 2116.22$ lbf/ft^2

$\rho_0 = 0.076474$ lbm/ft$^3 = 0.002376$ slugs/ft^3

$\mu_0 = 1.2024 \times 10^{-5}$ lbm/ft · s $= 3.740 \times 10^{-7}$ lbf · s/ft^2

perpendicular to that surface. Furthermore, the pressure acting at a point in a fluid at rest is the same in all directions.

From the definition of the word static, it is clear that a fluid at rest is a static medium. However, if the fluid particles, when viewed as a continuum, are either all at rest or all moving with the same velocity, the fluid is said to be a *static medium*. Thus, the term *static fluid properties* may be applied to situations in which the elements of the fluid are moving, providing there is no relative motion between finite elements. Since there is no relative motion between adjacent layers of the fluid, there are no shear forces. With no relative motion between fluid elements, the viscosity of the fluid is of no concern. For these inviscid flows, the only forces acting on the surface of a fluid element are the pressure forces.

Standard atmospheric pressure at sea level is defined as the pressure that can support a column of mercury 760 mm in length when the density of the mercury is 13.5951 g/

cm^3 and the acceleration due to gravity is the standard value. The standard atmospheric pressure at sea level is 1.01325×10^5 N/m^2.

Atmospheric pressure decreases with vertical distance from sea level (i.e., altitude). Atmospheric pressure is presented as a function of altitude in Table 1.1. These values are taken from the *U.S. Standard Atmosphere, 1962* (Ref. 1.1). For all practical purposes, this atmosphere is in agreement with the *International Civil Aviation Organization* (ICAO) *Standard Atmosphere* over their common altitude range.

The magnitude of the pressure is expressed relative to a reference level. The two most common reference levels are absolute zero and the local atmospheric pressure. When pressure is expressed as the difference between its value and absolute zero, that is, a complete vacuum, it is called an *absolute pressure*. When pressure is expressed as the difference between its value and the local atmospheric value, it is called a *gage pressure*. If the difference is negative, the difference is called *vacuum pressure*. The relationships of these pressure levels are illustrated in Fig. 1.1.

Many devices are available for measuring pressure. All these devices take advantage of the fact that pressure applied to a finite area of material causes a force that will produce a stress and/or a displacement in the material. These mechanical effects can then be quantified in one of several different ways. Devices that can be used to measure pressure are shown in Figs. 1.2 and 1.3. A Bourdon-tube device, such as that illustrated in Fig. 1.2, is a relatively simple, reliable device that provides a direct displacement measurement. The deflection can be measured by a linkage attached to a calibrated dial-gage pointer. If the tube and linkage assembly are located in a vacuum environment, the device provides a measure of absolute pressure. More often the casing in which the tube and linkage assembly are located is not airtight, and the instrument provides a measure of gage pressure.

The displacement (or stress) of the sensing element can be measured by electrical

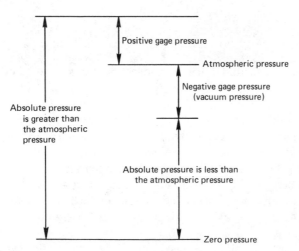

Figure 1.1 Illustration of terms used in pressure measurements.

Section AA

Flattened tube deflects outward under pressure

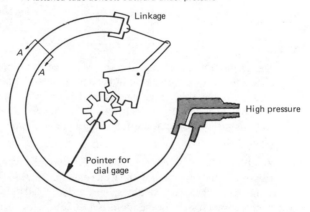

Figure 1.2 Photographs and sketch of a Bourdon-tube device for mechanical measurement of gage pressure.

means. Photographs of two typical electromechanical transducers are presented in Fig. 1.3. For both transducers, the tube that can be seen extending from each instrument on the side away from the sensing element exposes the interior surface of the sensing element to atmospheric pressure. Thus, both transducers provide a measure of gage pressure. The diaphragm of the transducer designed to measure unsteady pressures is installed flush with the wall and reacts almost instantaneously to a change in the local pressure. Since the dynamic response is excellent, these sensors are used to measure rapid transient-pressure measurements such as occur in blast-wave passage or turbulent flows.

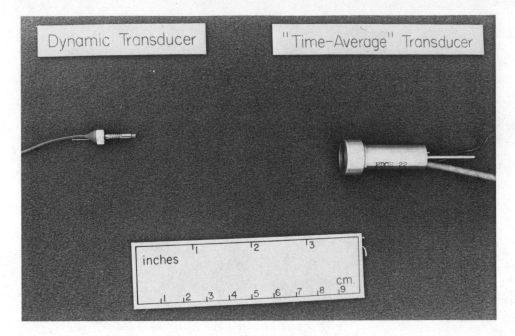

Figure 1.3 Photograph of pressure transducers.

Example 1.1

The output from a differential transducer used in a laboratory experiment indicates that the local pressure (at a specific location on the model) is 4.50×10^3 N/m² below the atmospheric value. The atmospheric pressure in the laboratory is determined using a mercury barometer. The column of mercury in the barometer is 75.2 cm in length. Calculate the absolute pressure and the gage pressure in the following units: (a) N/m², (b) bars, and (c) lbf/in.², which is often written psi.

Solution. The 75.2-cm column of mercury in the barometer indicates that the atmospheric pressure in the room during the experiment is 752/760 = 0.98947 of the standard sea-level value. Since the standard atmospheric value is 1.01325×10^5 N/m² or 14.696 lbf/in², the atmospheric pressure in the room is 1.00258×10^5 N/m² or 14.541 lbf/in.².

For the units of part (a), the gage pressure is that given by the differential transducer, that is, -4.50×10^3 N/m² or 4.50×10^3 N/m² vacuum. The absolute pressure is

$$p = 1.00258 \times 10^5 - 0.04500 \times 10^5 = 0.95758 \times 10^5 \text{ N/m}^2 \text{ (abs)}$$

In order to express the pressure in the units of part (b), note that the unit N/m² is also known as the pascal, with the abbreviation Pa. Furthermore, a pressure of 10^5 Pa is called 1 bar. Thus, the gage pressure is

$$4.50 \times 10^3 \text{ Pa} \times \frac{1 \text{ bar}}{10^5 \text{ Pa}} = 4.50 \times 10^{-2} \text{ bar vacuum} = 45.0 \text{ mbar vacuum}$$

The millibar units for pressure are often used in meteorological applications. The absolute pressure is 0.95758 bar.

In psi, the units for part (c), the gage pressure is

$$(4.50 \times 10^3 \text{ N/m}^2) \frac{14.696 \text{ psi}}{1.01325 \times 10^5 \text{ N/m}^2} = 0.653 \text{ psi vacuum}$$

The absolute pressure is 13.889 lbf/in.[2] (abs).

Note: If the pressure is not specifically stated to be a gage pressure, the reader should assume that the value given is the absolute pressure.

Example 1.2

If the atmosphere corresponds to the U.S. Standard Atmosphere, use Table 1.1 to calculate the altitude of the laboratory of Example 1.1 relative to sea level.

Solution.   At sea level, the standard atmospheric pressure is 760 mm Hg and, at 1 km, it is 674.127 mm Hg. Thus, atmospheric pressure decreases by 85.873 mm Hg over 1 km. Since the atmospheric pressure in the laboratory is 8 mm Hg below the standard sea-level pressure, the laboratory is at an altitude of

$$8 \text{ mm Hg} \frac{1000 \text{ m}}{85.873 \text{ mm Hg}} = 93.2 \text{ m}$$

above sea level.

Density

The *density* of a fluid at a point in space is the mass of the fluid contained in an incremental volume surrounding the point. As is the case when evaluating other fluid properties, the incremental volume must be large compared to molecular dimensions yet very small relative to the dimensions of the vehicle whose flow field we seek to analyze. Thus, provided that the fluid may be assumed to be a continuum, the density at a point is defined as

$$\rho = \lim_{\delta(\text{vol}) \to 0} \frac{\delta(\text{mass})}{\delta(\text{volume})} \tag{1.1}$$

The dimensions of density are mass/(length)^3.

In general, the density of a gas is a function of the composition of the gas, its temperature, and its pressure. The relation

$$\rho(\text{composition}, T, p) \tag{1.2}$$

is known as an equation of state. For a thermally perfect gas, the equation of state is

$$\rho = \frac{p}{RT} \tag{1.3}$$

R, which has a particular value for each substance, is called the *gas constant.* The gas constant for air has the value 287.05 N · m/kg · K. The gas constants for selected gases are presented in Table 1.2.

TABLE 1.2 GAS CONSTANTS
OF SELECTED GASES

Gas	R (N · m/kg · K)
Air	287.05
Carbon dioxide	189.
Helium	2077.
Hydrogen	4127.
Methane	518.
Nitrogen	297.
Oxygen	260.

Example 1.3

Calculate the density of air when the pressure is 1.01325×10^5 N/m^2 and the temperature is 288.15 K. Since air at this pressure and temperature behaves as a perfect gas, we can use Eq. (1.3).

Solution

$$\rho = \frac{1.01325 \times 10^5 \text{ N/m}^2}{(287.05 \text{ N} \cdot \text{m/kg} \cdot \text{K})(288.15 \text{ K})}$$

$$= 1.2250 \text{ kg/m}^3$$

For vehicles that are flying at approximately 100 m/s, or less, the density of the air flowing past the vehicle is assumed constant when obtaining a solution for the flow field. Rigorous application of Eq. (1.3) would require that the pressure and temperature remain constant (or change proportionally) in order for the density to remain constant throughout the flow field. We know that the pressure around the vehicle is not constant, since the aerodynamic forces and moments in which we are interested are the result of pressure variations associated with the flow pattern. However, the assumption of constant density for velocities of 100 m/s is a valid approximation, because the pressure changes that occur from one point to another in the flow field are small relative to the absolute value of the pressure.

The density of a liquid usually decreases slightly when the temperature increases and increases moderately when the pressure increases. However, since these changes are very small for most of the flow problems discussed in this book, the density of a liquid will be assumed to be constant throughout the flow field. The density of water is 1000 kg/m^3 (i.e., 1.0 g/cm^3) at 4°C. The density of any other liquid can be calculated if its specific gravity σ is known. The specific gravity of a substance is defined as the ratio of its density to the density of a standard substance. The standard usually employed for liquids is water. The specific gravities of some common liquids are presented in Table 1.3.

Seawater is a mixture of water and salt. Therefore, to determine its density one must know the composition as well as the temperature and pressure. The composition of seawater is expressed in terms of its *salinity,* which is the weight of the dissolved salt

TABLE 1.3 SPECIFIC GRAVITIES OF SOME
COMMON LIQUIDS

Liquid	Specific gravity, σ	Temperature, °C
Benzene	0.899	0
Ethyl alcohol	0.807	0
Gasoline	0.66–0.72	—
Glycerine	1.260	0
SAE 30 oil	0.918	20
Castor oil	0.969	15
Turpentine	0.873	16
Kerosene	0.81	20
Seawater	1.034	20
Water	1.0000	4
Water	0.9982	20
Water	0.9584	100
Mercury	13.5951	—

divided by the weight of the mixture. For seawater whose average salinity is 0.035 (i.e., 35 parts per thousand), the average density is 1030 kg/m^3.

Specific Weight

The weight per unit volume of a fluid is defined as its *specific weight,* which is given the symbol γ. The specific weight of air, when the pressure is 1.01325×10^5 N/m^2 and the temperature is 288.15 K, is 12.013 N/m^3. Water at 4°C has a specific weight of 9.8066×10^3 N/m^3.

The specific weight of other liquids can be calculated if their specific gravity is known. Because the ratio of the densities of two substances is equal to the ratio of the specific weights of the two substances, the specific gravity may be used to calculate the specific weight of a liquid.

Viscosity

In all real fluids, a shearing deformation is accompanied by a shearing stress. Although all real fluids resist a force tending to cause one layer to move over another, the resistance occurs only while the shearing motion takes place. When the flow stops, the fluid particles stay in the position they have reached. There is no tendency for them to revert to their original positions, as is the case for solids.

Consider the fluid element *ABCD* sheared in one plane by a single shear stress τ, as shown in Fig. 1.4. The shear strain angle $d\theta$ increases continuously with time as long as the shear stress τ is applied. As a result of the shearing force, the upper surface moves at a speed $u + \Delta u$, whereas the lower surface moves at a speed u. The transverse velocity gradient is given by $\Delta u/\Delta y$, which becomes $\partial u/\partial y$ in the limit as $\Delta y \rightarrow 0$. A partial derivative is used here because the velocity also varies in the other directions for a general

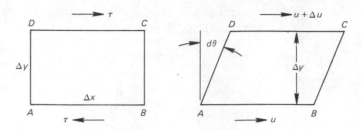

Figure 1.4 Shear deformation caused by shear stress in a fluid.

flow. It is only the transverse velocity gradient, that in the y direction for the element *ABCD,* that is of concern for this example.

The magnitude of the viscous shearing stress is proportional to the transverse velocity gradient. The constant of proportionality is the *coefficient of viscosity* or, more simply, the *viscosity* of the fluid, which is designated by the symbol μ. Thus, the shear stress is equal to μ times the transverse gradient of velocity, or in the nomenclature of Fig. 1.4,

$$\tau = \mu \frac{\partial u}{\partial y} \tag{1.4}$$

It is important to note that Eq. (1.4) applies to the velocity gradient and to the stress at a point. The change in velocity occurs over an infinitesimal layer of fluid, and the shear stress acts on an infinitesimal area.

For many fluids, the magnitude of the viscosity is independent of the rate of shear. For these *Newtonian fluids,* viscosity is a property of the fluid and a scalar quantity. The viscosity of a fluid relates to the transport of momentum in the direction of the velocity gradient (but opposite in sense). Therefore, viscosity is a *transport* property.

In gases, the interchange of momentum through the motion of the molecules forms the principal cause of viscosity. For a general gas, the coefficient of viscosity is a function of its composition, temperature, and pressure. However, in many situations, the viscosity of a gas is independent of the pressure (except at very low or very high pressures) and, because the molecular motion increases with temperature, the viscosity also increases with temperature. For most gases, viscosity can be calculated using a generalized form of Sutherland's formula:

$$\mu = C_1 \frac{T^{1.5}}{T + C_2} \tag{1.5}$$

Values for the two Sutherland's constants are tabulated for several gases in Table 1.4. For temperatures below 3000 K, the viscosity of air is independent of pressure. In this temperature range, we shall use Sutherland's equation for the viscosity of air:

$$\mu = 1.458 \times 10^{-6} \frac{T^{1.5}}{T + 110.4} \tag{1.6}$$

where T is the temperature (in K) and the units for μ are kg/s $\cdot$ m.

TABLE 1.4 SUTHERLAND'S CONSTANTS
FOR VARIOUS GASES

Gas	$C_1 \times 10^6$ $\left(\dfrac{kg}{s \cdot m \cdot K^{0.5}}\right)$	C_2 (K)
Air	1.458	110.4
Carbon dioxide	1.55	233.
Carbon monoxide	1.40	109.
Freon-12	1.48	317.
Helium	1.52	97.8
Hydrogen	0.649	70.6
Methane	0.983	155.
Nitrogen	1.39	102.
Oxygen	1.65	110.

Source: N.A. Hall, *Thermodynamics of Fluid Flow*.
Englewood Cliffs, N.J.: Prentice-Hall, Inc., © 1951,
renewed 1979, p. 20. Reprinted by permission of
Prentice-Hall, Inc., Englewood Cliffs, N.J.

Example 1.4

Calculate the viscosity of air when the temperature is 288.15 K.

Solution

$$\mu = 1.458 \times 10^{-6} \frac{(288.15)^{1.5}}{288.15 + 110.4}$$

$$= 1.7894 \times 10^{-5} \text{ kg/s} \cdot \text{m}$$

Although the process of momentum exchange also occurs in liquids, the molecules of a liquid are sufficiently close together for there to be appreciable forces between them. The relative movement of layers in a liquid modifies these intermolecular forces, thereby causing a net shear force that resists the relative movement. For nearly all liquids, viscosity decreases as temperature increases. Except at very high pressures, the viscosity of a liquid is independent of pressure. The viscosities of some representative liquids are presented as a function of temperature in Fig. 1.5.

Since viscosity is defined as the ratio of a shear stress to a velocity gradient, the dimensions of viscosity are (force)(time)/(length)^2. Thus, the units of viscosity could be $N \cdot s/m^2$ or $Pa \cdot s$, which are the units used in Fig. 1.5. When converting to English units, the reader should note that 1.0 lbf $\cdot$ s/ft^2 = 47.88 N $\cdot$ s/m^2. In the CGS system of units, where the unit of force is the dyne, the units of viscosity are dyne $\cdot$ s/cm^2. This grouping is known as the poise in honor of J. L. M. Poiseuille. Since the units of force are equal to (mass)(length)/(time)^2, the dimensions of viscosity could also be expressed in terms of (mass)/(time)(length). These are the units used in Sutherland's equation and its application in Example 1.4.

Based on Eq. (1.4), it is clear that the shear stress is zero when there is no relative

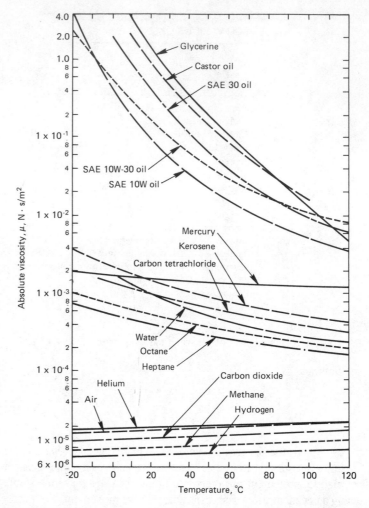

Figure 1.5   Absolute viscosity of common fluids as a function of temperature. R. W. Fox and A. T. McDonald, *Introduction to Fluid Mechanics, 2nd ed*. New York: John Wiley & Sons, Inc., 1978.

motion between adjacent layers of fluid, no matter what the value of μ is. Thus, even though no real fluid has a zero coefficient of viscosity, the effects of viscosity can be negligible. In many problems of interest to us, the effects of viscosity can be neglected. In such problems, the magnitudes of the coefficient of viscosity of the fluid and of the velocity gradients in the flow field are such that their product is negligible relative to the inertia and pressure forces acting on the fluid particles. We shall use the term *inviscid flow* in these cases to emphasize the fact that it is the character of both the velocity field and the fluid that allows us to neglect viscous effects. For such flows, the only forces acting on the surface of a fluid element are the pressure forces.

Note also that $\partial u/\partial y$ must be everywhere finite. If the velocity varies in the flow field, it does so continuously and does not change abruptly between adjacent layers of the fluid. This condition of continuous variation of the velocity also must be satisfied at solid boundaries. Thus, the fluid particles immediately adjacent to the surface of a configuration located in the flow field do not move relative to the surface, or, conversely, the velocity of the fluid at the surface must be equal to the velocity of the surface. Thus, in a viscous fluid, a boundary condition for fluid motion that must always be satisfied is that there should be no slipping at a solid boundary. This no-slip boundary condition is not required of gas flows at extremely low pressures. However, in such cases the concept of the gas as a continuum is no longer valid.

Example 1.5

There is a thin film of SAE 10W oil (at room temperature) between two parallel plates that are infinite in extent. As indicated in the sketch of Fig. 1.6, the upper plate moves at a constant speed of 10 m/s, while the lower plate is fixed. As a result, there is a linear variation of velocity for the oil particles in the film:

$$u = U_0 \frac{y}{h}$$

If the oil film is 0.5 cm thick (i.e., the vertical distance between the plates is 0.5 cm), what is the shear force per unit area of plate?

Solution. As shown in the sketch of Fig. 1.6, the velocity of the oil particles is

$$u = U_0 \frac{y}{h}$$

Note that at the two boundaries (i.e., at the plates) the oil particles move at the same speed as the plates. This is the no-slip condition. Thus, the shear at any point in the oil is

$$\tau = \mu \frac{\partial u}{\partial y} = \mu \frac{U_0}{h}$$

Note that the shear force is independent of y, that is, is constant across the oil film. Using Fig. 1.5, we find that the viscosity of SAE 10W oil at room temperature (which we will say is 25°C) is approximately 0.07 N · s/m². Thus,

$$\tau = 0.07 \ (\text{N} \cdot \text{s/m}^2) \frac{10 \text{ m/s}}{0.005 \text{ m}} = 140 \text{ N/m}^2$$

which does indeed have the units of force per unit area.

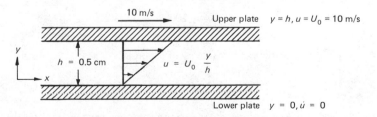

Figure 1.6 Sketch for Example 1.5.

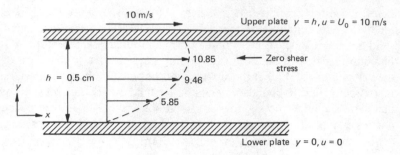

Figure 1.7 Sketch for Example 1.6.

Example 1.6

If there is a streamwise pressure gradient acting on the oil film separating the two plates of Example 1.5, the velocity of the oil particles in the film varies as

$$u = \frac{U_0}{h} y + \frac{h^2}{2\mu} \frac{dp}{dx} \left\{ \left(\frac{y}{h}\right)^2 - \left(\frac{y}{h}\right) \right\}$$

The velocity profile is illustrated in the sketch of Fig. 1.7. (Note that this velocity distribution is the solution to Prob. 4.12).

Again, $U_0 = 10$ m/s, $h = 0.5$ cm, and the oil is SAE 10W oil at 25°C. The pressure gradient *(dp/dx)* is $-100,000$ N/m² per meter. The negative sign indicates that the pressure decreases in the streamwise direction; that is, the pressure at the left of a fluid element is greater than that on the right. Thus, the pressure differential tends to push the fluid particle to the right.

(a) Calculate the maximum shear stress in the oil film. At what value of y does this occur?
(b) Calculate the y location where the shear stress in the oil goes to zero. Locate this point on the sketch of the velocity distribution presented in Fig. 1.7.

Solution. Let us first substitute the numerical values for the parameters into the expression for the velocity distribution:

$$u = \frac{10}{0.005} y - \frac{(0.005)}{2(0.07)} [10^5] \left\{ \frac{y^2}{(0.005)} - y \right\}$$

Note that the factor h has been rearranged in the second term.

$$u = 2000y - 3571(200y^2 - y)$$

Thus, the velocity gradient in the y direction is

$$\frac{du}{dy} = 2000 - 3571(400y - 1) = 5.571 \times 10^3 - 1.428 \times 10^6 \, y$$

Since the shear stress is directly proportional to the velocity gradient, let us determine where the velocity gradient is a maximum. To do this, we see that the second derivative

$$\frac{d^2u}{dy^2} = -1.428 \times 10^6 = \frac{d}{dy}\left(\frac{du}{dy}\right)$$

is always negative. Thus, the gradient is a maximum where $y = 0$, that is, at the lower wall.

(a) The maximum shear is

$$\tau_{max} = \mu \left.\frac{du}{dy}\right|_{y\,=\,0} = 0.07\,(5.571 \times 10^3) = 390 \text{ N/m}^2$$

(b) The shear is zero when $du/dy = 0$. This occurs when

$$y = \frac{5.571 \times 10^3}{1.428 \times 10^6} = 0.0039 \text{ m} = 0.78h$$

The shear is zero at the point where the velocity of the oil particles is a maximum, as shown in Fig. 1.7.

For the majority of fluids, viscosity is independent of the velocity gradient, and so Newton's hypothesis is fulfilled. There is, however, a fairly large group of liquids for which viscosity is not independent of the rate of shear. These liquids are referred to as non-Newtonian. Liquids that have a reduced viscosity when the rate of shear is large are said to be pseudoplastic. Gelatin, milk, and blood are in this category. Liquids that have an increased viscosity when the rate of shear is large are said to be *dilatant*. Concentrated solutions of sugar in water are in this category.

Other liquids exhibit non-Newtonian behavior if their apparent viscosity changes with time when shearing forces are applied. Liquids for which the apparent viscosity increases with the duration of the stress are called *rheopectic*. Those for which the apparent viscosity decreases with the duration are termed *thixotropic*. For additional information about non-Newtonian fluids, the reader is referred to Ref. 1.4.

Kinematic Viscosity

Many equations of fluid mechanics include the ratio μ/ρ as a parameter. Because this ratio appears frequently, it has been given a special name, *kinematic viscosity*. The symbol used to represent the kinematic viscosity is ν:

$$\nu = \frac{\mu}{\rho} \qquad (1.7)$$

In this ratio the force units (or, equivalently, the mass units) cancel. Thus, ν has the units of L^2/T (e.g., square meters per second or square feet per second).

Speed of Sound

The speed at which a disturbance of infinitesimal strength propagates through a fluid that is at rest is known as the *speed of sound*, which is designated in this book as a. As will be discussed in Chapter 10, a sound wave produces only infinitesimal changes in pressure

TABLE 1.5 SPEED OF SOUND
IN VARIOUS FLUIDS AT 15.5°C
AND 1 ATMOSPHERE

Medium	a (m/s)
Gas	
Air	340.3
Argon	217.0
Carbon dioxide	266.1
Helium	1000.0
Hydrogen	1294.2
Methane	185.0
Liquid	
Ethyl alcohol	1200.9
Glycerine	1859.3
Mercury	1450.8
Water	1490.5

Source: From *Fluid Mechanics* by
F.M. White. Copyright © 1979 by
McGraw-Hill Book Company. Used
with the permission of McGraw-Hill
Book Company.

and density. Since it produces negligible heat transfer, sound-wave propagation may be considered as an isentropic process. The speed of sound is the ratio of the change in pressure to the change in density that occurs during the isentropic process:

$$a^2 = \left(\frac{\partial p}{\partial \rho}\right)_s \tag{1.8}$$

This equation is valid for the speed of sound in any material.

For many materials the relationship between p and ρ at constant entropy is not known. For a perfect gas, however, $a = \sqrt{kRT}$, where k is the ratio of the specific heats and R is the gas constant. For the range of temperature over which air behaves as a perfect gas, $k = 1.4$ and the speed of sound is given by

$$a = 20.047\sqrt{T} \tag{1.9}$$

where T is the temperature (in K) and the units for the speed of sound are m/s. Representative values of the speed of sound in various fluids are presented in Table 1.5.

Bulk Modulus of Elasticity

Since all matter is compressible to some extent, a change in the compressive stress applied to an elemental volume of the substance produces some change in its volume. For liquids and solids, the degree of compressibility of a substance is characterized by the *bulk modulus, K,* which is defined for an isentropic process by the relation

$$K = +\rho\left(\frac{\partial p}{\partial \rho}\right)_s \tag{1.10}$$

The bulk modulus of water is approximately 2.1×10^9 N/m^2 at standard conditions. As a liquid is compressed, its molecules become more tightly spaced and its resistance to further compression increases; that is, K increases. The bulk modulus of water, for example, roughly doubles as the pressure increases from 1 to 3500 atm. Similarly, as the temperature decreases, K increases.

Since gases are very compressible, the term bulk modulus is seldom applied to gases. Compressible gas flows will be discussed in Chapter 10.

Vapor Pressure

Because all liquids tend to evaporate, there is continual movement of molecules in and out of a liquid at a free surface. If the space above the free surface is enclosed and if a sufficient quantity of liquid is available, an equilibrium state will be reached such that the rate at which molecules escape from the liquid is balanced by the rate at which they return to it. The pressure at which the net exchange of molecules between the liquid and the vapor is zero is called the *vapor pressure*.

Because molecular activity depends upon the temperature, the vapor pressure is a function of the temperature of the liquid. Thus, a liquid can be made to boil either by increasing its temperature or by decreasing the pressure of the gas bounding the liquid surface. If water is heated to 100°C, its vapor pressure will be 1.01325×10^5 N/m^2. That is, water exposed to standard atmospheric pressure will boil at 100°C. However, when the pressure of the air outside the water is decreased to 2345 N/m^2, or 0.023 times the standard atmospheric pressure, the boiling temperature of water is 20°C. Water boils even at room temperature if the pressure of the air above the water is reduced sufficiently.

Effects similar to boiling can be produced by changing the pressure of a liquid containing dissolved gases. When the pressure of the liquid is sufficiently reduced, the dissolved gases are liberated in the form of bubbles. The reduction of pressure required for the release of the dissolved gases is less than that required for boiling of the liquid. A subsequent increase in pressure may cause the bubbles to collapse, such that very high impact forces result. This phenomenon is known as *cavitation* and has serious consequences in fluid machinery.

Surface Tension

Surface tension arises from the forces between the molecules of a liquid and the forces between the liquid molecules and those of any adjacent substance. This produces a surface on the liquid that acts like a stretched membrane. Because of this membrane effect, the liquid exerts "tension" upon adjacent portions of the surface or upon objects that are in contact with the liquid. The molecules of a liquid are bound to each other by forces of molecular attraction, and it is these forces that give rise to cohesion. *Cohesion* is the tendency of the liquid to remain as one assemblage of particles, rather than to behave as a gas and fill the entire space within which it is confined. Forces between the molecules of a fluid and the molecules of a solid boundary surface give rise to *adhesion* between the fluid and the boundary.

If the forces of adhesion between the molecules of a particular liquid and a particular solid are greater than the forces of cohesion between the liquid molecules themselves, the liquid molecules tend to crowd toward the solid surface, and the area of contact between the liquid and the solid boundary increases. The liquid then spreads over the solid, wetting it as shown in the sketch of Fig. 1.8. Water will wet clean glass; mercury will not. Water will not wet wax or a greasy surface.

The relation between these forces explains the capillary rise or depression that occurs when a free liquid surface meets a solid boundary. The surface tension (σ) for a water–air surface is 0.073 N/m at room temperature. The surface tension force acts around the circumference of the tube in the direction indicated in the sketch of Fig. 1.8.

Example 1.7

Calculate the capillary rise (h) of the water in a clean glass tube, as shown in Fig. 1.8, if the inside diameter of the glass tube is 1.5 mm. It may be assumed that θ is equal to 0° for water against clean glass.

Solution. By summing the forces acting on the volume of water in the tube that has risen above the reservoir level, we see that

$$\sigma \pi d - \gamma_{H_2O} \left(\frac{\pi d^2}{4} h \right) = 0$$

$$h = \frac{4\sigma}{\gamma_{H_2O} d} = \frac{4(0.073)}{(9.8066 \times 10^3)(0.0015)} = 0.0199 \text{ m} = 1.99 \text{ cm}$$

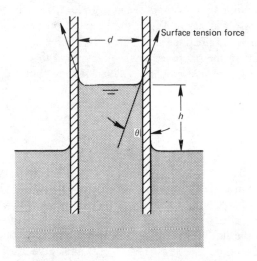

Figure 1.8 Capillary action in a tube.

Most organic liquids have values of surface tension between 0.020 and 0.030 N/m. The value for mercury is approximately 0.50 N/m. These values are for the liquid in contact with air. For all liquids, surface tension decreases as the temperature rises. The surface tension of water may be considerably reduced by the addition of small quantities of organic solutes, such as soap or detergent.

PROBLEMS

1.1. Using Table 1.1, calculate the standard atmospheric pressure of air at an altitude of 35,000 ft. Calculate the pressure in the following units: N/m^2, kPa, psi, and psf (lbf/ft^2).

1.2. Calculate the density of air when the pressure is 14.696 $lbf/in.^2$ and the temperature is 519°R. Air at this pressure and temperature can be assumed to behave as a perfect gas. In English units, $R = 53.34$ ft $\cdot$ lbf/lbm $\cdot$ °R. Express the density using units of lbm/ft^3 and of $slugs/ft^3$. To accomplish the conversion, note that $g_c = 32.174$ ft $\cdot$ lbm/lbf $\cdot$ s^2. (This is the English unit equivalent of Example 1.3.)

1.3. Using the gas constants presented in Table 1.2, calculate the densities for the following gases at the specified conditions. The densities are to be calculated in the following units: kg/m^3, $slugs/ft^3$, and lbm/ft^3.
   (a) Nitrogen at 350°F and 150 psi.
   (b) Helium at 20°C and 1.013×10^5 N/m^2.
   (c) Methane at 70°F and atmospheric pressure.

1.4. The specific gravity of a gas (SG) is the dimensionless ratio of its density to the density of air at standard conditions, as given in Example 1.3 or Prob. 1.2. What is the specific gravity of hydrogen at 150°C and 1.5×10^6 Pa?

1.5. A perfect gas undergoes a process whereby its pressure is doubled and its density is decreased to three-quarters of its original value. If the initial temperature is 200°F, what is the final temperature in °F? in °C?

1.6. Using the specific gravities presented in Table 1.3, calculate the densities and specific weights of the following liquids: **(a)** benzene, **(b)** gasoline, **(c)** SAE 30 oil, and **(d)** seawater. Values should be calculated for the following units: density in kg/m^3, $slugs/ft^3$, and lbm/ft^3; and specific weight in N/m^3 and lbf/ft^3.

1.7. Calculate the viscosity of air when the temperature is 519°R. Use the expression

$$\mu = 2.27 \times 10^{-8} \frac{T^{1.5}}{T + 198.6}$$

where T is the temperature in °R and the units for μ are lbf $\cdot$ s/ft^2. (This is the English unit equivalent of Example 1.4.)

1.8. Using Eq. (1.6), calculate the viscosity of air for temperatures from 250 K to 3000 K. So that you only need to calculate values for a limited number of temperatures, present the results in graphical form; that is, graph μ as a function of T. (You should be able to do this with four or five specific values for μ.)

1.9. Using the values for Sutherland's constants for various gases presented in Table 1.4, calculate the viscosities for the following gases at the specified conditions. The units for the calculated values are to be in Pa $\cdot$ s, lbf $\cdot$ s/ft^2, and poise.

(a) Nitrogen at 350°F and 150 psi.

(b) Helium at 20°C and 1.013 × 10⁵ N/m².

(c) Methane at 70°F and atmospheric pressure.

1.10. Using the results of Probs. 1.2, 1.3, 1.7, and 1.9, calculate the values for the kinematic viscosity for the following:

(a) Nitrogen at 350°F and 150 psi.

(b) Helium at 20°C and 1.013 × 10⁵ N/m².

(c) Methane at 70°F and atmospheric pressure.

(d) Air at standard atmospheric conditions for sea level.

1.11. A block weighing 500 N slides down an inclined surface on which there is a thin film of SAE 30 oil at room temperature. As shown in Fig. P1.11, the inclination angle is 20°. The block is a cube 0.2 m on a side. What is the terminal speed of the block as it slides down the incline? The oil thickness is 0.003 cm. Assume a linear variation of the velocity across the oil film.

1.12. Water at 80°F moves through a pipe, as shown in Fig. P1.12. The radial velocity distribution at any cross section is given by

$$U = U_0 \left[1 - \left(\frac{r}{R} \right)^2 \right]$$

where U_0 is the centerline velocity. If the diameter of the pipe is 6 in. and the centerline velocity is 10 ft/s, what is the shear stress at the wall of the pipe in lbf/ft²? in N/m²? What is the total shear force acting on the wall per meter of length and per foot of length of pipe?

1.13. Consider two infinite parallel plates, a distance h apart (Fig. P1.13). The velocity distribution between the plates is

$$u = \frac{1}{2\mu} \frac{dp}{dx} y^2 + C_1 y + C_2$$

Use the boundary conditions for a viscous flow to evaluate the constants C_1 and C_2.

1.14. A square, thin flat plate, 1 ft on a side, slides over an infinite plane at a constant speed of 30 ft/s. There is a thin film of oil whose viscosity is 1.4 × 10⁻⁴ lbf · s/ft² between the plate and the infinite plane. The oil film is 0.05 in. thick. If 1 hp = 550 ft · lbf/s, what is the horsepower required to keep the plate moving at 30 ft/s?

1.15. A schematic view of a concentric-cylinder viscometer is shown in Fig. P1.15. When the speed of rotation is ω rpm and the radius is r_2 feet, the fluid velocity at the surface of the outer cylinder is $r_2\omega$. With a clearance of b feet,

$$\frac{du}{dy} = \frac{r_2\omega}{b}$$

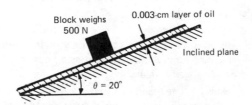

Figure P1.11   Sketch for Prob. 1.11

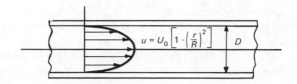

Figure P1.12 Sketch for Prob. 1.12

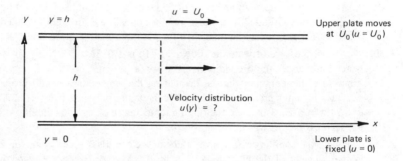

Figure P1.13 Sketch for Prob. 1.13

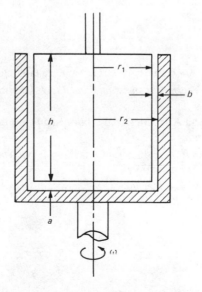

Figure P1.15 Concentric-cylinder viscometer.

If we use a viscometer with $a = 0.01$ in., $b = 0.02$ in., $r_2 = 2.52$ in., and $h = 4.00$ in. to measure the viscosity of glycerine at room temperature, what is the horsepower required when the speed of rotation is 120 rpm?

1.16. Using Table 1.1 and Eq. (1.7), calculate the kinematic viscosity of air at sea level. Then calculate the kinematic viscosity of air at 12 km. Comparing the answers, how does the ratio of the kinematic viscosities at these two altitudes relate the ratio of the ambient pressures?

1.17. What is the kinematic viscosity of water at 20°C?

1.18. A bomb explodes on a coastal plain where the atmosphere is at standard sea-level conditions. Three seconds after you see the flash of the explosion its sound reaches you. Assuming the blast wave travels at the speed of sound and that the speed of light is infinite by comparison, how far away is the explosion?

1.19. An airplane is flying at an air speed of 565 mph at an altitude of 35,000 ft. What is its Mach number at this altitude? The Mach number equals the air speed divided by the speed of sound. What is its Mach number if it flies at the same air speed at sea level?

1.20. The vapor pressure of water at 100°C (212°F) is 1.013×10^5 N/m^2 (14.696 lbf/in.^{2}), since water boils under these conditions. The vapor pressure of water is approximately a linear function of temperature; that is, decreasing the temperature would produce a proportional decrease in vapor pressure. Specifically, the vapor pressure decreases 3.10×10^3 N/m^2/°C (0.25 lbf/in.^{2}/°F). Calculate the boiling temperature of water at an altitude of 3000 m (9843 ft). Express the answer in °C and in °F.

1.21. Calculate the capillary rise (h) of water in a clean glass tube, as shown in Fig. 1.8, if the inside diameter of the glass tube is $^1/_8$ in. The surface tension of water in English units is approximately 0.005 lbf/ft. The density of water is 1.9404 slugs/ft^3.

1.22. What diameter of glass tube is required if the capillary effects on the water within the tube are not to exceed 0.5 mm?

REFERENCES

1.1. *U.S. Standard Atmosphere, 1962*, Government Printing Office, Washington, D.C., Dec. 1962.

1.2. Hall, N. A., *Thermodynamics of Fluid Flow*, Prentice-Hall, Inc., Englewood Cliffs, N.J., 1951.

1.3. Fox, R. W., and A. T. McDonald, *Introduction to Fluid Mechanics*, 2nd ed., John Wiley & Sons, New York, 1978.

1.4. Reiner, M., *Deformation, Strain and Flow: An Elementary Introduction to Rheology*, 3rd ed., Lewis, London, 1969.

1.5. White, F. M., *Fluid Mechanics*, McGraw-Hill Book Company, New York, 1979.

CHAPTER TWO

Fluid Statics

If fluid particles, when viewed as a continuum, are either all at rest or all moving with the same velocity, the fluid is said to be a *static medium*. Thus, the term *static fluid properties* may be applied to situations in which the elements of the fluid are moving, providing there is no relative motion between finite elements. Since there is no relative motion between adjacent layers of the fluid, there are no shear forces. With no relative motion between fluid elements, the viscosity of the fluid is of no concern. For these inviscid flows, the only forces acting on the surface of a fluid element are pressure forces.

PRESSURE VARIATION IN A STATIC FLUID

Consider the small fluid element whose center is defined by the coordinates x, y, and z, as shown in Fig. 2.1. A first-order Taylor's series expansion is used to evaluate the pressure at each face. Thus, the pressure at the back face of the element is $p - (\partial p/\partial x)(\Delta x/2)$; that at the front face is $p + (\partial p/\partial x)(\Delta x/2)$. If the fluid is at rest, the element must be in equilibrium. For equilibrium, the sum of the forces in any direction must be zero. Thus,

$$-\left(p + \frac{\partial p}{\partial x}\frac{\Delta x}{2}\right)\Delta y\,\Delta z + \left(p - \frac{\partial p}{\partial x}\frac{\Delta x}{2}\right)\Delta y\,\Delta z = 0 \qquad (2.1a)$$

$$-\left(p + \frac{\partial p}{\partial y}\frac{\Delta y}{2}\right)\Delta x\,\Delta z + \left(p - \frac{\partial p}{\partial y}\frac{\Delta y}{2}\right)\Delta x\,\Delta z = 0 \qquad (2.1b)$$

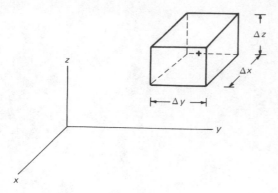

Figure 2.1 Derivation of Eqs. (2.1) through (2.3).

$$-\left(p + \frac{\partial p}{\partial z}\frac{\Delta z}{2}\right)\Delta x\,\Delta y + \left(p - \frac{\partial p}{\partial z}\frac{\Delta z}{2}\right)\Delta x\,\Delta y - \rho g\,\Delta x\,\Delta y\,\Delta z = 0 \quad (2.1c)$$

Note that the coordinate system has been chosen such that gravity acts in the negative z direction. Combining terms and dividing by $\Delta x\,\Delta y\,\Delta z$,

$$\frac{\partial p}{\partial x} = 0 \tag{2.2a}$$

$$\frac{\partial p}{\partial y} = 0 \tag{2.2b}$$

$$\frac{\partial p}{\partial z} = -\rho g \tag{2.2c}$$

The three equations can be written as one using vector notation:

$$\nabla p = \rho \vec{f} = -\rho g\hat{k} \tag{2.3}$$

where, $\vec{f}$ represents the body force per unit mass. For the cases of interest to this book, the body force is gravity.

These equations will illustrate two important principles for a nonaccelerating, hydrostatic, or shear-free, flow: (1) There is no pressure variation in the horizontal direction, that is, the pressure is constant in a plane perpendicular to the direction of gravity, and (2) the vertical pressure variation is proportional to gravity, density, and change in depth. Furthermore, as the element shrinks to zero volume (i.e., as $\Delta z \rightarrow 0$), it can be seen that the pressure is the same on all faces. The pressure at a point in a static fluid is independent of orientation.

Since the pressure only varies with z, that is, it is not a function of x or y, an ordinary derivative may be used and Eq. (2.2c) may be written:

$$\frac{dp}{dz} = -\rho g \tag{2.4}$$

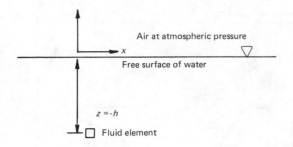

Figure 2.2 Sketch for Example 2.1.

Example 2.1

Referring to Fig. 2.2, if the water in a lake is everywhere at rest, what is the pressure as a function of the distance from the surface? The air above the surface of the water is at standard-atmosphere sea-level conditions. How far down must one go before the pressure is 1 atm greater than the pressure at the surface?

Solution.   To relate the pressure to the distance from the surface, let us examine Eq. (2.4):

$$\frac{dp}{dz} = -\rho g$$

Integrating,

$$p - p_{\text{surface}} = -\rho g(z - z_{\text{surface}}) \tag{2.5}$$

Since $z_{\text{surface}} = 0$ and $p_{\text{surface}} =$ atmospheric pressure, the static pressure at any depth $z = -h$ is given by the relation

$$p = p_{\text{atm}} + \rho gh \tag{2.6}$$

Thus, the pressure increases linearly with the distance below the surface. Note that this equation applies to the pressure variation in any fluid where the density and gravity are constant.

To determine how far below the surface one must go before the pressure is 1 atm greater than the pressure at the surface, use Eq. (2.6) as follows:

$$2_{\text{atm}} = 1_{\text{atm}} + \rho gh$$

$$\rho gh = 1_{\text{atm}} = 1.01325 \times 10^5 \text{ N/m}^2$$

The density of water is 1.0 g/cm^3 = 1.0 × 10^3 kg/m^3, and the acceleration due to gravity is 9.8066 m/s^2. Thus,

$$h = \frac{1.01325 \times 10^5}{(1.0 \times 10^3)(9.8066)} = 10.3323 \text{ m}$$

This sample problem illustrates that the pressure in a continuously distributed, uniform, static fluid varies only with the vertical distance from the surface and is independent of the shape of the container. The pressure is the same at all points in a particular horizontal plane in the fluid. An illustration of this is shown in Fig. 2.3. The free surface

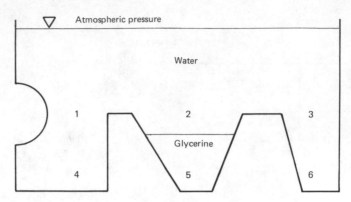

Figure 2.3 Hyrdostatic-pressure distribution.

of the fluid is subjected to atmospheric pressure and forms a horizontal plane. Points 1, 2, and 3 are all located in the water and are the same distance below the surface. Therefore, static pressure is the same at all three points. Static pressure at point 4 is equal to that at point 6, being greater than the pressure in the water above them. However, the pressure at point 5 is not equal to the pressure at point 4 since it is beneath a different fluid, glycerine, which is isolated from the other legs of the container.

Equation (2.6) describes the variation of pressure with depth for a single fluid whose free surface is at atmospheric pressure. If more than one fluid is present, the density would change as a step function as we move from one fluid to another. We must account for density variations when using Eq. (2.4). The static pressures of the fluids of adjacent layers are equal at their common fluid–fluid interface. To illustrate the variation in pressure with depth for different fluids, Eq. (2.4) will be applied to the layered fluid shown in the sketch of Fig. 2.4. Note that the fluids are arranged in order from the lightest at the top to the heaviest at the bottom. (Refer to the specific weights presented in Table 1.3.) This is the only stable configuration. If they were initially arranged in a different order, the fluids would overturn until they achieved the stable arrangement.

The static pressure at some point in the oil located a distance z below the free surface is given by

$$p = p_1 - \rho_2 g z$$

Since z is negative, the second term will add to the first, indicating that the pressure increases with depth. At the oil–water interface, the pressure in either fluid is given by

$$p = p_1 + \rho_2 g h_2$$

At some point in the glycerine,

$$p = p_1 + \rho_2 g h_2 + \rho_3 g h_3 - \rho_4 g(z + h_2 + h_3)$$

Since $z = -h_2 - h_3 - h_4$ at the bottom of the glycerine layer, the static pressure there is

$$p = p_1 + \rho_2 g h_2 + \rho_3 g h_3 + \rho_4 g h_4$$

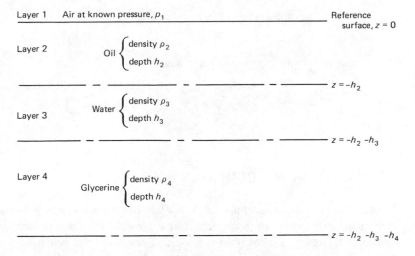

Figure 2.4 Static-pressure variation for layers of different fluids.

Example 2.2

A gasoline tank is vented to the standard sea-level atmospheric conditions, as shown in the sketch of Fig. 2.5. The output of the fuel gage for the gasoline tank is proportional to the gage pressure at the bottom of the tank. If the tank is 30.0 cm deep and contains 2.0 cm of water, how many centimeters of air remain at the top if the fuel gage indicates that the tank is full? The density of water is 1.0 g/cm^3, and the specific gravity of gasoline is 0.69.

Solution.   Assume there are h cm of air. Then there are $(28.0 - h)$ cm of gasoline. Since the weight of the air above the gasoline has a negligible effect on the pressure, the pressure at the free surface of the gasoline is equal to the standard atmospheric value. Thus, the gage pressure at the bottom of the tank is

$$p_{\text{bottom}} - p_{\text{atm}} = \rho_{\text{gas}}g(28.0 - h) + \rho_{\text{water}}g(2.0)$$

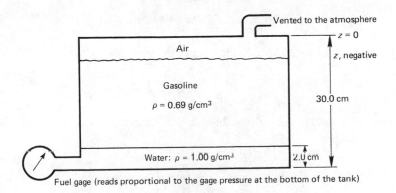

Figure 2.5 Sketch for Example 2.2.

However, this value is equal to the pressure that would exist if the tank were full of gasoline:

$$p_{\text{bottom}} - p_{\text{atm}} = \rho_{\text{gas}}g(30.0)$$

Equating the two expressions and noting that $\rho_{\text{gas}} = 0.69$ g/cm^3,

$$0.69g(28.0 - h) + 1.00g(2.0) = 0.69g(30.0)$$

$$0.69h = 0.69(28.0) + 1.00(2.0) - 0.69(30.0)$$

$$h = 0.90 \text{ cm}$$

PRESSURE VARIATION IN A COMPRESSIBLE FLUID

In the examples discussed thus far, Eq. (2.4) has been applied to fluids whose density is constant everywhere or is constant over a considerable distance between step-function changes. However, the equation is a valid statement of the condition for equilibrium of any fluid. For a compressible fluid, however, the density depends upon the pressure. Thus, to integrate this equation and determine the variation of pressure with position, one must define the relation between density and pressure. For many processes involving a gas, the pressure is proportional to the density raised to the power n. Such processes are termed *polytropic*. Thus,

$$p = C\rho^n \tag{2.7}$$

Atmospheric Models

The polytropic relation may be used with Eq. (2.4) to develop relations describing the variation of pressure with altitude in the earth's atmosphere.

For an isothermal process involving a perfect gas, $n = 1$. Thus,

$$p = C\rho = \rho RT$$

Equation (2.4) may be written

$$\frac{dp}{dz} = -\rho g = -\frac{pg}{RT}$$

Separating the variables and integrating between two points,

$$\int \frac{dp}{p} = \ln\frac{p_2}{p_1} = -\frac{g}{RT}\int dz = -\frac{g}{RT}(z_2 - z_1)$$

where the integration reflects the fact that the temperature has been assumed constant. Rearranging,

$$p_2 = p_1 \exp\left\{\frac{g(z_1 - z_2)}{RT}\right\} \tag{2.8}$$

The pressure variation described by Eq. (2.8) is a reasonable approximation of that in the atmosphere near the earth's surface.

An improved correlation for pressure variation in the earth's atmosphere can be obtained if one accounts for the temperature variation with altitude. The earth's mean atmospheric temperature decreases almost linearly with z up to an altitude of nearly 11,000 m. That is,

$$T = T_0 - Bz \tag{2.9}$$

where T_0 is the sea-level temperature (absolute) and B is the lapse rate, both of which vary from day to day. The following standard values will be assumed to apply from 0 to 11,000 m:

$$T_0 = 288.15 \text{ K} \quad \text{and} \quad B = 0.0065 \text{ K/m}$$

Substituting Eq. (2.8) into the relation,

$$\int \frac{dp}{p} = -\int \frac{g \, dz}{RT}$$

and integrating,

$$p = p_0 \left(1 - \frac{Bz}{T_0} \right)^{g/RB} \tag{2.10}$$

The exponent g/RB, which is dimensionless, is equal to 5.26 for air.

Example 2.3

Using Eqs. (2.9) and (2.10), calculate the temperature and pressure of air at an altitude of 10 km. Compare the tabulated values with those presented in Table 1.1.

Solution.   The ambient temperature at 10,000 m is

$$T = T_0 - Bz = 288.15 - 0.0065(10^4) = 223.15 \text{ K}$$

The tabulated value from Table 1.1 is 223.252 K. The calculated value for the ambient pressure is

$$p = p_0 \left(1 - \frac{Bz}{T_0} \right)^{g/RB}$$

$$= 1.01325 \times 10^5 \left(1 - \frac{0.0065(10^4)}{288.15} \right)^{5.26}$$

$$= 1.01325 \times 10^5 (0.26063) = 2.641 \times 10^4 \text{ N/m}^2 = 198.08 \text{ mm Hg}$$

The comparable value in Table 1.1 is 198.765 mm Hg.

PRESSURE MEASUREMENT TECHNIQUES

There are many devices for measuring pressure. Because pressure is a force applied to an area, a device can be built to "measure" the pressure by converting that force to a stress or a displacement, which is the actual parameter measured. These mechanical effects can then be quantified in different ways, including using measurement of one of the following parameters:

1. Height of a liquid column (a manometer).
2. Direct displacement measurement (a Bourdon-tube gage).
3. Indirect (electrical) measurement of displacement (a transducer).

The second and third techniques were discussed in Chapter 1.

Manometer

As illustrated by Eq. (2.4), the pressure in a column of fluid varies directly with the depth of the liquid. Manometers are devices in which a static column (or columns) of one or more liquids is used to measure the difference between the pressure at two points.

A common type of manometer employs a transparent U-tube set in a vertical plane, as shown in Fig. 2.6. In this application, the manometer is used to provide a measure of the pressure difference between points 1 and 2 due to fluid flow in the variable-area channel. With this arrangement one can determine the pressure difference but not the absolute pressure at either station. Tubes connecting the flush-mounted orifices located in the channel wall to the U-tube transmit the static pressures from the two orifices. The liquid contained in the lower part of the U-tube (fluid B) is denser and does not mix with

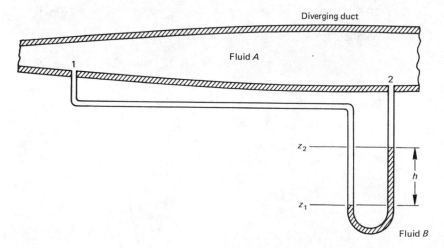

Figure 2.6   Sketch for Example 2.4.

fluid A. The density of fluid B is chosen to give a suitable height differential (h) for the expected difference in pressure between stations 1 and 2.

Example 2.4

A U-tube manometer is used to measure the change in static pressure between points 1 and 2 in the diverging duct, as shown in Fig. 2.6. Fluid A is air; fluid B is mercury. If the differential height, h, is

$$h = z_2 - z_1 = 10.8 \text{ cm}$$

what is the pressure differential between points 1 and 2?

Solution. The weight of air in the tubing leading to the U-tube manometer has a negligible effect on the pressure acting on the mercury. Thus, p_1 is the static pressure applied to the mercury at z_1 (on the left) and p_2 is that at z_2 (on the right). The static pressure is the same in a particular horizontal plane where there is a continuous path through the mercury in the two legs. Thus,

$$p_1 = p_2 + \rho_{Hg}gh$$

Noting that the density of mercury (ρ_{Hg}) is 13.5951 g/cm^3 or 13.5951 $\times$ 10^3 kg/m^3,

$$p_1 - p_2 = (13.5951 \times 10^3 \text{ kg/m}^3)(9.8066 \text{ m/s}^2)(0.108 \text{ m}) = 1.4399 \times 10^4 \text{ N/m}^2$$

The pressure at station 1 is 1.4399×10^4 N/m^2 greater than that at station 2.

As illustrated in Fig. 2.7, a simple, open manometer can be used to measure the pressure in a closed chamber (or a duct) relative to the atmospheric pressure. Recall that the difference between a particular pressure and the local atmospheric pressure is known as the gage pressure. Thus, the device shown in Fig. 2.7 measures the gage pressure directly. This open manometer uses two fluids: the fluid in the chamber (or duct), fluid A, and a second fluid, fluid B. This two-fluid arrangement might be used (1) if the chamber

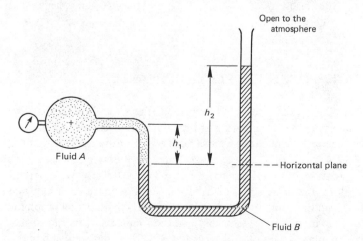

Figure 2.7 Sketch for Example 2.5.

fluid were corrosive or (2) to obtain a suitable height, h_2; for example, a relatively heavy fluid B would reduce h_2 so that the open tube could be relatively short, or a lighter fluid B would increase h_2 so that the experimental error in reading the fluid level would be relatively small.

Example 2.5

An open manometer, such as the one shown in Fig. 2.7, is used to measure the pressure at the centerline of a pipe containing oil. Fluid A is oil, whose specific gravity is 0.90; fluid B is water. If h_1 is 3.6 cm and h_2 is 15.0 cm, what is the pressure at the centerline of the pipe, p_{cl}?

Solution.   The pressure is constant in the horizontal plane containing the oil–water interface in the left leg of the U-tube. Since the weight of air above the water has a negligible effect on the pressure in the right leg, the pressure in the horizontal plane of interest is

$$p = p_{atm} + \rho_{H_2O}gh_2$$

where p_{atm} denotes the value of the atmospheric pressure. The pressure in the left leg of the U-tube in that plane is

$$p = p_{cl} + \rho_{oil}gh_1$$

Equating the two expressions:

$$p_{cl} = p_{atm} + \rho_{H_2O}gh_2 - \rho_{oil}gh_1$$

$$= p_{atm} + (1.00 \times 10^3 \text{ kg/m}^3)(9.8066 \text{ m/s}^2)(0.150 \text{ m})$$

$$- (0.90 \times 10^3 \text{ kg/m}^3)(9.8066 \text{ m/s}^2)(0.036 \text{ m})$$

$$= p_{atm} + (1.4710 \times 10^3 - 0.3177 \times 10^3) \text{ N/m}^2$$

$$= p_{atm} + 1.1533 \times 10^3 \text{ N/m}^2$$

Thus p_{cl} is 1.1533×10^3 N/m^2 greater than the atmospheric value; that is, 1.1533×10^3 N/m^2 gage.

HYDROSTATIC FORCES ON PLANE SURFACES

Figure 2.8 shows a plane surface submerged in a fluid that is at rest. Since there can be no shear stresses in a static fluid medium, the force on the plane is due to pressure only and must act normal to the surface. If variations in the density of the fluid are negligible, Eq. (2.4) or (2.6) can be used to define the pressure field in the fluid. Thus, we see that the pressure on a submerged surface varies linearly with depth. For a plane surface, therefore, the linear stress distribution is analogous to combined bending and compression of a beam in strength-of-materials theory. The hydrostatic problem thus reduces to simple formulas involving the centroid and the moments of inertia of the plate cross section.

A plane panel of arbitrary shape that is completely submerged in a liquid is shown

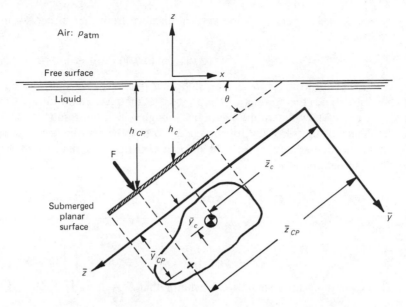

Figure 2.8 Coordinate system and nomenclature for the forces on a submerged planar surface.

in Fig. 2.8. The panel is inclined to the horizontal free surface by the angle θ. The xyz coordinate system is such that $-h$ is the vertical depth to any point on the plate, so the pressure at that point would be

$$p = p_{atm} + \rho g h \tag{2.6}$$

A $\bar{y}$, $\bar{z}$ coordinate system is in the plane of the plate, as shown in Fig. 2.8. The force acting on an element dA ($= d\bar{y}\, d\bar{z}$) is

$$dF = p\, dA = (p_{atm} + \rho g h)\, d\bar{y}\, d\bar{z}$$

Integrating over the total area of the plate, the total hydrostatic force on one side of the plate is given by

$$F = p_{atm} \int\int d\bar{y}\, d\bar{z} + \rho g \int\int h\, d\bar{y}\, d\bar{z} \tag{2.11}$$

The second integral can be evaluated by noting that

$$h = \bar{z} \sin \theta$$

So Eq. (2.11) can be written

$$F = p_{atm}A + \rho g \sin \theta \int\int \bar{z}\, dA \tag{2.12}$$

Noting that $\int\int \bar{z}\, dA$ is the first moment of the plate area about the $\bar{y}$ axis, we may replace the integral by $\bar{z}_c A$, where $\bar{z}_c$ is the $\bar{z}$ coordinate of the centroid. Finally, noting that

$h_c = z_c \sin \theta$, where h_c is the vertical distance from the surface to the plate centroid, we can write

$$F = (p_{atm} + \rho g h_c)A = p_c A \qquad (2.13)$$

Thus, the resultant force on one side of a plane surface due to a linearly increasing pressure equals the product of the pressure at the plate centroid times the plate area.

Let us now determine the point through which the resultant force acts, known as the center of pressure, CP, of the plate. To find the coordinates $(\bar{y}_{CP}, \bar{z}_{CP})$, we sum the moments due to the pressure field and equate them to the moment of the resultant force. Thus, to determine $\bar{z}_{CP}$,

$$F\bar{z}_{CP} = \int\int \bar{z}p \, d\bar{y} \, d\bar{z} = \int\int \bar{z}(p_{atm} + \rho g \bar{z} \sin \theta) \, d\bar{y} \, d\bar{z}$$

Thus,

$$F\bar{z}_{CP} = p_{atm} \int\int \bar{z} \, dA + \rho g \sin \theta \int\int \bar{z}^2 \, dA \qquad (2.14)$$

This equation can be simplified by noting that $F = p_c A$, $\int\int \bar{z} \, dA = \bar{z}_c A$, and

$$\int\int \bar{z}^2 \, dA = I_{\bar{y}_c \bar{y}_c} + \bar{z}_c^2 A$$

which is the transfer theorem for the second moment of the area about the $\bar{y}$ axis. $I_{\bar{y}_c \bar{y}_c}$ is the area moment of inertia of the plate area about its centroidal axis $\bar{y}_c$ computed in the plane of the plate. Thus, Eq. (2.14) becomes

$$p_c A \bar{z}_{CP} = p_{atm} \bar{z}_c A + \rho g \sin \theta \, I_{\bar{y}_c \bar{y}_c} + \rho g h_c \bar{z}_c A$$

This equation can be rewritten as

$$\bar{z}_{CP} = \bar{z}_c + \frac{\rho g \sin \theta \, I_{\bar{y}_c \bar{y}_c}}{p_c A} \qquad (2.15)$$

Note that the resultant force does not act at the centroid of the plate $(\bar{z}_c)$ but below it, toward the high-pressure side. Furthermore, $\bar{z}_{CP}$ depends on the angle θ.

To determine the location of $\bar{y}_{CP}$, we follow a similar procedure for the moment about the $\bar{z}$ axis. Thus, we calculate the moment due to the pressure field and equate it to the moment of the resultant force.

$$F\bar{y}_{CP} = \int\int \bar{y}p \, d\bar{y} \, d\bar{z} = \int\int \bar{y}(p_{atm} + \rho g \bar{z} \sin \theta) \, d\bar{y} \, d\bar{z}$$

Thus,

$$p_c A \bar{y}_{CP} = p_{atm} \bar{y}_c A + \rho g \sin \theta \int\int \bar{y}\bar{z} \, d\bar{y} \, d\bar{z} \qquad (2.16)$$

The integral of the second term on the right of Eq. (2.16) is the product of inertia $I_{\bar{y}\bar{z}}$. Using the parallel axis theorem for the product of inertia, we can write Eq. (2.16) as

$$p_c A \bar{y}_{CP} = \bar{y}_c A(p_{atm} + \rho g \bar{z}_c \sin \theta) + \rho g \sin \theta \, I_{\bar{y}_c \bar{z}_c}$$

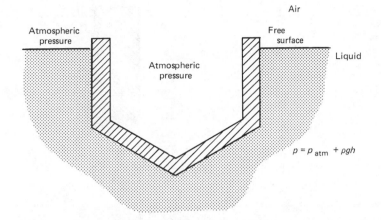

Figure 2.9 Case where the atmospheric pressure can be eliminated from the formulation.

Noting that the term in parentheses is the pressure at the centroid of the plate area, we obtain

$$\bar{y}_{CP} = \bar{y}_c + \frac{\rho g \sin \theta\, I_{\bar{y}_c \bar{z}_c}}{p_c A} \qquad (2.17)$$

If $I_{\bar{y}_c \bar{z}_c} = 0$, which is true for symmetric configurations,

$$\bar{y}_{CP} = \bar{y}_c$$

That is, the center of pressure is in the same vertical plane as the centroid.

For many applications, the other side of the plate is inside a ship or is the dry side of a sluice gate or a dam, as shown in Fig. 2.9. Thus, the pressure at the centroid of the plate (p_c) on the side exposed to the liquid is $p_{atm} + \rho g h_c$ and that on the side exposed to the air is p_{atm}. For problems in which we are interested in the pressure difference, the atmospheric pressure can be eliminated from the formulation. Thus, p_c can be replaced by $\rho g h_c$ for applications where atmospheric air acts on the opposite side of the plate. For applications such as shown in Fig. 2.9,

$$\bar{z}_{CP} = \bar{z}_c + \frac{I_{\bar{y}_c \bar{y}_c} \sin \theta}{h_c A} = \bar{z}_c + \frac{I_{\bar{y}_c \bar{y}_c}}{\bar{z}_c A} \qquad (2.18)$$

and

$$\bar{y}_{CP} = \bar{y}_c + \frac{I_{\bar{y}_c \bar{z}_c} \sin \theta}{h_c A} = \bar{y}_c + \frac{I_{\bar{y}_c \bar{z}_c}}{\bar{z}_c A} \qquad (2.19)$$

Example 2.6

A rectangular gate, 2 m wide, is hinged at point B and rests against a smooth wall at point A, as shown in Fig. 2.10. Calculate (a) the pressure force on the gate due to the seawater, (b) the force exerted by the wall at point A, (c) the forces at hinge B, and (d) the location of the center of pressure.

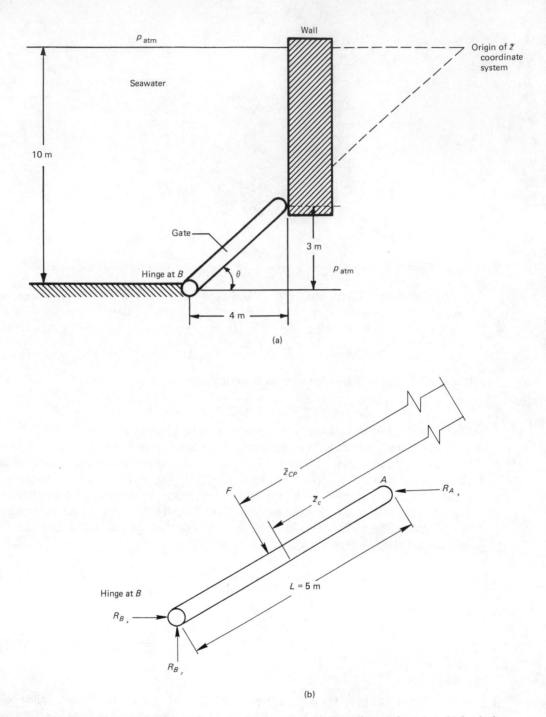

Figure 2.10 Sketch for configuration for Example 2.6: (a) complete configuration; (b) free-body diagram for the gate.

Solution. From the geometry of Fig. 2.10, $\theta = 36.87°$ and the gate is 5 m long. Thus, the area of the plate is 10 m². The centroid of a rectangle is at its midpoint. Thus,

$$h_c = 8.5 \text{ m}$$

$$\bar{z}_c = \frac{8.5}{\sin \theta} = 14.167 \text{ m}$$

The net pressure force on the gate is the difference between the hydrostatic pressure due to the seawater acting on one side of the gate and the atmospheric pressure acting on the other side of the plate.

$$F = p_c A - p_{atm} A = \rho g h_c A$$

From Table 1.3, the specific gravity of seawater is 1.034. Thus,

$$F = 1.034 \, (1000 \text{ kg/m}^3)(9.8066 \text{ m/s}^2)(8.5 \text{ m}) (10 \text{ m}^2)$$

$$= 8.619 \times 10^5 \text{ N}$$

is the answer to part (a).

Before we can determine the answers to parts (b) and (c), we must calculate the point at which the resultant pressure force acts. By symmetry, $\bar{y}_{CP}$ is in the plane of the paper. To calculate $\bar{z}_{CP}$ using Eq. (2.18), we need to evaluate $I_{\bar{y}_c \bar{y}_c}$. For a rectangular plate, the second moment of the area about the $\bar{y}_c$ axis is

$$I_{\bar{y}_c \bar{y}_c} = \frac{wL^3}{12} = \frac{2(125)}{12} = 20.833 \text{ m}^4$$

where w is the width (into the paper) and L is the length of the plate. Thus,

$$\bar{z}_{CP} = \bar{z}_c + \frac{I_{\bar{y}_c \bar{y}_c}}{\bar{z}_c A} = 14.167 + \frac{20.833}{14.167(10)} = 14.314 \text{ m}$$

As discussed earlier, the center of pressure is slightly deeper than the centroid of the rectangular plate. Thus, we have determined the answer to part (d).

To calculate the forces at the ends of the gate, refer to the free-body diagram of the forces acting on the gate that is presented in Fig. 2.10b. Summing the moments about point B and assuming that R_{A_x} acts toward the left, as shown in Fig. 2.10b,

$$\Sigma M_B = 0 = F(2.353) - R_{A_x}(3)$$

$$R_{A_x} = 6.760 \times 10^5 \text{ N}$$

Since the sign of R_{A_x} is positive, we have assumed the correct direction for this force. Thus, R_{A_x} does indeed act to the left (as it should, since the gate rests against the wall).

Summing the forces in the x direction,

$$R_{B_x} + F \sin \theta - R_{A_x} = 0$$

$$R_{B_x} = 6.760 \times 10^5 - 0.6(8.619 \times 10^5) = 1.589 \times 10^5 \text{ N}$$

Finally, summing the forces in the z direction,

$$R_{B_z} - F \cos \theta = 0$$

$$R_{B_z} = 0.8(8.619 \times 10^5) = 6.895 \times 10^5 \text{ N}$$

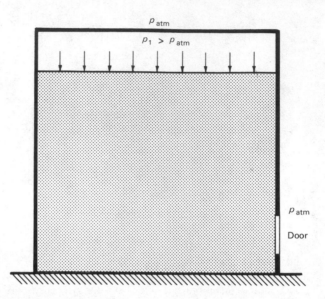

Figure 2.11 Case where the pressure at the surface of the liquid is greater than the atmospheric pressure.

If the situation is as shown in Fig. 2.11, where the pressure at the free surface of the liquid p_1 is above the pressure of the atmosphere outside the tank, we may proceed by imagining the surface of the liquid to be raised by an equivalent height h_{eq}. Thus,

$$p_1 = p_{atm} + \rho g h_{eq} \qquad (2.20)$$

Once we determine h_{eq}, we can use equations such as (2.18) and (2.19) to obtain solutions to the problem. We could also use the basic formulation, noting that the pressure at any point in the liquid is

$$p = p_1 + \rho g h$$

With this approach, we could not use Eqs. (2.18) and (2.19), since atmospheric pressure does not appear in the expressions for the pressure on both sides of the plate.

HYDROSTATIC FORCES ON CURVED SURFACES

Let us now consider the forces on curved surfaces due to the pressure field in a fluid at rest. As we shall see, the forces on curved surfaces submerged in any static fluid can be determined using techniques similar to those developed in the previous section.

Consider the pressure force acting on a curved surface, as shown in Fig. 2.12. The force on an arbitrary area element dA of this surface is directed along the normal to the area element and is given by

$$\vec{dF} = -p\,\vec{dA} \qquad (2.21)$$

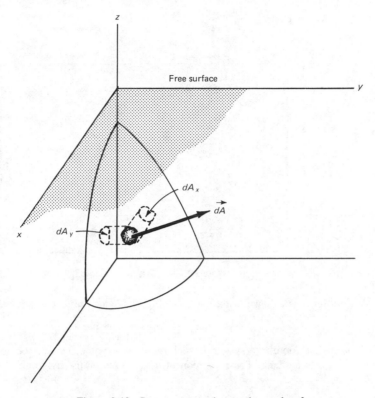

Figure 2.12   Pressure on a submerged curved surface.

The negative sign is used in Eq. (2.21) because the normal is directed outward from the surface and the pressure force is compressive. The application of this sign convention will be demonstrated in Example 2.7. To determine the component of the force in the x direction, we take the dot product of the vector quantities in Eq. (2.21) times the unit vector $\hat{i}$. But $\vec{dA} \cdot \hat{i}$ is the projection of the area element onto a plane normal to the x axis (dA_x). Thus,

$$\vec{dF} \cdot \hat{i} = dF_x = -p\, \vec{dA} \cdot \hat{i} = -p\, dA_x$$

where the resultant negative sign indicates that the force is in the negative x direction. The force in the x direction due to the pressure acting on a surface element is equal to the pressure times the projection of the surface element onto a plane perpendicular to the x axis. This can be extended as a general rule when determining the force component in any direction due the pressure acting on an arbitrary area element.

Example 2.7

Compare the pressure force acting on the end walls of the tank due to the water. As shown in Fig. 2.13, the depth (D) of the water in the tank is $3R$, where R is the radius of the cylindrical-segment protrusion. The axis of the cylindrical protrusion is in the horizontal plane of the free surface of the water.

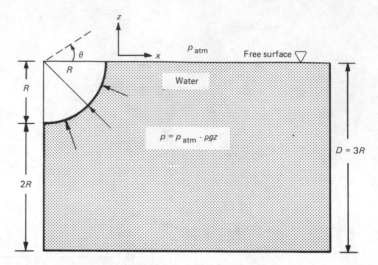

Figure 2.13   Tank for Example 2.7.

Solution.   As shown in the sketch of Fig. 2.13, the pressure at any point in the water is

$$p = p_{\text{atm}} - \rho g z \tag{2.22}$$

where the coordinate system is such that $z = 0$ is the free surface and $z = -3R$ is the bottom of the tank. The x component of the force on the right end of the tank due to the water is

$$F_{R_x} = -\int_{-3R}^{0} p(-dA\ \hat{i}) \cdot \hat{i}$$

The minus sign appears on the factor $(-dA\ \hat{i})$, since the outward directed normal (see Fig. 2.12) acts in the negative x direction. Since the differential area $dA = dz(1)$, where the 1 represents a unit depth into the paper, we find

$$F_{R_x} = +\int_{-3R}^{0} (p_{\text{atm}} - \rho g z)\ dz$$

We obtain a positive sign for the x component of the pressure force (as we would expect) as a result of the consistent application of the sign convention. Integrating,

$$F_{R_x} = p_{\text{atm}} z \ \bigg|_{-3R}^{0} - \rho g \frac{z^2}{2} \ \bigg|_{-3R}^{0}$$

Thus,

$$F_{R_x} = p_{\text{atm}}(3R) + \rho g \frac{9R^2}{2} = p_{\text{atm}}D + \rho g \frac{D^2}{2} \tag{2.23}$$

This is the pressure force acting on the right-end wall due to the water in the tank. Suppose we were interested in the net force on the wall, which would be the difference between the internal and the external forces. Since atmospheric pressure acts uniformly over the external surface of the wall, the net force on the right wall is $\rho g(D^2/2)$.

The x component of the pressure force on the left-end wall is

$$F_{L_x} = -\int_{-\pi/2}^{0} p(R\,d\theta\,\hat{e}_\theta) \cdot \hat{i} - \int_{-3R}^{-R} p(dA\,\hat{i}) \cdot \hat{i}$$

where we have used mixed coordinates r, θ to describe the pressure force on the cylindrical segment protrusion and x, z to describe the pressure force on the rest of the wall. Let us express all the parameters of the first term as a function of the θ variable. Thus,

$$\hat{e}_\theta \cdot \hat{i} = \cos\theta$$

$$p = p_{\text{atm}} - \rho g R \sin\theta$$

Using these substitutions, F_{L_x} becomes

$$F_{L_x} = -\int_{-\pi/2}^{0} (p_{\text{atm}} - \rho g R \sin\theta)\,R\cos\theta\,d\theta - \int_{-3R}^{-R} (p_{\text{atm}} - \rho g z)\,dz$$

$$= -p_{\text{atm}} R \sin\theta \Big|_{-\pi/2}^{0} + \rho g\,R^2\,\tfrac{1}{2}\sin^2\theta \Big|_{-\pi/2}^{0} - p_{\text{atm}} z \Big|_{-3R}^{-R} + \tfrac{1}{2}\rho g z^2 \Big|_{-3R}^{-R}$$

$$= -p_{\text{atm}} R - \tfrac{1}{2}\rho g R^2 + p_{\text{atm}} R - p_{\text{atm}}(3R) + \tfrac{1}{2}\rho g R^2 - \tfrac{1}{2}\rho g(9R^2)$$

Thus,

$$F_{L_r} = -\left[p_{\text{atm}}\,(3R) + \rho g\left(\frac{9R^2}{2}\right)\right] = -\left[p_{\text{atm}} D + \rho g\,\frac{D^2}{2}\right] \tag{2.24}$$

Comparing Eqs. (2.23) and (2.24), we see that the x component of the force on the right end is the negative of that on the left end. The shape of the wall does not affect the resultant force, since the force component in a given direction is the product of the pressure times the projected area for that direction, integrated over the entire surface.

There is a difference in the z components of the forces on the end walls. For the right-end wall,

$$F_{R_z} = 0$$

since the wall is vertical. For the left-end wall,

$$F_{L_z} = -\int_{-\pi/2}^{0} p(R\,d\theta\,\hat{e}_\theta) \cdot (\hat{k})$$

Since $\hat{e}_\theta \cdot (\hat{k}) = \sin\theta$,

$$F_{L_z} = -\int_{-\pi/2}^{0} (p_{\text{atm}} - \rho g R \sin\theta)\,R\,d\theta\,\sin\theta$$

$$= p_{\text{atm}} R \cos\theta \Big|_{-\pi/2}^{0} + \rho g R^2\left[\frac{\theta}{2} - \frac{\sin 2\theta}{4}\right]_{-\pi/2}^{0} \tag{2.25}$$

$$= p_{\text{atm}} R + \rho g\,\frac{\pi R^2}{4}$$

If we are interested in the net force on the arc in the z direction, we must account for the atmospheric pressure acting over the external surface of the cylindrical-segment protrusion. Since the pressure on the external surface is constant over the entire arc, the force in any direction is the product of the pressure times the projected area normal to that direction. Thus, the z component of force due to the external atmospheric pressure is $-p_{atm}R$, and the net force in the z direction is $\rho g(\pi R^2/4)$. Note that the net vertical force on the left-end wall is equal to the weight of the fluid displaced from the quadrant of the cylinder.

Let us now analyze the hydrostatic pressure forces acting on the two-dimensional curved surface AB, as shown in Fig. 2.14. Since the configuration is two-dimensional, we will calculate the various force components per unit depth (into the paper). To solve for the forces acting on the curved surface AB, let us draw a free-body diagram of the forces acting on the fluid in the control volume AOB. As shown in Fig. 2.15, the forces acting on the mass of fluid are (1) F_H, the horizontal force of the surrounding fluid, (2) F_V, the downward force of the surrounding fluid, (3) W, the weight of the fluid in AOB, and (4) and (5) F_{R_x} and F_{R_z}, the force components of AB on the fluid in the control volume.

Summing the forces in the horizontal direction,

$$F_{R_x} = F_H \tag{2.26}$$

and in the vertical direction,

$$F_{R_z} = F_V + W \tag{2.27}$$

In Eq. (2.26), we see that the magnitude of the horizontal reaction of the curved surface is equal to the hydrostatic force that acts on a vertical projection of the curved surface. From Eq. (2.27), we see that the vertical reaction is equal to the sum of the vertical forces acting above the curved surface. These general principles apply to any curved surface. Furthermore, the line of action of the horizontal force is the same line

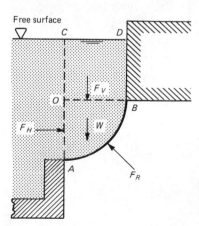

Figure 2.14 Hydrostatic pressure acting on the two-dimensional curved surface AB.

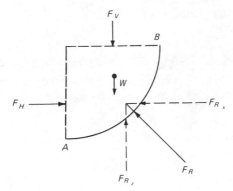

Figure 2.15 Free-body diagram for forces acting on curved surface AB.

of action as the force on the projected area, and the line of action of the vertical force is the line of action of the weight of water (plus atmospheric pressure, if necessary).

Since we have found the forces that make up the reaction of the curved surface AB, we need only reverse the signs of the components to determine the resultant hydrostatic forces of the water on the arc. By vectorially adding the component forces, we can determine both the magnitude and the line of action of the resultant force.

Example 2.8

Let us determine the hydrostatic force on the curved surface AB for the following conditions. AB is a circular arc whose radius is 1 m. The distance OC is 10 m. Water is the liquid supported by the surface AB, and air at standard atmospheric pressure is outside the arc.

Solution. Using Eq. (2.26), we can calculate F_{R_x}, which is equal to F_H, the horizontal force due to the pressure acting on the length OA.

$$F_{R_x} = F_H = p_c A = (p_{\text{atm}} + \rho g h_c)A$$

The product ρg, which is also known as γ (the specific weight), is 9.8066×10^3 N/m^3 for water. We will use a unit depth for our calculations of the area. Noting that the centroid of the projected area is located 10.5 m below the surface (i.e., $h_c = 10.5$ m),

$$F_{R_x} = [1.01325 \times 10^5 + (9.8066 \times 10^3)(10.5)]1 = 2.043 \times 10^5 \text{ N}$$

Since atmospheric pressure acts on the outside of the arc, the net force in the x direction is

$$F_{N_x} = F_H - p_{\text{atm}}(\overline{OA})(1) = 1.030 \times 10^5 \text{ N}$$

Using Eq. (2.27), the force in the vertical direction is

$$F_{R_z} = F_V + W = [p_{\text{atm}} + \rho g(\overline{OC})]1 + \rho g\left(\frac{\pi R^2}{4}\right)$$

$$= [1.01325 \times 10^5 + (9.8066 \times 10^3)(10)]1 + 9.8066 \times 10^3\left(\frac{\pi}{4}1\right)$$

$$= 2.071 \times 10^5 \text{ N}$$

The net force on the arc AB in the z direction is

$$F_{N_z} = F_{R_z} - p_{\text{atm}}(\overline{OB})(1) = 1.058 \times 10^5 \text{ N}$$

Note that the net force on the gate is equal to the weight of the water in the volume $OCDBA$ directly above the gate. Thus, for this case where atmospheric pressure acts downward at the free surface and upward on the underside of the arc, the atmospheric pressure terms cancel each other.

BUOYANCY

The buoyant force on a body is defined as the net vertical force that is produced by the fluid, or fluids, in contact with the body. The same basic principles used to compute the hydrostatic forces on surfaces can be applied to determine the net pressure force on a completely submerged body or on a floating body. The results may be summarized by the two laws of buoyancy discovered by Archimedes in the third century B.C:

1. A body immersed in a fluid experiences a vertical buoyant force equal to the weight of the fluid that it displaces.
2. A floating body displaces its own weight in the liquid in which it floats.

The first statement is consistent with our calculations of the vertical force on the cylindrical-segment protrusion, as discussed in Example 2.7. The net force was found to be equal to the weight of the fluid displaced by the quadrant of the cylinder. The second statement reflects the fact that the weight of the air displaced by the floating body is usually negligible and, therefore, the displaced liquid supplies the necessary buoyant force. The mathematical formulation of the first statement is

$$F_B = (\rho g)(\text{body volume}) = (\gamma)(\text{body volume}) \qquad (2.28)$$

where F_B is the buoyant force acting on a body immersed in a single fluid, where the fluid has a uniform specific weight. The line of action of the buoyant force passes through the center of volume of the displaced fluid, the point CB (center of buoyancy) of Fig. 2.16. The point CB is also the center of mass of the displaced fluid, but it is not necessarily the center of mass of the body's own material, since the body may be of variable density. The stability of an immersed body depends on the relative positions of the center of gravity of the body and the centroid of the displaced volume of the fluid, or the center of buoyancy.

Equation (2.28) can be generalized for a body immersed in a layered fluid, that is, one in which there are layers of immiscible fluids of different densities. The buoyant force acting on a body in a layered fluid is

$$(F_B)_{LF} = \sum_i \rho_i g \, (\text{displaced volume})_i \qquad (2.29)$$

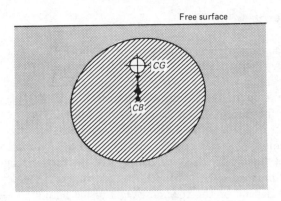

Figure 2.16 Sketch showing body (with nonuniform properties, as indicated by the relatively high *CG*) submerged in a liquid.

Each of the *i* layers would have its own center of volume, and one would have to sum the moments for the incremental buoyant forces in order to determine the resultant center of buoyancy. However, in nautical work, where we are interested in a body floating at the interface of air–water media, we would generally neglect the specific weight of air. In this case, the center of buoyancy is at the centroid of the volume of water displaced by the floating body.

Example 2.9

You are an engineer for a salvage company that is to raise a treasure chest from the sunken hull of an ancient ship. The item that you are to raise weighs 3 kN in air and has a volume of 0.10 m³. You plan to use oil drums filled with air as flotation devices for the chest. An empty oil drum weighs 225 N in seawater and has an internal volume of 0.20 m³. What is the minimum number of drums needed to lift the treasure?

Solution.   Let us first calculate the effective weight of the treasure chest in seawater.

$$W_{tr,sw} = W_{tr,a} - \rho_{sw}gV_{tr}$$

$$= 3000 - 1.034(9.8066 \times 10^3)(0.1) = 1986.0 \text{ N}$$

Let us now calculate the lifting power of one oil drum, which is the negative of the weight of the oil drum in seawater minus the buoyant force of the air contained in the drum.

$$L_{od} = -\left(W_{od,sw} - \rho_{sw}gV_{od}\right)$$

$$= -[225 - 1.034(9.8066 \times 10^3)(0.2)] = +1803.0 \text{ N}$$

Thus, one drum lifts slightly less than the required weight. It will take a minimum of two drums to lift the treasure.

Hydrometry

The precise measurement of the specific weight of a liquid can be made using the principle of buoyancy. The device used for this task is the hydrometer, which consists of a relatively large glass bulb, weighted on one end, with a relatively slender stem of constant diameter extending from the other end, as shown in Fig. 2.17. The design of the hydrometer is such that the weighted end ensures the stability of the device. Furthermore, only the slender stem extends above the liquid surface. Because of the relatively small cross section of the stem, appreciable vertical movement of the hydrometer is required to change the volume of liquid displaced by the device. Because the buoyant force is equal to the weight of the hydrometer, it must be constant. Thus, the depth to which the hydrometer sinks will depend on the specific weight of the liquid. Consequently, a graduated scale on the stem can provide a direct measure of the specific weight (or, equivalently, of the specific gravity) of the liquid being measured.

STABILITY

Submerged Bodies

The stability of a completely submerged body depends upon the relative positions of the center of gravity of the body and the centroid of the displaced volume of fluid, called the *center of buoyancy*. If the center of buoyancy is above the center of gravity, any tipping of the body will automatically produce a restoring moment. Thus, for the balloon and basket configuration shown in Fig. 2.18, any displacement (position 2) from the normal position (position 1) produces a moment that tends to restore the system to the original position. The system is, therefore, stable.

If the center of gravity is above the center of buoyancy, the system is unstable. Consider the configuration shown in Fig. 2.16. Any displacement from the orientation shown, that is, with the center of gravity directly above the center of buoyancy, will produce an overturning moment that causes the body to continue turning until the stable configuration is reached.

If the center of buoyancy and the center of gravity are coincident, the body is neutrally stable.

Floating Bodies

Determining whether or not a configuration is stable is a much more difficult problem for floating bodies than for submerged bodies, because the location of the center of buoyancy changes as the floating body pitches and rolls. The position of the center of buoyancy relative to the center of gravity depends upon the shape of the body and the position in which it floats. For example, consider the ship shown in Fig. 2.19a, where the center of gravity is above the center of buoyancy. Assuming the weight does not shift

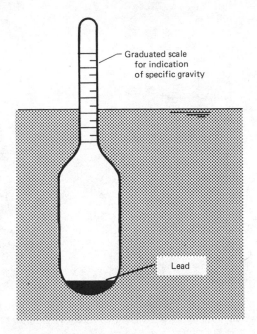

Figure 2.17 Sketch of a hydrometer.

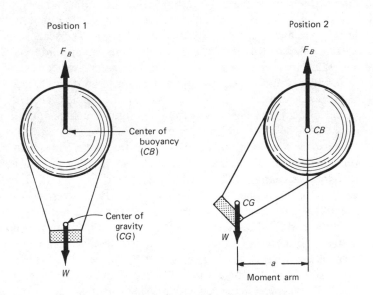

Figure 2.18 Stability of a submerged body.

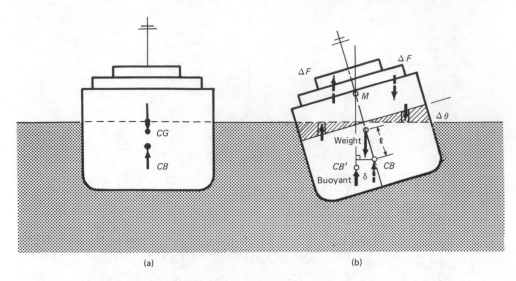

Figure 2.19 Ship cross section, illustrating stability of floating body: (a) initial position; (b) perturbed position.

as the ship rolls, the center of gravity remains fixed. However, the center of buoyancy shifts far enough to develop a restoring moment.

To investigate the stability of a floating body, consider the situation where the ship of Fig. 2.19 undergoes a small rotation $\Delta\theta$ about the longitudinal axis y. The perturbed position of the ship is illustrated in Fig. 2.19b. In rolling about the y axis in a counterclockwise sense, the ship displaces an additional volume of water from the left side, while it leaves a corresponding volume on the right. The sections of these volumes are indicated by the shaded areas of Fig. 2.19b. Thus, an upward force ΔF is developed on the left side of the ship as a result of the increased displacement of fluid on that side, and a downward force of equal value is developed on the right side of the ship because of the decreased displacement. These forces form a couple C about the y axis. As a result, the center of buoyancy has moved from its original, uptipped position at CB to the new position CB'. The center of gravity remains at CG.

Thus, the force system is equivalent to the single buoyant force $F_{CB'}$ at CB'. The point of intersection of the lines of action of the buoyant force before and after the roll is called the *metacenter, M*. The distance from M to the CG ($\overline{MG}$) is called the *metacentric height*. If M is above the CG, the weight W produces a restoring moment and the ship is stable. The greater the distance $\overline{MG}$, the greater is the restoring moment and the more stable is the vessel. If M falls on the CG, the configuration is neutrally stable. If M is below the CG, the vessel is unstable. It should be clear that any floating object with a center of gravity that is below its center of buoyancy will float in stable equilibrium.

Consider a floating block such as is shown in Fig. 2.20. The block is given a small rotational displacement in the counterclockwise direction. As a result of the displacement, a couple C is formed about the y (or longitudinal) axis. The total buoyant force system for the tipped configuration (see Fig. 2.20b) can be considered to be the sum of the force

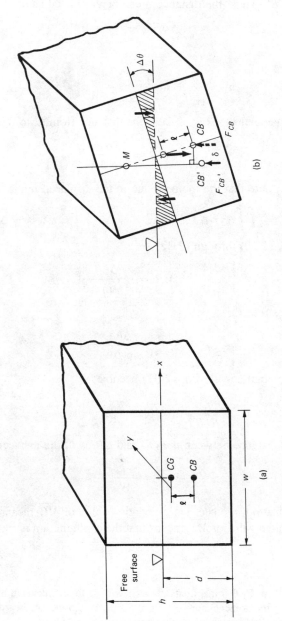

Figure 2.20 Nomenclature for stability of floating block: (a) unperturbed position; (b) perturbed position.

F_{CB} at the CB and the couple C. The force system is equivalent to the single force $F_{CB'}$ acting at CB'. Thus, the distance δ can be calculated using

$$-\delta F_{CB} + C = 0$$

or

$$\delta = \frac{C}{F_{CB}} = \frac{C}{W} \qquad (2.30)$$

From the geometry of Fig. 2.20b, the distance from M to the CB ($\overline{MB}$) is

$$\overline{MB} = \frac{\delta}{\sin \Delta\theta} \qquad (2.31)$$

To determine C, note that the moment due to the displaced liquid is

$$C = \int\int (\gamma x \, \Delta\theta \, dx \, dy)x = \gamma \, \Delta\theta \int\int x^2 \, dA = \gamma \, \Delta\theta \, I_{yy} \qquad (2.32)$$

Combining Eqs. (2.30) through (2.32),

$$\overline{MB} = \frac{\gamma \, \Delta\theta \, I_{yy}}{W \sin \Delta\theta} \qquad (2.33)$$

Using l'Hopital's rule,

$$\lim_{\Delta\theta \to 0} \frac{\Delta\theta}{\sin \Delta\theta} = 1$$

we see that, for small angles, Eq. (2.33) becomes

$$\overline{MB} = \frac{\gamma \, I_{yy}}{W} \qquad (2.34)$$

Designating the distance between the CG and CB as ℓ, the metacentric height $\overline{MG}$ is

$$\overline{MG} = \frac{\gamma \, I_{yy}}{W} - \ell \qquad (2.35)$$

From this formulation, we see that a negative value of $\overline{MG}$ means the configuration is unstable. A positive value of $\overline{MG}$ means that the configuration is stable (at least for small displacements).

Example 2.10

A board, 1.5 in. by 3.5 in., floats in water with its long dimension in the vertical direction; that is, using the nomenclature of Fig. 2.20a, $h = 3.5$ in. The board is 1 ft long. The γ of wood is 40 lbf/ft^3. Is this orientation stable?

Solution. The wood weighs

$$W = 40\left(\frac{1.5}{12}\right)\left(\frac{3.5}{12}\right)1 = 1.458 \text{ lbf}$$

In order to float, the wood must displace a volume of water weighing an equal amount.

$$62.43d\left(\frac{1.5}{12}\right)1 = 1.458$$

$$d = 0.1868 \text{ ft} = 2.24 \text{ in.}$$

Thus, the center of gravity is 1.75 in. from the top of the block, while the center of buoyancy is 2.38 in. from the top of the block. The distance between them (ℓ) is 0.63 in. Using Eq. (2.35),

$$\overline{MG} = \frac{\gamma\, I_{yy}}{W} - \ell = \frac{(62.43)\left[\frac{1}{12}\left(\frac{1.5}{12}\right)^3 1\right]}{1.458} - \frac{0.63}{12}$$

$$= 0.00697 - 0.05250 < 0$$

Since $\overline{MG}$ is negative, the board in this orientation is not stable.

PROBLEMS

As noted in Chapter 1, it will be stated specifically if the pressure is given or is to be calculated as a gage pressure. If not defined otherwise, the pressure is the absolute value.

2.1. Consider a situation where crude oil in a storage tank is everywhere at rest and the air above the free surface of the oil is at standard-atmosphere sea-level conditions. If the specific gravity of the crude oil is 0.86, what is the distance below the surface at which the pressure is 2 atm absolute? At what point is the pressure 1500 psfg?

2.2. A skin diver is swimming in fresh water at a depth of 45 m. What is the pressure acting at this depth in N/m² and in psig? What is the ratio of the absolute pressure at this depth to the pressure at the surface of the water? Assume that the temperature of the water is 25°C and that the density is 997.1 kg/m³.

2.3. Determine the heights of columns of (a) water, (b) ethyl alcohol, and (c) carbon tetrachloride (whose specific gravity is 1.59) that are equivalent to a column of mercury 250 mm high.

2.4. If the vapor pressure of water in Fig. P2.4 is 49 psf at 68°F, what is the maximum height (h) for the column of water before the dissolved gases are liberated in the form of bubbles?

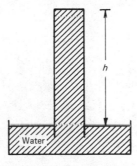

Figure P2.4   Sketch for Prob. 2.4.

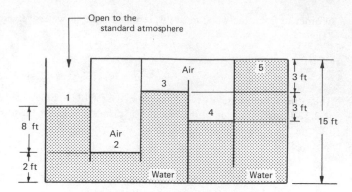

Figure P2.5 Sketch for Prob. 2.5.

2.5. A device contains air and water, as shown in Fig. P2.5. What are the pressures at points 1 through 5 in kPa and in psfg?

2.6. A device contains cells of air, water, and glycerine, as shown in Fig. P2.6. What are the pressures at points 1 through 5 in N/m^2 and in psf?

2.7. An irregular-shaped vessel contains water, glycerine, and mercury, as shown in Fig. P2.7. Sketch the pressure distribution along the three lines.

2.8. A hydraulic jack with the dimensions shown in Fig. P2.8 is used to work on a car. If the jack is to support a load of 4 kN, what force (F_1) must be applied to the handle of the jack?

2.9. A cylindrical diving bell, enclosed at the top and open at the bottom, is 10 ft high and 3 ft in diameter. The diving bell, which was originally full of air, is lowered until fresh water rises 4 ft into the interior. How far below the surface is the top of the bell for this condition? Assume isothermal compression of the air in the bell.

2.10. Two cylindrical diving bells (similar to that of Prob. 2.9) are lowered into fresh water until the water inside the first bell rises 3 ft into the interior while the water inside the second bell rises 1 ft into the interior. If the air cells in the two bells are connected, what will be the water levels in the two bells? Assume isothermal compression of the air in the bell.

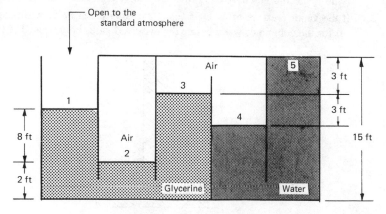

Figure P2.6 Sketch for Prob. 2.6.

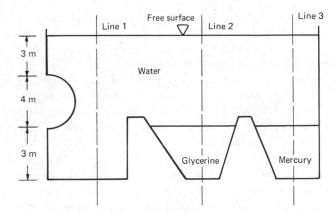

Figure P2.7   Sketch for Prob. 2.7.

2.11. Determine the pressure at the bottom of a container that is 20 ft deep and is filled with a liquid whose specific weight (in lbf/ft³) varies with depth according to the equation $\gamma = 45 + 0.5d$, where d is the depth in feet and is measured downward from the surface.

2.12. At what altitude is the static pressure one-half the sea-level value if one uses the isothermal relation, that is, Eq. (2.8)? Compare the calculated altitude with that presented in Table 1.1.

2.13. At what altitude is the static pressure one-half the sea-level value if one accounts for the temperature variation with altitude, that is, Eq. (2.10)? What is the temperature at this altitude? Compare the calculated values with those presented in Table 1.1.

2.14. For the model for the atmosphere using English units, the temperature at sea level is 59°F and decreases 1°F for every 280.5 ft. If the pressure at sea level is 2116 lbf/ft², and the gas constant for air is 53.34 ft lbf/lbm°R, what is the ambient pressure at 20,000 ft.

For Probs. 2.15 through 2.20, use the nomenclature of Fig. 2.7.

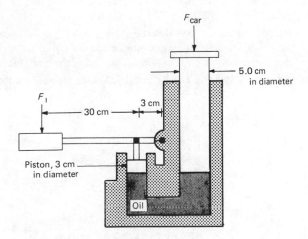

Figure P2.8.   Sketch for Prob. 2.8.

2.15. The pressure at the centerline of the pipe is 12 psfg. Fluid A is air. We can determine the height of the column of fluid B to within ± 0.02 in. If we wish to maintain an accuracy of $\pm 1\%$ or less, should we use unity-weight oil or mercury for fluid B? For unity-weight oil, $\sigma = 1.00$; for mercury, $\sigma = 13.5951$.

2.16. The pressure at the centerline of the pipe is 12 psig. Fluid A is air. We can determine the height of the column of fluid B to within ± 0.02 in. If we wish to maintain an accuracy of $\pm 1\%$ or less, should we use unity-weight oil or mercury for fluid B?

2.17. If fluid A is oil whose specific gravity is 0.93 and fluid B is water, what is the pressure at the centerline of the pipe if $h_1 = 5.0$ cm and $h_2 = 20.0$ cm?

2.18. What is the pressure at the centerline of the pipe if fluid A is water, fluid B is mercury, h_1 is 1.0 m, and $h_2 = 5.0$ cm? Determine the gage pressure in kPa and in psf.

2.19. Fluid A is water, while fluid B is a manometer fluid whose specific gravity is 2.94. If the gage pressure at the centerline of the pipe is 5 kPa and $h_1 = 10$ cm, what is h_2?

2.20. Fluid A is air; fluid B is mercury. What is the gage pressure at the pipe centerline if $h_1 = 10$ cm and $h_2 = 100$ cm?

2.21. Determine the difference in pressure between points A and B in Fig. P2.21.

2.22. What is the pressure p_A for the configuration of Fig. P2.22. The specific gravity of the oil is 0.80.

2.23. A vertical gate 5 ft high by 10 ft wide is used as a dam for fresh water. What is the necessary resisting moment at the bottom to hold the gate in position?

2.24. A vertical gate 3 m high by 15 m wide is used as a dam for fresh water. What is the necessary resisting moment at the bottom to hold the gate in position?

2.25. When concrete is poured into wooden forms, the forces on the forms can be estimated by assuming that the freshly poured concrete behaves as a liquid whose specific gravity is 2.40. Determine the force exerted by the concrete per foot of length of the form if the concrete is poured into forms for a wall that is to be 8 ft high. If the forms are held in place by pins that are located every 2 ft, as shown in Fig. P2.25, what force is exerted on the two bolts at a station?

2.26. Calculate the force and the center of pressure on one side of the vertical triangular panel ABC shown in Fig. P2.26.

2.27. A horizontal cylindrical tank that is 5 m long and 1.5 m in diameter is filled with oil whose specific gravity is 0.90. If the pressure inside the top of the tank is atmospheric, calculate the force exerted on the circular panel at the end of the tank. Where is the center of pressure?

2.28. Determine the forces at A and B due to hydrostatic pressure for the gate shown in Fig. P2.28.

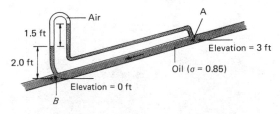

Figure P2.21   Sketch for Prob. 2.21.

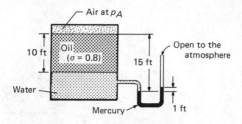

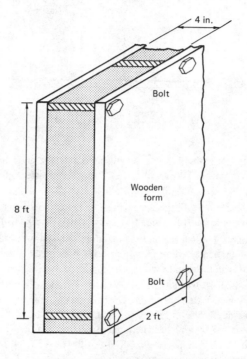

Figure P2.22 Sketch for Prob. 2.22.

Figure P2.25 Sketch for Prob. 2.25.

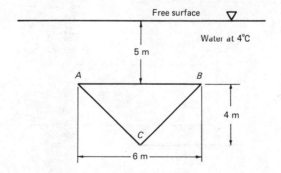

Figure P2.26 Sketch for Prob. 2.26.

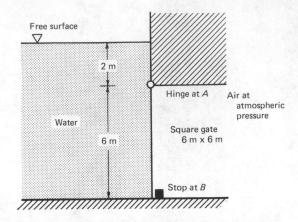

Figure P2.28   Sketch for Prob. 2.28.

2.29. At what height (h) will the water cause the gate shown in Fig. P2.29 to rotate in a clockwise sense? The gate is 10 m wide, L is 7 m, and W is 300,000 N. Neglect the weight of the gate.

2.30. At what height (h) will the water cause the gate shown in Fig. P2.29 to rotate in a clockwise sense? The gate is 10 ft wide, L is 15 ft, and W is 8000 lbf. Neglect the weight of the gate.

2.31. A gate that is 1 m square and is hinged at B, as shown in Fig. P2.31, is used as a valve. It opens automatically when the water level h exceeds a certain value. Determine the lowest height for which the gate will open.

2.32. A tank, which is divided at the center by a vertical partition, contains water on one side of the partition to a depth of 5 m. On the other side, nitric acid (specific gravity = 1.50) is stored to a depth of 6 m. There is a rectangular opening at the bottom of the center partition, which is sealed by a plate. The plate is 70 cm high by 40 cm wide. It is hinged at its upper edge, that is, 70 cm above the bottom of the tank. What force must be applied at the lower edge of the plate to keep it closed?

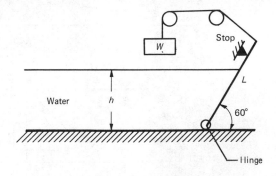

Figure P2.29   Sketch for Probs. 2.29 and 2.30.

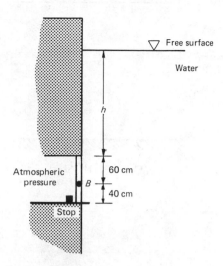

Figure P2.31   Sketch for Prob. 2.31.

2.33. Nitric acid ($\sigma = 1.50$) is stored under pressure and passes through a pipeline to a processor as shown in Fig. P2.33. A piston 2 in. in diameter is used to seal the line. What must be the pressure p_B in order to drive the piston into the closed position?

2.34. Calculate the resultant force acting on the wall shown in Fig. P2.34.

2.35. What is the resultant force on the wall shown in Fig. P2.35.

2.36. Calculate the resultant force on the hemispherical bulge on the bottom of the tank shown in Fig. P2.36.

2.37. The cylindrical element AB of Fig. P2.37, whose radius is 1.5 m, is a gate, 5 m wide. The gate is hinged at B and rests against a smooth wall at A. Neglecting the effects of friction, what are the forces at points A and B?

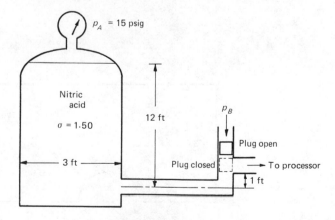

Figure P2.33   Sketch for Prob. 2.33.

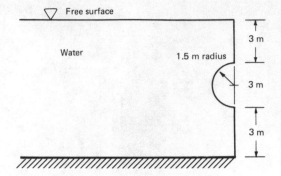

Figure P2.34 Sketch for Prob. 2.34.

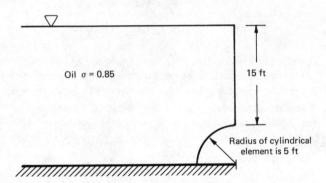

Figure P2.35 Sketch for Prob. 2.35.

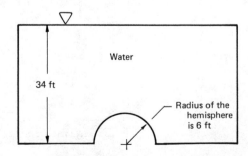

Figure P2.36 Sketch for Prob. 2.36.

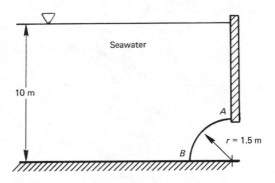

Figure P2.37 Sketch for Prob. 2.37.

2.38. The hemispherical dome shown in Fig. P2.38 weighs 5000 lbf and is filled with water. If the dome has no bottom, what force must be exerted through the bolts in order to hold the dome in place?

2.39. A butterfly valve is mounted in the vertical end wall of a large water basin. The valve consists of a circular disk, 4 ft in diameter, pivoted about a horizontal axis that passes through its center. Water stands to a level that is 6 ft above the top of the valve. Atmospheric pressure acts at the free surface of the water and on the outside of the valve. What torque is necessary to keep the valve closed?

2.40. A circular, cylindrical log, 3 ft in diameter and 10 ft long, rests on the bottom of a creek bed. The water, which is at rest, stands to a depth of 3 ft on one side of the log and 1.5 ft on the other side. If the specific weight of the log is 40 lbf/ft³, what is the net force on the log?

2.41. An iceberg floats in seawater. The specific weight of the ice is 57 lbf/ft³; that of seawater is 64.55 lbf/ft³. If a volume of 100,000 ft³ of the iceberg is visible protruding above the free surface, what is the total volume of the iceberg?

2.42. A ship displaces 130 m³ in seawater. What is the weight of the ship?

2.43. A balloon contains 10,000 ft³ of hydrogen, which has a specific weight of 0.0069 lbf/ft³. What is the lifting potential of the balloon at the earth's surface if the balloon weighs 300 lbf?

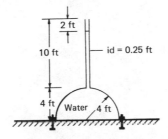

Figure P2.38 Sketch for Prob. 2.38.

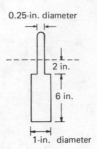

Figure P2.45 Sketch for Prob. 2.45.

2.44. A marker buoy, 1 m in diameter, is made of material that weighs 6400 N/m^3. The buoy is moored in seawater. If the tension in the mooring line is 600 N, what fraction of the buoy is above the surface?

2.45. A hydrometer, weighing 0.2 lbf, floats as shown in Fig. P2.45. What is the specific gravity of the liquid in which it floats?

2.46. A board, 1.5 in. by 3.5 in., floats in water so that the sides that are 3.5 in. are parallel to the surface; thus using the nomenclature of Fig. 2.20a, $h = 1.5$ in. If the board is 1 ft long and $\gamma = 40$ lbf/ft^3, is this orientation stable?

2.47. A cylindrical log 1 ft in diameter and 1 ft long floats in water. If the specific weight of the wood is 50 lbf/ft^3, will the log float in the water with its ends horizontal?

2.48. A cylindrical log 1 ft in diameter and 1 ft long floats in water. If the specific weight of the wood is 30 lbf/ft^3, will the log float in the water with its ends horizontal?

2.49. A spar buoy, 2 in. by 2 in. by 8 ft, is made of wood that weighs 40 lbf/ft^3. A metal weight of 4 lbf is placed at one end of the buoy. Is this buoy stable when floating in a vertical position with the weight at the bottom?

2.50. A barge that is 20 ft wide by 60 ft long is loaded with rock, as shown in Fig. P2.50. The rock and the barge weigh 480,000 lbf. If the center of gravity of the rock-laden barge is at the top surface of the barge, is this configuration stable?

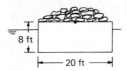

Figure P2.50 Sketch for Prob. 2.50.

CHAPTER THREE

Fundamentals of Flow Analysis and the Conservation of Mass

For many fluid mechanics problems, the engineer is interested in determining the forces and moments acting on an object located in a moving stream or moving through a static fluid medium. For other problems, the engineer may seek to determine the rate at which heat is transferred to or from an object owing to the relative motion of the fluid around an object. For such problems, the engineer must be able to describe the velocity field as a function of space and time. The flow may be such that the velocity field can be determined independently of the other flow parameters. In other flow situations, it may be necessary for the engineer to solve for several flow parameters (including the velocity) simultaneously. In this and subsequent chapters, the basic equations for describing fluid motion will be derived, and solution techniques will be developed for problems of varying difficulty.

VELOCITY FIELD

Fluid motion can be described in two ways. In one approach, the Lagrangian point of view, the motion of an individual particle is followed as it moves through space. However, the motion of a single fluid particle is inadequate to describe an entire flow field. The motion of the entire flow field is obtained by describing the motion of each and every particle in the field of flow. Because the relative positions of fluid particles change continuously with time, the Lagrangian description, which is often used in analyzing problems in solid mechanics, is seldom applied to fluid mechanics.

The alternative way, known as the Eulerian point of view, is to select a certain point in space and describe the motion of the fluid particles which pass that point as time goes on. In the Eulerian description, the fluid particle velocity depends on the point in space that is chosen and on time. Thus, in the Cartesian coordinate system, the velocity is given as

$$\vec{V} = u\hat{i} + v\hat{j} + w\hat{k} \tag{3.1a}$$

where

$$u(x, y, z, t), \quad v(x, y, z, t), \quad \text{and} \quad w(x, y, z, t) \tag{3.1b}$$

FLOW PATTERNS: STREAMLINES AND PATHLINES

Visualizations of fluid motion that can be generated numerically or experimentally provide the engineer with graphic insights into the flow field solution. Often it is desirable to define lines in the flow field that can be used to represent the speed and direction of flow. Lines that are constructed such that they are always tangent to the local velocity vectors of the fluid particles in a flow are called *streamlines*. Consequently, a tangent to the curve at any point along the streamline gives the direction of the velocity vector at that point in the flow field. This is illustrated in Fig. 3.1. Because the local velocity vector is tangent (parallel) to the streamline, there is no flow across a streamline. Since there is no flow through an impervious boundary (i.e., a solid wall adjacent to the fluid domain), the velocity vectors of the flow adjacent to such boundaries must be parallel to it. Therefore, the contour of a solid surface located in the flow field is a streamline.

Because every vector arc length $d\vec{r}$ along a streamline must be tangent to $\vec{V}$, their respective components must be in direct proportion; that is,

$$\frac{dx}{u} = \frac{dy}{v} = \frac{dz}{w} = \left|\frac{d\vec{r}}{\vec{V}}\right| \tag{3.2}$$

A closed pattern of streamlines is called a *streamtube*. By definition, the fluid within a streamtube is confined there, because it cannot cross the streamlines, that is, the lateral

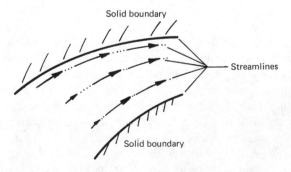

Figure 3.1   Streamlines for a steady, incompressible flow in a channel.

surface of the streamtube. The streamtube walls may be solid surfaces, such as the wall of a pipe, or they may be fluid surfaces across which there is no flow.

Since a streamline is a line everywhere tangent to the velocity vector at a given instant, it is an instantaneous line. Streamlines are difficult to generate experimentally in unsteady flow unless one is able to mark a great many fluid particles and define their

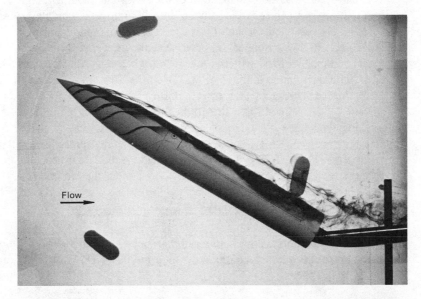

Figure 3.2 Tangent ogive-cylinder with and without tapered nose boom at zero sideslip (in a water tunnel). Photographs supplied by Northrop Corporation.

direction of motion during a short time interval. For steady flow, streamlines are easy to identify.

A *pathline* is the trajectory of a fluid particle of fixed identity. A pathline can be found by a time exposure of a single marked particle moving through the flow field. Streamlines and pathlines are identical in a steady flow.

Clearly, an accurate visualization of the flow field about a vehicle is a valuable aid to the engineer and can provide valuable insights into very complex, three-dimensional flow fields. Dye injected through the surface of a model mounted in a water tunnel can provide excellent flow visualization because of the light-reflecting characteristics of a dye in water. Examples of the patterns that result when dye is injected through the surface of a missile model that is inclined to the oncoming flow are presented in the photographs of Fig. 3.2. The photographs were taken during a test program conducted in the Northrop Diagnostic Water Tunnel. The streamlines for the flow on the windward (or upstream) side of the model are clearly evident. For the leeward surface of the model, the dye reflects the more complex flow pattern of a three-dimensional flow separation. Part of the dye diffuses (i.e., fans out) in the separated viscous flow near the surface, and part of it marks the core of a vortex that breaks down near the tail end of the model.

DESCRIPTION OF THE FLOW AROUND A MOVING OBJECT

If one is to calculate the flow field around an object moving through a fluid medium, it is necessary to solve the equations governing the flow. The governing equations can be

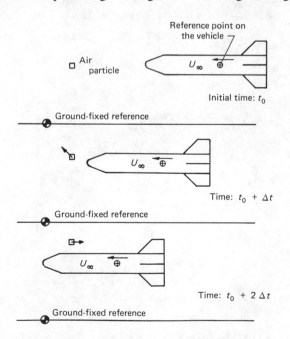

Figure 3.3   The (nonsteady) air flow around a missile in the ground-fixed coordinate system.

formulated either from the point of view of an observer at a fixed point who watches the object move past him or from the point of view of an observer moving with the object who watches the fluid move around the object. Providing the two observers apply the appropriate boundary conditions to the governing equations, both observers will obtain the same values for the forces acting on the object.

To an observer on the ground, that is, at a fixed point, the object is "flying" through a mass of fluid that is substantially at rest. The neighboring fluid particles are accelerated and decelerated by the object. The reaction of the particles to the acceleration results in a force on the object. The motion of a typical fluid particle is shown in Fig. 3.3. The particle, which is initially at rest well ahead of the object, is accelerated by its passage. The description of the flow field in a ground-fixed coordinate system must represent the time-dependent motion of the fluid particles. Thus, even if the object moves at a constant speed and at a constant altitude, the flow is nonsteady.

As viewed by an observer moving with the object, the fluid moves past the object in response to its geometry. If the object moves at a constant velocity, at a constant altitude, and with a constant attitude, the terms of the flow-field equations that contain derivatives with respect to time are zero in this object-fixed coordinate system. Thus, as shown in Fig. 3.4, the velocity and the flow properties of the fluid particles that pass through a specific location relative to the object are independent of time. The flow is steady relative to a set of axes fixed to the object (or vehicle). Therefore, the equations are easier to solve in the object-fixed coordinate system than in the ground-fixed coordinate

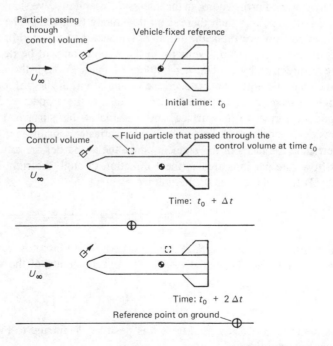

Figure 3.4 The (steady) air flow around a missile in an object-fixed coordinate system.

system. Because of the resulting simplification of the mathematics, many problems in fluid mechanics are formulated as the flow of a stream of fluid past a body at rest. Note that the subsequent locations of the fluid particle that passed through the control volume at time t_0 are included for comparison in Fig. 3.4.

In the majority of applications in this text, the object-fixed coordinate system will be used. Thus, instead of describing the fluid motion around an object moving through a fluid, the fluid will be viewed as flowing around a fixed object. At points far from the vehicle, that is, the undisturbed free stream, the fluid particles are moving toward the vehicle with the velocity U_∞ (see Fig. 3.4), which is in reality the speed of the object (see Fig. 3.3). The subscript ∞ will be used throughout the text to denote the undisturbed (or free-stream) flow conditions (i.e., those conditions far from the vehicle). Since all the fluid particles in the free stream are moving with the same velocity, there is no relative motion between them, and hence there are no shearing stresses in the free-stream flow. Recall that when there is no relative motion between the fluid particles the fluid is termed a *static medium*. The values of the static fluid properties (e.g., pressure and temperature) are the same for either coordinate system.

GENERAL FORMS OF THE CONTINUITY EQUATION

Let us apply the principle of conservation of mass to a small volume of space through which the fluid can move freely. For convenience, we shall use a Cartesian coordinate system *(x, y, z)*. Furthermore, in the interest of simplicity, we shall treat a two-dimensional flow, that is, one in which there is no flow along the z axis. The flow patterns for a two dimensional flow are the same for any xy plane. As indicated in the sketch of Fig. 3.5, the component of the fluid velocity in the x direction will be designated by u, and that in the y direction by v. The net outflow of mass through the surface surrounding the volume must be equal to the decrease of mass within the volume. The mass flow rate through a surface bounding the element is equal to the product of the density, the velocity component normal to the surface, and the area of that surface. Flow out of the volume is considered positive. A first-order Taylor series expansion is used to evaluate the flow properties at the faces of the element, since the properties are a function of position. The mass flow rate per unit area in the x direction through the right-hand surface, which is ($+ \Delta x/2$) from the center of the volume element, is

$$\rho u + \frac{\partial}{\partial x}(\rho u)\left(\frac{\Delta x}{2}\right)$$

and is positive (i.e., is an *efflux*) if u is positive. The mass flow rate per unit area through the left-hand surface, which is ($- \Delta x/2$) from the center of the volume is

$$\rho u + \frac{\partial}{\partial x}(\rho u)\left(-\frac{\Delta x}{2}\right)$$

and is negative (i.e., is an *influx*) if u is positive. Referring to Fig. 3.4, the net outflow of mass per unit time is

$$\left[\rho u + \frac{\partial(\rho u)}{\partial x}\frac{\Delta x}{2}\right]\Delta y + \left[\rho v + \frac{\partial(\rho v)}{\partial y}\frac{\Delta y}{2}\right]\Delta x - \left[\rho u - \frac{\partial(\rho u)}{\partial x}\frac{\Delta x}{2}\right]\Delta y - \left[\rho v - \frac{\partial(\rho v)}{\partial y}\frac{\Delta y}{2}\right]\Delta x$$

which must equal the rate at which the mass contained within the element decreases:

$$-\frac{\partial\rho}{\partial t}\,\Delta x\,\Delta y$$

Equating the two expressions, combining terms, and dividing by $\Delta x\,\Delta y$,

$$\frac{\partial\rho}{\partial t} + \frac{\partial}{\partial x}(\rho u) + \frac{\partial}{\partial y}(\rho v) = 0$$

If the approach were extended to include flow in the z direction, we would obtain the general differential form of the continuity equation in Cartesian coordinates:

$$\frac{\partial\rho}{\partial t} + \frac{\partial}{\partial x}(\rho u) + \frac{\partial}{\partial y}(\rho v) + \frac{\partial}{\partial z}(\rho w) = 0 \tag{3.3}$$

In vector form, the differential form of the continuity is

$$\frac{\partial\rho}{\partial t} + \nabla\cdot(\rho\vec{V}) = 0 \tag{3.4}$$

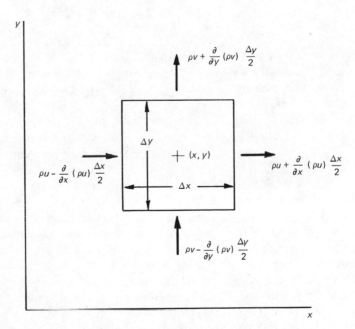

Figure 3.5 Velocities and densities for the mass flow balance through a fixed-volume element in two dimensions.

As will be shown in Example 3.3, the reader should start with this form of the continuity equation when developing the formulation for other coordinate systems.

If the details of the flow field are not of concern, the conservation principle can be applied directly to a relatively large region, or finite volume. Integrating Eq. (3.4) over a finite volume in our fluid space yields

$$\iiint\limits_{\text{vol}} \frac{\partial \rho}{\partial t} \, d(\text{vol}) + \iiint\limits_{\text{vol}} \nabla \cdot (\rho \vec{V}) \, d(\text{vol}) = 0$$

The volume integral can be transformed into a surface integral using Gauss's theorem, which is

$$\iiint\limits_{\text{vol}} \nabla \cdot (\rho \vec{V}) \, d(\text{vol}) = \oiint\limits_{A} \rho \vec{V} \cdot d\vec{A}$$

where $d\vec{A}$ is a vector normal to the surface dA, is positive when pointing outward from the enclosed volume, and is equal in magnitude to the surface area. The circle through the integral sign for the area indicates that the integration is to be performed over the entire surface bounding the volume. The resultant equation is the general integral expression for the conservation of mass:

$$\frac{\partial}{\partial t} \iiint\limits_{\text{vol}} \rho \, d(\text{vol}) + \oiint\limits_{A} \rho \vec{V} \cdot d\vec{A} = 0 \tag{3.5}$$

In words, the time rate of change of the mass within the volume plus the net efflux (outflow) of mass through the surface bounding the volume must be zero.

Note that, although a fluid is viscous, its viscosity does not appear explicitly in either form of the continuity equation. Nevertheless, the presence of viscosity strongly affects the velocity field. To determine this effect, one must include the momentum equation in the solution process, as will be discussed in subsequent chapters.

Two general forms of the continuity equation have been derived. Equation (3.4) is a differential equation that is valid at every point in the flow field and that can be used in obtaining a detailed solution of the flow. Equation (3.5) is an integral equation that is valid for a finite volume and that can be used in obtaining a less detailed solution. For a general flow problem, the continuity equation contains two unknowns, the density (ρ) and the velocity ($\vec{V}$). Since there are more unknowns (two) than equations (one), additional equations are needed before solutions for general flow problems can be obtained. However, as discussed in Chapter 1, in many problems of interest, variations in the fluid density are negligible, and density may be assumed to be constant. For such *incompressible* flows, there is only one unknown, the velocity vector. Therefore, if the boundary conditions are known, it is possible to obtain solutions of the velocity field for many incompressible flows using only the continuity equation. For the rest of this chapter, we will develop techniques to obtain solutions to the velocity field for flow cases whose solutions require use of only the continuity equation.

Differential Continuity Equation for Incompressible Flows

If the density variations in the flow field are sufficiently small so that the density may be assumed to be constant, the differential form of the continuity equation, Eq. (3.4), becomes

$$\nabla \cdot \vec{V} = 0 \tag{3.6}$$

Note that, for incompressible flows, the term

$$\frac{\partial \rho}{\partial t} = 0$$

whether or not the flow is steady. Thus, there is no term containing an explicit derivative with respect to time in the differential continuity equation when the flow is incompressible.

In Cartesian coordinates, the continuity equation for constant density flows becomes

$$\frac{\partial u}{\partial x} + \frac{\partial v}{\partial y} + \frac{\partial w}{\partial z} = 0 \tag{3.7}$$

Example 3.1

Consider a steady, low-speed flow of a viscous fluid in an infinitely long, two-dimensional channel of height h, which is known as Poiseuille flow. As shown in Fig. 3.6, the velocity variations take place in the x, y plane. Both the sketch and the statement that the flow is two-dimensional indicate that w, the z component of velocity, and the derivatives with respect to z are zero. Because the flow is confined between parallel plates that are infinitely long, the velocity components do not vary in the x direction. In this text, such a flow is termed a *fully developed* flow. Using the differential form of the continuity equation, what can be said about v, the velocity component in the y direction?

Solution. Because the flow is low speed, the density will be assumed to be constant. Thus, the continuity equation for this steady, two-dimensional, incompressible flow is

$$\frac{\partial u}{\partial x} + \frac{\partial v}{\partial y} = 0 \tag{3.8}$$

Since the velocity components do not change in the x direction, $\partial u / \partial x = 0$. Therefore, $\partial v / \partial y = 0$ also. Furthermore, since $v = 0$ at both walls (i.e., there is no flow through the solid

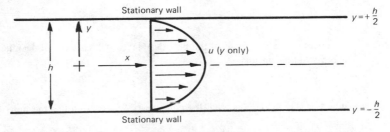

Figure 3.6 Steady, two-dimensional, fully developed flow between two parallel plates (for Example 3.1).

walls or, equivalently, the walls are streamlines), and since v does not depend on x or z, v = 0 everywhere. Thus, the flow is everywhere parallel to the x axis, and the streamlines are parallel to the walls.

Example 3.2

As a fluid flows past a flat plate, a viscous layer adjacent to the wall develops where the streamwise velocity component (u) varies from 0 at the wall (since the fluid particles do not "slip" past the wall in a viscous flow) to u_e at the outer edge of the viscous layer. A sketch of this *boundary layer* is presented in Fig. 3.7. Assume that, in the boundary layer, the streamwise velocity component is given by

$$u = \frac{y}{\delta} u_e$$

where δ, the boundary-layer thickness, is given by $\delta = 1.25 \times 10^{-2}\sqrt{x}$. Although the linear relation is a relatively crude approximation of the boundary layer, it serves for illustration in these examples. Outside the boundary layer, the streamwise velocity remains constant and equal to the upstream value, u_e. Using the continuity equation, determine the value of v at the edge of the boundary layer at a point $x = 0.5$ m. For this flow, $u_e = 2.337$ m/s.

Solution.   Use the differential form of the continuity equation for two-dimensional, incompressible flow:

$$\frac{\partial u}{\partial x} + \frac{\partial v}{\partial y} = 0$$

Thus,

$$\frac{\partial v}{\partial y} = -\frac{\partial}{\partial x}\left\{\frac{yu_e}{1.25 \times 10^{-2}\sqrt{x}}\right\} = \frac{yu_e}{2.50 \times 10^{-2} x^{1.5}}$$

Integrating,

$$v = \int \frac{\partial v}{\partial y} dy + C = \frac{u_e y^2}{5.0 \times 10^{-2} x^{1.5}} + C$$

To evaluate the constant of integration, apply the boundary condition that $v = 0$ when $y = 0$ (i.e., the wall is nonporous). Thus,

$$v = \frac{u_e y^2}{5.0 \times 10^{-2} x^{1.5}}$$

To evaluate v at the edge of the boundary layer (which we will designate by the symbol v_e), use the definition that

$$y_e = \delta = 1.25 \times 10^{-2}\sqrt{x}$$

where it should be clear that the constant (1.25×10^{-2}) has the units of (length)$^{0.5}$. Thus,

$$\frac{v_e}{u_e} = \frac{1.5625 \times 10^{-4} x}{5.0 \times 10^{-2} x^{1.5}} = \frac{3.125 \times 10^{-3}}{\sqrt{x}}$$

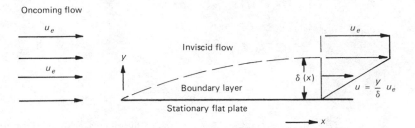

Figure 3.7 Boundary layer for flow past a stationary flat plate (for Example 3.2).

At $x = 0.5$ m

$$v_e = 4.42 \times 10^{-3} u_e = 1.03 \times 10^{-2} \text{ m/s}$$

Note that $v_e \neq 0$ and, therefore, the streamlines are not parallel to the wall for this boundary-layer flow. The reader should compare the results for this flow with those of Example 3.1. There are two significant differences for these flows. The fully developed flow of Example 3.1 is confined between two plates and is a flow where viscosity affects the entire flow field. In the boundary-layer flow of Example 3.2, the flow is initially inviscid (for $x \leqslant 0$). For $x > 0$, the effect of viscosity diffuses outward, so the region influenced by viscosity (the boundary layer) grows with the $\sqrt{x}$.

Example 3.3

Derive the continuity equation for incompressible flow in cylindrical coordinates, starting with the general vector form

$$\nabla \cdot \vec{V} = 0 \qquad (3.6)$$

where

$$\nabla = \hat{e}_r \frac{\partial}{\partial r} + \frac{\hat{e}_\theta}{r} \frac{\partial}{\partial \theta} + \hat{e}_z \frac{\partial}{\partial z} \qquad (3.9)$$

and

$$\vec{V} = \hat{e}_r v_r + \hat{e}_\theta v_\theta + \hat{e}_z v_z \qquad (3.10)$$

in cylindrical coordinates.

Solution. Substituting Eqs. (3.9) and (3.10) into Eq. (3.6),

$$\left(\hat{e}_r \frac{\partial}{\partial r} + \frac{\hat{e}_\theta}{r} \frac{\partial}{\partial \theta} + \hat{e}_z \frac{\partial}{\partial z} \right) \cdot (v_r \hat{e}_r + v_\theta \hat{e}_\theta + v_z \hat{e}_z)$$

$$- \hat{e}_r \cdot \hat{e}_r \frac{\partial v_r}{\partial r} + \hat{e}_r \cdot v_r \frac{\partial \hat{e}_r}{\partial r} + \hat{e}_r \cdot \hat{e}_\theta \frac{\partial v_\theta}{\partial r} + \hat{e}_r \cdot v_\theta \frac{\partial \hat{e}_\theta}{\partial r}$$

$$+ \hat{e}_r \cdot \hat{e}_z \frac{\partial v_z}{\partial r} + \hat{e}_r \cdot v_z \frac{\partial \hat{e}_z}{\partial r} + \frac{\hat{e}_\theta}{r} \cdot \hat{e}_r \frac{\partial v_r}{\partial \theta} + \frac{\hat{e}_\theta}{r} \cdot v_r \frac{\partial \hat{e}_r}{\partial \theta}$$

$$+ \frac{\hat{e}_\theta}{r} \cdot \hat{e}_\theta \frac{\partial v_\theta}{\partial \theta} + \frac{\hat{e}_\theta}{r} \cdot v_\theta \frac{\partial \hat{e}_\theta}{\partial \theta} + \frac{\hat{e}_\theta}{r} \cdot \hat{e}_z \frac{\partial v_z}{\partial \theta} + \frac{\hat{e}_\theta}{r} \cdot v_z \frac{\partial \hat{e}_z}{\partial \theta}$$

$$+ \hat{e}_z \cdot \hat{e}_r \frac{\partial v_r}{\partial z} + \hat{e}_z \cdot v_r \frac{\partial \hat{e}_r}{\partial z} + \hat{e}_z \cdot \hat{e}_\theta \frac{\partial v_\theta}{\partial z} + \hat{e}_z \cdot v_\theta \frac{\partial \hat{e}_\theta}{\partial z}$$

$$+ \hat{e}_z \cdot \hat{e}_z \frac{\partial v_z}{\partial z} + \hat{e}_z \cdot v_z \frac{\partial \hat{e}_z}{\partial z}$$

To evaluate the odd-numbered terms of the right-hand side of the equation, we use the relations for the dot (or scalar) product of unit vectors:

$$\hat{e}_r \cdot \hat{e}_r = \hat{e}_\theta \cdot \hat{e}_\theta = \hat{e}_z \cdot \hat{e}_z = 1$$

and

$$\hat{e}_r \cdot \hat{e}_\theta = \hat{e}_\theta \cdot \hat{e}_z = \hat{e}_z \cdot \hat{e}_r = 0$$

To evaluate the even-numbered terms of the right-hand side, we need to consider the derivatives of unit vectors. From vector calculus, we know that a vector can change in length and/or in direction. Obviously, a unit vector cannot change in length. From vector calculus for the unit vectors of cylindrical coordinates, we know that

$$\frac{\partial \hat{e}_r}{\partial \theta} = \hat{e}_\theta \quad \text{and} \quad \frac{\partial \hat{e}_\theta}{\partial \theta} = -\hat{e}_r$$

All other derivatives of the unit vectors are zero:

$$\frac{\partial \hat{e}_r}{\partial r} = \frac{\partial \hat{e}_\theta}{\partial r} = \frac{\partial \hat{e}_z}{\partial r} = \frac{\partial \hat{e}_z}{\partial \theta} = \frac{\partial \hat{e}_r}{\partial z} = \frac{\partial \hat{e}_\theta}{\partial z} = \frac{\partial \hat{e}_z}{\partial z} = 0$$

Substituting these relations into the expanded form of the continuity equation, we obtain the scalar equation:

$$\frac{\partial v_r}{\partial r} + \frac{v_r}{r} + \frac{1}{r} \frac{\partial v_\theta}{\partial \theta} + \frac{\partial v_z}{\partial z} = 0 \tag{3.11}$$

This equation will be most useful in obtaining solutions for many flows.

STREAM FUNCTION IN A TWO-DIMENSIONAL INCOMPRESSIBLE FLOW

Examining the continuity equation for an incompressible, two-dimensional flow in Cartesian coordinates,

$$\nabla \cdot \vec{V} = \frac{\partial u}{\partial x} + \frac{\partial v}{\partial y} = 0$$

it is obvious that the equation is satisfied by a stream function ψ, for which the velocity components can be calculated as

$$u = \frac{\partial \psi}{\partial y} \tag{3.12a}$$

$$v = -\frac{\partial \psi}{\partial x} \tag{3.12b}$$

Note that the continuity equation is also satisfied identically if $u = -\partial\psi/\partial y$ and $v = \partial\psi/\partial x$. Since many authors use this convention, the reader should be aware that there is no essential difference in the application of the two sign conventions.

Thus, the equation of continuity for an incompressible, two-dimensional flow is the necessary and sufficient condition for the existence of a stream function. The flow need be two-dimensional only in the sense that it requires only two spatial coordinates to describe the motion. Therefore, stream functions exist both for plane flow and for axially symmetric flow. The reader might note, although it is not relevant to this chapter, that stream functions exist for compressible two-dimensional flows, if they are steady. A corollary to this is that the existence of a stream function is a necessary condition for a physically possible flow (i.e., one that satisfies the continuity equation).

Since ψ is a point function,

$$d\psi = \frac{\partial \psi}{\partial x} dx + \frac{\partial \psi}{\partial y} dy \tag{3.13}$$

so that

$$d\psi = -v\, dx + u\, dy \tag{3.14}$$

From Eq. (3.2), the definition of a streamline in a two-dimensional flow is

$$\frac{dx}{u} = \frac{dy}{v}$$

Rearranging, it can be seen that

$$u\, dy - v\, dx = 0 \tag{3.15}$$

along a streamline. Equating Eqs. (3.14) and (3.15), one finds that

$$d\psi = 0$$

along a streamline. Thus, the change in ψ is zero along a streamline or, equivalently, ψ is a constant along a streamline. A corollary statement is that lines of constant ψ are streamlines of the flow. It follows, then, that the volume flow rate (per unit depth) between any two points in the flow is the difference between the values of the stream function at the two points of interest.

Example 3.4

Does the velocity field given by

$$\vec{V} = a(x^2 - y^2)\hat{i} - 2axy\hat{j}$$

represent an incompressible flow that conserves mass? If it does, find the stream function for this velocity field, graph it, and discuss it.

Solution.   To determine if the velocity field represents an incompressible flow that conserves mass, verify that the continuity equation is satisfied.

$$u = a(x^2 - y^2), \qquad v = -2axy$$

Does $(\partial u/\partial x) + (\partial v/\partial y) = 0$? Yes, since $2ax + (-2ax) = 0$! Therefore, the continuity equation is satisfied. Since the flow is two-dimensional and incompressible, we are certain that a stream function exists. To find the stream function, integrate the expressions given by Eqs. (3.12a) and (3.12b). Thus, ψ must satisfy both of the following equations:

$$\psi = \int u \, dy + f(x) \tag{3.16a}$$

and

$$\psi = -\int v \, dx + g(y) \tag{3.16b}$$

Thus, the stream function is

$$\psi = \int a(x^2 - y^2) \, dy + f(x)$$

$$= ax^2y - \frac{ay^3}{3} + f(x) \tag{3.17a}$$

But it is also

$$\psi = -\int (-2axy) \, dx + g(y)$$

$$= ax^2y + g(y) \tag{3.17b}$$

The stream function that satisfies both Eqs. (3.17a) and (3.17b) is

$$\psi = ax^2y - \frac{ay^3}{3} + C$$

To graph this, set $C = 0$ for convenience so that

$$3x^2y - y^3 = \frac{3\psi}{a}$$

for constant values of ψ. Streamlines for $\psi = 0$, $\psi = \pm a$, and $\psi = \pm 2a$ are presented in Fig. 3.8. Since any streamline represents a surface across which there is no flow, sketches of three possible flows are presented in Fig. 3.9. Since the velocity is zero only at the origin, the condition that the velocity of a viscous fluid goes to zero at a stationary wall (i.e., the no-slip condition) is not satisfied for these streamlines. Thus, these streamlines could represent the walls only for the flow of a frictionless fluid.

Example 3.5

What is the significance of the spacing between the streamlines for the flow into a 60° corner, as shown in Fig. 3.9a?

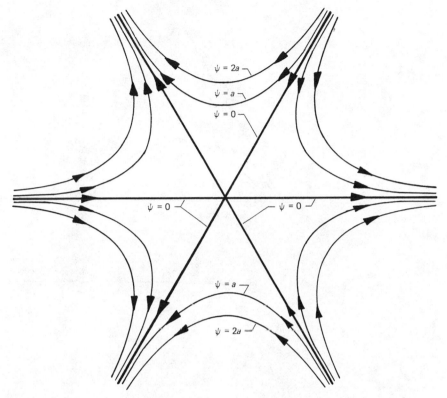

Figure 3.8 Streamlines for $\vec{V} = a(x^2 - y^2)\hat{i} - 2axy\hat{j}$ of Example 3.4.

Solution. To determine the significance of the streamline spacing, consider the values in the following table.

ψ	x	y	$\vec{V}$	$|\vec{V}|$
0	0.000	0.000	0	0.0
a	0.000	-1.442	$-2.079a\hat{i}$	$2.1a$
$2a$	0.000	-1.817	$-3.301a\hat{i}$	$3.3a$
0	$+1.732$	-3.000	$-6.000a\hat{i} + 10.392a\hat{j}$	$12.0a$
a	$+1.633$	-3.000	$-6.333a\hat{i} + 9.798a\hat{j}$	$11.7a$
$2a$	$+1.528$	-3.000	$-6.665a\hat{i} + 9.168a\hat{j}$	$11.3a$

Thus, it is clear that the higher the local velocity, the closer the distance between streamlines.

Since many of the flows to be discussed in Chapter 5 are most easily formulated in cylindrical coordinates, let us work through a sample problem illustrating the techniques.

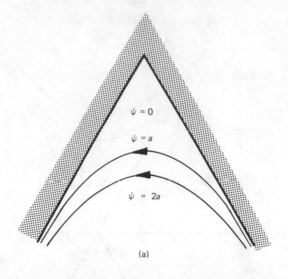

$\psi = 0$

$\psi = a$

$\psi = 2a$

(a)

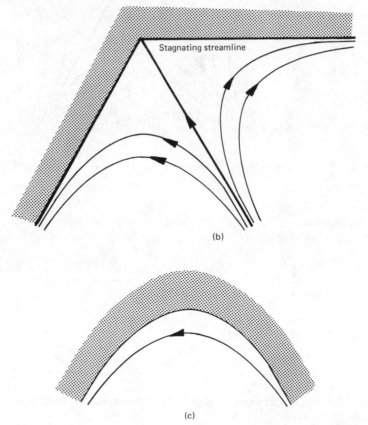

Stagnating streamline

(b)

(c)

Figure 3.9 Possible inviscid flows for the streamlines of Fig. 3.8: (a) flow into a 60°
sharp corner; (b) flow into a 120° sharp corner; (c) flow into a rounded 60° corner.

Example 3.6

Consider an incompressible, steady flow going toward a two-dimensional sink such that the velocity field in cylindrical coordinates is given by

$$\vec{V} = -\frac{K}{2\pi r}\hat{e}_r$$

The term "two-dimensional" indicates that the flow field produced by the sink is independent of z.

(a) Show that this flow satisfies the differential form of the continuity equation.

(b) If

$$v_r = \frac{1}{r}\frac{\partial\psi}{\partial\theta} \quad \text{and} \quad v_\theta = -\frac{\partial\psi}{\partial r} \tag{3.18}$$

determine the stream function for this flow.

Solution. (a) To illustrate that this flow satisfies the continuity equation, we can either substitute the velocity itself into Eq. (3.6) or substitute the velocity components into Eq. (3.11). For purposes of illustration, we will do both. Using Eq. (3.6),

$$\nabla \cdot \vec{V} = \left[\hat{e}_r\frac{\partial}{\partial r} + \frac{\hat{e}_\theta}{r}\frac{\partial}{\partial\theta} + \hat{e}_z\frac{\partial}{\partial z}\right] \cdot \left[\frac{-K}{2\pi r}\hat{e}_r\right]$$

Neglecting the terms that are zero,

$$\nabla \cdot \vec{V} = \hat{e}_r \cdot \hat{e}_r\frac{\partial}{\partial r}\left(\frac{-K}{2\pi r}\right) - \frac{\hat{e}_\theta}{r}\frac{K}{2\pi r} \cdot \frac{\partial\hat{e}_r}{\partial\theta}$$

Noting that $\partial\hat{e}_r/\partial\theta = \hat{e}_\theta$,

$$\nabla \cdot \vec{V} = +\frac{K}{2\pi r^2} - \frac{K}{2\pi r^2} = 0$$

Using Eq. (3.11) and noting that

$$v_r = -\frac{K}{2\pi r}, \qquad v_\theta = v_z = 0$$

we see that

$$\frac{\partial}{\partial r}\left(\frac{-K}{2\pi r}\right) + \frac{1}{r}\left(\frac{-K}{2\pi r}\right) = 0$$

Thus, we have shown by both approaches that the continuity equation is indeed satisfied for this velocity function.

(b) To determine the stream function for this velocity field, we rearrange the expressions of Eq. (3.18). Thus, we find that the stream function must simultaneously satisfy the two relations

$$\psi = \int v_r r\, d\theta + f(r)$$

and

$$\psi = - \int v_\theta \, dr + g(\theta)$$

The first relation gives

$$\psi = - \frac{K\theta}{2\pi} + f(r)$$

while the second gives

$$\psi = g(\theta)$$

The stream function that satisfies both of these is

$$\psi = - \frac{K\theta}{2\pi} + C$$

where C is a constant, usually chosen to be zero. Note the streamlines are lines of constant θ, that is, straight lines radiating toward the origin. Note that, since the only nonzero velocity component is v_r (the radial component of velocity), this streamline pattern should not be surprising.

The reader can visualize a physical model for this flow by imagining a large flat surface (or floor) covered by a thin layer of water. If a drain is opened at the center of the room (i.e., the origin of the coordinate system), the water will flow in radially toward the drain (sink) with the velocity increasing as the sink is approached. There are two significant differences between the "theoretical" velocity field and the actual flow. The actual velocity will not go to infinity as $r \rightarrow 0$. Furthermore, the effects of the fact that a point on the earth is actually in an accelerating coordinate system (i.e., the Coriolis force), which cause the swirl in the bathtub drain, are not included in the model. This effect is negligible in most of the flows that we will discuss in this book.

INTEGRAL CONTINUITY EQUATION FOR INCOMPRESSIBLE FLOWS

Let us examine the integral form of the continuity equation as applied to an incompressible flow involving a single species of fluid in the domain of our control volume. In this case, ρ is constant throughout the domain and for all time. The first term is zero and Eq. (3.5) can be written

$$\oiint_A \vec{V} \cdot d\vec{A} = 0 \tag{3.19}$$

Note that the dimensions of the term represented by the integral of Eq. (3.19) are (length)^3/time or, equivalently, volume/time. Thus, for an incompressible flow involving a single species of fluid, the requirement for the conservation of mass reduces to the requirement for the conservation of volume.

Example 3.7

Apply the integral form of the continuity equation to the boundary-layer flow of Example 3.2 to obtain information about the flow in the vertical direction.

Solution. Let us choose a rectangular control volume whose length is L and whose height is H, as shown in Fig. 3.10. As will be discussed further, the exact value of H does not matter as long as it is greater than the boundary-layer thickness (δ) at L. Let us evaluate the integral of Eq. (3.19) for each of the four elements that comprise the surface bounding the control volume. The vector expressions for each of the differential areas are illustrated in Fig. 3.10. The convention is used that $d\vec{A}$ is a vector normal to the surface dA, which is positive when pointing outward from the enclosed volume and which is equal in magnitude to the surface area. As illustrated in the sketch of Fig. 3.10b, the differential area can be written as $d\vec{A}_3 = dy\, dz\, \hat{i}$ for surface 3 and $d\vec{A}_4 = dx\, dz\, \hat{j}$ for surface 4. However, since the flow is two-dimensional it is independent of z. Thus, the depth of the control volume (the distance into the paper) can be chosen to be 1. Since there are no variations in the z direction, there need be no integration with respect to this variable, and the double integration

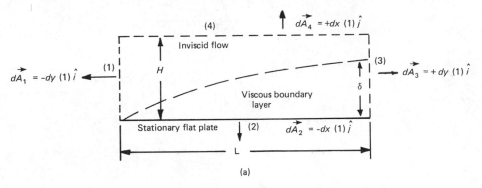

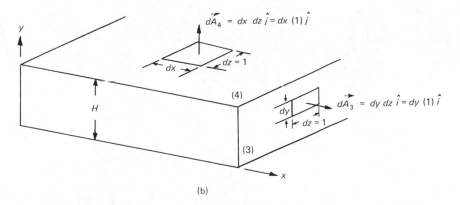

Figure 3.10 Control volume for the boundary layer for flow past a stationary flat plate (for Example 3.7). (See Fig. 3.7 for the velocity field.)

associated with the area is replaced by a single integral times a unit depth. The continuity equation for this boundary-layer flow is

$$\oint_A \vec{V} \cdot d\vec{A} = 0$$

$$= \int_0^H u_e\hat{i} \cdot (-dy\,\hat{i}) + \int_0^L 0(-dx\,\hat{j})$$

$$\underbrace{\qquad}_{(1)} \qquad \underbrace{\qquad}_{(2)}$$

$$+ \int_0^\delta (\frac{y}{\delta}u_e\hat{i} + v\hat{j}) \cdot (dy\,\hat{i}) + \int_\delta^H (u_e\hat{i} + v_e\hat{j}) \cdot (dy\,\hat{i})$$

$$\underbrace{\qquad\qquad\qquad\qquad}_{(3)}$$

$$+ \int_0^L (u_e\hat{i} + v_e\hat{j}) \cdot (dx\,\hat{j})$$

$$\underbrace{\qquad}_{(4)}$$

$$= 0$$

The y component of velocity (v) that appears in the third term is a function of x and y but will not enter into the final formulation, since $\hat{j} \cdot \hat{i} = 0$. The term v_e, which is a function of x, is the parameter that we seek to evaluate.

Evaluating the integrals,

$$-u_e H + u_e \frac{\delta}{2} + u_e(H - \delta) + \int_0^L v_e\,dx = 0$$

Rearranging,

$$\int_0^L v_e\,dx = u_e \frac{\delta}{2} \qquad (3.20)$$

Note that as long as we require that H be greater than δ at L (i.e., the entire boundary layer is within the control volume) its specific value will not matter.

If we use the additional fact that

$$\delta = 1.25 \times 10^{-2} \sqrt{x}$$

and differentiate the expressions of Eq. (3.20)

$$v_e = \frac{0.3125 \times 10^{-2}}{\sqrt{x}} u_e$$

we find that $v_e = 4.42 \times 10^{-3}u_e$, when $x = 0.5$ m. This is exactly the same result that was obtained in Example 3.2 using the differential form of the continuity equation. However, we cannot evaluate v at other points in the flow field using the integral equation, whereas we could and did using the differential equation.

Average Velocity

In many problems we are interested in the average velocity of the fluid passing through some cross section. By definition, the average velocity is

$$V_{av} = \overline{V} = \frac{Q}{A} = \frac{1}{A} \iint \vec{V} \cdot d\vec{A} \tag{3.21}$$

Example 3.8

For the viscous boundary layer of Example 3.7, we found that:

$$v_e = \frac{0.3125 \times 10^{-2}}{\sqrt{x}} u_e$$

What is the average velocity $(\overline{v}_e)$ over the length L?

Solution.   To find the average value of v_e over the length L, we use Eq. (3.21):

$$\overline{v}_e = \frac{1}{L(1)} \int_0^L \frac{0.3125 \times 10^{-2} \, u_e}{\sqrt{x}} \, dx \tag{1}$$

Note that, since the flow is two-dimensional, the z component of the area has been chosen to be unity, and the integration is performed only with respect to x. Thus,

$$\overline{v}_e = \frac{0.3125 \times 10^{-2} \, u_e}{L} \, (2\sqrt{x} \, \big|_0^L = \frac{0.625 \times 10^{-2} \, u_e}{\sqrt{L}}$$

One-Dimensional Flow

Consider the application of the integral form of the continuity equation to a one-dimensional, incompressible steady flow, such as is shown in Fig. 3.11. Since the flow is steady, the partial derivative with respect to time in Eq. (3.5) is zero. Furthermore, the requirement that the flow be incompressible (i.e., ρ = constant) allows us to write

$$\oiint \vec{V} \cdot d\vec{A} = 0 \tag{3.19}$$

When we apply the equation to the flow shown in Fig. 3.11, it is clear that the shape of the control volume between the inlet and outlet stations does not matter since the walls are streamlines. The statement that the flow is one-dimensional implies that the velocity and other properties are constant across each cross section. Thus,

$$\oiint \vec{V} \cdot d\vec{A} = \iint_{A_1} V_1 \hat{n} \cdot (-dA \, \hat{n}) + \iint_{A_2} V_2 \hat{n} \cdot (dA \, \hat{n})$$

$$= -V_1 \iint_{A_1} dA + V_2 \iint_{A_2} dA = 0$$

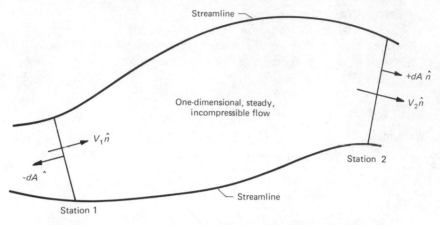

Figure 3.11   One-dimensional flow in a variable-area streamtube.

Rearranging,

$$V_1A_1 = V_2A_2 = VA, \quad \text{a constant} \tag{3.22}$$

Thus, we have derived the almost obvious relation that the flow is the same across any planar surface in a steady, incompressible, one-dimensional flow.

Viscous Flow in a Variable-Area Steamtube

A slightly more complicated flow is illustrated in Example 3.9.

Example 3.9

Consider water flowing in a variable-area, circular pipe, whose dimensions are shown in Fig. 3.12. The flow is steady and incompressible. The velocity is uniform (independent of r) at the inlet, station 1. Because of viscous effects, the velocity at station 2 varies with r, being zero at the wall and a maximum, U_0, at the centerline. Calculate U_0 for this flow, which is shown in Fig. 3.12.

Solution.   This is a steady, incompressible flow in a streamtube. Because the velocity varies in both the axial and radial directions (at station 2), it is not one-dimensional. Therefore, we cannot use Eq. (3.22). Using Eq. (3.19),

$$\oiint \vec{V} \cdot d\vec{A} = -U_1 \iint_{A_1} dA + \int_0^{3.0} \int_0^{2\pi} U_2 r \, d\theta \, dr = 0$$

The negative sign on the first integral results since $d\vec{A}$ is a vector directed outward from the control volume and is, therefore, opposite to the velocity vector. For an axisymmetric flow, the velocity is independent of θ, as is the case for this flow. Therefore, the second term can be written

$$\int_0^{3.0} U_2(2\pi r \, dr)$$

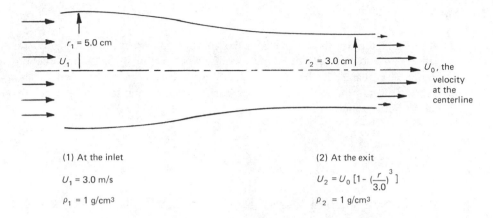

(1) At the inlet

$U_1 = 3.0$ m/s

$\rho_1 = 1$ g/cm3

(2) At the exit

$U_2 = U_0 \left[1 - (\frac{r}{3.0})^3\right]$

$\rho_2 = 1$ g/cm3

Figure 3.12   Flow for Example 3.9.

This θ integration will not be worked in detail in subsequent problems involving axisymmetric flows. Thus, because the flow is independent of one of the variables (θ in this case), the integration over the area requires an integration over only one variable. Recall the discussion with Example 3.7. Substituting the expression for U_2,

$$2\pi U_0 \int_0^{3.0} \left[1.0 - \left(\frac{r}{3.0}\right)^3\right] r \, dr = U_1 \pi (5.0)^2$$

Therefore,

$$U_0 = \frac{25.0 U_1}{2(2.7)} = 4.630 U_1 = 13.89 \text{ m/s}$$

Example 3.10

What is the average velocity at station 1 and at station 2 for the flow of Example 3.9?

Solution.   Since the velocity is constant over the cross section at station 1, it is clear that

$$U_{av,1} = U_1 = 3.0 \text{ m/s}$$

At station 2, we will let the symbol R_2 represent the radius of the streamtube (3.0 cm), so that

$$U_{av,2} = \frac{1}{\pi R_2^2} \int_0^{R_2} U_0 \left[1 - \left(\frac{r}{R_2}\right)^3\right] 2\pi r \, dr$$

$$= \frac{2\pi U_0}{\pi R_2^2} \left[\frac{r^2}{2} - \frac{r^5}{5 R_2^3}\right]_0^{R_2} = \frac{2 U_0}{R_2^2} \left(\frac{3 R_2^2}{10}\right) = 0.6 U_0$$

The value of U_0 was obtained in Example 3.9. Thus, $U_{av,2} = 8.334$ m/s.

SUMMARY

In this chapter, we have solved for the velocity field in several relatively simple applications. The techniques developed will be very useful in obtaining solutions to more complex problems. In the next chapter, we will derive the momentum equation and use it to obtain information about the pressure distribution and the forces acting on an object due to fluid motion.

PROBLEMS

3.1. Consider the two-dimensional flow of a fluid for which the velocity is given by

$$\vec{V} = 2\hat{j} \quad \text{(m/s)}$$

during the time interval $t = 0$ to $t = 10$ s. From the time $t = 10$ s to $t = 20$ s, the velocity is given by

$$\vec{V} = 2\hat{i} - 2\hat{j} \quad \text{(m/s)}$$

The path of a particle in the fluid is traced from a point in the flow field starting at time $t = 0$. Draw the path line of the particle and streamlines at time $t = 15$ s.

3.2. Consider the two-dimensional, unsteady flow of a fluid for which the velocity is given by

$$\vec{V} = 3\hat{i} + 2t\hat{j} \quad \text{(m/s)}$$

Where t is time in seconds. If a particle is released at time $t = 0$, draw the pathline of the particle and a sketch of the streamlines at time $t = 5$ s.

3.3. Consider an incompressible, steady, viscous flow along a flat plate. Assume that, in the boundary layer, the streamwise velocity component is given by

$$\frac{u}{u_e} = \frac{3}{2}\frac{y}{\delta} - \frac{1}{2}\left[\frac{y}{\delta}\right]^3$$

where δ, the boundary-layer thickness is given by $\delta = 1.25 \times 10^{-2}\sqrt{x}$. Outside the boundary layer, the streamwise velocity component remains constant and equal to the upstream value, u_e. Using the differential form of the continuity equation, determine the value of v_e (the value of v at the edge of the boundary layer) when $x = 0.5$ m and $u_e = 2.337$ m/s.

3.4. Consider the incompressible steady flow for a two-dimensional potential vortex, such that

$$\vec{V} = \frac{\Gamma}{2\pi r}\hat{e}_\theta$$

Show that this flow satisfies the differential form of the continuity equation, Eq. (3.11). Using the velocity-component/stream-function relations of Eq. (3.18), determine the stream function for this flow. Sketch the streamlines.

3.5. Show that the velocity field given by

$$\vec{V} = -\frac{K}{2\pi r}\hat{e}_r + \frac{\Gamma}{2\pi r}\hat{e}_\theta$$

satisfies the continuity equation for an incompressible flow. Using Eq. (3.18), determine the stream function for this flow. Sketch the streamlines.

3.6. Show that the velocity field given by

$$\vec{V} = U_\infty \cos\theta \left[1 - \frac{R^2}{r^2}\right]\hat{e}_r - U_\infty \sin\theta \left[1 + \frac{R^2}{r^2}\right]\hat{e}_\theta$$

satisfies the continuity equation. In this expression for inviscid flow around a two-dimensional cylinder, U_∞ represents the free-stream velocity and R the radius of the cylinder. Both are constants for a given problem.

3.7. Two of the three velocity components for an incompressible flow are

$$u = x^2 + 2xz \quad \text{and} \quad v = y^2 + 2yz$$

What is the most general form of the fluid component $w(x, y, z)$ that satisfies the continuity equation?

3.8. A two-dimensional velocity field is given by

$$u = -\frac{Ky}{x^2 + y^2}, \qquad v = +\frac{Kx}{x^2 + y^2}$$

where K is a constant. Does this velocity field satisfy the continuity equation for incompressible flow? Transform these velocity components into the polar components v_r and v_θ in terms of r and θ. What type of flow might this velocity field represent?

3.9. The velocity components for a two-dimensional flow are

$$u = \frac{C(y^2 - x^2)}{(x^2 + y^2)^2} \quad \text{and} \quad v = \frac{-2Cxy}{(x^2 + y^2)^2}$$

where C is a constant. Does this flow satisfy the continuity equation?

3.10. A gas is flowing at relatively low speeds, so the density may be assumed constant. Consider the flow where the velocity components are

$$u = -\frac{2xyz}{(x^2 + y^2)^2} U_\infty L$$

$$v = -\frac{(x^2 - y^2)z}{(x^2 + y^2)^2} U_\infty L$$

$$w = \frac{y}{x^2 + y^2} U_\infty L$$

Here U_∞ and L are a reference velocity and a reference length, respectively. Does this flow satisfy the continuity equation?

3.11. Derive the continuity equation for incompressible flow in spherical coordinates, starting with the general vector form

$$\nabla \cdot \vec{V} = 0$$

where

$$\nabla = \hat{e}_r \frac{\partial}{\partial r} + \frac{\hat{e}_\theta}{r \sin \omega} \frac{\partial}{\partial \theta} + \frac{\hat{e}_\omega}{r} \frac{\partial}{\partial \omega}$$

and

$$\vec{V} = \hat{e}_r v_r + \hat{e}_\theta v_\theta + \hat{e}_\omega v_\omega$$

in spherical coordinates.

3.12. The velocity field for a spherical point source flow is given by

$$\vec{V} = \frac{Q}{4\pi r^2} \hat{e}_r$$

Show that this satisfies the differential form of the continuity equation, as derived in Prob. 3.11.

3.13. If the velocity field is given by the vector

$$\vec{V} = 2x\hat{i} - 2y\hat{j}$$

develop the expression for the stream function. Is the y axis a streamline?

3.14. A stream function ψ is given as

$$\psi = x^2 + 2xy + 4t^2 y$$

where ψ has the units of m²/s. When $t = 2$ s, what is the volumetric flow rate of water (per unit depth) across the semicircular arc AB, shown in Fig. P3.14? What is the volumetric flow rate across the straight line on the x axis from A to C?

3.15. In Example 3.2 we approximated the velocity field for the viscous boundary layer that exists when a field flows past a flat plate by

$$u = \frac{u_e\, y}{1.25 \times 10^{-2}\, x^{0.5}}, \qquad v = \frac{u_e\, y^2}{5.00 \times 10^{-2} \times x^{1.5}}$$

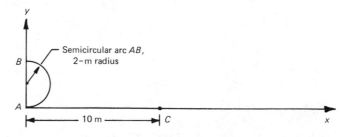

Figure P3.14   Configuration for Prob. 3.14.

These components are only for the viscous region near the wall (see Fig. 3.7). For the oncoming flow and for the inviscid flow outside the boundary layer, the velocity field is given by

$$u = u_e, \qquad v = 0$$

Find the stream functions for the two regions. Graph the streamlines. Note that the streamlines intersect (which they should not do) because the flow model that we have postulated for the velocity field is only an approximation. Note also that we can use stream functions to describe the flow whether it is viscous or inviscid, providing it is two-dimensional and incompressible.

3.16. Consider a one-dimensional, incompressible flow in a duct. If the cross-sectional area of the duct varies in the streamwise direction, derive a relation between the change in velocity as a function of the change in area.

3.17. Water flows through a pipe 15 cm in diameter at a velocity of 2 m/s. What is the volumetric flow rate in cubic meters per second and in cubic feet per second? What is the mass flow rate in kilograms per minute? Assume the temperature is 20°C.

3.18. Water flows through a circular pipe, as shown in Fig. P3.18, at a constant volumetric flow rate of 0.75 m³/s. Assuming that the velocities at stations 1, 2, and 3 are uniform across the cross section (i.e., the flow is one-dimensional), use the integral form of the continuity equation to calculate the velocities U_1, U_2, and U_3. The corresponding diameters are $d_1 = 0.5$ m, $d_2 = 10.0$ cm, and $d_3 = 0.3$ m.

3.19. Water from a reservoir drains from a constant-area pipe, as shown in Fig. P3.19. The water flow at the inlet (station 1) is essentially inviscid. Therefore, the velocity may be assumed to be constant at 5.0 m/s across the entire cross section; that is,

$$\vec{V}_1 = 5.0\hat{i}$$

The pipe is sufficiently long such that the effects of viscosity are felt across the entire cross section by the time station 2 is reached, so the velocity at station 2 is given by

$$\vec{V}_2 = U_0 \left[1 - \left(\frac{r}{R} \right)^2 \right] \hat{i}$$

U_0 is the velocity at the centerline and R is the radius of the pipe, 5.0 cm. If the flow is steady and incompressible, what is U_0?

3.20. Consider two infinite, parallel plates, a distance $h = 2$ cm apart (see Fig. P3.20). The velocity distribution between the plates is

$$u = \frac{1}{2\mu} \frac{dp}{dx} y^2 + C_1 y + C_2$$

(a) Use the boundary conditions for a viscous flow to evaluate the constants C_1 and C_2.
(b) If

$$\frac{dp}{dx} = +\ 50 \text{ N/m}^2\text{/m}, \qquad h = 2 \text{ cm}, \qquad \mu = 1 \times 10^{-4} \text{ N} \cdot \text{s/m}^2$$

what is the value of U_0 such that the net volumetric flow rate at any station is zero?

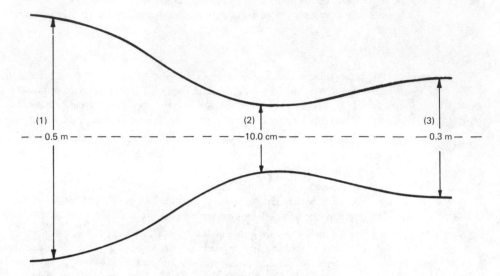

Figure P3.18 Variable-area duct for Prob. 3.18.

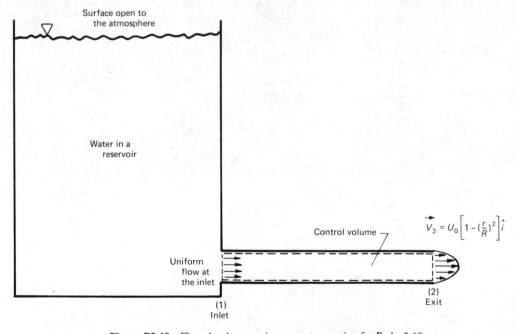

Figure P3.19 Flow development in constant-area pipe for Prob. 3.19.

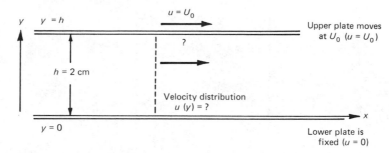

Figure P3.20   Sketch for Prob. 3.20.

3.21. Consider the flow system shown in Fig. P3.21. Assume that complete mixing between the two inflows occurs in the tank before the mixture discharges through pipe C. If the flow is steady, what is the mass rate of flow, the average velocity, and the specific gravity of the mixture in the pipe at C?

3.22. How long will it take the water surface of a tank, which is 60 cm in diameter (as shown in Fig. P3.22), to drop from $h = 2$ m to $h = 30$ cm? The velocity of the water at the drain hole, which is 5 cm in diameter, is given by the relation $V = \sqrt{2gh}$.

3.23. The velocity distribution in a horizontal open channel is given by $u = 3y^{0.15}$, where u is the streamwise velocity in m/s at a distance y meters above the floor of the channel. If the depth of the flow is 1 m and the width of the channel is 3 m, what is the volumetric flow rate in m³/s? What is the mean velocity?

3.24. A 10-m³ tank is initially filled with fresh water. At time $t = 0$, a salt solution containing 500 N of salt per cubic meter of solution begins entering at section 1 at 0.5 m³/s. Assume that an efficient mixing device produces a uniform salt solution throughout the tank at any instant. If 0.5 m³/s of the mixture is drained from the tank at section 2, how many newtons of salt will be dissolved in the tank at time $t = 1$ min? How long will it take before the solution in the tank contains 200 N/m³ of salt?

3.25. An ejector system is used to pump water through the elbow system shown in Fig. P3.25. The water-jet pump injects water at 30 m/s through a pipe 8.0 cm in diameter and entrains a secondary flow of water in the annular region around the small pipe of the jet pump. Assume that the velocity of the secondary flow is uniform at the "inlet" station and is equal to 3 m/s. After some distance, the two flows become fully mixed. Assuming that the flow

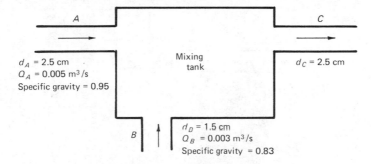

Figure P3.21   Sketch for Prob. 3.21.

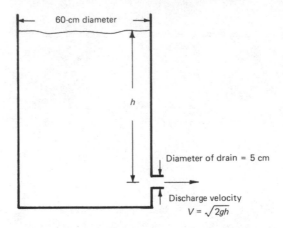

Figure P3.22   Sketch for Prob. 3.22.

is steady and incompressible and that the velocity of the mixed flow is uniform across the 25.0-cm pipe, calculate U_3.

3.26. Apply the integral form of the continuity equation to the boundary-layer flow of Prob. 3.3 in order to obtain information about the flow in the vertical direction. Choose a rectangular control volume whose length is L and whose height is H, which is greater than the boundary-layer thickness (δ) at L. Find the value of v_e when $x = 0.5$ m and $u_e = 2.337$ m/s.

3.27. One cubic meter per second of water enters a rectangular duct as shown in Fig. P3.27. Two of the surfaces of the duct are porous. Water is added through the upper surface at a rate shown by the parabolic curve, while it leaves through the front face at a rate that decreases linearly with the distance from the entrance. The maximum values of both flow rates, shown in the sketch, are given in cubic meters per second per unit length along the duct. What is the average velocity of the water leaving the duct if it is 1.0 m long and has a cross section of 0.1 m²?

3.28. For the conditions of Prob. 3.27, determine the position along the duct where the average velocity of flow is a minimum. What is the average velocity at this station?

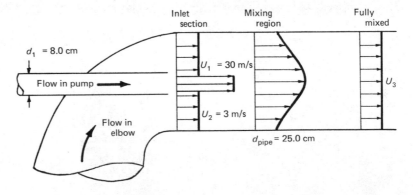

Figure P3.25   Sketch for Prob. 3.25.

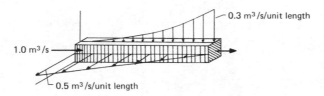

Figure P3.27   Sketch for Prob. 3.27.

3.29. As shown in Fig. P3.29, 1.5 m³/s of water leaves a rectangular duct. Two of the surfaces of the duct are porous. Water leaves through the upper surface at a rate shown by the parabolic curve, while it enters the front face at a rate that decreases linearly with distance from the entrance. The maximum values of both flow rates, shown in the sketch, are given in cubic meters per second per unit length along the duct. What is the average velocity of the water entering the duct if it is 1.0 m long and has a cross section of 0.1 m²?

3.30. The incompressible, steady flow emanating from a two-dimensional source is given by

$$\vec{V} = \frac{K}{2\pi r}\hat{e}_r$$

What is the flow rate across any cylindrical surface of unit depth centered on the origin, that is, a curved surface whose radius is $r = R$ (a constant) and for which $\Delta z = 1$? Note that a differential area for this surface is $\vec{dA} = R\,d\theta\,(1)\,\hat{e}_r$.

3.31. Oil flows through a pipe such that the velocity varies as

$$u = U_0\left[1 - \left(\frac{r}{R}\right)^3\right]$$

If the radius of the pipe (R) is 4 in., what is the centerline velocity (U_0) so that 20 gallons per minute flow through the pipe. The specific gravity of the oil is 0.86.

3.32. Consider the simple model for the flow in the near wake of a missile in free flight, as shown in Fig. P3.32. The velocity of the air far from the missile is U_0 ($= 100$ m/s). The propellant has been expended and, thus, there is no exhaust from the rocket. Because of friction on the missile's surface, there is a boundary layer that is δ thick, where $\delta = 0.10D$, in which the streamwise velocity varies as

$$u = U_0\left(\frac{y}{\delta}\right)^{0.15}$$

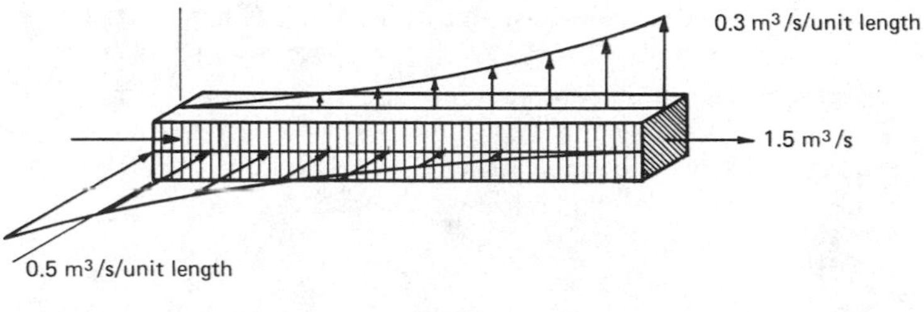

0.3 m³/s/unit length

1.5 m³/s

0.5 m³/s/unit length

Figure P3.29   Sketch for Prob. 3.29.

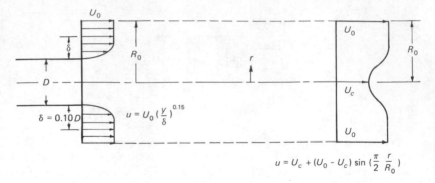

Figure P3.32   Sketch for Prob. 3.32.

After a complex mixing process in the base flow field, the velocity varies as

$$u = U_c + (U_0 - U_c) \sin\left(\frac{\pi r}{2R_0}\right)$$

If $U_c = 0.5U_0$, what is the value of R_0 (as a multiple of D)? Assume that the flow is incompressible.

3.33. Liquid propane has a variety of uses in motor homes. The tank containing liquid propane is vented to the atmosphere through an overflow valve whose opening is 0.055 in. in diameter. Propane flows through the valve as a liquid and vaporizes as it encounters the air. The pressure drop for the flow can be directly related to the air temperature, as follows:

Temperature (°F)	40	50	60	70	80	90
Vapor pressure (psig)	63	77	92	109	128	149

If the mass flow rate is given by

$$\dot{m} = C_1 A \sqrt{2 (\Delta p)\rho}$$

what is the mass flow rate when the temperature is 75°F? The density of liquid propane is 31.5 1bm/ft^3 and the discharge coefficient is 0.98. If the ratio of gas volume to liquid volume is 273, how many cubic feet of gaseous propane are released?

3.34. Consider liquid propane flowing through the overflow valve as discussed in Prob. 3.33. If the volumetric flow rate of liquid propane is 1.88×10^{-3} ft^3/s, what is the temperature?

3.35. You are relaxing on an international flight when a terrorist leaps up and tries to take over the airplane. The crew refuses the demands of the terrorist and he fires his pistol, shooting a small hole in the airplane. Panic strikes the crew and other passengers. But you leap up and shout, "Do not worry! I am an engineering major and I know it will take ——?—— seconds for the cabin pressure to drop from 0.5×10^5 N/m^2 to 0.25×10^5 N/m^2." Calculate how long it will take the cabin pressure to drop. Make the following assumptions.

(i) The air in the cabin behaves as a perfect gas:

$$\rho_c = \frac{p_c}{RT_c}$$

where the subscript c stands for cabin. $R = 287.05 \ N \cdot m/kg \cdot K$. Furthermore, $T_c = 22°C$ and is constant for the whole time.

(ii) The volume of air in the cabin is $71.0 \ m^3$. The bullet hole is 0.75 cm in diameter.

(iii) Air escapes through the bullet hole according to the equation

$$\dot{m}_c = - \ 0.040415 \ \frac{p_c}{\sqrt{T_c}} \left[A_{\text{bullet hole}} \right]$$

where p_c is in N/m^2, T_c is in K, $A_{\text{bullet hole}}$ is in m^2, and $\dot{m}_c$ is in kg/s.

3.36. The crew refuses the demands of a terrorist and he fires his pistol, shooting a small hole in the airplane. Panic strikes the crew and other passengers. But you leap up and shout, "Do not worry! I am an engineering major and I know it will take ———?——— seconds for the cabin pressure to drop from 7.0 psia to 3.5 psia." Calculate how long it will take the cabin pressure to drop. Make the following assumptions.

(i) The air in the cabin behaves as a perfect gas:

$$\rho_c = \frac{p_c}{RT_c}$$

where the subscript c stands for cabin, $R = 53.34 \ ft \cdot lbf/lbm \cdot °R$, and $T_c = 80°F$ and is constant for the whole time.

(ii) The volume of the cabin is $2513 \ ft^3$. The bullet hole is 0.3 in. in diameter.

(iii) Air escapes through the bullet hole according to the equation:

$$\dot{m}_c = - \ 0.5318 \ \frac{p_c}{\sqrt{T_c}} \left[A_{\text{bullet hole}} \right]$$

where p_c is in lbf/ft^2, T_c is in °R, $A_{\text{bullet hole}}$ is in ft^2, and $\dot{m}_c$ is in lbm/s.

3.37. Oxygen leaks slowly through a small orifice from an oxygen bottle. The volume of the bottle is $0.1 \ m^3$ and the diameter of the orifice is 0.1 mm. Assume that the temperature in the tank remains constant at 18°C and that the oxygen behaves as a perfect gas. The mass flow rate is given by

$$\dot{m}_{O_2} = - \ 0.6847 \ \frac{p_{O_2}}{\sqrt{R_{O_2} T_{O_2}}} \left[A_{\text{orifice}} \right]$$

(The units are those of Prob. 3.35.) How long does it take for the pressure in the tank to decrease from 10 to 5 MPa?

CHAPTER FOUR

The Conservation of Linear Momentum and of Angular Momentum

In Chapter 3 the continuity equation, together with the appropriate boundary conditions, was used to obtain solutions of the velocity field for several relatively simple flows. However, using only the continuity equation, we could not determine anything about pressure forces or viscous forces. The reader can think of many engineering applications where it is important to be able to determine pressure forces and viscous forces.

Aerodynamic forces act on vehicles that move through the air. The velocity and pressure variations that act on the moving aircraft not only produce a lifting component but also produce drag forces. Similarly, lift and drag forces acting on a car affect its performance and economy. There is an optimum inclination angle for the hatchback of a passenger car to achieve minimum drag. Hatchback configurations inclined at an angle lower or greater than the optimum result in greater drag forces and, therefore, greater fuel consumption. The optimum angle can be determined once the interrelation between the vehicle configuration and the velocity–pressure field is understood.

In the design of pump impellers, hydrofoils, and pipelines, the engineer must avoid the occurrence of cavitation. Cavitation is the phenomenon of boiling in a flowing liquid at normal temperatures, which occurs when the pressure drops below a critical value, the vapor pressure. If water is accelerated from rest to about 15 m/s, its pressure drops by almost 1 atm. As the liquid pressure drops below the vapor pressure, vapor bubbles begin to appear in the liquid. This flow-induced boiling is known as *cavitation*.

In this chapter, we will derive the equations for the conservation of linear momentum and of angular momentum. Using these equations together with the continuity equation, we will be able to solve simultaneously for the velocity field and pressure field for flows where the fluid properties (ρ and μ) are approximately constant. If the temperature variations are large enough to produce significant changes in the fluid properties, we must include the energy equation in our solution procedure. Such flows will be discussed in Chapter 8.

SYSTEM ANALYSIS

The laws of mechanics are written for a *system*, which is defined as an arbitrary quantity of mass of fixed identity. Everything external to this system is denoted by the term *surroundings*. The system is separated from its surroundings by its *boundaries*. The laws of mechanics define interactions between the system and its surroundings. The fixed quantity of mass for the system is denoted by *m*. Thus, the mass of the system is conserved and does not change. This statement is equivalent to the mathematical formulations of the continuity equation, as presented in Chapter 3.

ACCELERATION OF A FLUID PARTICLE

The equation for the conservation of linear momentum is obtained by applying Newton's law: the net force acting on a fluid particle is equal to the time rate of change of the linear momentum of the fluid particle. Thus, we require the total time derivative of the velocity $\vec{V}$, which is, in general, an explicit function of time t as well as of its position x, y, z. Furthermore, the position coordinates x, y, z of the fluid particle are themselves a function of time. Since $\vec{V}$ (x, y, z, t) and $x(t,)$ $y(t)$, and $z(t)$, then

$$\vec{a} = \frac{d\vec{V}}{dt} = \frac{\partial \vec{V}}{\partial x}\frac{dx}{dt} + \frac{\partial \vec{V}}{\partial y}\frac{dy}{dt} + \frac{\partial \vec{V}}{\partial z}\frac{dz}{dt} + \frac{\partial \vec{V}}{\partial t} \tag{4.1}$$

The infinitesimal changes in the position of a particle are directly related to the local velocity components:

$$\frac{dx}{dt} = u, \qquad \frac{dy}{dt} = v, \qquad \frac{dz}{dt} = w$$

Therefore, the acceleration of a fluid particle expressed in Cartesian coordinates is

$$\vec{a} = \frac{d\vec{V}}{dt} = \frac{\partial \vec{V}}{\partial t} + u\frac{\partial \vec{V}}{\partial x} + v\frac{\partial \vec{V}}{\partial y} + w\frac{\partial \vec{V}}{\partial z} \tag{4.2}$$

Using vector notation, the acceleration is

$$\vec{a} = \frac{d\vec{V}}{dt} = \frac{\partial \vec{V}}{\partial t} + (\vec{V} \cdot \nabla)\vec{V} \tag{4.3}$$

Note that the expanded form of the acceleration in cylindrical coordinates is given in Prob. 4.5.

Since the time differentiation follows a given particle in its motions, the derivative is frequently termed the *particle*, *total*, or *substantial* derivative of $\vec{V}$. The first term on the right-hand side of Eqs. (4.2) and (4.3) is called the local acceleration, or time-dependent change in velocity. The last three terms of Eq. (4.2), or equivalently the second term of Eq. (4.3), represent the convective acceleration of the fluid particle, that is, the changes in velocity that occur because the fluid particle moves around in space.

Problems where the local, time-dependent changes are zero, that is,

$$\frac{\partial \vec{V}}{\partial t} = 0$$

are known as *steady-state* flows. Note that, even when this is true, $d\vec{V}/dt$ is not necessarily zero, since the velocity of a fluid particle may change as it moves to different points in space.

Note that Eq. (4.3) contains a general expression for the Eulerian time-derivative operator following a fluid particle:

$$\frac{d}{dt} = \underset{\text{local}}{\frac{\partial}{\partial t}} + \underset{\text{convective}}{(\vec{V} \cdot \nabla)} \tag{4.4}$$

This operator can be applied to any fluid property, scalar or vector. Thus, to calculate the total, or substantial, derivative of the temperature T with respect to time,

$$\frac{dT}{dt} = \frac{\partial T}{\partial t} + (\vec{V} \cdot \nabla)T \tag{4.5}$$

The total time derivative follows a particle of fixed identity, making it convenient for expressing laws of particle mechanics in the Eulerian fluid-field description. The increased complexity occurs because we are following the motion of identified particles in a deformable, continuous medium.

Example 4.1

You are attending the bonfire before the homecoming football game. The temperature of the air varies inversely with distance from the fire, so any circle centered at the fire is a constant temperature contour. However, the fire increases in intensity with time, so the temperature of the air at a given point increases with time. Assume that the temperature (K) of the air is given by

$$T = 285 + \frac{2t}{r}$$

where the constant 2 has the units of m · K/s. Two students are following different air particles, as shown in Fig. 4.1. Particle a moves tangentially to a circle whose radius is 2 m. Particle b moves directly toward the fire. What is the total change in temperature for the air particles shown in the sketch for $r = 2$ m and $t = 10$ s?

(a) The air particle moves tangentially to the isotherm (i.e., a circle), so $\vec{V}_a = 2\hat{e}_\theta$.

(b) The air particle moves directly toward the fire, so $\vec{V}_b = -2\hat{e}_r$.

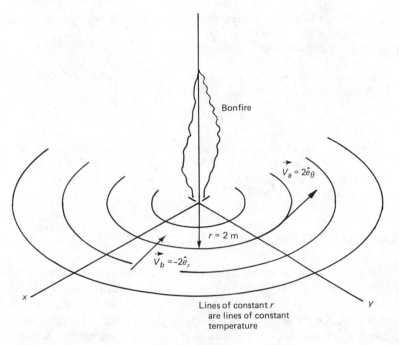

Figure 4.1 Bonfire of Example 4.1.

Solution. For both cases, the local change in temperature with respect to time is

$$\frac{\partial T}{\partial t} = \frac{2}{r}$$

The temperature gradient is

$$\nabla T = \left(\hat{e}_r \frac{\partial}{\partial r} + \frac{\hat{e}_\theta}{r} \frac{\partial}{\partial \theta} + \hat{e}_z \frac{\partial}{\partial z} \right) \left(285 + \frac{2t}{r} \right)$$

$$= -\frac{2t}{r^2} \hat{e}_r$$

Therefore, the temperature gradient is in the radial direction, increasing with time and decreasing with distance from the fire.

For case (a), where $\vec{V} = 2\hat{e}_\theta$,

$$\frac{dT}{dt} = \frac{\partial T}{\partial t} + \left(\vec{V} \cdot \nabla \right) T$$

$$= \frac{2}{r} + \left(\frac{2}{r} \frac{\partial}{\partial \theta} \right) \left(285 + \frac{2t}{r} \right) = 1.0 \ \text{K/s}$$

There is no convective change in temperature for this air particle since its motion is perpendicular to the spatial temperature gradient. Thus, the substantial, or total, time derivative of the temperature is equal to the partial (unsteady component) derivative with respect to time for the motion of case (a).

For case (b),

$$\frac{dT}{dt} = \frac{2}{r} + \left(-2\frac{\partial}{\partial r}\right)\left(285 + \frac{2t}{r}\right) = \frac{2}{r} + \frac{4t}{r^2}$$

$$= 1.0 + \frac{4(10)}{4} = 11.0 \text{ K/s}$$

This air particle experiences a large increase in temperature because it moves directly toward the fire. Note, for this case, we are moving parallel to the temperature gradient. So its total temperature change is due both to local, time-dependent (or unsteady) changes and to convective (or those due to fluid motion) changes.

GENERAL FORM OF THE MOMENTUM EQUATION

The equation for the conservation of linear momentum is the mathematical representation of Newton's law, which states that the net force acting on a fluid particle is equal to the time rate of change of the linear momentum of the fluid particle. As the fluid element moves in space, its shape and volume may change, but its mass is conserved. Thus, using an inertial coordinate system (i.e., one that is neither accelerating nor rotating), we can write

$$\vec{F} = m\frac{d\vec{V}}{dt} \tag{4.6}$$

The principal forces with which we are concerned are those that act directly on the mass of the fluid element, the body forces, and those that act on its surface, the pressure forces and shear forces. The stress system acting on an element of the surface is illustrated in Fig. 4.2. The stress components τ acting on the small cube are assigned subscripts. The first subscript indicates the direction of the normal to the surface on which the stress acts, and the second indicates the direction in which the stress acts. Thus, τ_{xy} denotes a stress acting in the y direction on the surface whose normal points in the x direction.

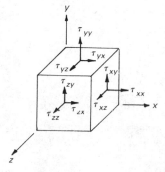

Figure 4.2   Nomenclature for the normal stresses and shear stresses acting on a fluid element.

Similarly, τ_{xx} denotes a normal stress acting on that surface. The stresses are described in terms of a right-hand coordinate system in which the outwardly directed surface normal indicates the positive direction.

The properties of most fluids have no preferred direction in space; that is, fluids are isotropic. Furthermore, the stresses do not explicitly depend on either the position coordinate or the velocity of the fluid. As a result,

$$\tau_{xy} = \tau_{yx}, \qquad \tau_{yz} = \tau_{zy}, \qquad \tau_{zx} = \tau_{xz} \tag{4.7}$$

In general, the various stresses change from point to point. Thus, they produce net forces on the fluid particle, which cause it to accelerate. The forces acting on each surface are obtained by taking into account the variations of stress with position by using the center of the element as a reference point. To simplify the illustration of the force balance on the fluid particle, we shall again consider a two-dimensional flow, as indicated in Fig. 4.3. The resultant force in the x direction (for a unit depth in the z direction) is

$$\rho f_x \, \Delta x \, \Delta y + \frac{\partial}{\partial x} (\tau_{xx}) \, \Delta x \, \Delta y + \frac{\partial}{\partial y} (\tau_{yx}) \, \Delta y \, \Delta x$$

where f_x is the body force per unit mass in the x direction. The most common body force for the flow fields of interest to this text is that of gravity.

Including flow in the z direction, the resultant force in the x direction would be

$$F_x = \rho f_x \, \Delta x \, \Delta y \, \Delta z + \frac{\partial}{\partial x} (\tau_{xx}) \, \Delta x \, \Delta y \, \Delta z + \frac{\partial}{\partial y} (\tau_{yx}) \, \Delta y \, \Delta x \, \Delta z$$

$$+ \frac{\partial}{\partial z} (\tau_{zx}) \, \Delta z \, \Delta y \, \Delta x$$

which, by Eq. (4.6), is equal to

$$ma_x = \rho \, \Delta x \, \Delta y \, \Delta z \, \frac{du}{dt} = \rho \, \Delta x \, \Delta y \, \Delta z \left[\frac{\partial u}{\partial t} + (\vec{V} \cdot \nabla) u \right]$$

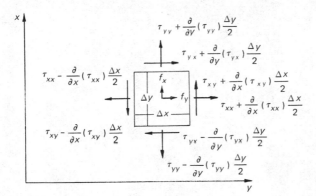

Figure 4.3 Stresses acting on a two-dimensional element of fluid.

Equating the two and dividing by the volume of the fluid particle $\Delta x\,\Delta y\,\Delta z$ yields

$$\rho\,\frac{du}{dt} = \rho f_x + \frac{\partial}{\partial x}\,\tau_{xx} + \frac{\partial}{\partial y}\,\tau_{yx} + \frac{\partial}{\partial z}\,\tau_{zx} \tag{4.8a}$$

Similarly, we obtain the equation of motion for the y direction,

$$\rho\,\frac{dv}{dt} = \rho f_y + \frac{\partial}{\partial x}\,\tau_{xy} + \frac{\partial}{\partial y}\,\tau_{yy} + \frac{\partial}{\partial z}\,\tau_{zy} \tag{4.8b}$$

and for the z direction,

$$\rho\,\frac{dw}{dt} = \rho f_z + \frac{\partial}{\partial x}\,\tau_{xz} + \frac{\partial}{\partial y}\,\tau_{yz} + \frac{\partial}{\partial z}\,\tau_{zz} \tag{4.8c}$$

Next, we need to relate the stresses to the motion of the fluid. For a fluid at rest or for an inviscid fluid motion, there is no shearing stress, and the normal stress is in the nature of a pressure. For fluid particles, the stress is related to the rate of strain by a physical law based on the following assumptions:

1. Stress components may be expressed as a linear function of the components of the rate of strain. The friction law for one-dimensional flow of a Newtonian fluid is a special case of this linear stress/rate-of-strain relation: $\tau = \mu(\partial u/\partial y)$.
2. The relations between the stress components and the rate-of-strain components must be invariant to a coordinate transformation consisting of either a rotation or a mirror reflection of axes, since a physical law cannot depend upon the choice of the coordinate system.
3. When all velocity gradients are zero (i.e., the shear stress vanishes), the stress components must reduce to the hydrostatic pressure, p.

For a fluid that satisfies these criteria,

$$\tau_{xx} = -p - \frac{2}{3}\mu\nabla\cdot\vec{V} + 2\mu\,\frac{\partial u}{\partial x} \tag{4.9a}$$

$$\tau_{yy} = -p - \frac{2}{3}\mu\nabla\cdot\vec{V} + 2\mu\,\frac{\partial v}{\partial y} \tag{4.9b}$$

$$\tau_{zz} = -p - \frac{2}{3}\mu\nabla\cdot\vec{V} + 2\mu\,\frac{\partial w}{\partial z} \tag{4.9c}$$

$$\tau_{xy} = \tau_{yx} = \mu\left(\frac{\partial u}{\partial y} + \frac{\partial v}{\partial x}\right) \tag{4.10a}$$

$$\tau_{xz} = \tau_{zx} = \mu\left(\frac{\partial u}{\partial z} + \frac{\partial w}{\partial x}\right) \tag{4.10b}$$

$$\tau_{yz} = \tau_{zy} = \mu\left(\frac{\partial v}{\partial z} + \frac{\partial w}{\partial y}\right) \tag{4.10c}$$

With the appropriate expressions for the surface stresses substituted into Eq. (4.8), one obtains

$$\rho \frac{\partial u}{\partial t} + \rho(\vec{V} \cdot \nabla)u = \rho f_x - \frac{\partial p}{\partial x} + \frac{\partial}{\partial x}\left[2\mu \frac{\partial u}{\partial x} - \frac{2}{3}\mu \nabla \cdot \vec{V}\right]$$

$$+ \frac{\partial}{\partial y}\left[\mu\left(\frac{\partial u}{\partial y} + \frac{\partial v}{\partial x}\right)\right] + \frac{\partial}{\partial z}\left[\mu\left(\frac{\partial w}{\partial x} + \frac{\partial u}{\partial z}\right)\right] \quad (4.11a)$$

$$\rho \frac{\partial v}{\partial t} + \rho(\vec{V} \cdot \nabla)v = \rho f_y + \frac{\partial}{\partial x}\left[\mu\left(\frac{\partial u}{\partial y} + \frac{\partial v}{\partial x}\right)\right] - \frac{\partial p}{\partial y}$$

$$+ \frac{\partial}{\partial y}\left[2\mu \frac{\partial v}{\partial y} - \frac{2}{3}\mu \nabla \cdot \vec{V}\right] + \frac{\partial}{\partial z}\left[\mu\left(\frac{\partial w}{\partial y} + \frac{\partial v}{\partial z}\right)\right] \quad (4.11b)$$

$$\rho \frac{\partial w}{\partial t} + \rho(\vec{V} \cdot \nabla)w = \rho f_z + \frac{\partial}{\partial x}\left[\mu\left(\frac{\partial w}{\partial x} + \frac{\partial u}{\partial z}\right)\right] + \frac{\partial}{\partial y}\left[\mu\left(\frac{\partial v}{\partial z} + \frac{\partial w}{\partial y}\right)\right]$$

$$- \frac{\partial p}{\partial z} + \frac{\partial}{\partial z}\left[2\mu \frac{\partial w}{\partial z} - \frac{2}{3}\mu \nabla \cdot \vec{V}\right] \quad (4.11c)$$

These general differential equations for the conservation of linear momentum are known as the *Navier–Stokes equations*. Note that the viscosity μ is considered to be dependent on the spatial coordinates. This is done since, for a compressible flow, the changes in velocity and pressure, together with the heat due to friction, bring about considerable temperature variations. The temperature dependence of viscosity in the general case should, therefore, be incorporated into the governing equations.

For a general application, the unknown parameters that appear in the Navier–Stokes equations are the three velocity components (u, v, and w), the pressure (p), the density (ρ), and the viscosity (μ). As we discussed in Chapter 1, for a fluid of known composition that is in equilibrium, the density and viscosity are unique functions of pressure and temperature. Thus, there are five primary (or primitive) variables for a general flow problem: the three velocity components, the pressure, and the temperature. However, at present we have only four equations: the continuity equation, Eq. (3.4), and the three components of the momentum equation, Eqs. (4.11a) through (4.11c). Until we derive the energy equation in Chapter 8, we will not be able to solve general problems for which the temperature variations are so large that they must be included in the solution algorithm.

For many flows, however, temperature variations are sufficiently small that the density and viscosity may be assumed constant throughout the flow field. Such flows will be termed *constant-property* flows in this text. The terms *low-speed* and/or *incompressible* flows will also be used in the description of these flows. A gas flow is considered incompressible if the Mach number is less than 0.4. For these flows, there are only four unknowns: the three velocity components (u, v, and w) and the pressure (p). Thus, we have a system of four independent equations that can be solved for the four unknowns.

Since Eqs. (4.11a) through (4.11c) are the general differential equations for the conservation of linear momentum, the equations for a static medium can be obtained by neglecting the terms relating to the acceleration of the fluid particles and to the viscous forces. Neglecting these terms in Eqs. (4.11a) through (4.11c) and assuming the body force is gravity and that it acts in the negative z direction, the reader would obtain Eqs. (2.2a) through (2.2c).

EXACT SOLUTIONS OF THE DIFFERENTIAL
MOMENTUM EQUATION

The Navier–Stokes equations for a general viscous flow are nonlinear partial differential equations. For most applications, it is impossible to obtain solutions for the complete Navier–Stokes equations, even for constant-property flows. In most flow problems, simplifying assumptions are made so that approximate solutions can be obtained in order to generate design information. The engineer evaluates the relative magnitude of the terms in Eqs. (4.11a) through (4.11c), neglecting terms that are relatively unimportant for the particular application. As a result, the equations are simplified to the point where *approximate* solutions can be obtained. These approximate solutions yield valuable engineering information, providing the simplifying assumptions are valid for the application of interest. Examples will be presented in Chapters 5 through 7 to illustrate typical simplifying assumptions, the appropriate solution techniques, and the validity (and/or limitations) of these assumptions.

Nevertheless, there are certain flow problems for which exact solutions of the Navier–Stokes equations can be generated, for example, steady, fully developed, incompressible flow. The analysis of a fully developed flow is illustrated in Example 4.2.

Example 4.2

Consider a steady, low-speed flow of a viscous fluid between two infinitely long, parallel, *vertical* plates, spaced a distance h apart. As shown in Fig. 4.4, the velocity variations take place in the x, z plane. The flow is completely independent of y. Because the flow is confined between parallel plates that are infinitely long, the velocity components do not vary in the z direction. Hence, this flow is fully developed in the z (or vertical) direction.

The wall on the left ($x = 0$) is stationary; the wall on the right ($x = h$) is moving upward at a constant speed, w_0. Assume that all pressure gradients are negligible, but that we cannot neglect the effects of gravity, which acts in the negative z direction.
(a) Find expressions for u, v, and w.
(b) What is the value of w at the midpoint of the channel, that is, at $x = h/2$?
(c) Develop the relation between w_0, g, h, ρ, and μ so that there is zero net mass flow across any horizontal plane, that is, any plane for which $z =$ constant.

Solution.   As was the case in Example 3.1, we will assume that the density is constant for this low-speed flow. Thus, the continuity equation for this steady, two-dimensional, incompressible flow is

$$\frac{\partial u}{\partial x} + \frac{\partial w}{\partial z} = 0$$

Since the flow is fully developed in the z direction, $\partial w/\partial z = 0$. Therefore, $\partial u/\partial x = 0$, also. Furthermore, since $u = 0$ at both walls and since u does not depend on y or z, $u = 0$ everywhere.

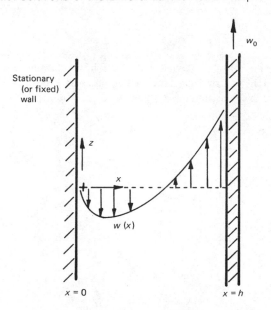

Figure 4.4 Fully developed flow in a vertical channel (Example 4.2).

$x = 0$ $x = h$

(a) At this point, we know that $u = 0$ everywhere, $v = 0$ everywhere, and w is a function of x only (since it does not depend on y, z, or t). We also know that the only body force is gravity and that it acts in the negative z direction. We have been told to assume that all pressure gradients are negligible.

Thus, all the terms in Eqs. (4.11a) and (4.11b) are zero and the equations need not be considered further. Consider now Eq. (4.11c).

$$\rho \frac{\partial w}{\partial t} + \rho(\vec{V} \cdot \nabla)w = \rho f_z + \frac{\partial}{\partial x}\left[\mu\left(\frac{\partial w}{\partial x} + \frac{\partial u}{\partial z}\right)\right]$$

$$+ \frac{\partial}{\partial y}\left[\mu\left(\frac{\partial v}{\partial z} + \frac{\partial w}{\partial y}\right)\right] - \frac{\partial p}{\partial z} + \frac{\partial}{\partial z}\left[2\mu \frac{\partial w}{\partial z} - \frac{2}{3}\mu\nabla \cdot \vec{V}\right]$$

Because we are considering low-speed flow of a simple fluid, μ is a constant throughout the flow field. Thus, we can rewrite the viscous terms of this equation as follows:

$$\frac{\partial}{\partial x}\left[\mu\left(\frac{\partial w}{\partial x} + \frac{\partial u}{\partial z}\right)\right] + \frac{\partial}{\partial y}\left[\mu\left(\frac{\partial v}{\partial z} + \frac{\partial w}{\partial y}\right)\right] + \frac{\partial}{\partial z}\left[2\mu \frac{\partial w}{\partial z} - \frac{2}{3}\mu\nabla \cdot \vec{V}\right]$$

$$= \mu \frac{\partial^2 w}{\partial x^2} + \mu \frac{\partial}{\partial z}\left(\frac{\partial u}{\partial x}\right) + \mu \frac{\partial}{\partial z}\left(\frac{\partial v}{\partial y}\right) + \mu \frac{\partial^2 w}{\partial y^2} + \mu \frac{\partial}{\partial z}\left(\frac{\partial w}{\partial z}\right) + \mu \frac{\partial^2 w}{\partial z^2} - \frac{2}{3}\mu \frac{\partial}{\partial z}(\nabla \cdot \vec{V})$$

$$= \mu\left[\frac{\partial^2 w}{\partial x^2} + \frac{\partial^2 w}{\partial y^2} + \frac{\partial^2 w}{\partial z^2}\right] + \mu \frac{\partial}{\partial z}\left(\frac{\partial u}{\partial x} + \frac{\partial v}{\partial y} + \frac{\partial w}{\partial z}\right) - \frac{2}{3}\mu \frac{\partial}{\partial z}(\nabla \cdot \vec{V})$$

Noting that

$$\frac{\partial u}{\partial x} + \frac{\partial v}{\partial y} + \frac{\partial w}{\partial z} = \nabla \cdot \vec{V}$$

and that $\nabla \cdot \vec{V} = 0$ (since this is the continuity equation for a constant density flow), we can replace the viscous terms of Eq. (4.11c) by

$$\mu \left[\frac{\partial^2 w}{\partial x^2} + \frac{\partial^2 w}{\partial y^2} + \frac{\partial^2 w}{\partial z^2} \right]$$

Since we must include the effect of gravity, which acts in the negative z direction, $f_z = -g$. However, we are told we can neglect the pressure gradient. Thus, we can write the z momentum equation for this constant-property flow as

$$\rho \frac{\partial w}{\partial t} + \rho u \frac{\partial w}{\partial x} + \rho v \frac{\partial w}{\partial y} + \rho w \frac{\partial w}{\partial z} = -\rho g + \mu \frac{\partial^2 w}{\partial x^2} + \mu \frac{\partial^2 w}{\partial y^2} + \mu \frac{\partial^2 w}{\partial z^2} \qquad (4.12)$$

Note that

$$\rho \frac{\partial w}{\partial t} = 0, \quad \text{because the flow is steady}$$

$$\rho u \frac{\partial w}{\partial x} = 0, \quad \text{because } u = 0$$

$$\rho v \frac{\partial w}{\partial y} = 0, \quad \text{because } v = 0 \text{ and } w = w(x \text{ only})$$

$$\rho w \frac{\partial w}{\partial z} = \mu \frac{\partial^2 w}{\partial y^2} = \mu \frac{\partial^2 w}{\partial z^2} = 0, \quad \text{because } w = w(x \text{ only})$$

Thus, the equation to be solved is

$$\mu \frac{d^2 w}{dx^2} = \rho g$$

and note d^2w/dx^2 is written as an ordinary differential (instead of a partial differential), since w is a function of x only. Furthermore, ρg is a constant and not a function of x or y. Integrating twice (noting that μ, ρ, and g are constants), we obtain

$$w = \frac{\rho g}{2\mu} x^2 + C_1 x + C_2$$

To evaluate the two constants of integration, we must introduce the two boundary conditions:

(i) $w(0, y, z) = 0$

(ii) $w(h, y, z) = w_0$

These two equations represent the requirement that the viscous fluid particles immediately adjacent to a solid surface adhere to that surface (i.e., the no-slip condition). Using boundary condition (i), it is clear that

$$C_2 = 0$$

Using boundary condition (ii), we find that

$$C_1 = \frac{w_0}{h} - \frac{\rho g}{2\mu} h$$

Thus,

$$w(x, y, z) = \frac{\rho g h^2}{2\mu} \left[\left(\frac{x}{h}\right)^2 - \frac{x}{h} \right] + w_0 \frac{x}{h}$$

Note that the boundary conditions are satisfied by this expression.

(b) At the middle of the channel, $x = h/2$. Thus,

$$w\left(\frac{h}{2}, y, z\right) = -\frac{\rho g h^2}{8\mu} + \frac{w_0}{2}$$

If w_0 is zero (i.e., both walls are stationary), w is negative (downward), as we would expect it to be.

(c) To obtain the desired relation for part (c), we must determine exactly what is sought. Referring to the sketch of Fig. 4.4, we see that, with one wall fixed and the other wall moving upward, part of the flow is going upward and part of the flow is going downward. There is obviously a situation in which these flows balance and there is zero net flow across a horizontal plane. Using the relations developed in Chapter 3, the mass flow rate across a plane is given by

$$\dot{m} = \iint \rho \vec{V} \cdot d\vec{A} = \iint \rho w \, dx \, dy$$

We know that w is independent of y. Therefore, we will choose dy to be 1 (i.e., a unit depth). Thus,

$$\dot{m} = \int_0^{x=h} \rho w \, dx \, (1) = 0$$

Noting that ρ is a constant, we obtain the expression to be integrated as

$$\int_0^h \left(\frac{\rho g h^2}{2\mu} \left[\left(\frac{x}{h}\right)^2 - \left(\frac{x}{h}\right) \right] + w_0 \frac{x}{h} \right) dx = 0$$

Integrating, we find that

$$w_0 = \frac{\rho g h^2}{6\mu}$$

is the relation between w_0, g, h, ρ, and μ so that there is zero net mass flow across any horizontal plane.

REYNOLDS NUMBER, FROUDE NUMBER, EULER NUMBER, AND MACH NUMBER AS SIMILARITY PARAMETERS

For the flow field discussed in the previous example, so many of the terms of the momentum equation had zero value that we were left with a relatively simple equation for which we could obtain an exact analytical solution. However, such simplifications cannot be made for the majority of flow problems. Thus, it is impossible to obtain analytical solutions for most flows. For many applications, the engineer can introduce reasonable approximations, for example, that certain terms of the equation are negligible in comparison to others, that the fluid behaves as a perfect gas, or that the fluid is incompressible. These assumptions simplify the equation to be solved while retaining its essential characteristics. Having introduced these simplifications, the engineer often can solve the resulting equations. Despite rapid advancements in computer hardware and the analytical techniques used in numerical formulations, many problems, even after the appropriate simplifying assumptions have been introduced, cannot be solved analytically or numerically. In such cases, the engineer often conducts experimental programs to measure directly the parameters that define the flow field. Some objectives of such test programs are as follows:

1. To obtain information necessary to develop a flow model that could be used in theoretical solutions.
2. To investigate the effect of various geometric parameters on the flow field.
3. To verify that theoretical predictions of the flow field for a particular configuration are correct.
4. To measure directly the flow field around the complete configuration.

Usually, either scale models of the complete configuration or large-scale simulations of elements of the configuration (such as the wing of an airplane) are used in these test programs. Furthermore, in many test programs the free-steam conditions (such as the velocity and static pressure) for the tests cannot be made equal to the values for the condition that is to be simulated.

It is important then to determine under what conditions the experimental results obtained for one flow are applicable to another flow that is confined by boundaries that are geometrically similar (but of different size). For geometric similarity, all length scales must be the same. It is as if you took a photograph of the prototype and reduced it (or enlarged it) until it matched exactly the model configuration. To do this, consider the x momentum equation as applied to the two flows of Fig. 4.5. For simplicity, let us limit ourselves to constant-property flows. Recall that for a constant-property flow, the continuity equation requires that

$$\nabla \cdot \vec{V} = 0$$

With this limitation, Eq. (4.11a) can be written as

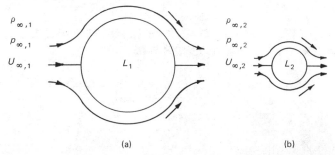

(a)   (b)

Figure 4.5   Nomenclature for a flow around a prototype configuration and that around a scale model: (a) prototype flow; (b) model flow.

$$\rho \frac{\partial u}{\partial t} + \rho u \frac{\partial u}{\partial x} + \rho v \frac{\partial u}{\partial y} + \rho w \frac{\partial u}{\partial z} = \rho f_x - \frac{\partial p}{\partial x} + \mu \frac{\partial^2 u}{\partial x^2} + \mu \frac{\partial^2 u}{\partial y^2} + \mu \frac{\partial^2 u}{\partial z^2} \quad (4.13)$$

Let us divide each of the thermodynamic properties by the value of that property at a point far from the vehicle (i.e., the free-stream value of the property) for each of the two flows. Thus, for the first flow,

$$p_1^* = \frac{p}{p_{\infty,1}}, \qquad \rho_1^* = \frac{\rho}{\rho_{\infty,1}}, \qquad \mu_1^* = \frac{\mu}{\mu_{\infty,1}}$$

and for the second flow,

$$p_2^* = \frac{p}{p_{\infty,2}}, \qquad \rho_2^* = \frac{\rho}{\rho_{\infty,2}}, \qquad \mu_2^* = \frac{\mu}{\mu_{\infty,2}}$$

Note that the free-stream values for all three nondimensionalized (*) thermodynamic properties are unity for both cases. Similarly, let us divide the velocity components by the free-stream velocity. Thus, for the first flow,

$$u_1^* = \frac{u}{U_{\infty,1}}, \qquad v_1^* = \frac{v}{U_{\infty,1}}, \qquad w_1^* = \frac{w}{U_{\infty,1}}$$

and for the second flow,

$$u_2^* = \frac{u}{U_{\infty,2}}, \qquad v_2^* = \frac{v}{U_{\infty,2}}, \qquad w_2^* = \frac{w}{U_{\infty,2}}$$

With the velocity components thus nondimensionalized, the free-stream boundary conditions are the same for both flows. That is, at points far from the vehicle,

$$u_1^* = u_2^* = 1 \quad \text{and} \quad v_1^* = v_2^* = w_1^* = w_2^* = 0$$

A characteristic dimension L is used to nondimensionalize the independent variables.

$$x_1^* = \frac{x}{L_1}, \qquad y_1^* = \frac{y}{L_1}, \qquad z_1^* = \frac{z}{L_1}, \qquad t_1^* = \frac{tU_{\infty,1}}{L_1}$$

and

$$x_2^* = \frac{x}{L_2}, \qquad y_2^* = \frac{y}{L_2}, \qquad z_2^* = \frac{z}{L_2}, \qquad t_2^* = \frac{tU_{\infty,2}}{L_2}$$

Let us divide the body force per unit mass by g, which is the gravitational constant, to nondimensionalize this parameter. Since gravity is the body force of interest in this text, g is the appropriate characteristic quantity. That gravity is the body force of interest is shown in Chapters 2 and 5. Thus,

$$f_{x1}^* = \frac{f_x}{g}, \qquad f_{x2}^* = \frac{f_x}{g}$$

Note that g is the same for both flows.

In terms of these dimensionless parameters, Eq. (4.13) becomes

$$\rho_1^* \frac{\partial u_1^*}{\partial t_1^*} + \rho_1^* u_1^* \frac{\partial u_1^*}{\partial x_1^*} + \rho_1^* v_1^* \frac{\partial u_1^*}{\partial y_1^*} + \rho_1^* w_1^* \frac{\partial u_1^*}{\partial z_1^*}$$

$$= \left[\frac{gL_1}{U_{\infty,1}^2}\right] \rho_1^* f_{x1}^* - \left[\frac{p_{\infty,1}}{\rho_{\infty,1} U_{\infty,1}^2}\right] \frac{\partial p_1^*}{\partial x_1^*}$$

$$+ \left[\frac{\mu_{\infty,1}}{\rho_{\infty,1} U_{\infty,1} L_1}\right] \left(\mu_1^* \frac{\partial^2 u_1^*}{\partial x_1^{*2}} + \mu_1^* \frac{\partial^2 u_1^*}{\partial y_1^{*2}} + \mu_1^* \frac{\partial^2 u_1^*}{\partial z_1^{*2}}\right) \qquad (4.14a)$$

for the first flow. For the second flow,

$$\rho_2^* \frac{\partial u_2^*}{\partial t_2^*} + \rho_2^* u_2^* \frac{\partial u_2^*}{\partial x_2^*} + \rho_2^* v_2^* \frac{\partial u_2^*}{\partial y_2^*} + \rho_2^* w_2^* \frac{\partial u_2^*}{\partial z_2^*}$$

$$= \left[\frac{gL_2}{U_{\infty,2}^2}\right] \rho_2^* f_{x2}^* - \left[\frac{p_{\infty,2}}{\rho_{\infty,2} U_{\infty,2}^2}\right] \frac{\partial p_2^*}{\partial x_2^*}$$

$$+ \left[\frac{\mu_{\infty,2}}{\rho_{\infty,2} U_{\infty,2} L_2}\right] \left(\mu_2^* \frac{\partial^2 u_2^*}{\partial x_2^{*2}} + \mu_2^* \frac{\partial^2 u_2^*}{\partial y_2^{*2}} + \mu_2^* \frac{\partial^2 u_2^*}{\partial z_2^{*2}}\right) \qquad (4.14b)$$

Both the dependent and independent variables have been nondimensionalized, as indicated by the * quantities. The dimensionless *boundary-condition values* for the dependent variables are the same for the two flows around geometrically similar configurations. As a consequence, the solutions of the two problems in terms of the dimensionless variables will be identical, provided that the differential equations are identical. The differential equations will be identical if the dimensionless parameters in the brackets have the same values for both problems. In this case, the flows are said to be dynamically similar, as well as geometrically similar.

Let us examine the first similarity parameter from Eq. (4.14),

$$\left[\frac{U_\infty^2}{gL}\right] \qquad (4.15)$$

The square root of this similarity parameter is known as the *Froude number*. It is named after William Froude, a nineteenth-century British naval architect, and will be designated by the symbol Fr in this text. The Froude number is a dominant similarity parameter for free-surface flows (e.g., ship resistance, surface waves, and open channels). The Froude number is not significant for a flow in which there is no free surface.

Let us now consider the second similarity parameter in Eq. (4.14),

$$\left[\frac{p_\infty}{\rho_\infty U_\infty^2}\right] \qquad (4.16)$$

The pressure coefficient in this form is known as the *Euler number* (Eu) and is important when the pressure drops low enough to cause vapor formation (i.e., cavitation) in a liquid. We can also interpret this similarity parameter in relation to gas flows. Recall that for a perfect gas the equation of state is

$$p_\infty = \rho_\infty R T_\infty$$

and the free-stream speed of sound is given by

$$a_\infty = \sqrt{k R T_\infty}$$

Substituting these relations into Eq. (4.16) yields

$$\frac{p_\infty}{\rho_\infty U_\infty^2} = \frac{R T_\infty}{U_\infty^2} = \frac{a_\infty^2}{k U_\infty^2} = \frac{1}{k M_\infty^2} \tag{4.17a}$$

since the Mach number is defined as

$$M_\infty = \frac{U_\infty}{a_\infty} \tag{4.17b}$$

Thus, the second dimensionless similarity parameter can be interpreted in terms of the free-steam Mach number for a gas flow or in terms of the Euler number for a liquid.

The inverse of the final similarity parameter is written

$$\left[\frac{\rho_\infty U_\infty L}{\mu_\infty} \right] \tag{4.18}$$

which is the *Reynolds number,* a measure of the ratio of inertia forces to viscous forces. Named after Osborne Reynolds, a British engineer, the Reynolds number is important for all flows in which we account for the effects of viscosity. Since the coefficient of viscosity is never zero, the Reynolds number is one of the most important similarity parameters. However, there are many regions of the flow field where the product of the viscosity times the shear velocity gradient is negligible. Since the viscous terms of Eqs. (4.11a) through (4.11c), the Navier–Stokes equations, are negligible for these inviscid flows, the Reynolds number would not be important. Inviscid flows are discussed in Chapter 5.

INTEGRAL FORM OF THE MOMENTUM EQUATION

The integral form of the momentum equation can be obtained by returning to Newton's law. The sum of the forces acting on a system of fluid particles is equal to the rate of change of momentum of the fluid particles. Thus, the sum of the body forces and of the surface forces equals the time rate of change of momentum within the volume plus the net efflux of momentum through the surface bounding the volume. In vector form,

$$\vec{F}_{body} + \vec{F}_{surface} = \frac{\partial}{\partial t} \iiint_{vol} \rho \vec{V} \, d(vol) + \oiint_A \vec{V}(\rho \vec{V} \cdot d\vec{A}) \tag{4.19}$$

Solutions of the Integral Form of the Momentum Equation

For some problems, a detailed solution of the complete flow field is not required, and the desired information can be most easily determined by solving the integral form of the momentum equation. Since the momentum equation is primarily a relation between the velocity field and the distribution of forces, the control volume (or control volumes for complex problems) should be carefully chosen so that the velocities and forces that must be determined as part of the solution process can be readily calculated.

The reader is reminded that the momentum equation, Eq. (4.19), was developed by applying Newton's law to a fluid particle in a coordinate system that is neither accelerating nor rotating. Thus, the control volume, relative to which the velocities in the equation are measured, must be fixed in inertial space.

Example 4.3

Consider a fully developed, steady, constant-property flow in a pipe of constant diameter. The radial distribution of the streamwise component of velocity is given by

$$u = U_0 \left[1 - \left(\frac{r}{R} \right)^2 \right]$$

Since the flow is fully developed, the velocity is independent of x; that is, the velocity profiles are the same for every axial station. Develop the relation between the streamwise pressure gradient and ρ, μ, U_0, and R.

Solution.   Since we are interested in the forces and velocities in the x direction, we will neglect the effect of the body forces, that is, gravity which acts in the radial direction. Let us evaluate the terms of the integral form of the momentum equation:

$$\vec{F}_{\text{body}} + \vec{F}_{\text{surface}} = \frac{\partial}{\partial t} \iiint\limits_{\text{vol}} \rho \vec{V} \, d(\text{vol}) + \oiint\limits_{A} (\rho \, \vec{V} \cdot d\vec{A}) \vec{V} \tag{4.19}$$

The forces acting on the fluid within the control volume (represented by the dashed lines of Fig. 4.6) in the x direction are the pressure forces acting at stations 1 and 2 and the shear force acting at the surface of the pipe. Two choices are available for expressing the pressure forces. The first assumes that all the normal stresses act in the direction of the outward normal, in which case the pressure is treated as a negative stress. See Eqs. (4.9a) through (4.9c). The second approach makes use of the knowledge that pressure forces are compressive. Thus, the pressure forces on the control surface of Fig. 4.6 act inwardly. Using either approach, the sum of the forces in the x direction is

$$\sum F_x = p_1 A_1 - p_2 A_2 - |\tau_w| 2\pi R \, \Delta x \tag{4.20a}$$

The signs of the pressure terms reflect the direction in which the force acts. Since the viscous force (or shear) at the wall tends to retard the fluid motion, it is given a negative sign. That is, the force of the wall on the fluid is in the negative x direction.

Since the flow is steady, the first term on the right-hand side of Eq. (4.19) is zero. The second term, which is the net efflux of momentum from the control volume in the x direction, is

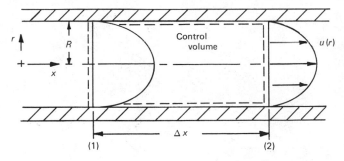

Figure 4.6 Fully developed, steady, constant-property flow in a pipe of constant diameter (Example 4.3).

$$\oiint (\rho \vec{V} \cdot d\vec{A})u = - \int_1 \rho \left\{ U_0 \left[1 - \left(\frac{r}{R} \right)^2 \right] \right\}^2 2\pi r \, dr$$

$$+ \int_2 \rho \left\{ U_0 \left[1 - \left(\frac{r}{R} \right)^2 \right] \right\}^2 2\pi r \, dr$$

$$= 0 \qquad\qquad (4.20b)$$

Note that there is zero net efflux of momentum from the control volume for the fully developed, steady flow in a constant-area streamtube. This would be true for any velocity distribution, where the flow is steady and fully developed.

When Eqs. (4.20a) and (4.20b) are substituted into Eq. (4.19), we obtain

$$(p_1 - p_2)\pi R^2 = |\tau_w| 2\pi R \, \Delta x$$

Rearranging,

$$\frac{dp}{dx} = \frac{p_2 - p_1}{\Delta x} = - \frac{2|\tau_w|}{R}$$

Since the velocity profile is known, we can calculate the shear at the wall using the relation for a Newtonian fluid, Eq. (1.4):

$$|\tau_w| = \left| \mu \left(\frac{du}{dr} \right)_{r=R} \right| = \frac{2\mu U_0}{R}$$

Thus, we obtain the relation

$$\frac{dp}{dx} = - \frac{4\mu U_0}{R^2} \qquad\qquad (4.21)$$

Note that when the flow is from left-to-right, as shown in the sketch, (i.e., $U_0 > 0$), then $dp/dx < 0$; that is, the pressure decreases in the streamwise direction. The pressure drop is due to the viscous forces acting on the walls of the pipe. An alternate way of viewing this result is that the pumping units in a pipeline are needed to overcome the pressure drop due to viscous forces. Such flows will be treated in considerable detail in Chapter 6.

Comment on Pressure Gradients. A pressure gradient for which the pressure decreases in the streamwise direction is termed a *favorable* pressure gradient. One for which the pressure increases in the streamwise direction is termed an *adverse* pressure gradient.

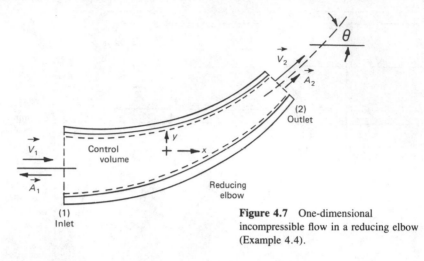

Figure 4.7 One-dimensional incompressible flow in a reducing elbow (Example 4.4).

Example 4.4

Use the integral form of the momentum equation to evaluate the resultant force of the fluid on the reducing elbow shown in Fig. 4.7 as a result of a steady, incompressible flow in the elbow. Let us assume that the flow is one-dimensional, that is, the flow parameters are constant across the pipe, varying only in the streamwise direction. Because we will not learn the techniques that are required to calculate the flow characteristics at the inlet and outlet until later, we will solve for the resultant force in terms of the parameters of the problem.

Solution.   The control volume is chosen so that it contains all the fluid in the elbow section, as indicated by the dashed line of Fig. 4.7. To determine the resultant force of the fluid on the reducing elbow, we will use the integral form of the momentum equation, determining first the force of the elbow on the fluid, which is the negative of the force we seek.

The forces acting on the surface of the fluid are the pressure forces acting at the inlet and exit stations, as well as the distribution of the normal and shear stresses at the wall of the reducer. We are not interested in determining the details of the force distribution along the wall but merely the resultant force on the fluid. The body force is simply the weight of the fluid within the control volume, which is the product of the specific weight (γ) times the internal volume of the elbow. For the coordinate system of Fig. 4.7, the weights acts in the negative y direction.

To simplify the analysis, let us apply the integral equation to the x direction and then to the y direction. Thus, since the flow is steady, the x component of the momentum equation is

$$\sum F_x = \oiint (\rho \vec{V} \cdot d\vec{A}) V_x \tag{4.22a}$$

and the y component of the momentum equation is

$$\sum F_y = \oiint (\rho \vec{V} \cdot d\vec{A}) V_y \tag{4.22b}$$

Evaluating the terms in the equation for the x direction, we obtain

$$p_1A_1 - p_2A_2 \cos \theta + F_{PFx} = (-\rho V_1A_1)(V_1) + (\rho V_2A_2)(V_2 \cos \theta)$$

where F_{PFx} is the resultant force of the pipe on the fluid in the x direction. Note that F_{PFx} has been arbitrarily chosen to be positive (i.e., to the right). Should the conditions of the flow be such that the force is to the left, a negative value of F_{PFx} would be obtained when the physical values for the various parameters are introduced into the equation.

Noting that the force of the fluid on the pipe is the negative of this,

$$F_{FPx} = -F_{PFx}$$

and that

$$\rho V_1A_1 = \rho V_2A_2 = \dot{m}$$

by continuity, we obtain

$$F_{FPx} = p_1A_1 - p_2A_2 \cos \theta + \dot{m}(V_1 - V_2 \cos \theta) \qquad (4.23a)$$

Similarly, we obtain for the y component of the momentum equation

$$-p_2A_2 \sin \theta - W + F_{PFy} = (\rho V_2A_2)(V_2 \sin \theta)$$

This equation can be solved for the resultant force of the pipe on the fluid in the y direction, which is

$$F_{PFy} = p_2A_2 \sin \theta + W + \dot{m}V_2 \sin \theta$$

Note that, since all the terms on the right-hand side of this equation are positive for the flow shown in Fig. 4.7, the force of the pipe on the fluid is in the positive y direction, as assumed.

The force of the fluid on the pipe in the y direction is

$$F_{FPy} = -p_2A_2 \sin \theta - W - \dot{m}V_2 \sin \theta \qquad (4.23b)$$

Example 4.5

Consider the situation where a stream of water is directed against a stationary, curved trough (or impeller blade), as shown in Fig. 4.8. Flow is steady and incompressible. Neglect body forces and determine the net force on the trough in the horizontal direction (F_{Tx}).

Solution. We will work the problem using two different control volumes. The first corresponds to the streamtube for the water in the trough. The second control volume surrounds the entire trough and cuts through the support in a plane perpendicular to the y axis.

Let us work the problem using the first control volume. Note that the streamtube surface of the jet of water is in contact with the atmospheric air on all sides except for the curved surface that is in contact with the trough. Thus, on all these "free-jet" surfaces the force per unit area is the atmospheric pressure, as shown in Fig. 4.8b. Although the pressure distribution on the surface that is in contact with the trough is not known, its integrated effect is the resultant force of the trough on the fluid (F_{TFx}). Applying the integral form of the momentum equation for a steady, incompressible flow to the water in the trough, we obtain

$$p_{atm}A_{t,x} + F_{TFx} = -(\rho V_1A_1)V_1 + (\rho V_2A_2)V_2 \cos \theta$$

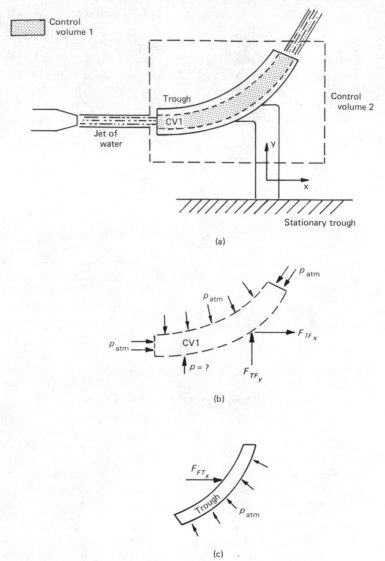

Figure 4.8   Stream of water impinging on a stationary curved trough (Example 4.5):
(a) overall flow field; (b) details for the first control volume, CV1; (c) forces on the
trough.

where $A_{t,x}$ is the net projected area of that part of the control surface exposed to the atmospheric
pressure. The term $(p_{atm}A_{t,x})$ reflects the fact that the resultant force in a certain direction
due to a constant pressure acting on a curved surface is the product of the pressure times
the projected area.

   If we neglect the effects of friction and gravity on the water flow, there will be no
change in the speed of the fluid particles as they move along the trough. Thus, $V_1 = V_2$.

Furthermore, using the integral form of the continuity equation, we can write

$$\rho V_1 A_1 = \rho V_2 A_2 = \dot{m}$$

Combining these expressions, we obtain

$$F_{TFx} = -p_{atm} A_{t,x} - \dot{m} V_1 (1 - \cos\theta) \tag{4.24}$$

Note that, since all five factors on the right-hand side of Eq. (4.24) are positive, the right-hand side is negative. That is, the force of the trough on the fluid is not in the positive x direction, as assumed and as shown in Fig. 4.8b, but is in the negative direction. This should seem intuitively reasonable to the reader, since the force of the trough should be against the initial jet in order to turn it from its original direction.

Since we want to calculate the net force on the trough, let us refer to Fig. 4.8c. The force acting on the trough in the x direction due to the impinging jet of water (F_{FTx}) is equal in magnitude but opposite in direction to the force of the trough on the water, which is given by Eq. (4.24). Thus,

$$F_{FTx} = p_{atm} A_{t,x} + \dot{m} V_1 (1 - \cos\theta)$$

However, as indicated in the sketch of Fig. 4.8c, atmospheric pressure acts on the other side of the trough and in opposition to the force of the fluid. Thus, the net force on the trough in the x direction (F_{Tx}) is

$$F_{Tx} = \dot{m} V_1 (1 - \cos\theta) \tag{4.25}$$

We could have obtained the same result more directly by working the problem using a different control volume, i.e., CV2 of Fig. 4.8a. The entire trough is contained in this control volume, which cuts through the support strut in a plane perpendicular to the y axis. Let us apply the integral form of the momentum equation to this control volume to analyze the forces in the x direction.

Since atmospheric pressure acts uniformly over the bounding surfaces of the control volume, there is no net force due to the pressure field. The only force acting in the x direction at the surface of CV2 is the force of the strut on the fluid in the control volume, (F_{SFx}). Again, we will assume that F_{SFx} acts in the positive x direction (i.e., to the right). Equating it to the net efflux of momentum, we obtain

$$F_{SFx} = -(\rho V_1 A_1) V_1 + (\rho V_2 A_2) V_2 \cos\theta$$

As before, $V_1 = V_2$ and $\rho V_1 A_1 = \rho V_2 A_2 = \dot{m}$, so

$$F_{SFx} = -\dot{m} V_1 (1 - \cos\theta)$$

To calculate the net force acting on the strut (which is equal to the net force acting on the trough since the strut carries that force), note that atmospheric pressure acts on all sides of the strut. Thus, considering a free-body diagram of the strut, we see that the net force on the strut is equal and opposite to F_{SFx}; that is,

$$F_{Tx} = \dot{m} V_1 (1 - \cos\theta)$$

which is the same as the result we obtained before.

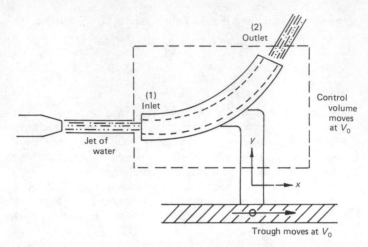

Figure 4.9   Stream of water impinging on a moving trough (Example 4.6).

Example 4.6

Consider next the case where the curved trough of Example 4.5 is moving at a constant speed (V_0) relative to the ground, as shown in Fig. 4.9. Again, we are to determine the net force on the trough in the x direction.

Solution.   To do this, let us select a control volume that encloses the entire trough and that moves with the same speed V_0, as shown in Fig. 4.9. Recall from mechanics that any reference system translating at a constant speed relative to an inertial coordinate system is itself an inertial reference system. Thus, the control volume selected for this problem is an inertial control volume.

Note that the velocity entering the control volume at station 1 is $(V_1 - V_0)$. Thus, equating the force of the strut on the fluid to the net efflux of momentum from the control volume, we obtain

$$F_{SFx} = -\left[\rho(V_1 - V_0)A_1\right](V_1 - V_0) + \left[\rho(V_2)A_2\right]V_2 \cos\theta$$

Neglecting the effects of friction and gravity on the water flow, $V_1 - V_0 = V_2$. Applying the continuity equation to the control volume yields the relation that

$$\rho(V_1 - V_0)A_1 = \rho V_2 A_2$$

Combining these relations, we find that

$$F_{SFx} = -\left[\rho(V_1 - V_0)^2 A_1\right](1 - \cos\theta)$$

Thus, the net force component in the x direction on the trough (or on the strut) is

$$F_{Tx} = +\left[\rho(V_1 - V_0)^2 A_1\right](1 - \cos\theta) \tag{4.26}$$

Example 4.7

A rocket is mounted on a test stand, as shown in the sketch of Fig. 4.10. A complex mixture of high-pressure, high-temperature gases is generated in the combustion chamber. These gases are accelerated through a convergent–divergent nozzle. The gases exhaust from the rocket at supersonic speeds, and the pressure in the nozzle exit plane (p_{ne}) is not necessarily equal to the atmospheric value. Let us assume that the flow properties are constant across the nozzle exit plane; that is, ρ_{ne} and V_{ne} are constant across the nozzle exit plane. Neglecting viscous effects and heat transfer, what is the net force (thrust) as measured by the test stand (T)?

Solution. Consider first the application of the momentum equation to the control volume corresponding to the propellant–exhaust gases as they are within the rocket, as shown in Fig. 4.10b.

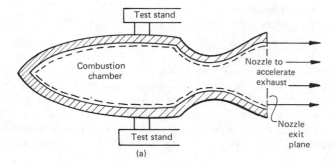

(a)

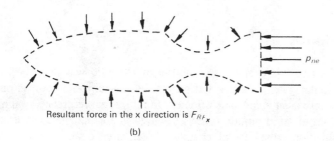

Resultant force in the x direction is F_{Rf_x}

(b)

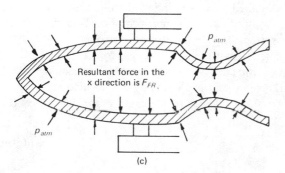

(c)

Figure 4.10 Rocket exhaust flow of Example 4.7: (a) sketch of overall flow field; (b) forces acting on fluid (rocket gases) in the control volume; (c) forces acting in rocket shell.

$$\sum F_x = F_{RFx} - p_{ne}A_{ne} = (\rho_{ne}V_{ne}A_{ne})V_{ne}$$

We have assumed that the force of the rocket on the fluid (i.e., the propellant–exhaust gases) is positive (i.e., to the right). Furthermore, there is only an efflux of momentum and it occurs at the exhaust plane. Noting that $\rho_{ne}V_{ne}A_{ne} = \dot{m}_{ne}$,

$$F_{RFx} = \dot{m}_{ne}V_{ne} + p_{ne}A_{ne}$$

Since both terms are positive, the force of the rocket on the fluid is to the right, as assumed.

Now consider the balance of forces acting on the rocket shell and test stand shown. A sketch of the setup is presented in Fig. 4.10c. We know that the force of the fluid on the rocket is

$$F_{FRx} = -\dot{m}_{ne}V_{ne} - p_{ne}A_{ne} \tag{4.27}$$

and acts in the negative x direction (as indicated by the signs).

Writing the force balance on the rocket shell and test stand:

$$T + F_{FRx} + p_{atm}A_{ne} = 0 \tag{4.28}$$

Using Eq. (4.27) for F_{RFx} will yield the correct signs, since the force acts to the left and should be negative in Eq. (4.28). The last term represents the effect of the atmospheric pressure acting on the shell of the rocket. If the shell was a closed surface, there would be no net force. However, since the nozzle exit plane is a "hole" in the shell, there is a net force in the positive x direction due to the atmospheric pressure that acts on the nose of the vehicle not being canceled by a pressure acting on a corresponding surface at the aft end of the rocket. Thus,

$$T = \dot{m}V_{ne} + (p_{ne} - p_{atm})A_{ne} \tag{4.29}$$

NONINERTIAL REFERENCE FRAME

For the previous applications of this chapter, the motion of the fluid was described in terms of an inertial coordinate system. Recall that an inertial coordinate system is one that is either at rest or that moves at a constant velocity. In an inertial reference system, the deviation of a body from uniform motion (or rest) is always attributable to external influences. For such applications, the rate of change of velocity equals the absolute acceleration, and Newton's law can be applied directly to the fluid motion. In this section, we shall develop the momentum equation for a general, noninertial coordinate system.

Consider an inertial coordinate system X, Y, Z and a local coordinate system x, y, z, which is moving in a general manner within the X, Y, Z system, as shown in Fig. 4.11. The origin O of the noninertial coordinate system is defined by the position vector $\vec{R}$. A point P in the noninertial coordinate system is defined by the position vector $\vec{r}$ in the x, y, z reference system. The inertial coordinates of the point P are defined by the position vector $\vec{r}_0$, where

$$\vec{r}_0 = \vec{R} + \vec{r} \tag{4.30}$$

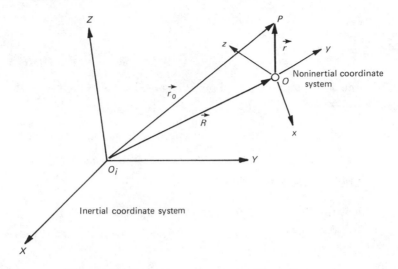

Figure 4.11   Nomenclature for a noninertial coordinate system.

The velocity of a fluid particle is given by

$$\vec{V}_0 = \dot{\vec{r}}_0 = \dot{\vec{R}} + \vec{V}_{xyz} + \vec{\omega} \times \vec{r}$$

Thus, the linear velocity in the primary (inertial) coordinate system is the sum of the following:

1. Translational movement of the origin, O, of the noninertial coordinate system ($\dot{\vec{R}}$).
2. Translational velocity of the fluid particle, as observed in the moving coordinate system ($\vec{V}_{xyz}$).
3. Velocity due to the rotation of the x, y, z axis ($\vec{\omega} \times \vec{r}$).

The acceleration of a fluid particle relative to the inertial reference frame is given by

$$\vec{a}_0 = \frac{d\vec{V}_0}{dt} = \ddot{\vec{R}} + \dot{\vec{V}}_{xyz} + \dot{\vec{\omega}} \times \vec{r} + \vec{\omega} \times \dot{\vec{r}}$$

But

$$\dot{\vec{V}}_{xyz} = \vec{a}_{xyz} + \vec{\omega} \times \vec{V}_{xyz}$$

and

$$\dot{\vec{r}} = \vec{V}_{xyz} + \vec{\omega} \times \vec{r}$$

Combining these three relations, one obtains

$$\vec{a}_0 = \ddot{\vec{R}} + \vec{a}_{xyz} + 2\vec{\omega} \times \vec{V}_{xyz} + \dot{\vec{\omega}} \times \vec{r} + \vec{\omega} \times (\vec{\omega} \times \vec{r}) \qquad (4.32)$$

Thus, the acceleration of a fluid particle in the inertial coordinate system $(\vec{a}_0)$ is the sum of the following:

1. Acceleration of the noninertial origin in the inertial coordinate system $(\ddot{\vec{R}})$.

2. Apparent acceleration relative to an observer in the x, y, z system $(\vec{a}_{xyz})$.

3. Coriolis acceleration $(2\vec{\omega} \times \vec{V}_{xyz})$.

4. Rotational acceleration of the moving system $(\dot{\vec{\omega}} \times \vec{r})$.

5. Centrifugal acceleration, directed from the particle normal to the axis of rotation, $\vec{\omega} \times (\vec{\omega} \times \vec{r})$.

The Coriolis acceleration is named after G. G. Coriolis, a French mathematical physicist who first demonstrated its effects quantitatively in 1844. The Coriolis acceleration is important to the oceanographer and meteorologist. It is important to note that if one applies Newton's law in a noninertial system (such as a system fixed on the surface of the rotating earth), then the Coriolis acceleration must be viewed as being due to the action of an external Coriolis force. The Coriolis force occurs only when the fluid particle is in motion relative to the rotating axes.

Earth's Atmosphere

Consider the coordinate system in which the center of the earth O_i is fixed; that is, we neglect the earth's motion about the sun. Furthermore, $\omega = \Omega$ and $\dot{\vec{\omega}} = 0$, as shown in Fig. 4.12. The acceleration of a fluid particle at point P relative to O_i is given by

$$\vec{a}_0 = \ddot{\vec{R}} + \vec{a}_{xyz} + 2\vec{\Omega} \times \vec{V}_{xyz} + \vec{\Omega} \times (\vec{\Omega} \times \vec{r}) \qquad (4.33)$$

For a spherical earth rotating about its axis,

$$\ddot{\vec{R}} = \vec{\Omega} \times (\vec{\Omega} \times \vec{R}) \qquad (4.34a)$$

The acceleration $\vec{a}_0$ is

$$\vec{a}_0 = \frac{\vec{F}}{m} + \vec{g}_0 \qquad (4.34b)$$

where $\vec{g}_0$ is the force exerted by the earth and is equal to the sum of $\vec{g}$, the acceleration due to gravity, and the centrifugal acceleration due to the earth's rotation.

$$\vec{g}_0 = \vec{g} + \vec{\Omega} \times (\vec{\Omega} \times \vec{R}) \qquad (4.34c)$$

Note that in many cases the last term in Eq. (4.33) is relatively small and can be neglected. Thus,

$$\vec{a}_{xyz} = \frac{\vec{F}}{m} + \vec{g} - 2\vec{\Omega} \times \vec{V}_{xyz} \qquad (4.35)$$

When viewed from above the Northern Hemisphere, the earth rotates in a counterclockwise manner. Thus, the angular velocity vector would point outward along the axis of rotation at the North Pole. At the South Pole, it would point inward. At any point on the earth, other than at the poles or on the equator, the rotation can be resolved into two components: a radial component and a tangential component. At the poles it is all radial, and at the equator it is only tangential. For a spherical earth the tangential component is directed northward.

Consider the motion of the atmosphere at a latitude represented by the angle ϕ, as shown in Fig. 4.12. Gravity acts in the negative z direction. For motion in a plane parallel to the earth's surface, that is, $\dot{z} = 0$, the accelerations in the x, y, z system are

$$\ddot{x} = F_x + 2\Omega\dot{y} \sin \phi \qquad (4.36a)$$

$$\ddot{y} = F_y - 2\Omega\dot{x} \sin \phi \qquad (4.36b)$$

$$\ddot{z} = F_z - g + 2\Omega\dot{y} \cos \phi \qquad (4.36c)$$

where F_x, F_y, and F_z represent the force components per unit mass. For an inviscid flow, the force per unit mass is proportional to the negative of the pressure gradient. The Coriolis acceleration has been moved to the right-hand side of the equations where it appears as an effective force. Thus, if the forces acting on a fluid particle are balanced (i.e., there is no acceleration), we obtain

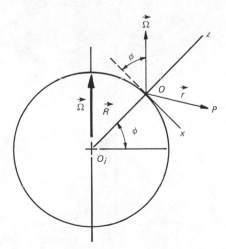

Figure 4.12 Nomenclature for describing the motion of the earth's atmosphere.

$$\frac{1}{\rho}\frac{\partial p}{\partial x} = 2\Omega\dot{y}\sin\phi \qquad (4.37a)$$

$$\frac{1}{\rho}\frac{\partial p}{\partial y} = -2\Omega\dot{x}\sin\phi \qquad (4.37b)$$

$$\frac{1}{\rho}\frac{\partial p}{\partial z} = 2\Omega\dot{y}\cos\phi - g \qquad (4.37c)$$

Let us examine the vertical component first. The earth's angular velocity is 2π radians per sidereal day, or 7.292×10^{-5} rad/s. The maximum value of $\cos\phi$ is 1. Thus, assuming a value of $\dot{y}$ of 30 m/s (or 58 knots),

$$2\Omega\dot{y}\cos\phi = 2(7.292 \times 10^{-5})(30)1 = 4.38 \times 10^{-3} \text{ m/s}^2$$

But g is 9.8066 m/s², and a typical value of

$$\frac{1}{\rho}\frac{\partial p}{\partial z} \approx \frac{1}{1.2 \text{ kg/m}^3}\frac{1.2 \times 10^4 \text{ N/m}^2}{1000 \text{ m}} = 10 \text{ m/s}^2$$

where the approximate value of $\partial p/\partial z$ was determined from Table 1.1. The term $2\Omega\dot{y}$ $\cos\phi$ is negligible by comparison to the other two terms, and Eq. (4.37c) can be replaced by the approximation

$$\frac{\partial p}{\partial z} \approx -\rho g \qquad (4.38)$$

Thus, we can neglect the component of the Coriolis force and write the vertical balance in the form of the hydrostatic equation, as was done in Chapter 2. See Eq. (2.4).

For inviscid flow in a straight path in a horizontal plane, the Coriolis force and the pressure gradient force are in balance. This is known as the *geostrophic balance* and is represented by Eqs. (4.37a) and (4.37b). The velocities $\dot{x}$ and $\dot{y}$ are components of the geostrophic wind. The horizontal, geostrophic velocities are perpendicular to the hori-

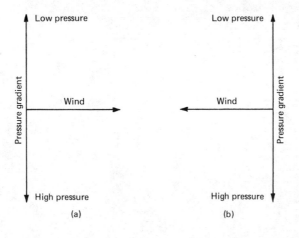

Figure 4.13 Buys Ballot's law:
(a) Northern Hemisphere;
(b) Southern Hemisphere.

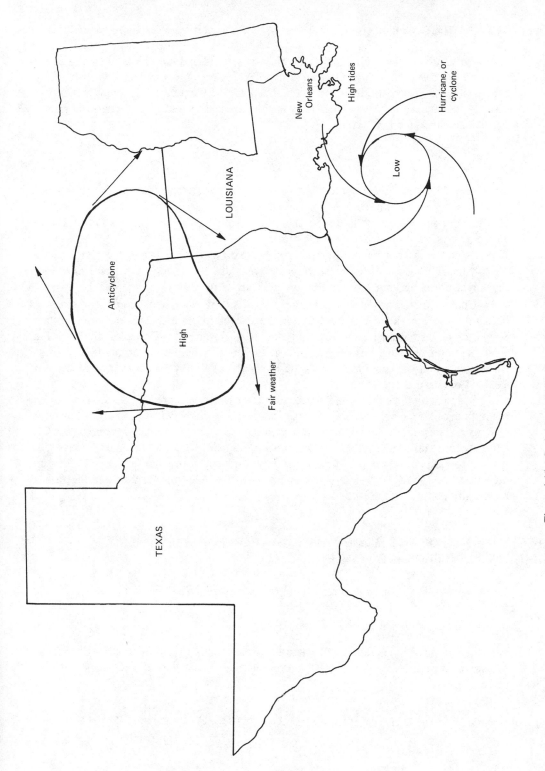

Figure 4.14 Cyclones, anticyclones, and Buys Ballot's law.

125

zontal pressure gradient. Note that the fluid flows along and not across lines of constant pressure (isobars). It is this feature that enables isobars on a weather map to be representative of the flow patterns in the free atmosphere. If the pressure gradient is measured directly to determine $\partial p/\partial n$, where n is the distance measured in a direction normal to the isobars, then we may write

$$\frac{1}{\rho}\frac{\partial p}{\partial n} = -2\Omega u_g \sin \phi \tag{4.39}$$

where u_g is the total geostrophic-wind velocity. The geostrophic wind has a magnitude of $\sqrt{\dot{x}^2 + \dot{y}^2}$ and is directed 90° to the right of the pressure gradient in the Northern Hemisphere and to the left in the Southern Hemisphere. This is illustrated in Fig. 4.13. These results are summarized in a rule of meteorology, *Buys Ballot's law,* which follows. If you stand with your back to the wind in the Northern Hemisphere, the high pressure is on your right and the low pressure is on your left. In the Southern Hemisphere, the high pressure is on your left and the low pressure is on your right.

Centers (or areas) of low pressure are called *cyclones,* and centers (or areas) of high pressure are called *anticyclones*. In the Northern Hemisphere, the circulation is counterclockwise around a cyclone and clockwise for an anticyclone, as shown in Fig. 4.14. As a result of the circulation pattern, high tides would occur in the first quadrant (in the direction of New Orleans) as the hurricane of Fig. 4.14 comes ashore near the Texas–Louisiana border.

Viscosity reduces the wind speed near the earth's surface and, hence, reduces the magnitude of the Coriolis force. However, the pressure gradient is essentially independent of height. Thus, since the wind speed decreases as the earth's surface is approached, the Coriolis force no longer balances the pressure gradient. Thus, the air moves across the isobars toward the lower pressure. In free atmosphere, above the first 500 to 1000 m, the effect of viscosity is relatively small in relation to the other forces, and the flow is essentially parallel to the isobars.

INTEGRAL FORM OF THE MOMENTUM EQUATION FOR A NONINERTIAL REFERENCE FRAME

Newton's law for an infinitesimal system of fluid particles can be written as

$$d\vec{F} = dm\,\vec{a}_0 = dm[\vec{a}_{xyz} + \ddot{\vec{R}} + 2\vec{\omega} \times \vec{V}_{xyz} + \dot{\vec{\omega}} \times \vec{r} + \vec{\omega} \times (\vec{\omega} \times \vec{r})] \tag{4.40}$$

Let us rearrange this equation and integrate over a finite system of fluid particles, such as shown in Fig. 4.15. As before, $\vec{F}$ represents the sum of the surface forces and body forces, so

$$\vec{F}_{\text{surface}} + \vec{F}_{\text{body}} - \iiint [\ddot{\vec{R}} + 2\vec{\omega} \times \vec{V}_{xyz} + \dot{\vec{\omega}} \times \vec{r} + \vec{\omega} \times (\vec{\omega} \times \vec{r})]\rho d(\text{vol})$$

$$= \iiint \vec{a}_{xyz}\,dm = \frac{d}{dt}\iiint \vec{V}_{xyz}\,\rho d(\text{vol}) \tag{4.41}$$

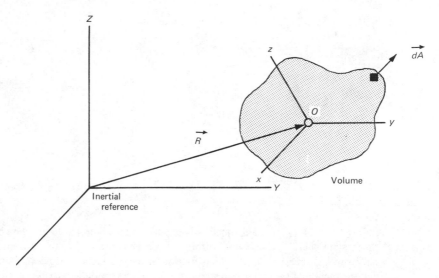

Figure 4.15 Integral form of the momentum equation for a noninertial reference frame.

The right-hand side of this equation represents the time derivative of the linear momentum as viewed in the xyz coordinate system. The set of terms in the integral of the left-hand side can be viewed as a set of hypothetical forces (e.g., the Coriolis force and the centrifugal force). The control volume for this formulation will be fixed in the xyz coordinate system and, hence, will be a noninertial reference frame.

$$\vec{F}_{\text{surface}} + \vec{F}_{\text{body}} - \iiint [\ddot{\vec{R}} + 2\vec{\omega} \times \vec{V}_{xyz} + \dot{\vec{\omega}} \times \vec{r} + \vec{\omega} \times (\vec{\omega} \times \vec{r})]\rho d(\text{vol})$$

$$= \frac{\partial}{\partial t} \iiint \rho \vec{V}_{xyz} \, d(\text{vol}) + \oiint (\rho \vec{V}_{xyz} \cdot \vec{dA})\vec{V}_{xyz} \quad (4.42)$$

Since the control volume is fixed in xyz, it is convenient to use it when evaluating velocities and time derivatives in solving problems. Thus, $\ddot{\vec{R}}$ is the acceleration of the origin of the control volume relative to inertial reference system X, Y, Z, and $\vec{\omega}$ is the angular velocity of the control volume measured from X, Y, Z with the axis of rotation going through the point O. Thus, Eq. (4.42) represents the following physical statement: the sum of the surface forces and body forces acting on the fluid particles in the control volume minus the total of the "hypothetical" body forces (that occur because the control volume is noninertial) equals the net efflux of momentum from the control volume plus the rate of increase of momentum within the control volume, relative to an observer in the control volume.

Example 4.8

A jet of fluid from the nozzle shown at the left of Fig. 4.16 strikes the vertical plate, causing the cart to accelerate to the right. If the cart starts from rest and is unrestrained, develop the equation describing the velocity of the cart as a function of time.

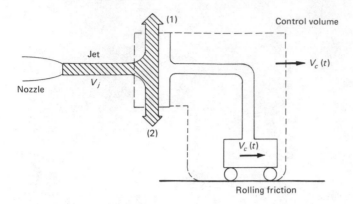

Figure 4.16 Sketch for Example 4.8.

Solution. The momentum equation is applied to the control volume, shown in Fig. 4.16. Since atmospheric pressure acts uniformly over the entire surface of the control volume, the only surface force is that of rolling friction in the x direction. However, since it is stated that the motion of the cart is unrestrained, the rolling friction will be neglected. In evaluating the terms of Eq. (4.42), $\vec{\omega}$ and $\dot{\vec{\omega}}$ are zero. Furthermore,

$$\ddot{\vec{R}} = a_{x,\text{rel}} = \frac{d}{dt}(V_c)$$

is the rate of change of the cart speed. Thus, Eq. (4.42) can be written:

$$-\iiint a_{x,\text{rel}}\, dm = \frac{\partial}{\partial t} \iiint \rho u\, d(\text{vol}) + \oiint (\rho \vec{V} \cdot d\vec{A}) u$$

Only for the influx is u nonzero. Let us assume that the mass and x momentum of the fluid within the control volume are relatively small with respect to the mass and x momentum of the cart. Thus, the triple (or volume) integrals can be replaced by

$$\frac{\partial}{\partial t} \iiint \rho u\, d(\text{vol}) \approx 0 \quad \text{and} \quad \iiint a_{x,\text{rel}}\, dm \approx m_c \frac{dV_c}{dt}$$

Thus,

$$-m_c \frac{dV_c}{dt} = -\rho A_j (V_j - V_c)^2$$

We can separate variables to obtain

$$\frac{dV_c}{(V_j - V_c)^2} = \frac{\rho A_j}{m_c}\, dt$$

Note that ρ, A_j, and m_c are constants. Since the cart starts from rest, the velocity of the cart (V_{c1}) at some time (t_1) is obtained by integration:

$$\frac{1}{V_j - V_c}\bigg|_0^{V_{c1}} = \frac{\rho A_j}{m_c} t\bigg|_0^{t_1}$$

As a result,

$$\frac{V_{c1}}{V_j} = \frac{\rho A_j V_j t_1}{m_c + \rho A_j V_j t_1}$$

INTEGRAL FORM OF THE ANGULAR MOMENTUM EQUATION

If the surroundings exert a net moment $\vec{dM}$ on an infinitesimal system of fluid particles about some reference point in the system, there will be a rotation about that point. The moment of the total force on the system of particles about a point of an inertial reference frame is equal to the time rate of change of the moment of momentum, as seen in this inertial space:

$$\vec{dM} = \vec{r} \times \vec{dF} = \frac{d}{dt}(\vec{r} \times dm\,\vec{V}) \tag{4.43}$$

Applying this equation to a finite system of particles,

$$\vec{M}_{\text{total}} = \vec{M}_{\text{surface}} + \vec{M}_{\text{body}} = \int \vec{r} \times \vec{dF} = \frac{\vec{dH}}{dt} \tag{4.44}$$

where $\vec{H}$ is the moment of momentum of the system. Note that the total moment is the sum of the moments due to the surface forces acting on the system of particles and the moments due to the body forces acting through the system. For this form of the moment-of-momentum equation for a finite system, the moments and time derivatives are evaluated in an inertial coordinate system.

The total time rate of change of the moment of momentum $\vec{H}$ for the system at any time t is equal to the rate of change of $\vec{H}$ within the control volume having the shape of the system at time t, plus the net rate of efflux of $\vec{H}$ across the control surface. Thus,

$$\frac{\vec{dH}}{dt} = \frac{\partial}{\partial t}\iiint (\vec{r} \times \vec{V})\rho\,d(\text{vol}) + \oiint (\vec{r} \times \vec{V})\rho\vec{V} \cdot \vec{dA}$$

$$= \vec{M}_{\text{surface}} + \vec{M}_{\text{body}} \tag{4.45}$$

Since the system of fluid particles and the control volume occupy the same space at time t, we can interpret $\vec{M}_{\text{surface}}$ and $\vec{M}_{\text{body}}$ in Eq. (4.45) to be equal to the total moments about a point a in the inertial coordinate system XYZ, as shown in Fig. 4.17.

In many applications, such as turbomachines, the motion takes place in a plane and can be described as a rotation about an axis rather than a point. For such applications, we need employ only a single scalar component of the moment-of-moment equation, Eq. (4.45). The motion can be best formulated using cylindrical coordinates, such as shown in Fig. 4.18. Instead of using the moments about a point, $\vec{M}_{\text{surface}}$ and $\vec{M}_{\text{body}}$, we shall use the torques, T_{surface} and T_{body}, which are the torques about the axis AA that goes

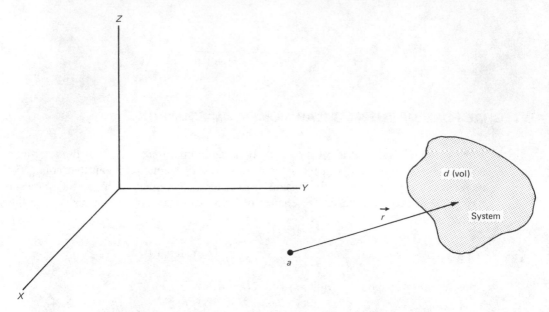

Figure 4.17   Nomenclature for the integral form of the moment-of-momentum equation.

through the point a. In this scalar formulation, the term $\vec{r} \times \vec{V}$ is replaced by rV_θ, where r is the radial distance from the axis to a particle and V_θ is the velocity of the particle. The geometry is such that V_θ is perpendicular to r and, with r, forms a plane that is normal to the axis AA. The scalar component of the moment-of-momentum equation is

$$T_{\text{surface}} + T_{\text{body}} = \frac{\partial}{\partial t} \iiint rV_\theta \rho \, d(\text{vol}) + \oiint rV_\theta \, \rho \vec{V} \cdot d\vec{A} \qquad (4.46)$$

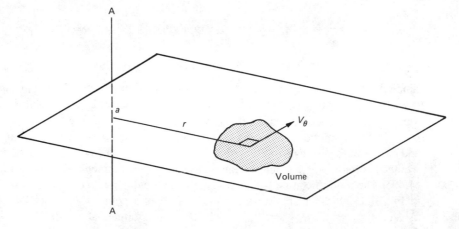

Figure 4.18   Nomenclature for planar motion.

Example 4.9

The sprinkler of Fig. 4.19 discharges 0.005 cfs through each nozzle. The diameters of the nozzle openings are 0.375 in. each. Each jet is discharged outward so that it makes an angle $\phi = 30°$ with the normal to the sprinkler arm. Neglecting friction, what is the steady-state speed of rotation?

Solution. We will use as our control surface the cylindrical area enclosing the rotating sprinkler head. The resisting torques due to the bearings and the seals are to be neglected. The fluid entering the sprinkler has no moment of momentum. Since the rotation is steady and clockwise, application of Eq. (4.46) gives

$$-\rho_1 r_1 V_{\theta_1} Q_1 - \rho_2 r_2 V_{\theta_2} Q_2 = 0$$

To verify the sign, the reader may want to use the vector cross product in Eq. (4.45). Since $\rho_1 = \rho_2 = \rho$, $r_1 = r_2 = r_0$, and $Q_1 = Q_2 = Q$,

$$-\rho r_0 Q (V_{\theta_1} + V_{\theta_2}) = 0$$

where V_{θ_1} and V_{θ_2} are the absolute tangential velocities of the jets.

$$V_{\theta_1} = V_{\theta_2} = V_r \cos \phi - r_0 \Omega$$

Since $d = 0.375$ in., $A = 0.000767$ ft^2. Thus, the relative velocity is

$$V_r = \frac{Q}{A} = \frac{0.005}{0.000767} = 6.519 \text{ ft/s}$$

For the moment of momentum to be zero,

$$V_{\theta_1} + V_{\theta_2} = 0 = 2(V_r \cos \phi - r\Omega)$$

Thus,

$$\Omega = \frac{V_r \cos\phi}{r} = 11.29 \text{ rad/s} = 107.82 \text{ rpm}$$

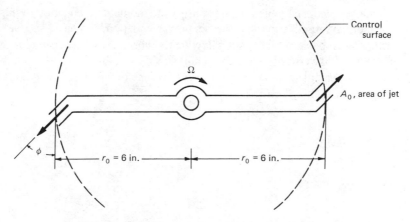

Figure 4.19   Sprinkler for Examples 4.9 and 4.10.

Example 4.10

The sprinkler shown in Fig. 4.19 discharges water at a total volumetric flow rate of Q. Each nozzle has a cross-sectional area A_0 and makes an angle ϕ with a normal to the sprinkler arm. If the sprinkler arm starts from rest (i.e., $\Omega = 0$ when $t = 0$), determine the equation for Ω as a function of time. The resisting torque due to the bearings and the seals will be assumed to be constant at T_{res}. The moment of inertia of the empty rotating sprinkler arm is I_{sp}.

Solution.   Again we will choose the cylindrical area enclosing the rotating sprinkler head, as shown in Fig. 4.19, as our control surface. Since the inflow is along the axis, it has no moment of momentum. Applying Eq. (4.46),

$$-T_{res} = \frac{d}{dt} \int_0^{r_0} r(r\Omega) \, \rho 2A_0 \, dr + I_{sp} \frac{d\Omega}{dt} - r_0(V_r \cos \phi - r_0\Omega)\rho Q$$

where $V_r = Q/2A_0$. Rearranging the terms in this equation,

$$\frac{d\Omega}{dt} (I_{sp} + \frac{2}{3} \, \rho r_0^3 A_0) = \rho Q r_0(V_r \cos \phi - r_0\Omega) - T_{res}$$

Note that the steady-state value of Ω is found by setting $d\Omega/dt = 0$. Thus,

$$\Omega = \frac{V_r \cos \phi}{r_0} - \frac{T_{res}}{\rho Q r_0^2}$$

Neglecting the resisting torque (T_{res}), we obtain a relation that is consistent with Example 4.9.

Additional applications of the moment-of-momentum equation will be discussed in Chapter 12.

SUMMARY

We have developed generalized forms of the momentum equation in this chapter. Using the momentum equation and the continuity equation, we have obtained equations governing some basic but interesting flow fields. For many of the examples, we cannot obtain numerical answers unless we are given considerable information about the flow, because we cannot calculate it ourselves with our present knowledge. We will learn in subsequent chapters how to make these calculations.

PROBLEMS

4.1. Given the velocity field

$$\vec{V} = 10y\hat{i} + (x^2 + y^2)\hat{j} - 2xy\hat{k}$$

What is the acceleration of a particle at the point $(3, 1, 1)$ when $t = 1$?

4.2. Given the velocity field

$$\vec{V} = 10yt^2\hat{i} + (x^2 + y^2)t\hat{j} - 2x^2y\hat{k}$$

What is the acceleration of a particle at the point $(3, 1, 1)$ when $t = 1$?

4.3. A two-dimensional velocity field is given by

$$\vec{V} = (x^2 + x - y^2)\hat{i} - (2xy + y)\hat{j}$$

At $x = 2$ and $y = 1$ compute (a) the acceleration components, a_x and a_y, and (b) the velocity component in the direction $\theta = 30°$.

4.4. Consider the one-dimensional motion of a fluid particle moving on the centerline of the converging channel, as shown in Fig. P4.4. The vertical dimension of the channel (and, thus, the area per unit depth) varies as

$$2y = 2h - h\sin\left(\frac{\pi}{2}\frac{x}{L}\right)$$

Assume that the flow is steady and incompressible. Use the integral form of the continuity equation to describe the velocity along the channel centerline. Also determine the corresponding axial acceleration. If u at $x = 0$ is 2 m/s, h is 1 m, and $L = 1$ m, calculate the acceleration when $x = 0$ and when $x = 0.5L$.

4.5. Show that the acceleration for steady flow in a cylindrical coordinate system is given by

$$\vec{a} = \left(v_r\frac{\partial v_r}{\partial r} + \frac{v_\theta}{r}\frac{\partial v_r}{\partial \theta} - \frac{v_\theta^2}{r} + v_z\frac{\partial v_r}{\partial z}\right)\hat{e}_r$$

$$+ \left(v_r\frac{\partial v_\theta}{\partial r} + \frac{v_\theta}{r}\frac{\partial v_\theta}{\partial \theta} + \frac{v_\theta v_r}{r} + v_z\frac{\partial v_\theta}{\partial z}\right)\hat{e}_\theta$$

$$+ \left(v_r\frac{\partial v_z}{\partial r} + \frac{v_\theta}{r}\frac{\partial v_z}{\partial \theta} + v_z\frac{\partial v_z}{\partial z}\right)\hat{e}_z$$

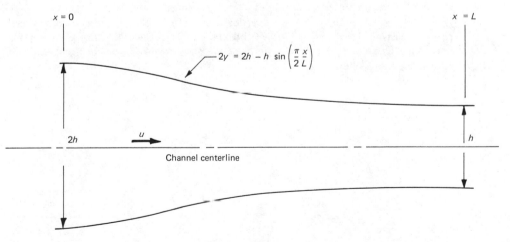

Figure P4.4 Sketch for Prob. 4.4.

Note that

$$\vec{V} = v_r \hat{e}_r + v_\theta \hat{e}_\theta + v_z \hat{e}_z$$

and

$$\nabla = \hat{e}_r \frac{\partial}{\partial r} + \frac{\hat{e}_\theta}{r} \frac{\partial}{\partial \theta} + \hat{e}_z \frac{\partial}{\partial z}$$

4.6. Given the velocity field for two-dimensional, inviscid flow around a cylinder of radius R:

$$\vec{V} = U_\infty \cos \theta \left[1 - \frac{R^2}{r^2} \right] \hat{e}_r - U_\infty \sin \theta \left[1 + \frac{R^2}{r^2} \right] \hat{e}_\theta$$

   (a) Derive the expression for the acceleration of a fluid particle.
   (b) What is the acceleration at points far from the surface of the cylinder, that is, $r \to \infty$? What is the acceleration at the following three points on the surface of the cylinder, that is, $r = R$: (i) $\theta = 0$, (ii) $\theta = 30°$, and (iii) $\theta = 90°$?

4.7. Consider the incompressible, steady flow from a two-dimensional source, which is described by the velocity function

$$\vec{V} = \frac{K}{2\pi r} \hat{e}_r$$

Derive the expression for the acceleration at a general point in the flow field.

4.8. The density of a fluid varies inversely with the radial distance from the origin so that

$$\rho = \frac{K}{r}$$

where k is a constant. What is $d\rho/dt$ for the fluid motion where the velocity is given by

$$\vec{V} = r\omega \hat{e}_\theta$$

as shown in Fig. P4.8?

4.9. We are to obtain a solution for a steady, constant-property flow. The only body force is gravity, which acts in the negative z direction. Converting these statements into the appropriate mathematical formulations, rewrite Eqs. (4.11a) through (4.11c) as they apply to this flow. That is, simplify the general form of the Navier–Stokes equations into the form appropriate for this flow.

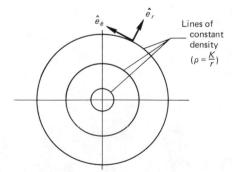

Figure P4.8   Sketch for Prob. 4.8.

4.10. The velocity field of a constant-property flow is given by

$$\vec{V} = a(x^2 - y^2)\hat{i} - 2axy\hat{j}$$

The flow is incompressible and the fluid properties are constant (i.e., unchanged throughout the flow field). What must be the pressure field in order for this velocity field to satisfy the Navier–Stokes equations? Assume that z is "up" and the only body force is gravity, which acts in the negative z direction.

4.11. Consider the steady, low-speed viscous flow in an infinitely long, two-dimensional channel of height h (i.e., the flow is fully developed). Since this is a low-speed flow, we will assume that the viscosity and density are constant. Let us also assume that the body forces are negligible. Develop the expression for

$$u(y)$$

given a pressure gradient of dp/dx, where the upper plate moves at the velocity $u = U_0$ and the lower plate is fixed. As shown in Fig. P4.11, the coordinate system is such that the plates are located at $y = \pm h/2$. What is the relation between U_0, dp/dx, h, and μ, if the mass flow rate per unit depth across a plane $x = $ constant is zero?

4.12. Consider the steady, low-speed flow of a viscous fluid in an infinitely long, two-dimensional channel of height h (i.e., the flow is fully developed). Since this is a low-speed flow, we will assume that the viscosity and density are constant. Let us assume the body forces are negligible. The upper plate (which is at $y = h$) moves in the x direction at the speed U_0, while the lower plate (which is at $y = 0$) is stationary. As shown in Fig. P4.12, the coordinate system is such that the plates are located at $y = 0$ and $y = +h$.
  (a) Develop expressions for u, v, and w (which satisfy the boundary conditions) as functions of U_0, h, μ, dp/dx, and y.
  (b) Write the expressions for dp/dx in terms of μ, U_0, and h, if $u = 0$ at $y = h/2$.

4.13. Consider the steady, laminar, incompressible flow between two parallel plates as shown in Fig. P4.13. The upper plate moves at velocity U_0 to the right, and the lower plate is stationary. The pressure gradient is zero. The lower half of the region between the plates (i.e., $0 \leqslant y \leqslant h/2$) is filled with fluid with density ρ_1 and viscosity μ_1, and the upper half ($h/2 \leqslant y \leqslant h$) is filled with fluid of density ρ_2 and viscosity μ_2. The fluids do not mix.
  (a) State the condition that the shear stress must satisfy for $0 < y < h$.
  (b) State the four boundary conditions that must be satisfied by the fluid velocity at the walls and at the interface of the two fluids.

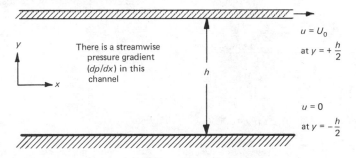

Figure P4.11   Sketch for Prob. 4.11.

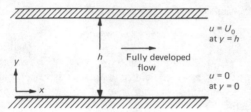

Figure P4.12 Sketch for Prob. 4.12.

(c) Obtain the velocity profile in each of the two regions and sketch the result for $\mu_1 > \mu_2$.
(d) Calculate the shear stress at the lower wall.
Neglect the body forces for this problem.

4.14. Consider the fully developed flow in a circular pipe, as shown in Fig. P4.14. The velocity u is a function of the radial coordinate only:

$$u = U_{CL} \left(1 - \frac{r^2}{R^2} \right)$$

where U_{CL} is the magnitude of the velocity at the centerline (or axis) of the pipe. Use the integral form of the momentum equation, Eq. (4.19), to show how the pressure drop per unit length dp/dx changes if the radius of the pipe is doubled while the mass flux through the pipe is held constant at the value $\dot{m}$. Neglect the weight of the fluid in the control volume and assume the fluid properties are constant.

4.15. The equation defining an ellipsoid is

$$\left(\frac{x}{a} \right)^2 + \left(\frac{y}{b} \right)^2 + \left(\frac{z}{c} \right)^2 = 1$$

where a, b, and c are the reference lengths for their respective coordinates. If the prototype ellipsoid has $a = 5$ m, $b = 3$ m, and $c = 1$ m, what should b and c be for the model ellipsoid if $a = 1$ m?

4.16. The design speed of a transport aircraft is 550 mph at 35,000 ft. The characteristic dimension of the aircraft is 28 ft. What are the flight design values of the Mach number and the Reynolds number? If a one-twentieth scale model is to be tested in a pressurized wind tunnel, what should be the static pressure (in pounds force per square inch, absolute) and the wind speed in the test section in order to simulate both the Reynolds number and the Mach number? Assume the static temperature of the air in the test section is 60°F and that the air behaves as a perfect gas. What is the effect of the static pressure in the test section on the Mach number?

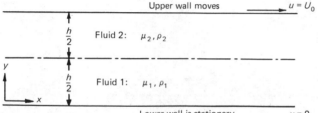

Figure P4.13 Sketch for Prob. 4.13.

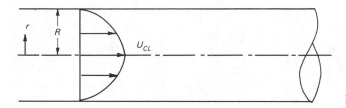

Figure P4.14 Sketch for Prob. 4.14.

4.17. A sphere 3.0 cm in diameter falls through glycerine at a speed of 15 cm/s. What is the Reynolds number for this flow, if the temperature of the glycerine is 20°C?

4.18. A 1:50 scale model of a proposed dam is to be used in a design study. If the design value of the discharge over the spillway at flood stage is 15,000 m³/s, what water flow rate should be established in the model to simulate this flow? Also, if a velocity of 1.2 m/s is measured at a point in the model, what is the velocity at a corresponding point in the prototype flow?

4.19. Oil with a kinematic viscosity of 5×10^{-5} ft²/s is pumped through a 12-in. smooth pipe at 8 ft/s. If water at 68°F flows in a 2-in. smooth pipe, what should the velocity be in order to have dynamic similarity?

4.20. Oil with a kinematic viscosity of 4×10^{-6} m²/s is pumped through a 20-cm smooth pipe at 2 m/s. If water at 20°C flows in a 5-cm smooth pipe, what should the velocity be in order to have dynamic similarity?

4.21. Determine the relationship between the ratio of the kinematic viscosities, ν_m/ν_p, and the scale factor if both the Reynolds number and the Froude number are to be simulated in a given model test.

4.22. A one-tenth scale model of an automobile is to be tested in a pressurized wind tunnel. The test is to simulate an automobile traveling at 80 km/h in air at standard sea-level atmospheric conditions; that is, $p_\infty = 101.325$ kPa and $T_\infty = 288.15$ K. If static temperature in the wind tunnel is 288.15 K, what is the static pressure in the test section in order to match simultaneously the Mach number and the Reynolds number? Assume that the air at this temperature behaves as a perfect gas so that the speed of sound is 340.3 m/s.

4.23. A jet of liquid discharges vertically downward into a tank of the liquid. For a volumetric flow rate of 2 cfs, a velocity of 40 ft/s, compute the force exerted on the tank by the jet. The specific gravity of the liquid is 0.75.

4.24. A jet of water, as shown in Fig. P4.24, issues from a nozzle that is 10 cm in diameter at a speed of 5 m/s. The jet impinges on a plate that is normal to the axis of the jet. Neglecting gravity and friction, calculate the force required to hold the plate fixed.

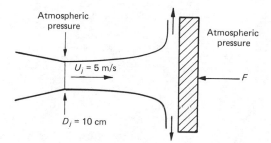

Figure P4.24 Sketch for Prob. 4.24.

Assume the jet of
water is straight
(unaffected by gravity)
from the nozzle to
the person.

Figure P4.25   Sketch for Prob. 4.25.

4.25. A steady flow of water from a hose is used for crowd control at a marathon rock concert.
If the jet issues from a nozzle that is 3 in. in diameter at a velocity of 50 ft/s, what is the
force of the water on the person shown in Fig. P4.25? Neglect the effects of gravity and
friction.

4.26. What are the forces of the water on the reducing elbow shown in Fig. P4.26? The pressure
at station 1 is 2500 lbf/ft²; that at station 2 is 2116 lbf/ft² (i.e., standard atmospheric). The
velocity at station 2 is 20 ft/s. The water in the elbow weighs 60 lbf.

4.27. What is the force of the water on the nozzle shown in Fig. P4.27? $D_1 = 5$ cm; $D_2 = 3$ cm;
$p_1 = 5$ kPa, gage; $p_2 = 0$ Pa, gage; and $U_2 = 5.00$ m/s.

4.28. A jet of water impinges on a 180° turning vane, as shown in Fig. P4.28. If the vane is fixed
(i.e., $V_b = 0$) what is the force on the vane?

4.29. A jet of water impinges on a 180° turning vane, as shown in Fig. P4.28. If the vane moves
at a speed of 20 ft/s, what is the force on the vane? What horsepower is imparted to the
vane?

4.30. A dredger is loading sand ($\sigma = 2.65$) onto a moored barge, as shown in Fig. P4.30. The
sand leaves the dredger pipe at 5 ft/s with a weight flux of 750 lbf/s. What is the tension
on the mooring line caused by the impinging sand?

4.31. A jet of water is deflected 180° by a vane attached to the cart shown in Fig. P4.31. The jet
is 2.0 in. in diameter and has a velocity of 50 ft/s. The cart weighs 100 lbf. Neglecting the
effects of viscosity, what is the distance traveled by the cart 10 s after the jet is directed
against the vane?

4.32. Calculate the forces acting on the vane of Fig. P4.32 if $\rho_j = 1.25$ slugs/ft³, $A_j = 0.02$ ft²,
$V_j = 15$ ft/s, $\theta = 30°$, and $V_v = 0$.

4.33. Calculate the forces acting on the vane of Fig. P4.32 if $\rho_j = 2.0$ slugs/ft³, $A_j = 0.1$ ft², V_j
$= 20$ ft/s, $\theta = 90°$, and $V_v = 10$ ft/s.

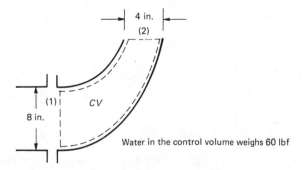

4 in.

(2)

(1)

8 in.

CV

Water in the control volume weighs 60 lbf

Figure P4.26   Sketch for Prob. 4.26.

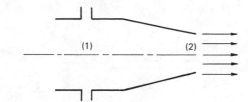

Figure P4.27 Sketch for Prob. 4.27.

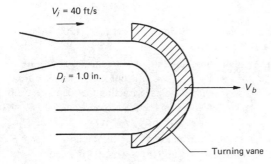

V_j = 40 ft/s

D_j = 1.0 in.

V_b

Turning vane

Figure P4.28 Sketch for Probs. 4.28 and 4.29.

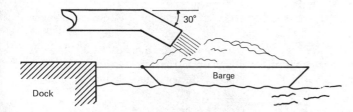

30°

Barge

Dock

Figure P4.30 Sketch for Prob. 4.30.

V_c

V_j = 50 ft/s
D_j = 2 in.

Figure P4.31 Sketch for Prob. 4.31.

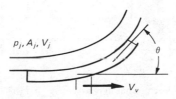

p_j, A_j, V_j

θ

V_v

Figure P4.32 Sketch for Probs. 4.32 through 4.34.

139

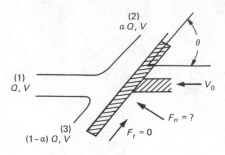

Figure P4.35   Sketch for Probs. 4.35 through 4.38.

4.34. Calculate the forces acting on the vane of Fig. P4.32 if $\rho_j = 1200$ kg/m³, $A_j = 0.02$ m², $V_j = 10$ m/s, $\theta = 30°$, and $V_v = 5$ m/s.

4.35. A jet strikes an inclined fixed plate, breaking into two streams, as shown in Fig. P4.35. The velocity is unchanged (i.e., $V_1 = V_2 = V_3 = V$), but the volumetric flow rates are not equal: $Q_2 = \alpha Q$ and $Q_3 = (1 - \alpha)Q$, α being a fraction that depends on θ. Assume the flow is inviscid so that the tangential force on the plate is zero; that is, $F_t = 0$. What is α as a function of θ?

4.36. For the conditions of Prob. 4.35, develop an expression for the normal force F_n as a function of θ. What is F_n for a jet of water if $V = 20$ ft/s, $A = 0.05$ ft², and $\theta = 60°$?

4.37. If the flat plate of Fig. P4.35 moves directly toward the jet at a velocity of V_0, what is the power required to move the plate?

4.38. If the flat plate of Fig. P4.35 moves away from the jet at a velocity of V_0, what is the power developed by the plate?

4.39. Water from a reservoir drains from a constant-area pipe, as shown in Fig. P4.39. The water flow at the inlet station (station 1) is essentially inviscid. Thus, the velocity is constant at 5.0 m/s across the entire cross section. The pipe is sufficiently long so that the effects of

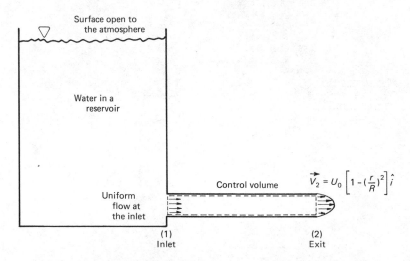

Figure P4.39   Flow development in constant-area pipe for Probs. 4.39 and 4.40.

viscosity are felt across the entire cross section by the time station 2 is reached. As a result, the velocity at station 2 is given by

$$U_2 = U_0 \left[1 - \left(\frac{r}{R} \right)^2 \right]$$

where U_0 is the velocity at the centerline and R is the radius of the pipe, 5.0 cm. If the flow is steady and incompressible, what is the total friction force between stations 1 and 2? Neglect body forces.

4.40. Consider the flow of oil ($\sigma = 0.86$) between stations 1 and 2 of Fig. P4.39. If $U_1 = 0.5$ m/s, $R = 3$ cm, $p_2 = 101$ kPa, and the measured wall-friction drag between stations 1 and 2 is 15 N, what is the pressure p_1 at station 1?

4.41. Using the results of Example 4.3, what is the pressure drop per foot of length if SAE30 oil at 68°F flows in a pipe whose diameter is 1 ft? Assume U_0 is 15 ft/s. Express the answer as lbf/ft²/ft.

4.42. Using the results of Example 4.3, what is the pressure drop per meter of length if water at 20°C flows in a pipe whose diameter is 10 cm? Assume U_0 is 10 m/s. Express the answer as N/m²/m.

4.43. A jet engine (Fig. P4.43) on a test stand takes in air at standard sea-level atmospheric conditions at the inlet (station 1). $V_1 = 200$ m/s and $A_1 = 0.3$ m². The fuel–air ratio is 1/40. The exhaust gases leave the engine at atmospheric pressure such that $V_2 = 1000$ m/s and $A_2 = 0.25$ m². Compute the test stand reaction that balances the thrust of the engine in steady flow.

4.44. The jet engine of an airplane that is flying at 900 km/h takes in 700 N/s of air, burns 17.5 N/s of fuel, and discharges the mixture to the atmosphere as exhaust gases. If the thrust of the engine is 40,000 N, what is the absolute velocity of the exhaust gases?

4.45. A rocket is mounted on a test stand in standard sea-level conditions. The area of the nozzle exit plane is 0.2 ft². The velocity of exhaust gases is 5000 ft/s and the mass flow rate is 2.0 lbm/s. If the static pressure in the nozzle exit plane is 10 atm, what is the thrust developed by the rocket?

4.46. The rocket of Fig. P4.46 has four nozzles, each canted at 10° with respect to the rocket's axis. The gases exhaust at 2000 m/s through a total exit area of 1 m². The density of the

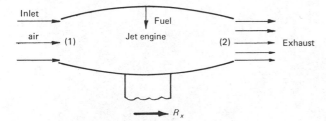

Figure P4.43 Sketch for Prob. 4.43.

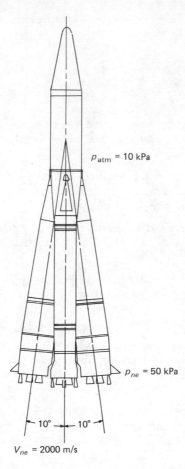

p_{atm} = 10 kPa

p_{ne} = 50 kPa

10°   10°

V_{ne} = 2000 m/s

Figure P4.46   Sketch for Prob. 4.46.

exhaust gas is 0.3 kg/m^3. The pressure in the nozzle exit plane is 50 kPa. If the atmospheric pressure is 10 kPa, what is the thrust on the rocket in newtons?

4.47. What is the horizontal pressure gradient ($\partial p/\partial x$) due to the Coriolis force when the wind speed is 45 m/s, the altitude is 2 km, and $\phi = 30°$?

4.48. How long does it take the cart of Example 4.8 to reach a speed of 0.5 V_j? A stream of water whose velocity is 20 m/s strikes the cart, which has a mass of 3 kg. The nozzle has an area of 5 cm^2.

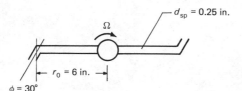

d_{sp} = 0.25 in.

Ω

r_0 = 6 in.

$\phi = 30°$

Figure P4.49   Sketch for Probs. 4.49 through 4.51.

4.49. The horizontal lawn sprinkler shown in Fig. P4.49 has a total flow rate of 0.01 ft^3/s introduced vertically through the center. If $\phi = 30°$, $d_{sp} = 0.25$ in., and $r_0 = 6$ in., what is the torque required to keep the arms from rotating?

4.50. If the sprinkler shown in Fig. P4.49 rotates freely (i.e., $T_{res} = 0$), what will be the steady-state value of Ω (in rpm)?

4.51. If the sprinkler shown in Fig. P4.49 rotates with $T_{res} = 0.05$ ft lbf, what will be the steady-state value of Ω (in rpm)?

CHAPTER FIVE

Dynamics of an Incompressible, Inviscid Flow

In this chapter, we will analyze flow fields for which the effects of viscosity are negligible. As often discussed in previous chapters, no real fluid has zero coefficient of viscosity. However, in many flows involving real fluids, the magnitude of the coefficient of viscosity of the fluid and the velocity gradients in the flow field are such that their product is negligible relative to the inertia and pressure forces acting on the fluid particles. We will use the term *inviscid flow* in these cases to emphasize the fact that it is the character of both the velocity field and the fluid viscosity that allows us to neglect the viscous forces. In regions of the flow field where viscous shear stresses are negligibly small (i.e., in regions where the flow is inviscid), the components of the momentum equation, Eqs. (4.11a) through (4.11c), become

$$\rho \frac{du}{dt} = \rho f_x - \frac{\partial p}{\partial x} \tag{5.1a}$$

$$\rho \frac{dv}{dt} = \rho f_y - \frac{\partial p}{\partial y} \tag{5.1b}$$

$$\rho \frac{dw}{dt} = \rho f_z - \frac{\partial p}{\partial z} \tag{5.1c}$$

In vector form, the equation is

$$\frac{d\vec{V}}{dt} = \frac{\partial \vec{V}}{\partial t} + (\vec{V} \cdot \nabla)\vec{V} = \vec{f} - \frac{1}{\rho} \nabla p \tag{5.2}$$

144

No assumption has been made about the density at this point, so these equations apply to both a compressible and an incompressible flow. These equations, derived in 1755 by Leonhard Euler, are called the *Euler equations*.

In addition to the assumption that the flow is inviscid, in this chapter we will consider only flows for which the fluid properties do not vary through the flow field. Since the flows are inviscid, density is the only fluid property that appears in Eqs. (5.1) and (5.2). Since the fluid properties do not vary for the flow fields discussed in this chapter, density is constant for a given flow. The term *incompressible flow* will be used in describing these flows in this text.

Example 5.1

The tank of a tank-truck rig is completely filled with gasoline. The specific gravity of the gasoline is 0,7, so its specific weight is 6.86×10^3 N/m³. The tank on the trailer is 7 m long by 2 m high, as shown in Fig. 5.1. The tank is vented so that the pressure at the surface of the gasoline at the top rear end of the tank is atmospheric. What is the pressure at the top front of the tank, when the truck decelerates steadily at a rate of 3 m/s²? What is the maximum pressure in the tank?

Solution. Rewriting Eq. (5.1a) for this one-dimensional problem,

$$dp = -\rho a_x \, dx$$

Since a_x is constant, we can integrate this expression to obtain

$$p_{tf} - p_{tr} = -\rho a_x(x_{tf} - x_{tr})$$

Noting that the pressure at the top rear (p_{tr}) is the atmospheric value and that $x_{tr} = 0$, the pressure at the top front (p_{tf}) is

$$p_{tf} = p_{\text{atm}} - \rho a_x x_{tf}$$

$$= 1.01325 \times 10^5 - (700)(-3)(7)$$

$$= 1.160 \times 10^5 \text{ N/m}^2, \text{ abs} = 1.47 \times 10^4 \text{ N/m}^2, \text{ gage}$$

Since the vertical variation in pressure follows the hydrostatic relations of Chapter 2 [e.g., Eqs. (2.4) and (2.6)], the maximum pressure occurs at the bottom front of the tank.

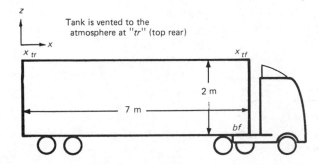

Figure 5.1   Sketch for Example 5.1.

Noting that the specific weight ($\gamma = \rho g$) of gasoline is 6.86×10^3 N/m^3, the pressure at the bottom front is

$$p_{bf} = p_{tf} + \rho g h = p_{atm} + 14{,}700 + (6.86 \times 10^3)2$$

$$= p_{atm} + 2.842 \times 10^4 \text{ N/m}^2 = 28.42 \text{ kPa, gage}$$

BERNOULLI'S EQUATION

As stated previously, the flows of interest in this chapter are inviscid and incompressible. Furthermore, let us consider only body forces that are conservative (such as is the case for gravity),

$$\vec{f} = -\nabla F \tag{5.3}$$

and flows that are steady:

$$\frac{\partial \vec{V}}{\partial t} = 0$$

Using the vector identity that

$$(\vec{V} \cdot \nabla)\vec{V} = \nabla\left(\frac{V^2}{2}\right) - \vec{V} \times (\nabla \times \vec{V})$$

Eq. (5.2) becomes (for these assumptions)

$$\nabla\left(\frac{V^2}{2}\right) + \nabla F + \frac{1}{\rho}\nabla\rho - \vec{V} \times (\nabla \times \vec{V}) = 0 \tag{5.4}$$

In these equations V is the scalar magnitude of the velocity $\vec{V}$.

Let us calculate the change in the magnitude of each of these terms along an arbitrary path whose length and direction are defined by the vector $\vec{dr}$. To do this, we take the dot product of each term in Eq. (5.4) and the vector $\vec{dr}$. The result is

$$d\left(\frac{V^2}{2}\right) + dF + \frac{dp}{\rho} - \vec{V} \times (\nabla \times \vec{V}) \cdot \vec{dr} = 0 \tag{5.5}$$

Note that, since $\vec{V} \times (\nabla \times \vec{V})$ is a vector perpendicular to $\vec{V}$, the last term is zero (1) for any displacement $\vec{dr}$ if the flow is irrotational, or (2) for a displacement along a streamline if the flow is rotational. Thus, for a flow that is

1. inviscid,
2. incompressible,
3. steady, and
4. irrotational (or, if the flow is rotational, we consider only displacements along a streamline), and for which
5. the body forces are conservative,

the first integral of Euler's equation is

$$\int d\left(\frac{V^2}{2}\right) + \int dF + \int \frac{dp}{\rho} = \text{constant} \tag{5.6}$$

Since each term involves an exact differential,

$$\frac{V^2}{2} + F + \frac{p}{\rho} = \text{constant} \tag{5.7}$$

The force potential most often encountered is that due to gravity. Let us take the z axis to be positive when pointing upward and normal to the surface of the earth. The force per unit mass due to gravity is directed downward and is of magnitude g. Therefore, referring to Eq. (5.3),

$$\vec{f} = -\frac{\partial F}{\partial z}\,\hat{k} = -g\hat{k} \tag{5.8}$$

so

$$F = gz$$

For these five assumptions, the first integral of the momentum equation becomes

$$\frac{V^2}{2} + gz + \frac{p}{\rho} = \text{constant} \tag{5.9}$$

Equation (5.9) is known as Bernoulli's equation.

Because the density has been assumed constant, it is not necessary to include the energy equation in the procedure to solve for the velocity and pressure fields. Note, in deriving Eq. (5.9), we have assumed that dissipative mechanisms do not significantly affect the flow. As a corollary, Bernoulli's equation is valid only for flows where there is no mechanism for dissipation, such as viscosity. In thermodynamics, the flow process would be called *reversible*.

Note that, if the velocity is zero throughout the entire flow field, the pressure variation in a static fluid as given by Eq. (5.9) is identical to that given by Eq. (2.5). This is as it should be, since the five conditions required for Bernoulli's equation are valid for the static fluid.

When we worked Example 4.4, we solved for the resultant force in terms of parameters of the problem, since we did not then know how to calculate the flow characteristics at the inlet and outlet of the section. We are now able to calculate the flow characteristics.

Example 5.2

Water flows through a 180° vertical reducing elbow, as shown in Fig. 5.2. The water discharges into the atmosphere at station 2 with a volumetric flow rate of 0.1 m³/s. The volume of the water contained in the reducing elbow is 0.1 m³, and the metal walls of the bend weigh 450 N. At the inlet (station 1) the diameter of the elbow is 20 cm. At the outlet the diameter of the elbow is 10 cm. As shown, the distance from the centerline of the inlet

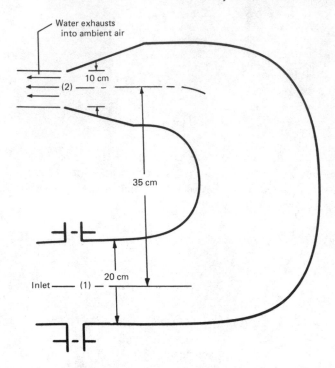

Water exhausts
into ambient air

10 cm

(2)

35 cm

20 cm

Inlet —— (1)

Figure 5.2   Reducing elbow for Example 5.2.

to the centerline of the outlet is 35 cm. Assuming that the flow is steady, incompressible, and inviscid, calculate the force required to hold the bend in place.

Solution.   Let us use the integral form of the momentum equation to generate expressions for the force of the fluid on the pipe in the x and z directions. We can either derive the expressions from the basic equation, Eq. (4.19), or we can adapt the equations derived in Example 4.4 to this specific problem. Let us proceed with the latter approach.

Using Eq. (4.23a), we obtain the expression for the force of the fluid on the pipe in the x direction as

$$F_{FPx} = p_1 A_1 - p_2 A_2 \cos \theta + \dot{m}(V_1 - V_2 \cos \theta)$$

Let us now obtain numerical values for the terms. Note that, since the flow direction is completely reversed by the elbow, $\theta = 180°$. Thus,

$$F_{FPx} = p_1 A_1 + p_2 A_2 + \dot{m}(V_1 + V_2) \tag{5.10}$$

Since all terms are positive, the force of the fluid on the pipe is to the right, as assumed. The reader should verify that this result is logically correct.

The water is discharged to the atmosphere at station 2. Because the streamlines of the exhaust jet are straight, there is no variation in pressure across them. Thus, since air at atmospheric pressure surrounds the exhausting jet of water and since there is no pressure variation across the streamlines,

$$p_2 = p_{atm} = 1.01325 \times 10^5 \text{ N/m}^2$$

Using the continuity equation,

$$\rho V_1 A_1 = \rho V_2 A_2 = \rho(0.1 \text{ m}^3/\text{s})$$

Thus,

$$V_1 = \frac{0.1}{[\pi(0.2)^2]/4} = 3.183 \text{ m/s}, \qquad V_2 = \frac{0.1}{[\pi(0.1)^2]/4} = 12.732 \text{ m/s}$$

Having determined the static pressure at station 2 and the velocities at both stations, we can use Bernoulli's equation to calculate the static pressure at the inlet, station 1. Using Eq. (5.9) and solving for p_1,

$$p_1 = p_2 + \rho g(z_2 - z_1) + \tfrac{1}{2}\rho V_2^2 - \tfrac{1}{2}\rho V_1^2$$

Substituting the numerical values for the parameters,

$$p_1 = 1.01325 \times 10^5 \text{ N/m}^2 + 1000 \text{ kg/m}^3 (9.8066 \text{ m/s}^2) (0.35 \text{ m})$$

$$+ \tfrac{1}{2} 1000 \text{ kg/m}^3 [162.114 - 10.132] \text{ m}^2/\text{s}^2$$

$$= (1.01325 + 0.03432 + 0.75991) \times 10^5 \text{ N/m}^2$$

Thus,

$$p_1 = 1.80748 \times 10^5 \text{ N/m}^2$$

The reader should make a practice of noting the relative magnitude of the various terms. In many flow problems, certain terms are neglected as being small relative to other terms. Studying the three terms that sum to give p_1, the reader can see that even though the density of water is relatively high (in comparison to the density of gases) the change in potential energy represents only a few percent of the change in pressure from station 2 to station 1. Substituting these numerical values for the parameters in Eq. (5.10), we obtain

$$F_{FPx} = 1.80748 \times 10^5 \left[\frac{\pi(0.2)^2}{4} \right]$$

$$+ 1.01325 \times 10^5 \left[\frac{\pi(0.1)^2}{4} \right] + 1000(0.1)(3.183 + 12.732)$$

$$= 5678.4 + 795.8 + 1591.5 = 8065.7 \text{ N}$$

Referring to Fig. 5.3, we see that over most of the external surface of the elbow, the force of the atmospheric pressure acting to the left is balanced by the atmospheric pressure force acting toward the right on the opposite side of the elbow. However, the atmospheric pressure forces on the surfaces opposite the inlet and outlet do not have balancing forces. Thus, there is a net force on the elbow in the x direction due to the external atmospheric pressure. The force is equal to the product of the atmospheric pressure times the projected, "unbalanced" area and acts to the left. Thus, the net force on the elbow in the x direction is

$$F_{Nx} = F_{FPx} - P_{\text{atm}}(A_1 + A_2) = 8065.7 - 3979.0 = 4086.7 \text{ N}$$

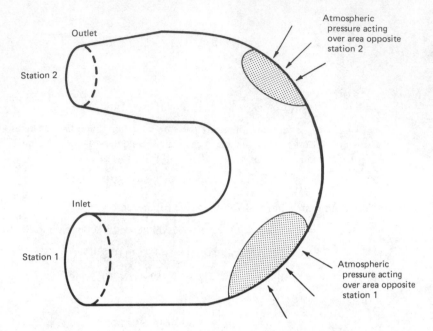

Figure 5.3   External surface of reducing elbow.

The horizontal component of the force (R_x) required to hold the elbow in place is the negative of this, or 4086.6 N toward the left.

Using Eq. (4.23b), the force of the fluid on the elbow in the vertical direction is

$$F_{FPz} = -W = -\gamma \, [\text{Vol}] = -980.66 \text{ N} \qquad (5.11)$$

The vertical force required to hold the pipe in place must not only be able to support the force of the fluid in the pipe, but it must support the weight of the metal pipe itself. Thus,

$$R_z = 980.66 + 450.0 = 1430.7 \text{ N}$$

Example 5.3

Consider a large tank containing a liquid, as shown in Fig. 5.4. The liquid in the tank is maintained under pressure so that the pressure of the gas in the tank (above the free surface of the liquid) is p_1. The liquid exhausts to the atmosphere through a small, well-rounded opening located a distance h below the free surface of the liquid in the tank. Assuming that the density is constant, develop the relation for the velocity of the jet of liquid (V_2) issuing from the tank.

Solution.   Since the distance h decreases with time as the liquid drains from the tank, this is not strictly a steady flow. However, since the diameter of the tank is large relative to the size of the opening, the velocity of the free surface is relatively small. Thus, the distance h will change slowly with time, and no serious error will be introduced if one calculates the jet velocity at a given time using the value of h that exists at that time. The flow is thus assumed to be *quasi-steady*.

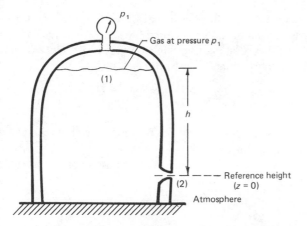

Figure 5.4 Sketch for Example 5.3.

If one neglects the thin, viscous layer near the wall, the liquid motion can be assumed to be irrotational. Under these conditions and in light of the fact that all streamlines have the same total energy at the free surface (i.e., the same Bernoulli constant), we may use Bernoulli's equation to relate conditions at the free surface in the tank to those at the exit. Thus, using the height of the exhaust opening as the reference level in Eq. (5.9), we obtain

$$p_1 + \tfrac{1}{2}\rho V_1^2 + \rho g h = p_{\text{atm}} + \tfrac{1}{2}\rho V_2^2$$

Note that we have already used the fact that, for a subsonic flow exhausting to the atmosphere, the pressure of the exhaust flow is atmospheric. Using the integral continuity equation, we find that

$$V_1 = \frac{A_2}{A_1} V_2 = \frac{d_2^2}{d_1^2} V_2$$

Since $d_1 \gg d_2$, the term containing V_1 is negligibly small. Thus,

$$V_2 = \sqrt{2gh + \frac{2}{\rho}(p_1 - p_{\text{atm}})} \qquad (5.12)$$

If the pressure in the tank is atmospheric (which would be the case if the free surface of the liquid is vented to the atmosphere), the exhaust velocity of the liquid is

$$V_2 = \sqrt{2gh} \qquad (5.13)$$

Note that for this case the exhaust velocity is independent of the properties of the liquid. This formula, which was developed by Torricelli in the seventeenth century, states that the discharge velocity equals the speed that a frictionless particle would attain if it fell freely from point 1 to point 2.

For more accurate results, one may account for friction by introducing an experimentally determined *velocity coefficient* (C_v). The velocity coefficient depends on the size and shape of the opening as well as the distance from the free surface to the opening *(h)*. For well-designed, rounded openings, the value of C_v is usually between 0.98 and 1.00.

For other than a well-rounded opening, the jet stream will contract as it leaves the container. The smallest cross section of the jet is called the *vena contracta,* as shown in Fig. 5.5. The area at this section is determined experimentally. A *coefficient of contraction* (C_c) is used to describe the reduction in area and is defined as

$$C_c = \frac{A_c}{A} \tag{5.14}$$

This coefficient depends on the shape and size of the opening as well as the distance h. A representative value of C_c for a sharp-edged outlet is 0.62.

To determine the volumetric flow-rate of the liquid, we use expressions (5.13) and (5.14) in the definition for the volumetric flow rate:

$$Q = VA_c = C_v\sqrt{2gh}\, C_c A \tag{5.15}$$

The product of the coefficients can be represented by a single parameter, the *coefficient of discharge* (C_d), where $C_d = C_v C_c$. Tables and charts for the various coefficients can be found in hydraulic engineering handbooks.

Example 5.4

Water flows from a very large reservoir, as shown in Fig. 5.6. Neglecting friction in the pipes and assuming the density is constant, determine the output of the turbine for the data given in the sketch.

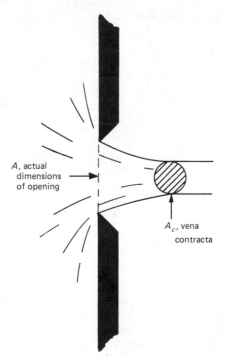

A, actual dimensions of opening

A_c, vena contracta

Figure 5.5   Reduction in area relating to the coefficient of contraction.

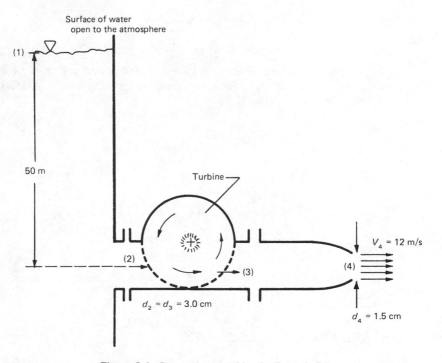

Figure 5.6 Reservoir and turbine for Example 5.4.

Solution. As was the case in Example 5.3, the flow in this example can be assumed to be quasi-steady. Together with the stated assumptions, the conditions required to apply Bernoulli's equation between different points in the pipe are satisfied. Thus, we can use Bernoulli's equation to define the flow at the inlet of the turbine, station 2, and at the outlet, station 3.

Using the integral form of the continuity equation, we can solve for V_2 and V_3:

$$V_2 = \frac{V_4 A_4}{A_2} = \frac{V_4 d_4^2}{d_2^2} = 3.0 \text{ m/s} = V_3$$

Because the reservoir is very large, the velocity at the free surface is negligible. Relating the flow at points 1 and 2 and solving for the static pressure at station 2,

$$p_2 = p_{atm} + \tfrac{1}{2}\rho(V_1^2 - V_2^2) + \rho g(z_1 - z_2)$$

$$= p_{atm} - \tfrac{1}{2}(1000 \text{ kg/m}^3)(9 \text{ m}^2/\text{s}^2) + 1000 \text{ kg/m}^3 \, (9.8066 \text{ m/s}^2) \, 50 \text{ m}$$

$$= p_{atm} + 4.8583 \times 10^5 \text{ N/m}^2$$

Because we are interested in the change in pressure across the pump, we can leave the parameter p_{atm} in the expression for p_2, since it will also appear in the expression for p_3.

Relating the flow at points 3 and 4 and solving for the static pressure at station 3,

$$p_3 = p_{\text{atm}} + \tfrac{1}{2}\rho(V_4^2 - V_3^2) + \rho g(z_4 - z_3)$$

$$= p_{\text{atm}} + \tfrac{1}{2}\,1000(144 - 9) = p_{\text{atm}} + 0.675 \times 10^5 \text{ N/m}^2$$

Neglecting heat transfer and changes in the internal energy of the water as it goes through the turbine, the first law of thermodynamics can be used to calculate the output of the turbine. The equation is

$$\frac{V_2^2}{2} + \frac{p_2}{\rho} = \frac{V_3^2}{2} + \frac{p_3}{\rho} + \frac{\dot{W}_s}{\dot{m}} \tag{5.16}$$

(The derivation of this equation will be discussed in Chapter 8.) Thus,

$$\dot{W}_s = \dot{m}\left[\left(\frac{V_2^2}{2} - \frac{V_3^2}{2}\right) + \left(\frac{p_2}{\rho} - \frac{p_3}{\rho}\right)\right] = V_4 A_4(p_2 - p_3)$$

Since $V_2 = V_3$ and $\dot{m} = \rho V_4 A_4$,

$$\dot{W}_s = (12 \text{ m/s})(1.767 \times 10^{-4} \text{ m}^2)(4.1833 \times 10^5 \text{ N/m}^2) = 887.1 \text{ N} \cdot \text{m/s} = 887.1 \text{ W}$$

Note that 1 watt = 1 joule/s = 1 N · m/s.

HYDRAULIC AND ENERGY GRADE LINES

The relation between the terms of the Bernoulli equation, Eq. (5.9), can be interpreted in terms of two grade lines. The energy grade line (EGL) corresponds to the height of the total Bernoulli constant h_0, where

$$\text{EGL} = \frac{V^2}{2g} + z + \frac{p}{\rho g} = h_0 \tag{5.17}$$

In a frictionless flow, where there is no work or heat transfer, the value of h_0 is constant. The hydraulic grade line (HGL) corresponds to the height equal to the sum of elevation and static pressure head. Thus:

$$\text{HGL} = z + \frac{p}{\rho g} = \text{EGL} - \frac{V^2}{2g} \tag{5.18}$$

In these two equations, the pressure is the gage value. Recall that in the previous example the atmospheric pressure was not important since we were interested in the changes in pressure.

These two heights can be visualized using the appropriate pressure sensors, as illustrated in Fig. 5.7. A pitot tube senses the total head of the stream, which corresponds to the EGL. The height of the energy grade line is constant along the duct. A piezometer tube, which is an open tube connected to the wall of the channel, provides a measure of the hydraulic grade line. As shown in Fig. 5.7, the HGL rises as the velocity decreases.

For a more general flow, that is, flow in which the viscous effects are considered, the EGL will drop slowly due to friction losses and will drop sharply due to a major loss

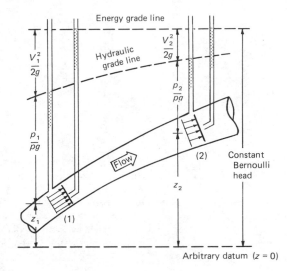

Figure 5.7 Hydraulic and energy grade lines for frictionless flow in a duct.

(e.g., a valve or obstruction) or due to the extraction of work (e.g., at a turbine). The EGL will rise if there is an input of work (e.g., from a pump or a propeller). The HGL generally follows the behavior of the EGL with respect to losses or work transfer, and it also rises (or falls) when the velocity decreases (or increases).

BERNOULLI'S EQUATION FOR GASEOUS FLOWS

For most gas flows the changes in potential energy between two points in the flow field are negligible. (One exception would be in describing the atmospheric flow field where we must account for large changes in distance.) Neglecting the change in potential energy, Eq. (5.9) may be written

$$p + \tfrac{1}{2}\rho V^2 = \text{constant}$$

This equation establishes a direct relation between pressure and velocity. Thus, if either parameter is known, the other can be uniquely determined provided that the flow does not violate the assumptions required to apply Bernoulli's equation. The equation can be used to relate the flow at various points around the vehicle, for example, (1) a point far from the vehicle (i.e., the free stream), (2) a point where the velocity relative to the vehicle is zero (i.e., a stagnation point), and (3) a general point just outside the boundary layer. The nomenclature for these points is illustrated in Fig. 5.8. Note that the free-stream parameters are designated by the subscript ∞.

$$p_\infty + \tfrac{1}{2}\rho_\infty V_\infty^2 = p_2 = p_3 + \tfrac{1}{2}\rho_\infty V_3^2 = p_t \tag{5.19}$$

The stagnation (or total) pressure (p_t), which is the constant of Eq. (5.19), is the sum of the free-stream static pressure (p_∞) and the free-stream dynamic pressure $(\tfrac{1}{2}\rho_\infty V_\infty^2$, which is designated by the symbol q_∞).

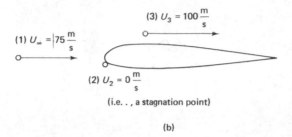

Figure 5.8 Flow for Example 5.5: (a) ground-fixed coordinate system; (b) vehicle-fixed coordinate system. (From John J. Bertin and Michael L. Smith, *Aerodynamics for Engineers*, © 1979, p. 40. Reprinted by permission of Prentice-Hall, Inc., Englewood Cliffs, N.J.)

Example 5.5

The airfoil of Fig. 5.8a moves through the air at 75 m/s at an altitude of 2 km. The fluid at point 3 moves downstream at 25 m/s relative to the ground-fixed coordinate system. What are the values of the static pressure at points 1, 2, and 3?

Solution. To solve this problem, let us superimpose a velocity of 75 m/s to the right so that the airfoil is at rest in the transformed coordinate system. In this vehicle-fixed-coordinate system, the fluid "moves" past the airfoil, as shown in Fig. 5.8b. The velocity at point 3 is 100 m/s relative to the stationary airfoil. The resultant flow is steady.

Point 1: p_∞, the static pressure of the undisturbed free stream, is found directly in Table 1.1

$$p_\infty = \frac{596.309 \text{ mm Hg}}{760.000 \text{ mmHg/atm}} (1.01325 \times 10^5 \frac{\text{N/m}^2}{\text{atm}}) = 79,501 \text{ N/m}^2$$

Point 2: $p_t = p_\infty + \frac{1}{2}\rho_\infty V_\infty^2$

$$= 79,501 \text{ N/m}^2 + \frac{1}{2}(1.0066 \text{ kg/m}^3)(75 \text{ m/s})^2 = 82,332 \text{ N/m}^2$$

Point 3: $p_3 + \frac{1}{2}\rho_\infty V_3^2 = p_\infty + \frac{1}{2}\rho_\infty V_\infty^2$

$$p_3 = 82,332 \text{ N/m}^2 - \frac{1}{2}(1.0066 \text{ kg/m}^3)(100 \text{ m/s})^2 = 77,299 \text{ N/m}^2$$

PRESSURE COEFFICIENT

The engineer often uses experimental data or theoretical solutions for one flow condition to gain insight into the flow field that exists at another flow condition. Wind-tunnel data, where scale models are exposed to flow conditions that simulate the design flight environment, are used to gain insight to describe the full-scale flow field at other flow conditions. Therefore, it is most desirable to present (experimental or theoretical) correlations in terms of dimensionless coefficients that depend only on the configuration geometry and the angle of attack. One such dimensionless coefficient is the pressure coefficient:

$$C_p = \frac{p - p_\infty}{\frac{1}{2}\rho_\infty V_\infty^2} = \frac{p - p_\infty}{q_\infty} \tag{5.20}$$

This particular choice of a parameter to nondimensionalize the local static pressure can be understood by referring to Bernoulli's equation without the potential energy term, Eq. (5.19). Rearranging,

$$C_p = \frac{p - p_\infty}{\frac{1}{2}\rho_\infty V_\infty^2} = 1 - \frac{V^2}{V_\infty^2} \tag{5.21}$$

Thus, at the stagnation point, where the local velocity is zero, $C_p = C_{p,t} = 1.0$ for an incompressible flow. Note that the stagnation point value is independent of the free-stream flow conditions and the configuration geometry.

PRESSURE COEFFICIENT AS A SIMILARITY PARAMETER

Equation (5.20) is the definition of the pressure coefficient and, therefore, can be used for any and all flows. It is important to note that the pressure coefficient for actual flows may vary with changes in the Reynolds number, the Mach number, and the geometry. Examples of Reynolds-number-dependent variations in the pressure-coefficient distributions for flow around a cylinder will be discussed later in this chapter.

Equation (5.21) is a dimensionless form of Bernoulli's equation for flows where the hydrostatic variation of pressure is negligible. It is, therefore, valid only for those flows that satisfy the conditions for Bernoulli's equation. As we will see in this chapter, when the flow is steady, inviscid, incompressible, and irrotational, the pressure coefficient depends only on the geometry. That is, it is independent of the Reynolds number. This should be expected, since as was discussed in Chapter 4 the Reynolds number is not a required similarity parameter for inviscid flows.

The objective of presenting the pressure in terms of the pressure coefficient is to generate the experimental or theoretical values of the pressure that are similar for different flow conditions. Thus, whereas the local static pressure at point 3 as defined by Eq. (5.19) always depends on the free-stream velocity (V_∞), the altitude (p_∞ and ρ_∞), and the configuration geometry (V_3), the corresponding value of the pressure coefficient, as defined by Eq. (5.21), would depend only on the configuration geometry (V_3^2/V_∞^2) under ideal conditions.

COMMENTS ABOUT BERNOULLI'S EQUATION

By rearranging the parameters in Bernoulli's equation, the terms (or, equivalently, the Bernoulli constant) have different units. Thus, the units of the terms in Eq. (5.9) represent energy, those in Eq. (5.17) represent the pressure head (in length), and those in Eq. (5.19) represent pressure (as force/area).

In Examples 5.2 through 5.5, we applied Bernoulli's equation to solve flows that ~ady, inviscid, incompressible, and irrotational with conservative body forces. However, there are many flows for which viscous effects cause significant losses in total pressure. Although the presence of significant viscous effects violates the flow model for which Bernoulli's equation is valid, these flows can be solved using a modified form of Bernoulli's equation. The losses in the total pressure head are solved using empirical coefficients. The modified Bernoulli equation will be discussed in Chapter 6, in which solutions for viscous flows are presented.

VELOCITY POTENTIAL FOR IRROTATIONAL FLOW

The assumption that the flow was irrotational was introduced when deriving Bernoulli's equation. For an irrotational flow, the curl of the velocity is zero:

$$\nabla \times \vec{V} = 0 \tag{5.22}$$

From vector calculus, the curl of any gradient is necessarily zero:

$$\nabla \times \nabla \phi = 0 \tag{5.23}$$

Thus, it is clear that the velocity field for an irrotational flow can be represented by a velocity potential:

$$\vec{V} = \nabla \phi \tag{5.24}$$

For Cartesian coordinates, the velocity components may be written in terms of derivatives of the potential function as

$$u = \frac{\partial \phi}{\partial x}, \qquad v = \frac{\partial \phi}{\partial y}, \qquad w = \frac{\partial \phi}{\partial z} \tag{5.25}$$

For cylindrical coordinates, the velocity components are

$$v_r = \frac{\partial \phi}{\partial r}, \qquad v_\theta = \frac{1}{r}\frac{\partial \phi}{\partial \theta}, \qquad v_z = \frac{\partial \phi}{\partial z} \tag{5.26}$$

If a fluid starts from rest, or if the fluid in some region is uniform and parallel, the rotation in this region is zero. The reader can verify this by showing that Eq. (5.22) is satisfied when the velocity is uniform and parallel (i.e., $\vec{V} = V_\infty \hat{i}$). Lord Kelvin showed that the entire flow will remain irrotational in the absence of viscous forces and discontinuities provided that the fluid is homogeneous and the body forces can be described by a potential function.

In many flow problems, the undisturbed, free-stream flow is a uniform parallel flow in which there are no shear stresses. Kelvin's theorem implies that, although the fluid particles in the subsequent flow patterns may follow curved paths, the flow remains irrotational except in those regions where the dissipative mechanisms (such as viscosity) are an important factor.

LAPLACE'S EQUATION FOR INCOMPRESSIBLE, IRROTATIONAL FLOWS

For an incompressible flow, the continuity equation is

$$\nabla \cdot \vec{V} = 0 \tag{3.6}$$

Combining Eqs. (3.6) and (5.24), one finds that for an incompressible, irrotational flow

$$\nabla^2 \phi = 0 \tag{5.27}$$

Thus, the governing equation for this motion, which is known as Laplace's equation, is a linear, second-order, partial differential equation.

In Chapter 3, we learned that the equation of continuity for an incompressible, two-dimensional flow is the necessary and sufficient condition for the existence of a stream function. Since the flow need be two-dimensional in the sense that only two spatial coordinates are needed to describe the motion, stream functions exist for both plane flows and axially symmetric flows. Thus, the velocity components in Cartesian coordinates that identically satisfy the continuity equation are

$$u = \frac{\partial \psi}{\partial y} \quad \text{and} \quad v = -\frac{\partial \psi}{\partial x} \tag{3.12}$$

(The reader may be familiar with texts, e.g., Ref. 5.1, that use the definition that $u = -\partial \psi/\partial y$ and $v = \partial \psi/\partial x$. Although this formulation also identically satisfies the continuity equation, Eq. (3.12) will be used throughout this text.) In cylindrical coordinates,

$$v_r = \frac{1}{r}\frac{\partial \psi}{\partial \theta} \quad \text{and} \quad v_\theta = -\frac{\partial \psi}{\partial r}$$

If the flow is also irrotational,

$$\nabla \times \vec{V} = 0$$

Then writing the velocity components in terms of the stream function, as defined in Eq. (3.12), we obtain

$$\nabla^2 \psi = 0 \tag{5.28}$$

Thus, for an irrotational, two-dimensional incompressible flow, the stream function is also governed by Laplace's equation.

RELATION BETWEEN STREAMLINES AND EQUIPOTENTIAL LINES

If a flow is incompressible, irrotational, and two-dimensional, the velocity field may be calculated using either a potential function or a stream function. Using the potential function, the velocity components in Cartesian coordinates are

$$u = \frac{\partial \phi}{\partial x}, \quad v = \frac{\partial \phi}{\partial y}$$

For a potential function,

$$d\phi = \frac{\partial \phi}{\partial x} \, dx + \frac{\partial \phi}{\partial y} \, dy = u \, dx + v \, dy$$

Therefore, for lines of constant potential ($d\phi = 0$),

$$\left(\frac{dy}{dx}\right)_{\phi \, = \, c} = -\frac{u}{v} \qquad (5.29)$$

Since a streamline is everywhere tangent to the local velocity, the slope of a streamline, which is a line of constant ψ, is

$$\left(\frac{dy}{dx}\right)_{\psi \, = \, c} = \frac{v}{u} \qquad (5.30)$$

Comparing Eqs. (5.29) and (5.30),

$$\left(\frac{dy}{dx}\right)_{\phi \, = \, c} = -\frac{1}{(dy/dx)_{\psi \, = \, c}} \qquad (5.31)$$

The slope of an equipotential line is the negative reciprocal of the slope of a streamline. Therefore, streamlines (ψ = constant) are perpendicular to equipotential lines (ϕ = constant), except at stagnation points, where the components vanish simultaneously.

Example 5.6.

Consider the incompressible, irrotational, two-dimensional flow, where the stream function is

$$\psi = 2xy$$

(a) What is the velocity at $x = 1$, $y = 1$? at $x = 2$, $y = \frac{1}{2}$? (Note that both points are on the same streamline.)

(b) Sketch the streamline pattern and discuss the significance of the spacing between the streamlines.

(c) What is the velocity potential for this flow?

(d) Sketch the lines of constant potential. How do the lines of equipotential relate to the streamlines?

Solution. (a) The stream function can be used to calculate the velocity components:

$$u = \frac{\partial \psi}{\partial y} = 2x, \quad v = -\frac{\partial \psi}{\partial x} = -2y$$

Therefore,

$$\vec{V} = 2x\hat{i} - 2y\hat{j}$$

At $x = 1$, $y = 1$, $\vec{V} = 2\hat{i} - 2\hat{j}$, and the magnitude of the velocity is

$$U = 2.8284$$

At $x = 2$, $y = \frac{1}{2}$, $\vec{V} = 4\hat{i} - \hat{j}$, and the magnitude of the velocity is

$$U = 4.1231$$

(b) A sketch of the streamline pattern is presented in Fig. 5.9. Results are presented only for the first quadrant (x positive, y positive). Mirror-image patterns would exist in other quadrants. Note that the $x = 0$ and $y = 0$ axes represent the $\psi = 0$ streamline.

Since the flow is incompressible, the integral form of continuity, Eq. (3.19), indicates that the product of the velocity times the distance between the streamlines is a constant. That is, since $\rho = $ constant,

$$\oiint \vec{V} \cdot d\vec{A} = 0$$

Therefore, the distance between the streamlines decreases as the magnitude of the velocity increases.

(c) Since $u = \partial\phi/\partial x$ and $v = \partial\phi/\partial y$,

$$\phi = \int u \, dx + g(y) = \int 2x \, dx + g(y) \tag{5.32a}$$

Also,

$$\phi = \int v \, dy + f(x) = -\int 2y \, dy + f(x) \tag{5.32b}$$

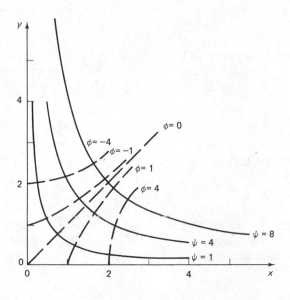

Figure 5.9 Equipotential lines and streamlines of Example 5.6. (From Bertin and Smith, *Aerodynamics for Engineers*, p. 47.)

The potential function that will satisfy both Eqs. (5.32a) and (5.32b) is

$$\phi = x^2 - y^2 + C$$

where C is an arbitrary constant.

(d) The equipotential lines are included in Fig. 5.9, where C, the arbitrary constant, has been set equal to zero. The lines of equipotential are perpendicular to the streamlines, as required by Eq. (5.31).

SUPERPOSITION OF FLOWS

Since Eq. (5.27) for the potential function and Eq. (5.28) for the stream function are linear, functions that individually satisfy these (Laplace's) equations may be added together to describe a desired, complex flow. The boundary conditions are that the resultant velocity is equal to the free-stream value at points far from the surface and that the component of the velocity normal to the surface is zero (i.e., the surface is a streamline). There are numerous two-dimensional and axisymmetric solutions available through *inverse* methods. These inverse methods do not begin with a prescribed boundary surface and directly solve for the potential flow, but instead assume a set of known singularities in the presence of an onset flow. The total potential function (or stream function) for the singularities and the onset flow are then used to determine the streamlines, any one of which may be considered to be a *boundary surface*. If the resultant boundary surface corresponds to that of the desired configuration, the desired solution has been obtained. The singularities most often used in such approaches, which were suggested by William Rankine in 1871, include a source, a sink, a doublet, and a vortex.

For a constant-density potential flow, the velocity field can be determined using only the continuity equation and the condition of irrotationality. Thus, the equation of motion is not used, and the velocity may be determined independently of the pressure. Once the velocity field has been determined, Bernoulli's equation can be used to calculate the corresponding pressure field. It is important to note that the pressures of the component flows cannot be superimposed (or added together), since they are nonlinear functions of the velocity. Referring to Eq. (5.9), the reader can see that the pressure is a quadratic function of the velocity.

ELEMENTARY TWO-DIMENSIONAL FLOWS

Uniform Flow

The simplest flow is a *uniform stream* moving in a fixed direction at a constant speed (i.e., the onset flow of the previous paragraph). Thus, the streamlines are straight and parallel to each other everywhere in the flow field (see Fig. 5.10). Using a cylindrical

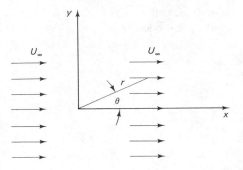

Figure 5.10 Streamlines for a uniform flow parallel to the x axis. (From Bertin and Smith, *Aerodynamics for Engineers*, p. 48.)

coordinate system, the potential function for a uniform flow moving parallel to the x axis is

$$\phi = U_\infty r \cos \theta \qquad (5.33)$$

where U_∞ is the velocity of the fluid particles. (Note that both U_∞ and V_∞ are used in this text to designate the free-stream velocity. Which symbol is used in a particular application is a matter of choice and/or convention.) Using a Cartesian coordinate system, the potential function for the uniform stream of Fig. 5.10 is

$$\phi = U_\infty x \qquad (5.34)$$

Source or Sink

A *source* is defined as a point from which fluid issues and flows radially outward (see Fig. 5.11) such that the continuity equation is satisfied everywhere but at the singularity that exists at the source's center. The potential function for the two-dimensional (planar) source centered at the origin is

$$\phi = \frac{K}{2\pi} \ln r \qquad (5.35)$$

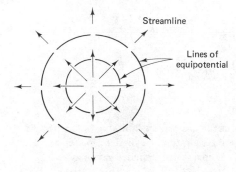

Figure 5.11 Equipotential lines and streamlines for flow from a two dimensional source. (From Bertin and Smith, *Aerodynamics for Engineers*, p. 49.)

where r is the radial coordinate from the center of the source and K is the source strength. The resultant velocity field in cylindrical coordinates is

$$\vec{V} = \nabla\phi = \hat{e}_r \frac{\partial\phi}{\partial r} + \frac{\hat{e}_\theta}{r}\frac{\partial\phi}{\partial\theta} \tag{5.36}$$

Since

$$\vec{V} = \hat{e}_r v_r + \hat{e}_\theta v_\theta$$

$$v_r = \frac{\partial\phi}{\partial r} = \frac{K}{2\pi r} \tag{5.37a}$$

and

$$v_\theta = \frac{1}{r}\frac{\partial\phi}{\partial\theta} = 0 \tag{5.37b}$$

Note that the resultant velocity has only a radial component and that this component varies inversely with the radial distance from the source.

A sink is a negative source. That is, fluid flows into a sink along radial streamlines. Thus, for a sink of strength K centered at the origin,

$$\phi = -\frac{K}{2\pi}\ln r \tag{5.38}$$

The reader may want to compare the analysis of the two-dimensional sink discussed in Example 3.6 with that of the next two examples. Recall that in Chapter 3 we worked only with the continuity equation and its implications.

Example 5.7

Show that the mass flow rate passing through a cylinder of radius r and of unit depth is proportional to K, the strength of the two-dimensional source, and is independent of the radius.

Solution

$$\dot{m} = \iint \rho\vec{V}\cdot d\vec{A} = \int \rho\left[\frac{K}{2\pi r}\hat{e}_r\right]\cdot[r\,d\theta(1)\hat{e}_r]$$

$$= \int_0^{2\pi} \rho\left(\frac{K}{2\pi r}\right)r\,d\theta$$

$$= K\rho$$

Thus, as one would expect for this steady flow, the volumetric flow rate issuing from the source also passes through the walls of any cylinder centered on the origin, since the velocity varies as r^{-1} and the surface area of the cylinder varies as r.

Example 5.8

What is the stream function corresponding to the potential function for the two-dimensional source of Eq. (5.35)? Sketch the streamline pattern. Sketch lines of equipotential.

Solution

$$v_r = \frac{\partial \phi}{\partial r} = \frac{1}{r} \frac{\partial \psi}{\partial \theta} = \frac{K}{2\pi r}$$

and

$$v_\theta = \frac{1}{r} \frac{\partial \phi}{\partial \theta} = - \frac{\partial \psi}{\partial r} = 0$$

Integrating the first expression,

$$\psi = \int \frac{K}{2\pi} d\theta + f(r)$$

Integrating the second expression,

$$\psi = g(\theta)$$

A stream function that satisfies both of these expressions is

$$\psi = \frac{K\theta}{2\pi} + C$$

A sketch of the streamlines is presented in Fig. 5.11. Note that the streamlines are lines of constant θ, that is, radial lines issuing from the origin (as one would physically expect for a source-type flow). The equipotential lines are circles, that is, lines of constant radius. Thus, as indicated by Eq. (5.31), the streamlines are perpendicular to equipotential lines.

Example 5.9

In the two previous examples, we have considered flows involving a single element. Consider now the incompressible, irrotational, steady flow generated when a uniform flow (from right to left) encounters a source located at the origin, as shown in Fig. 5.12. Two of the streamlines in this flow form a horizontal plane passing through the origin. Locate the stagnation point

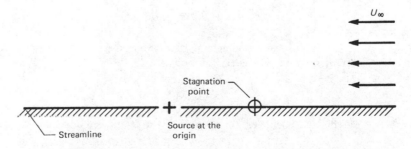

Figure 5.12 Uniform flow past a source as discussed in Example 5.9.

in this flow. Designating the stagnation-point location as x_0, determine the C_p distribution along the horizontal plane in terms of the dimensionless x coordinate (x_0/x).

Solution.   The potential function for a uniform flow from right to left is

$$\phi_{uf} = -U_\infty r \cos \theta$$

and that for a source at the origin is

$$\phi_s = \frac{K}{2\pi} \ln r$$

Since they each satisfy Laplace's equation, their sum will also satisfy Laplace's equation.

$$\phi = -U_\infty r \cos \theta + \frac{K}{2\pi} \ln r$$

The velocity components are

$$v_r = \frac{\partial \phi}{\partial r} = -U_\infty \cos \theta + \frac{K}{2\pi r}$$

$$v_\theta = \frac{1}{r} \frac{\partial \phi}{\partial \theta} = +U_\infty \sin \theta$$

Note that when $\theta = 0$ or $\theta = \pi$, $v_\theta = 0$; that is, velocity component normal to the horizontal plane of Fig. 5.12 is zero. Thus, as stated in the problem formulation, two streamlines form the horizontal plane. Furthermore, the total velocity on the plate (U) is

$$U = v_r = -U_\infty \cos \theta + \frac{K}{2\pi r}$$

To locate the stagnation point, note that v_r can be equal to zero only when $\theta = 0$. Thus, the radial location of the stagnation point is

$$r = x_0 = \frac{K}{2\pi U_\infty}$$

Since we are interested only in the flow along the plate, we can convert from the r, θ coordinates to x (since $y = 0$ along the plate). The v_r component of velocity can be written as

$$u = -U_\infty + \frac{K}{2\pi x}$$

To rewrite this expression in terms of x_0/x, note that $K = 2\pi x_0 U_\infty$. Noting also that u is the total velocity on the plate (U), we obtain

$$u = U = U_\infty \left(\frac{x_0}{x} - 1 \right)$$

The pressure coefficient on the plate can be determined using Eq. (5.21):

$$C_p = 1 - \frac{U^2}{U_\infty^2} = 1 - \left(\frac{x_0}{x} - 1 \right)^2 = \frac{2x_0}{x} - \left(\frac{x_0}{x} \right)^2$$

Note that this relation is consistent with our physical understanding of the flow, since

$$C_p = 0 \quad \text{when } x \to \pm\infty \text{ (i.e., at points far from the source)}$$
$$= 1 \quad \text{when } x = x_0 \text{ (i.e., at the stagnation point)}$$

There are other streamlines in the flow field produced by the superposition of a uniform flow and a source (or sink) that generate interesting flows (e.g., the Rankine half body). Examples of such flows are given in the problems at the end of this chapter.

Doublet

A *doublet* is defined to be the singularity resulting when a source and a sink of equal strength are made to approach each other (see Fig. 5.13) such that the product of their strengths (K) and their distance apart (a) remains constant at a preselected finite value in the limit as the distance between them approaches zero. The line along which the approach is made is called the *axis of the doublet*. The potential for a doublet for which the flow proceeds out from the origin in the negative x direction (i.e., the source is placed upstream) is

$$\phi = \frac{B}{r} \cos \theta \tag{5.39}$$

where B is a constant.

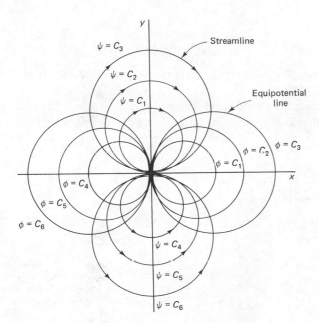

Figure 5.13 Equipotential line and streamlines for a doublet (flow proceeds out from the origin in the negative x direction). (From Bertin and Smith, *Aerodynamics for Engineers*, p. 51.)

Potential Vortex

A *potential vortex* is defined as a singularity about which fluid flows with concentric streamlines (see Fig. 5.14). The potential for a vortex centered at the origin is

$$\phi = -\frac{\Gamma\theta}{2\pi} \tag{5.40}$$

where Γ is the strength of the vortex. Differentiating the potential function, one finds the velocity distribution about an isolated vortex to be

$$v_r = \frac{\partial\phi}{\partial r} = 0 \tag{5.41a}$$

$$v_\theta = \frac{1}{r}\frac{\partial\phi}{\partial\theta} = -\frac{\Gamma}{2\pi r} \tag{5.41b}$$

Thus, there is no radial velocity component, and the circumferential component varies as the reciprocal of the radial distance from the vortex. Note that because we used a minus sign for the potential function, Eq. (5.40), the velocity is in the clockwise direction.

     The curl of the velocity vector for the potential vortex can be found using the definition for the curl of $\vec{V}$ in cylindrical coordinates:

$$\nabla \times \vec{V} = \frac{1}{r}\begin{vmatrix} \hat{e}_r & r\hat{e}_\theta & \hat{e}_z \\ \dfrac{\partial}{\partial r} & \dfrac{\partial}{\partial\theta} & \dfrac{\partial}{\partial z} \\ v_r & rv_\theta & v_z \end{vmatrix}$$

We find that

$$\nabla \times \vec{V} = 0$$

Thus, the flow is irrotational. We must remember, however, that the velocity is infinite at the origin (i.e., when $r = 0$).

     Two-dimensional vortex lines (or filaments) have an important role in the study of the flow around wings. Therefore, let us summarize the vortex theorems of Helmholtz.

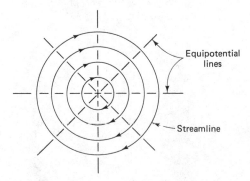

Equipotential lines

Streamline

Figure 5.14 Equipotential lines and streamlines for a potential vortex. (From Bertin and Smith, *Aerodynamics for Engineers*, p. 51.)

If there exists a potential for all forces acting on an inviscid fluid, the following statements are true:

1. The circulation around a given vortex line (i.e., the strength of the vortex filament) is constant along its length.

2. A vortex filament cannot end in a fluid. It must form a closed path, end at a boundary, or go to infinity. Examples of these three kinds of behavior are a smoke ring, a vortex bound to a two-dimensional airfoil that spans from one wall to the other in a wind tunnel, and the downstream ends of the horseshoe vortices representing the loading on a three-dimensional wing.

3. No fluid particle can have rotation, if it did not originally rotate. Or, equivalently, in the absence of rotational external forces, a fluid that is initially irrotational remains irrotational. Vortices can be generated by viscous forces. Furthermore, vortices are preserved as time passes. Only through the action of viscosity (or some other dissipative mechanism) can they decay or disappear.

The reader may be familiar with the rotation of a two-dimensional, solid body about its axis, such as the rotation of a record on a turntable. For solid-body rotation,

$$v_r = 0 \tag{5.42a}$$

$$v_\theta = r\omega \tag{5.42b}$$

where ω is the angular velocity. Substituting these velocity components into the definition

$$\nabla \times \vec{V} = \frac{1}{r}\left[\frac{\partial(rv_\theta)}{\partial r} - \frac{\partial v_r}{\partial \theta}\right]\hat{e}_z \tag{5.43}$$

we find that

$$\nabla \times \vec{V} = 2\omega\hat{e}_z \tag{5.44}$$

Thus, the vorticity, which is defined as the curl of the velocity, is equal to twice the angular velocity. We see that the velocity field that describes two-dimensional solid-body rotation is not irrotational and, therefore, cannot be defined using a potential function.

Example 5.10

A clockwise, two-dimensional, potential vortex is located near an infinite plane at a distance h above the plane. This may be viewed as the wing-tip vortex from the left wing of an airplane that is about to land. There is a cross wind such that the static pressure and the velocity at points very far from the vortex are p_∞ and U_∞, respectively. As shown in Fig. 5.15, the strength of the vortex is Γ. If the fluid is incompressible and inviscid, find the pressure distribution on the planar surface.

Solution. For the two-dimensional, potential vortex (PVl), which is located a distance h above the plane,

$$\phi_{\text{PVl}} = -\frac{\Gamma\theta_1}{2\pi} = -\frac{\Gamma}{2\pi}\tan^{-1}\left(\frac{y}{x}\right)$$

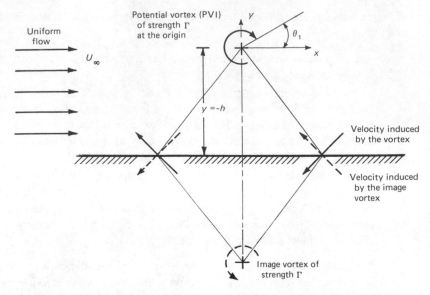

Figure 5.15   Vortex and uniform flow in the presence of a plane (Example 5.10).

where the x, y coordinate system is located at the origin of the vortex, as shown in the sketch. The velocities induced by this vortex at two representative points on the plane are represented by solid arrows in Fig. 5.15. Thus, we can see that the plane will not be a streamline if the only elements are the uniform flow and the one potential vortex, PVl. But the ground plane must be a streamline of the flow field. Therefore, we need to add an *image* vortex of equal strength, located a distance h below the plane. This image vortex induces velocities represented by the broken arrows. Note that the normal component of velocity induced at a point on the plane by the original vortex (PVl) is canceled by that induced by the image vortex. Thus, we satisfy the boundary condition that the resultant velocity be parallel to the plate. By including the image vortex, we model the fact that the flow field for a vortex near a wall is different than that for an isolated vortex.

To calculate the resultant velocity, let us first calculate the u component of velocity induced by PVl:

$$u = \frac{\partial \phi_{PVl}}{\partial x} = \frac{\partial}{\partial x} \left[-\frac{\Gamma}{2\pi} \tan^{-1} \left(\frac{y}{x} \right) \right]$$

$$= +\frac{\Gamma}{2\pi} \frac{y}{(x^2 + y^2)}$$

The velocity induced by the original vortex and its image is twice this value. (Since the image vortex serves to cancel the y component of velocity v induced by PVl, we do not need to calculate it.) Furthermore, note that $y = -h$ for the plane. Thus, adding the free-stream velocity to the vortex-induced velocity, we find that the net velocity at the surface of the plate is

$$U = U_\infty - \frac{\Gamma h}{\pi(x^2 + h^2)}$$

TABLE 5.1   STREAM FUNCTIONS AND POTENTIAL
FUNCTIONS FOR ELEMENTARY FLOWS

Flow	ψ	ϕ
Uniform flow	$U_\infty r \sin \theta$	$U_\infty r \cos \theta$
Source	$\dfrac{K\theta}{2\pi}$	$\dfrac{K}{2\pi} \ln r$
Doublet	$-\dfrac{B}{r} \sin \theta$	$\dfrac{B}{r} \cos \theta$
Vortex (with clockwise circulation)	$\dfrac{\Gamma}{2\pi} \ln r$	$-\dfrac{\Gamma\theta}{2\pi}$
90 ° corner flow	Axy	$\frac{1}{2} A(x^2 - y^2)$
Solid-body rotation	$\frac{1}{2} \omega r^2$	Does not exist

The pressure on the surface is given by Bernoulli's equation:

$$p = p_\infty + \tfrac{1}{2} \rho_\infty U_\infty^2 - \tfrac{1}{2} \rho_\infty U^2$$

Thus,

$$p = p_\infty - \tfrac{1}{2} \rho_\infty \left[\frac{\Gamma^2 h^2}{\pi^2 (x^2 + h^2)^2} - \frac{2 U_\infty \Gamma h}{\pi (x^2 + h^2)} \right]$$

Table 5.1 summarizes the potential functions and the stream functions for the elementary flows discussed in this section.

CIRCULATION

Circulation is defined as the line integral of the velocity around any closed curve. Referring to the closed curve C of Fig. 5.16, the circulation is given by

$$C = \oint_C \vec{V} \cdot \vec{dr} \tag{5.45}$$

where $\vec{V} \cdot \vec{dr}$ is the scalar product of the velocity vector and the differential vector length along the path of integration. As indicated by the circle through the integral sign, the integration is carried out for the complete closed path. The path of the integration is such that the area enclosed by the curve C is always on the left (i.e., counterclockwise for Fig. 5.16).

Consider the circulation around a small, square element in the x, y plane as shown in Fig. 5.17a. Integrating the velocity components along each of the sides and proceeding counterclockwise (i.e, keeping the area on the left of the path),

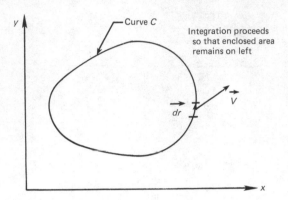

Figure 5.16   The concept of circulation.

$$\Delta C = u\,\Delta x + (v + \frac{\partial v}{\partial x}\,\Delta x)\Delta y - (u + \frac{\partial u}{\partial y}\,\Delta y)\Delta x - v\,\Delta y$$

Simplifying,

$$\Delta C = \left(\frac{\partial v}{\partial x} - \frac{\partial u}{\partial y}\right)\Delta x\,\Delta y$$

This procedure can be extended to calculate the circulation around a general curve C in the x, y plane, such as that of Fig. 5.17b. The result for this general curve in the x, y plane is

$$C = \oint_C \left(u\,dx + v\,dy\right) = \iint_A \left(\frac{\partial v}{\partial x} - \frac{\partial u}{\partial y}\right)dx\,dy \qquad (5.46)$$

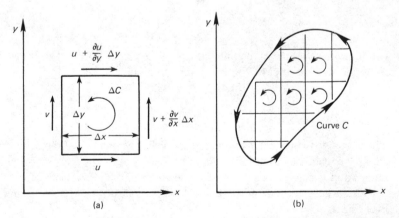

Figure 5.17   Circulation for elementary closed curves: (a) rectangular element; (b) general curve C.

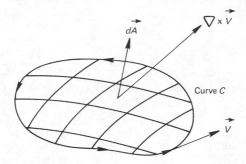

Figure 5.18 Nomenclature for Stokes's theorem.

Equation (5.46) represents Green's lemma for the transformation from a line integral to a surface integral in two-dimensional space. The transformation from a line integral to a surface integral in three-dimensional space is governed by Stokes's theorem:

$$\oint_C \vec{V} \cdot \vec{dr} = \iint_A (\nabla \times \vec{V}) \cdot \vec{dA} \tag{5.47}$$

where $\vec{dA}$ is a vector normal to the surface, positive when pointing outward from the enclosed volume, and equal in magnitude to the surface area (see Fig. 5.18). Note that Eq. (5.46) is a planar simplification of the more general equation, Eq. (5.47). In words, the integral of the normal component of the curl of the velocity vector over any surface A is equal to the line integral of the tangential component of the velocity around the curve C that bounds A. Stokes's theorem is valid when A represents a simply connected region in which $\vec{V}$ is continuously differentiable. Thus, Eq. (5.47) is not valid if the area A contains regions where the velocity is infinite.

RELATION OF CIRCULATION TO IRROTATIONAL FLOW

By means of Stokes's theorem, it is apparent that, if the curl of $\vec{V}$ (i.e., $\nabla \times \vec{V}$) is zero at all points in the region bounded by C, then the line integral of $\vec{V} \cdot \vec{dr}$ around the closed path is zero. When

$$\nabla \times \vec{V} \equiv 0 \tag{5.48}$$

and the flow contains no singularities, the flow is said to be irrotational. Stokes's theorem leads us to the conclusion that

$$\oint \vec{V} \cdot \vec{dr} = C = 0$$

For this irrotational velocity field, the line integral

$$\int \vec{V} \cdot \vec{dr}$$

is independent of path. A necessary and sufficient condition that

$$\int \vec{V} \cdot \vec{dr}$$

be independent of path is that the curl of $\vec{V}$ be everywhere zero. Thus, its value depends only on its limits. However, a line integral can be independent of the path of integration only if the integrand is an exact differential. Therefore,

$$\vec{V} \cdot \vec{dr} = d\phi \qquad (5.49)$$

where $d\phi$ is an exact differential. Expanding Eq. (5.49) in Cartesian coordinates,

$$u \, dx + v \, dy + w \, dz = \frac{\partial \phi}{\partial x} \, dx + \frac{\partial \phi}{\partial y} \, dy + \frac{\partial \phi}{\partial z} \, dz$$

it is apparent that

$$\vec{V} = \nabla \phi \qquad (5.50)$$

Note that Eq. (5.50) is the same as Eq. (5.24). We have used a second approach to show again that the velocity field for an irrotational flow can be represented by a velocity potential.

We have used both the differential and the integral forms of the continuity equation to study the flow field when a uniform free stream encounters a flat plate. As has been discussed, the no-slip condition creates a viscous boundary layer that grows in the stream-wise direction. Let us apply the definition of circulation and Stokes's theorem to study this flow field. As shown in Fig. 5.19, we will divide the flow field into two regions: (1) the inviscid flow upstream of the plate and (2) the rectangular area containing the viscous boundary layer on the plate.

Example 5.11

For the inviscid flow upsteam of the plate, demonstrate the validity of Stokes' theorem. Use the rectangular area designated region I in Fig. 5.19.

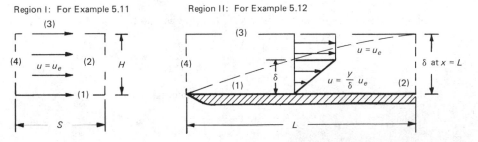

Figure 5.19   Flow past a flat plate (assuming a linear velocity profile in the boundary layer) (for Examples 5.11 and 5.12).

Solution.   Upstream of the plate

$$u = U_e \quad \text{and} \quad v = 0$$

To evaluate $\oint \vec{V} \cdot \vec{dr}$, let us note that $\vec{dr} = dx\,\hat{i} + dy\,\hat{j}$

Thus,

$$\oint \vec{V} \cdot \vec{dr} = \underbrace{\int_0^S (u_e\hat{i}) \cdot (dx\,\hat{i})}_{1} + \underbrace{\int_0^H (u_e\hat{i}) \cdot (dy\,\hat{j})}_{2}$$

$$+ \underbrace{\int_S^0 (u_e\hat{i}) \cdot (dx\,\hat{i})}_{3} + \underbrace{\int_H^0 (u_e\hat{i}) \cdot (dy\,\hat{j})}_{3}$$

Note that, because the velocity is perpendicular to $\vec{dr}$ along segments 2 and 4, these integrals are zero. The integrals for segments 1 and 2 are equal in magnitude but opposite in sign. Thus,

$$\oint \vec{V} \cdot \vec{dr} = 0$$

Note that, since $\vec{V} = u_e\hat{i}$, $\nabla \times \vec{V} = 0$ everywhere. Thus,

$$\iint (\nabla \times \vec{V}) \cdot \vec{dA} = 0$$

and we have demonstrated the validity of Stokes's theorem.

Example 5.12

Demonstrate the validity of Stokes's theorem for region II of Fig. 5.19.

Solution.   Recall that for our approximate flow model

$$\vec{V} = u_e\hat{i} \qquad \text{outside the boundary layer}$$

and

$$\vec{V} = \frac{u_e y}{1.25 \times 10^{-2}\,x^{0.5}}\,\hat{i} + \frac{u_e y^2}{5.00 \times 10^{-2}\,x^{1.5}}\,\hat{j}$$

for the viscous region, as was obtained in Example 3.2. Recall that the constant in the denominator has the units of (length)$^{0.5}$ so that each term does indeed have the units of velocity. The circulation around the perimeter of the rectangle designated region II is

$$\oint \vec{V} \cdot \vec{dr} = \underbrace{\int_0^L [0]\,dx}_{1} + \underbrace{\int_0^\delta \frac{u_e y^2}{5.00 \times 10^{-2}\,x^{1.5}}dy}_{2}$$

$$+ \underbrace{\int_L^0 u_e\,dx}_{3} + \underbrace{\int_\delta^0 [0]\,dy}_{4}$$

$$= \frac{u_e y^3}{15.00 \times 10^{-2}\,x^{1.5}}\bigg|_0^{\delta\,=\,1.25\,\times\,10^{-2}\,x^{0.5}} - u_e L$$

$$= 1.302 \times 10^{-5}\,u_e - u_e L$$

Note that the constant 1.302×10^{-5} has the units of (length) so that the two terms are dimensionally correct.

To calculate the curl of the velocity,

$$\nabla \times \vec{V} = \begin{vmatrix} \hat{i} & \hat{j} & \hat{k} \\ \dfrac{\partial}{\partial x} & \dfrac{\partial}{\partial y} & \dfrac{\partial}{\partial z} \\ u & v & w \end{vmatrix} = \hat{k} \left(\frac{\partial v}{\partial x} - \frac{\partial u}{\partial y} \right)$$

$$= \left[\frac{-3u_e y^2}{10.00 \times 10^{-2} \, x^{2.5}} - \frac{u_e}{1.25 \times 10^{-2} \, x^{0.5}} \right] \hat{k}$$

which is valid inside the boundary layer. Outside the boundary layer, $\nabla \times \vec{V} = 0$. However, this model is not rigorous since we know (by continuity) that v cannot be zero at the edge of the boundary layer. (Refer to the discussions of this flow in Chapter 3.)

$$\iint (\nabla \times \vec{V}) \cdot d\vec{A} = \int_0^L \int_0^{\delta \, = \, 1.25 \, \times \, 10^{-2} \, x^{0.5}} \left[-\frac{3u_e y^2}{10.00 \times 10^{-2} \, x^{2.5}} - \frac{u_e}{1.25 \times 10^{-2} \, x^{0.5}} \right] dx \, dy$$

$$= \int_0^L \left[-\frac{u_e y^3}{10.00 \times 10^{-2} \, x^{2.5}} - \frac{u_e y}{1.25 \times 10^{-2} \, x^{0.5}} \right]\Biggr|_0^{1.25 \, \times \, 10^{-2} \, x^{0.5}} dx$$

$$= \int_0^L \left[-\frac{1.953 \times 10^{-6} \, u_e}{10.00 \times 10^{-2} \, x} - u_e \right] dx$$

Since the coefficient of the first term is on the order of $0.1\delta^2$, we shall neglect it. However, in a rigorous analysis we would need special care here, since $\delta \to 0$ as $x \to 0$, and this term is undefined at the leading edge. In comparing the results, we see that the first terms for both expressions are small. Thus,

$$\oint \vec{V} \cdot d\vec{r} \simeq -u_e L$$

and

$$\iint (\nabla \times \vec{V}) \cdot dA \simeq -u_e L$$

The differences in the exact values of these integrals are due to the approximate model for v. The reader should review the example to verify that the first term in each integral is related to v.

Note also that the flow was irrotational for region I in Example 5.11 but is rotational for region II in Example 5.12. Referring to Kelvin's theorem, it should be clear that viscosity is the dissipative mechanism that produces the rotational character of the flow in region II. Because viscous forces are negligible outside the boundary layer, the flow away from the plate's surface remains irrotational.

ADDING ELEMENTARY FLOWS TO DESCRIBE FLOW AROUND A CYLINDER WITH ITS AXIS PERPENDICULAR TO THE FREE STREAM

Velocity Field

Consider the flow field represented by the sum of three potential functions, that is, those for a uniform flow, for a doublet, and for a vortex with clockwise circulation. Since each function satisfies Laplace's equation, so does their sum. The resultant potential function is

$$\phi = U_\infty r \cos \theta + \frac{B}{r} \cos \theta - \frac{\Gamma \theta}{2\pi} \tag{5.51}$$

Thus,

$$v_r = \frac{\partial \phi}{\partial r} = U_\infty \cos \theta - \frac{B}{r^2} \cos \theta \tag{5.52a}$$

and

$$v_\theta = \frac{1}{r} \frac{\partial \phi}{\partial \theta} = -U_\infty \sin \theta - \frac{B}{r^2} \sin \theta - \frac{\Gamma}{2\pi r} \tag{5.52b}$$

By examining Eq. (5.52a), we see that $v_r = 0$ at every point where $r = \sqrt{B/U_\infty}$, which is a constant and which we will designate as R. Note that the locus of points for which r is a constant is a circle (of radius R). Furthermore, since $v_r = 0$ for $r = R$, we know that the component of velocity normal to this circle is zero. Since the velocity normal to a streamline is zero (i.e., there is no flow across a streamline), these two statements mean that the circle may be considered a streamline of the flow field. Thus, the resultant potential function represents a two-dimensional, irrotational, incompressible flow around a cylinder of radius R whose axis is perpendicular to the free-stream direction.

Replacing B by $R^2 U_\infty$ allows us to rewrite the velocity components as

$$v_r = U_\infty \cos \theta \left(1 - \frac{R^2}{r^2} \right) \tag{5.53a}$$

$$v_\theta = -U_\infty \sin \theta \left(1 + \frac{R^2}{r^2} \right) - \frac{\Gamma}{2\pi r} \tag{5.53b}$$

The velocity field not only satisfies the surface boundary condition that the inviscid flow is tangent to a solid wall, but the velocity at points far from the cylinder is equal to the undisturbed free-stream velocity U_∞. Streamlines for the resultant inviscid flow field are illustrated in the sketches of Fig. 5.20. The streamline patterns are a function of the strength of the circulation (Γ). Note that Probs. 3.6 and 4.6 relate to this flow.

The velocity at the surface of the cylinder is equal to

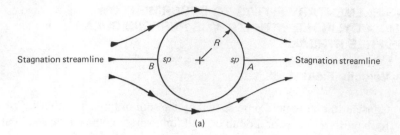

(a)

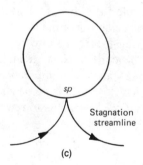

(b)

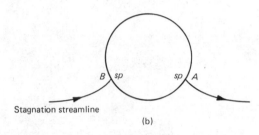

(c)

Figure 5.20 Two-dimensional flow around a cylinder (with and without circulation): (a) $\Gamma = 0$ (no circulation); (b) $\Gamma = 2\pi R U_\infty$; (c) $\Gamma = 4\pi R U_\infty$.

$$v_\theta = -2U_\infty \sin \theta - \frac{\Gamma}{2\pi R} \tag{5.54}$$

and, of course, as noted earlier, $v_r = 0$. Since the solution is for an inviscid model of the flow field, it is not inconsistent that the fluid adjacent to the surface moves relative to the surface (i.e., violates the no-slip condition that is required when one includes the effects of viscosity).

Pressure Distribution

Because the velocity at the surface of the cylinder is a function of θ, the local static pressure will also be a function of θ. Once the pressure distribution has been defined, it can be used to determine the forces and moments acting on the configuration. Using Bernoulli's equation Eq. (5.19), for a gas flow where the changes in potential energy can be neglected, one obtains the expression for the dimensional, local-static pressure distribution:

$$p = p_\infty + \tfrac{1}{2}\rho_\infty U_\infty^2 - \tfrac{1}{2}\rho_\infty\left[-\left(2U_\infty \sin\theta + \frac{\Gamma}{2\pi R}\right)\right]^2 \tag{5.55}$$

Expressing the pressure in terms of the dimensionless pressure coefficient,

$$C_p = 1 - \left[4\sin^2\theta + \frac{2\Gamma \sin\theta}{\pi R U_\infty} + \left(\frac{\Gamma}{2\pi R U_\infty}\right)^2\right] \tag{5.56}$$

The locations of the stagnation points also depend on the circulation. To locate the stagnation points, we need to find where

$$v_r = v_\theta = 0$$

Since $v_r = 0$ at every point on the cylinder, the stagnation points occur when $v_\theta = 0$. Therefore,

$$-2U_\infty \sin\theta - \frac{\Gamma}{2\pi R} = 0$$

or

$$\theta = \sin^{-1}\left(-\frac{\Gamma}{4\pi R U_\infty}\right) \tag{5.57}$$

If $\Gamma < 4\pi R U_\infty$, there are two stagnation points on the surface of the cylinder. They are symmetrically located about the y axis and both are on or below the x axis (see Fig. 5.20). If $\Gamma = 0$ (i.e., there is no circulation), the stagnation points are located at $\theta = 0$ and $\theta = \pi$ (points A and B of Fig. 5.20a). For no circulation, the flow around the cylinder is symmetric. If $\Gamma = 4\pi U_\infty R$, only one stagnation point exists on the cylinder and it exists at $\theta = 270°$, as shown in Fig. 5.20c.

Flow Field for $\Gamma = 0$

If there is no circulation, the pressure coefficient becomes

$$C_p = 1 - 4\sin^2\theta \tag{5.58}$$

The pressure coefficients calculated using this equation are presented in Fig. 5.21 as a function of θ. Recall that, in the nomenclature of this chapter, $\theta = 180°$ corresponds to

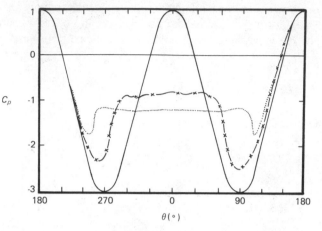

—— Theoretical distribution for inviscid flow, Eq. (5.58)

·········· Experimental distribution for subcritical Reynolds number,
      Re_d = 1.0 x 10^5

x——x Experimental distribution for supercritical Reynolds number,
      Re_d = 3.6 x 10^6

C_p

Figure 5.21   Theoretical pressure distribution around a circular cylinder, compared with data for a subcritical Reynolds number and that for a supercritical Reynolds number. (Data from E. Achenbach, *Journal of Fluid Mechanics*, vol. 34, pt. 4, 1968, 625–639. Reprinted by permission of Cambridge University Press.)

the plane of symmetry for the windward surface or forebody (i.e., that facing the free stream). Starting with the undisturbed free-stream flow and following the streamline that wets the surface, the flow decelerates from the free-stream velocity to zero velocity at the (windward) stagnation point in the plane of symmetry. The flow then accelerates, reaching a maximum velocity equal in magnitude to twice the free-stream velocity. From these maxima (which occur at θ = 90° and 270°), the flow tangent to the leeward surface decelerates to a stagnation point at the surface in the leeward plane of symmetry (at θ = 0°). As the flow decelerates, the pressure increases in the streamwise direction (as required by Euler's equation). The streamwise increase in pressure is known as an *adverse pressure gradient*.

However, even though the viscosity of air is relatively small, the actual flow field is radically different from the inviscid solution described in the previous paragraphs. When the air particles in the boundary layer, which have already been slowed by the action of viscosity, encounter the relatively large adverse pressure gradient associated with the deceleration of the leeward flow for this blunt configuration, boundary-layer separation occurs. The photograph of the smoke patterns for flow around a cylinder presented in Fig. 5.22 clearly illustrates the flow separation. Note that separation results when the fluid particles in the boundary layer (already slowed by viscosity) encounter an adverse pressure gradient that they cannot overcome. Not all boundary layers separate when they encounter an adverse pressure gradient. There is a relation between the characteristics of the boundary layer and the magnitude of the adverse pressure gradient required to produce separation. Thus, a turbulent boundary layer, which has relatively fast moving particles near the wall, would remain attached longer than a laminar boundary layer, which has slower-moving particles near the wall for the same value of the edge velocity. (Boundary layers are discussed in more detail in Chapter 7.) Therefore, the

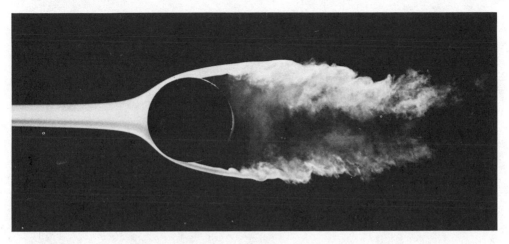

Figure 5.22 Smoke visualization of flow pattern for subcritical flow around a cylinder. (Photograph by F. N. M. Brown, courtesy of T. J. Mueller of University of Notre Dame.)

separation location, the size of the wake, and the surface pressure in the wake region depend on the character of the forebody boundary layer.

The experimentally determined separation locations for a circular cylinder as reported by Achenbach in Ref. 5.2 are presented as a function of Reynolds number in Fig. 5.23. As was discussed in Chapter 4, the Reynolds number is a dimensionless parameter (in this case, $Re_d = \rho_\infty U_\infty d / \mu_\infty$) that relates to the viscous characteristics of the flow. At subcritical Reynolds numbers (i.e., less than approximately 3×10^5), the boundary layer on the windward surface (or forebody) is laminar and separation occurs for $\theta \sim 100°$, that is, 80° from the windward stagnation point. Note the occurrence of separation so alters the flow that separation actually occurs on the windward surface where the inviscid solution, as given by Eq. (5.58) and presented in Fig. 5.21, indicates that there still should be a favorable pressure gradient (i.e., one for which the static pressure decreases in the streamwise direction). Above the critical Reynolds number, the forebody boundary layer is turbulent. Due to the higher levels of energy for the fluid particles near the surface in a turbulent boundary layer, the flow is able to run longer against the pressure gradient. In the critical region, Achenbach observed an intermediate "separation bubble" with final separation not occurring until $\theta = 40°$ (i.e., 140° from the stagnation point). For $Re_d > 1.5 \times 10^6$, the separation bubble no longer occurs, indicating that the supercritical state of flow has been reached. For supercritical Reynolds numbers, separation occurs in the range $70° < \theta < 60°$. (The reader should note that the critical Reynolds number is sensitive both to the turbulence level in the free stream and to surface roughness.)

Experimental pressure distributions are presented in Fig. 5.21 for the cases where the forebody boundary layer is laminar (a subcritical Reynolds number) and where the forebody boundary layer is turbulent (a supercritical Reynolds number). The subcritical pressure-coefficient distribution is essentially unchanged over a wide range of Reynolds

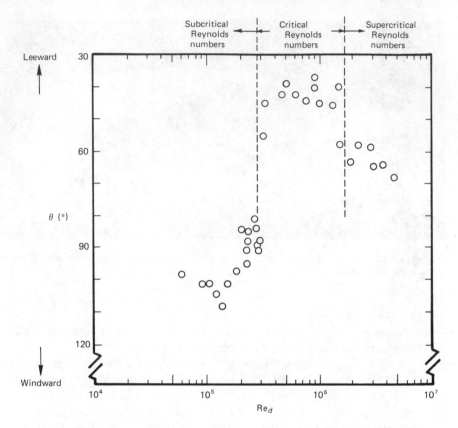

Figure 5.23 Location of the separation points on a circular cylinder as a function of the Reynolds number. (Data from Achenbach, *Journal of Fluid Mechanics*.)

numbers below the critical Reynolds number. Similarly, the supercritical pressure-coefficient distribution is independent of Reynolds number over a wide range of Reynolds numbers above the critical Reynolds number. For the flow upstream of the separation location, the boundary layer is thin, and the pressure-coefficient distribution is essentially independent of the character of the boundary layer for the cylinder. However, because the character of the attached boundary layer affects the separation location, it affects the pressure in the separated region. If the attached boundary layer is turbulent, separation is delayed and the pressure in the separated region is higher and closer to the inviscid level.

Lift and Drag for $\Gamma = 0$

The motion of the air particles around the cylinder produces forces that may be viewed as a normal (or pressure) component and a tangential (or shear) component. It is conventional to resolve the resultant force on the cylinder into a component perpendicular to the free-stream velocity direction (called the *lift*) and a component parallel to the free-stream velocity direction (called the *drag*). The nomenclature is illustrated in Fig. 5.24.

Lift per Unit Span. Since the expressions for the velocity distribution and pressure distribution were obtained for an inviscid flow, we shall consider only the contribution of the pressure to the lift and drag. As shown in Fig. 5.24, the lift per unit span of the cylinder is

$$l = -\int_0^{2\pi} p \sin\theta\, R\, d\theta \tag{5.59}$$

Referring to Eq. (5.55), the static pressure is given by

$$p = p_\infty + \tfrac{1}{2}\rho_\infty U_\infty^2 - 2\rho_\infty U_\infty^2 \sin^2\theta \tag{5.60}$$

Substituting Eq. (5.60) into Eq. (5.59), we find that the lift per unit span is

$$l = 0 \tag{5.61}$$

It is not surprising that there is zero lift per unit span of the cylinder, since the pressure distribution is symmetric about the x axis.

Instead of using Eq. (5.60), which is the expression for the static pressure, an aerodynamicist might be more likely to use Eq. (5.58), which is the expression for the dimensionless pressure coefficient. To do this, note that the net force in any direction due to a constant pressure acting on a closed surface is zero. As a result,

$$\int_0^{2\pi} p_\infty \sin\theta\, R\, d\theta = 0 \tag{5.62}$$

Adding Eqs. (5.59) and (5.62) yields

$$l = -\int_0^{2\pi} (p - p_\infty) \sin\theta\, R\, d\theta$$

Dividing both sides of this equation by the product $q_\infty 2R$, which is (the dynamic pressure) (area per unit span in the x plane), yields

$$\frac{l}{q_\infty 2R} = -\tfrac{1}{2}\int_0^{2\pi} C_p \sin\theta\, d\theta \tag{5.63}$$

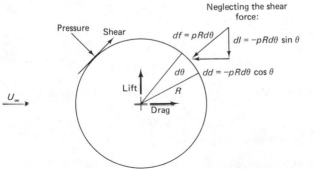

Figure 5.24 Forces acting on a cylinder whose axis is perpendicular to the free-stream flow. (From Bertin and Smith, *Aerodynamics for Engineers*, p. 58.)

Both sides of Eq. (5.63) are dimensionless. The expression of the left-hand side is known as the *section lift coefficient* for a cylinder:

$$C_l = \frac{l}{q_\infty 2R} \tag{5.64}$$

Using Eq. (5.58) to define C_p as a function of θ,

$$C_l = -\tfrac{1}{2} \int_0^{2\pi} (1 - 4 \sin^2 \theta) \sin \theta \, d\theta = 0$$

which, of course, is the same result as was obtained by integrating the pressure directly.

   Note: In this text a lowercase letter will be used to designate a section force (or section force coefficient), that is, the force per unit span, such as l in Eq. (5.59) or C_l in Eq. (5.64). Uppercase letters will be used to designate the force for a complete configuration, such as C_D in Eq. (5.79).

Example 5.13

   An infinitely long cylinder is used to "plug" a slot in a flat plate, as shown in Fig. 5.25. Consider the flow of the air to be steady, incompressible, and inviscid. The free-stream atmospheric conditions are

$$p_\infty = 1.01325 \times 10^5 \text{ N/m}^2$$

$$\rho_\infty = 1.2250 \text{ kg/m}^3$$

The cylinder is 7.5 cm in diameter and is made of a material whose density (ρ_c) is 98.00 kg/m³. What is the minimum velocity of the undisturbed free stream that will lift the cylinder off the plate (neglecting any effects of friction between the plug and the plate)?

Solution.   The cylindrical plug will lift off the plate when $l > w$, that is, when the lift per unit span exceeds the weight per unit span. Thus, let us first calculate the lift force per unit span acting on the cylinder. From Eq. (5.59),

$$l = -\int_0^{2\pi} pR \, d\theta \sin \theta$$

Since the net force due to a uniform (or constant) pressure acting over a closed surface is zero, we can add $\int_0^{2\pi} p_\infty R \sin \theta \, d\theta$ to this expression:

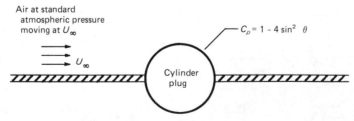

Air at standard
atmospheric pressure
moving at U_∞

$C_p = 1 - 4 \sin^2 \theta$

U_∞

Cylinder
plug

Air at rest at standard atmospheric pressure

Figure 5.25   Flow for Example 5.13.

$$l = - \int_0^{2\pi} (p - p_\infty) R \sin \theta \, d\theta$$

Using the definition for the pressure coefficient,

$$l = - q_\infty R \int_0^{2\pi} C_p \sin \theta \, d\theta$$

For the interval $0 \leqslant \theta \leqslant \pi$, $C_p = 1 - 4 \sin^2 \theta$, while for the interval $\pi < \theta < 2\pi$, $C_p = 0$. Thus, the lift force per unit span is

$$l = - q_\infty R \int_0^\pi (1 - 4 \sin^2 \theta) \sin \theta \, d\theta$$

$$= - q_\infty R \, [-\cos \theta \, |_0^\pi] + q_\infty R 4 [-\cos \theta + \frac{1}{3} \cos^3 \theta \, |_0^\pi]$$

$$= - 2q_\infty R + 8q_\infty R - \frac{8}{3} q_\infty R = 10 q_\infty R / 3$$

The weight per unit span of the cylinder is

$$w = \rho_c g A_c$$

Equating the two expressions,

$$\frac{10}{3} \frac{1}{2} (1.225 \text{ kg/m}^3) (U_\infty^2)(0.0375 \text{ m}) = (98.00 \text{ kg/m}^3) (9.8066 \text{ m/s}^2) \left[\frac{\pi}{4} (0.075)^2 \text{ m}^2 \right]$$

Solving for U_∞,

$$U_\infty = 7.447 \text{ m/s}$$

Drag per Unit Span.   Referring to Fig. 5.24, we can calculate the drag per unit span of the cylinder for the inviscid flow. The drag per unit span is

$$d = - \int_0^{2\pi} p \cos \theta \, R \, d\theta \tag{5.65}$$

Substituting Eq. (5.60) for the local pressure,

$$d = - \int_0^{2\pi} (p_\infty + \frac{1}{2} \rho_\infty U_\infty^2 - 2\rho_\infty U_\infty^2 \sin^2 \theta) \cos \theta \, R \, d\theta$$

we find that

$$d = 0 \tag{5.66}$$

A drag of zero is an obvious contradiction to the reader's experience (and is known as *d'Alembert's paradox*). Note that the actual pressure in the separated, wake region near the leeward plane of symmetry (in the vicinity of $\theta = 0$ in Fig. 5.21) is much less than the theoretical value. It is the resultant difference between the high pressures acting near the windward plane of symmetry (in the vicinity of $\theta = 180°$, i.e., the stagnation point) and the relatively low pressures acting near the leeward plane of symmetry that produces the large drag component.

A drag force that represents the streamwise component of the pressure force integrated over the entire configuration is termed *pressure* (or *form*) *drag*, C_{d_p}. The drag force that is obtained by integrating the streamwise component of the shear force over the vehicle is termed *skin friction drag*, C_{d_f}. Thus,

$$C_d = C_{d_p} + C_{d_f} \tag{5.67}$$

The data reported by Achenbach (Ref. 5.2) indicate that the friction drag was less than 3% of the total drag over the range of Reynolds numbers considered (see Fig. 5.23). Thus, in the case of real flow past a cylinder, the skin friction drag is small. However, significant form drag results because of the action of viscosity, which causes the boundary layer to separate and therefore radically alter the pressure field. The pressure near the leeward plane of symmetry is higher (and closer to the inviscid values) when the forebody boundary layer is turbulent. Thus, the difference between the pressure acting on the forward surface and that acting on the leeward surface is less in the turbulent case. As a result, the form drag for a turbulent boundary layer is markedly less than the corresponding value when the boundary layer on the forebody is laminar.

The drag coefficient per unit span for a cylinder is

$$C_d = \frac{d}{q_\infty 2R} \tag{5.68}$$

Experimental drag coefficients for a circular cylinder in a low-speed stream (Ref. 5.3) are presented as a function of Reynolds number in Fig. 5.26. For Reynolds numbers below 300,000, the drag coefficient is essentially constant (approximately 1.2), independent of Reynolds number. Recall that, when we were discussing the experimental values of C_p presented in Fig. 5.21, it was noted that the subcritical pressure distribution is essentially unchanged over a wide range of Reynolds numbers. Since both the drag coefficient and pressure coefficient are essentially independent of Reynolds number below the critical Reynolds number, we have further indication that the pressure (or form) drag is the dominant component for blunt bodies. Thus,

$$C_d \simeq -\frac{1}{2} \int_0^{2\pi} C_p \cos \theta \, d\theta$$

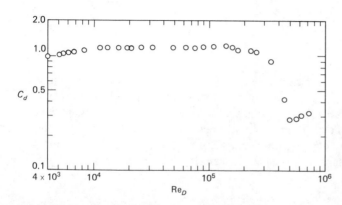

Figure 5.26 Drag coefficient for a circular cylinder as a function of the Reynolds number. (From *Boundary-Layer Theory* by H. Schlichting. Copyright © 1968 by McGraw-Hill Book Company. Used with the permission of McGraw-Hill Book Company.)

Above the critical Reynolds number (when the forebody boundary layer is turbulent), the drag coefficient is significantly lower. Reviewing the supercritical pressure distribution, we recall that the pressure in the separated region is closer to the inviscid level. In a situation where the Reynolds number would normally be subcritical, it may be desirable to induce boundary-layer transition by roughening the surface. An example of such transition-promoting roughness elements are the dimples on a golf ball or the vortex generators on aerodynamic surfaces. The dimples on a golf ball are intended to reduce drag; the vortex generators are designed to delay separation.

Example 5.14

Based on our knowledge of the blunt-body flow field, verify that dimpled golf balls are preferrable to smooth golf balls. The discussion should include an estimate of the Reynolds number.

Solution. For purposes of estimating the Reynolds number, note that a golf ball is approximately 4.32 cm in diameter. If we assume that the golf ball is moving at 61 m/s at sea level, the Reynolds number based on the diameter is

$$\text{Re}_d = \frac{\rho_\infty U_\infty d}{\mu_\infty} = \frac{(1.225 \text{ kg/m}^3) \ (61 \text{ m/s}) \ (0.0432 \text{ m})}{1.7894 \times 10^{-5} \text{ kg/s} \cdot \text{m}}$$

$$= 1.8 \times 10^5$$

Referring to the discussion of the drag on a round object, we see that this Reynolds number is below the critical value. Therefore, if the golf ball is smooth, the forebody boundary layer would be laminar and the form drag would be relatively large. Roughening the surface of the golf ball (such as with dimples) would cause the forebody boundary layer to be turbulent, resulting in a radically different separation pattern and reduced form drag. Since skin friction drag is small relative to the form drag for these blunt shapes, the increased skin friction for the dimpled golf ball that results because the boundary layer is turbulent would not be significant.

Flow Field for $\Gamma \neq 0$

If the expression for the pressure distribution for $\Gamma \neq 0$, Eq. (5.55), is substituted into the expression for the drag force per unit span of the cylinder,

$$d = -\int_0^{2\pi} p(\cos \theta)R \ d\theta = 0$$

The prediction of zero drag may be generalized to apply to any general, two-dimensional body in an irrotational, steady, incompressible flow. In any real two-dimensional flow, a drag force does exist and is due to viscous effects, which produce the shear force at the surface and which may also produce significant changes in the pressure field (causing form drag).

Integrating the pressure distribution to determine the lift force per unit span for the cylinder, one obtains

$$l = -\int_0^{2\pi} p(\sin \theta)R \ d\theta = \rho U_\infty \Gamma \qquad (5.69)$$

Thus, the lift per unit span is directly related to the circulation about the cylinder. This result, which is known as the *Kutta–Joukouski theorem*, applies to the potential flow about closed cylinders of arbitrary cross section.

INCOMPRESSIBLE, AXISYMMETRIC FLOW

The irrotational flows discussed thus far are two-dimensional. That is, the flow field that exists in the plane of the paper will exist in any and every plane parallel to the plane of the paper. Thus, although the sketches of the flow field defined by Eqs. (5.51) through (5.69) depict the flow around a circle of radius R, in reality they represent the flow around a cylinder whose axis is perpendicular to the plane of the paper. For these flows, $w \equiv 0$ and $\partial/\partial z \equiv 0$.

Let us now consider another type of "two-dimensional" flow: an axisymmetric flow. The coordinate system is illustrated in Fig. 5.27. There are no circumferential variations in an axisymmetric flow; that is,

$$v_\theta \equiv 0 \quad \text{and} \quad \frac{\partial}{\partial \theta} \equiv 0$$

Thus, the incompressible, continuity equation becomes

$$\frac{\partial v_r}{\partial r} + \frac{v_r}{r} + \frac{\partial v_z}{\partial z} = 0$$

Noting that r and z are the independent coordinates (i.e., variables), we can rewrite this expression as

$$\frac{\partial}{\partial r}(rv_r) + \frac{\partial}{\partial z}(rv_z) = 0 \tag{5.70}$$

As was discussed in Chapter 3, a stream function will exist for an incompressible, two-dimensional flow. The flow need be two-dimensional only in the sense that it requires

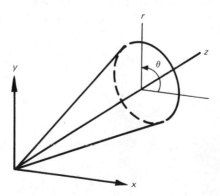

Figure 5.27 Coordinate system for an axisymmetric flow.

only two spatial coordinates to describe the motion. The stream function that identically satisfies Eq. (5.70) is

$$\frac{\partial \psi}{\partial z} = rv_r \quad \text{and} \quad \frac{\partial \psi}{\partial r} = -rv_z$$

Thus, in the coordinate system of Fig. 5.27,

$$v_r = \frac{1}{r} \frac{\partial \psi}{\partial z} \quad \text{and} \quad v_z = -\frac{1}{r} \frac{\partial \psi}{\partial r} \tag{5.71}$$

Flow Around a Sphere

To describe a steady, inviscid, incompressible flow around a sphere, we will add the axisymmetric potential functions for a uniform flow and for a doublet. We will first introduce the necessary relations in spherical coordinates. Referring to Prob. 3.11, we can see that

$$v_r = \frac{\partial \phi}{\partial r}, \qquad v_\omega = \frac{1}{r} \frac{\partial \phi}{\partial \omega}, \qquad v_\theta = \frac{1}{r \sin \omega} \frac{\partial \phi}{\partial \theta} \tag{5.72}$$

for an irrotational flow where $\vec{V} = \nabla \phi$. In Eq. (5.72), ϕ represents the potential function, and r, θ, and ω represent the independent coordinates. By symmetry,

$$v_\theta = 0 \quad \text{and} \quad \frac{\partial}{\partial \theta} = 0$$

The velocity potential for an axisymmetric doublet is

$$\phi = +\frac{B}{4\pi r^2} \cos \omega$$

where the doublet is so oriented that the source is placed upstream. The potential function for a uniform flow is

$$\phi = U_\infty r \cos \omega$$

Thus, the sum of the potential functions is

$$\phi = U_\infty r \cos \omega + \frac{B}{4\pi r^2} \cos \omega \tag{5.73}$$

The velocity components for this potential function are

$$v_r = \frac{\partial \phi}{\partial r} = U_\infty \cos \omega - \frac{B}{2\pi r^3} \cos \omega \tag{5.74a}$$

and

$$v_\omega = \frac{1}{r} \frac{\partial \phi}{\partial \omega} = -U_\infty \sin \omega - \frac{B}{4\pi r^3} \sin \omega \tag{5.74b}$$

As we did when modeling the inviscid flow around a cylinder, we note that

$$v_r = 0$$

when

$$r^3 = \frac{B}{2\pi U_\infty} = \text{constant} = R^3$$

Thus, if $B = 2\pi U_\infty R^3$, we can use the potential function described by Eq. (5.73) to describe steady, inviscid, incompressible flow around a sphere of radius R. For this flow,

$$v_r = U_\infty \left(1 - \frac{R^3}{r^3}\right) \cos \omega \qquad (5.75a)$$

and

$$v_\omega = -U_\infty \left(1 + \frac{R^3}{2r^3}\right) \sin \omega \qquad (5.75b)$$

On the surface of the sphere (i.e., for $r = R$), the resultant velocity is given by

$$U = |\vec{V}| = v_\omega = -\tfrac{3}{2}U_\infty \sin \omega \qquad (5.76)$$

The static pressure acting at any point on the sphere can be calculated using Eq. (5.76) to represent the local velocity in Bernoulli's equation:

$$p = p_\infty + \tfrac{1}{2}\rho_\infty U_\infty^2 - \tfrac{1}{2}\rho_\infty U_\infty^2 \left(\tfrac{9}{4}\sin^2 \omega\right) \qquad (5.77)$$

Rearranging the terms, we obtain the expression for the pressure coefficient for steady, inviscid, incompressible flow around a sphere:

$$C_p = 1 - \tfrac{9}{4}\sin^2 \omega \qquad (5.78)$$

Compare this expression with Eq. (5.58) for flow around a cylinder of infinite span whose axis is perpendicular to the free-stream flow:

$$C_p = 1 - 4\sin^2 \theta$$

Note that both θ and ω represent the angular coordinate relative to the axis, one for the two-dimensional flow, the other for axisymmetric flow. Thus, although the configurations have the same cross section in the plane of the paper (a circle) and both are described in terms of two coordinates, the flows are significantly different.

The drag coefficients for a sphere, as reported in Ref. 5.3, are presented as a function of the Reynolds number in Fig. 5.28. The drag coefficient for a sphere is defined as

$$C_D = \frac{\text{drag}}{q_\infty (\pi d^2/4)} \qquad (5.79)$$

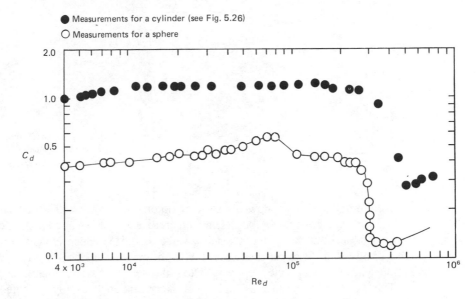

Figure 5.28   Drag coefficient for a sphere as a function of the Reynolds number. (From Schlichting, *Boundary-Layer Theory*.)

The Reynolds number dependence of the drag coefficient for a sphere is similar to that for a cylinder. Again, a significant reduction in drag occurs as the critical Reynolds number is exceeded and the windward boundary layer becomes turbulent.

AERODYNAMIC DRAG OF BLUFF BODY SHAPES CHARACTERISTIC OF HATCHBACK CARS

Based on the discussion of flow around cylinders and spheres, it should be evident that a substantial part of the drag force experienced by bluff bodies originates in the base area. This drag force component is a consequence of the relatively low pressure existing in the separated near wake, the level of which depends on the details of the body geometry and the fluid mechanics of the near wake. An investigation conducted by Morel (Ref. 5.4) explored the dependence of the near-wake flow on the geometry of the afterbody characteristics of hatchback automobiles.

The experimental investigation started with a study of a long axisymmetric cylinder aligned with the flow and placed in the free stream in the center of a test section of a 500 × 700 mm research wind tunnel. The downstream end of the cylinder was capped by interchangeable afterbodies that could be "sliced off." The inclination angle was varied from 20° slanted away from the horizontal to 90° slant (vertical base).

The drag coefficient data showed a very strong variation of C_D with the slant angle, as shown in Fig. 5.29. Going from the vertical base (β = 90°) toward smaller slant

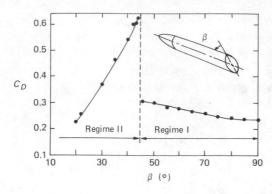

Figure 5.29 Drag coefficient for an axisymmetric cylinder with a slanted base. (From T. Morel, SAE Technical Paper 780267, 1978.)

angles, the drag coefficient showed a slow monotonic increase up to a "critical" angle $\beta = 42°$), where it increased abruptly. The increase was very large and the drag coefficient more than doubled at that point to reach a value of 0.625, which is unusually high for a slender body with a well-rounded nose. Below the critical angle, C_D had a much stronger variation with the slant angle, dropping below the vertical-base value around $\beta = 20°$.

The dramatic abrupt increase in drag at the critical angle clearly indicated a change in near-wake flow pattern. In recognition of this we denoted the two portions of the drag curve, above and below the critical angle, as regimes I and II, respectively. The base flow associated with regime I was found to be that associated with a flow separation pattern that in time-mean was quasi-axisymmetric, that is, one where the external flow passes over a closed recirculation region adjacent to the base in much the same manner as for purely axisymmetric bluff-based bodies, as shown in Fig. 5.30a. In regime II, the separation pattern was found to have been strongly three dimensional, with a strong edge vortex forming along each of the side edges, as the side flow tended to roll up over the side edges onto the slanted surface, as shown in Fig. 5.30b. This type of separation is well known to occur on delta wings placed at an angle of attack. Rolled-up vortices

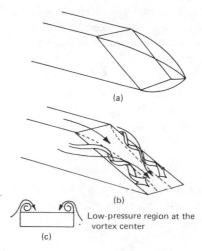

Figure 5.30 Two types of separated flow patterns on a separated afterbody: (a) quasi-axisymmetric separation pattern; (b) 3-d separation pattern; (c) cross-sectional view of the base flow for case (b). (From Morel, SAE Technical Paper 780267.)

always have a low pressure in their core, which can influence nearby surfaces, in this case those portions of the slanted surface that lie close to the side edges, as shown in Fig. 5.30c. The resulting strong suction force is thought responsible for the very high drag levels observed in regime II.

The flow behavior in regime II may be best explained by following its evolution with increasing slant angle. If one inclines the roof by a small angle β from the horizontal, an edge vortex is formed along each side edge. If the roof break is sharp, the top flow will separate from the roof at the break, only to reattach a short distance downstream and follow the slanted surface. As the angle β increases further, the two edge vortices grow stronger and supply air from the body sides onto the slanted surface and relieve the downstream pressure rise caused by the inward slope of the surface. This permits the top flow to reattach on the slanted surface and then stay attached up to relatively large slant angles. Eventually, however, the side inflow proves to be insufficient and the top flow cannot reattach. This happens at the critical angle above which the flow is fully separated, with only very weak vortices being formed along the side edges (i.e., regime I).

Drag coefficients for a vehiclelike body in the free-stream location indicate trends very similar to those found for the cylinder. These data are reproduced in Fig. 5.31. The trends in the drag data are very similar to those found for the cylinder. In regime I the drag coefficient was relatively constant, showing only a small variation over the whole range. In regime II the drag dropped initially, reaching a minimum at 9°, which was about 0.03 below the zero-slant value. This decrease is apparently a type of boat-tail effect, which is overpowered beyond $\beta = 9°$ by the growing strength of the edge vortices. The maximum drag occurred at $\beta = 30°$, where $C_D = 0.41$, and this was followed by a sharp drop to 0.25 at higher β. Lift data, which are presented in Fig. 5.32, had an even more pronounced variation with the slant angle. The lift coefficient was positive at all nonzero slant angles, as could be expected, because the base slant exposes an upward projection of the low-pressure base surface. On the other hand, the large magnitude of the lift coefficient is unusual.

The investigation by Morel (Ref. 5.4) included a study of the effects of four different factors relevant to road vehicles, free-stream turbulence, Reynolds numbers, ground

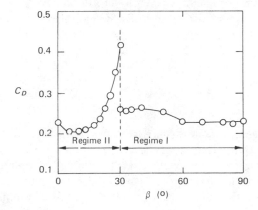

Figure 5.31 Drag coefficient of the vehiclelike body in the free-stream location. (From Morel, SAE Technical Paper 780267.)

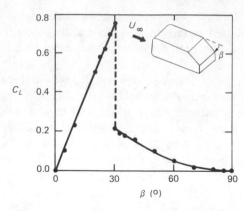

Figure 5.32 Lift coefficient of the vehiclelike body in the free-stream location. (From Morel, SAE Technical Paper 780267.)

proximity, and rounding of the upper edge, on the critical drag characteristics of two bluff bodies with slanted rear surfaces. Of these four factors the first three had only a small effect on the value of the critical slant angle and on the overall behavior in general. The rounding of the upper edge produced some important modifications, the most important of them being a shift of the critical slant angle to higher slant angles and an adverse effect on the drag characteristics at yaw. In summary, however, although there were some changes due to the four factors studied, the basic critical behavior with changing slant angle was always there.

Other design considerations that can yield reduced drag for automobiles include (Ref. 5.5) flush headlights, a radius at the leading edge of the hood (just above the headlamps), faired-in bumpers, windows set closer to the surface of the body to present a smoother surface, and a low-mounted air-dam under the bumper, ahead of the engine compartment, to reduce underbody drag.

LIFT AND DRAG COEFFICIENTS AS SIMILARITY PARAMETERS

Note that the formula for the drag coefficient for a sphere, as given by Eq. (5.79), differs from that for a cylinder of infinite span, as given by Eq. (5.68). Both forms of the drag coefficients, however, have common elements. Furthermore, the lift coefficient for a cylinder, Eq. (5.64), has the same elements. Thus, we can define a *force coefficient* as

$$C_F = \frac{\text{force}}{\underbrace{(\frac{1}{2}\rho_\infty U_\infty^2)}_{\substack{\text{dynamic} \\ \text{pressure}} } \text{ (reference area)}} \tag{5.80}$$

Note that, for a configuration of infinite span, a force per unit span would be divided by the reference area per unit span. This accounts for the difference between Eqs. (5.68) and (5.79). Ideally, the force coefficient would be a function of configuration geometry and of attitude only. However, the effects of viscosity and compressibility cause variations in the force coefficients. These efforts can be correlated in terms of parameters, such as the Reynolds number and Mach number. Such variations are evident in the drag coefficient measurements presented in this chapter.

PROBLEMS

5.1. If we neglect viscous effects, what pressure gradient is required to accelerate water in a horizontal pipe at a rate of 3 m/s²?

5.2. If we neglect viscous effects, what pressure gradient is required to accelerate water in a horizontal pipe at a rate of 5 ft/s²?

5.3. Water is accelerated from rest in a 200-ft-long, 12-in.-diameter horizontal pipe. If the water is accelerated at a rate of 12 ft/s², what is the pressure at the upstream end of the pipe if the pressure at the downstream end is 10 psi gage? Neglect viscous effects.

5.4. A column of water 3 m high stands in a vertical pipe that is open to the atmosphere at the top and is closed at the bottom by a piston. What upward acceleration of the piston is necessary to create a gage pressure of 60 kPa immediately above the piston?

5.5. An open, rectangular tank containing water is given a uniform acceleration along a straight line (a_x). After going through a complex motion at first, the surface ultimately achieves as a steady-state condition the inclined linear shape represented by the dashed line of Fig. P5.5. Are there any shear stresses in the volume of water? Why or why not? Using Euler's equation, show that the pressure variation along a vertical line from the free surface is hydrostatic; that is, the static pressure in the water increases linearly with distance from the free surface. Show that the tan $\theta = a_x/g$.

5.6. A truck carries an open tank, that is 6 m long, 2 m wide, and 3 m deep. Assuming that the driver will not accelerate or decelerate the truck at a rate greater than 2 m/s², what is the maximum depth to which the tank may be filled so that the water will not be spilled?

5.7. A truck carries an open tank that is 20 ft long, 6 ft wide, and 10 ft deep. Assuming that the driver will not accelerate or decelerate the truck at a rate greater than 6.3 ft/s², what is the maximum depth to which the tank may be filled so that the water will not be spilled?

5.8. Consider a liquid in a container that has being undergoing constant angular motion for a time interval which is of such duration that the liquid has assumed a fixed orientation in the container, as shown in Fig. P5.8. Are there any shear stresses in the volume of liquid? Why or why not? Using cylindrical coordinates, show that the pressure at any point in a horizontal plane (which is at the elevation $-z$) varies in the radial direction in the manner

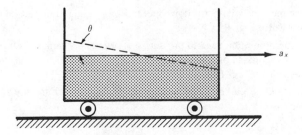

Figure P5.5 Accelerating rectangular tank for Prob. 5.5.

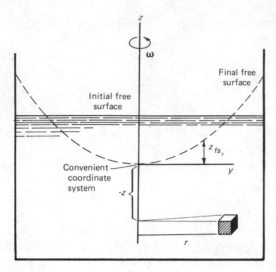

Figure P5.8 Sketch for Prob. 5.8.

$$p = p_1 + \gamma \frac{(r\omega)^2}{2g}$$

where p_1 is the pressure at the axis of rotation. Using the pressure distribution in the liquid, show that the free surface, whose elevation above the xy plane is designated as z_{fs}, as shown in Fig. 5.26, forms a parabolic surface given by

$$z_{fs} = \frac{(r\omega)^2}{2g}$$

5.9. (a) What conditions are necessary before you can use a stream function to solve for the flow field?

(b) What conditions are necessary before you can use a potential function to solve for the flow field?

(c) What conditions are necessary before you can apply Bernoulli's equation to relate two points in a flow field?

(d) Under what conditions does the circulation around a closed fluid line remain constant with respect to time?

5.10. Water drains from a tank and pipe system as a free jet, as shown in Fig. P5.10. If we neglect the effects of viscosity and the velocity of the water at the upper surface, what is the velocity of the water at the drain? Having found the velocity at the drain, what is the actual velocity at the upper surface?

5.11. Neglecting losses, determine the volumetric flow rate and the weight flow rate of the oil flowing from the tank shown in Fig. P5.11.

5.12. You are in charge of the pumping unit used to pressurize a large water tank on a fire truck. The fire that you are to extinguish is on the sixth floor of a building, 70 ft higher than the truck hose level, as shown in Fig. P5.12.

(a) What is the minimum pressure in the large tank for the water to reach the fire? Neglect pressure losses in the hose.

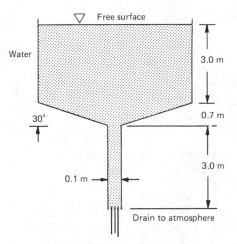

Figure P5.10   Sketch for Prob. 5.10.

(b) What is the velocity of the water as it exits the hose? The diameter of the nozzle is 3.0 in. What is the flow rate in gallons per minute? Note that 1 gal/min equals 0.002228 ft³/s.

5.13. A cylindrical tank open to the atmosphere at the top is filled with water. A drain hole 5 cm in diameter is opened on the side of the tank a distance h below the surface of the water. Use Bernoulli's equation to calculate how long it will take the water surface in the tank to drop from $h = 2.0$ m to $h = 30$ cm. See the sketch of Fig. P5.13.

5.14. A free jet of water leaves the tank horizontally, as shown in Fig. P5.14. Assuming that the tank is large and the losses are negligible, derive an expression for the distance X (from the tank to the point where the jet strikes the floor) as a function of h and H? What is X, if the liquid involved was gasoline for which $\sigma = 0.70$?

5.15. Shown in Fig. P5.15 is a siphon. If we neglect friction entirely, what is the velocity of the water leaving at C as a free jet? What are the pressures of the water in the tube at B and at A? If the vapor pressure of water at 68°F is given in the handbook as 0.79 ft of water, how high above the free surface can point B be before the siphon action breaks down?

5.16. A venturi meter is a device that is inserted into a pipeline to measure incompressible flow rates. As shown in Fig. P5.16, it consists of a convergent section that reduces the diameter to between one-half to one-fourth of the pipe diameter. This is followed by a divergent section through which the flow is returned to the original diameter. The pressure difference

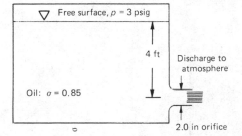

Figure P5.11   Sketch for Prob. 5.11.

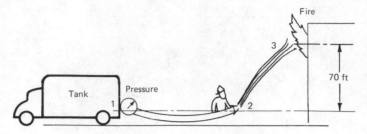

Figure P5.12 Sketch for Prob. 5.12.

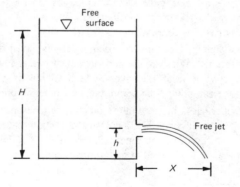

Figure P5.13 Sketch for Prob. 5.13.

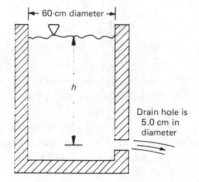

Figure P5.14 Sketch for Prob. 5.14.

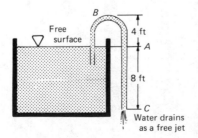

Figure P5.15 Sketch for Prob. 5.15.

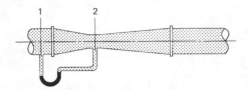

Figure P5.16 Sketch for Prob. 5.16.

between a location just before the venturi and one at the throat of the venturi is used to determine the volumetric flow rate (Q). Show that

$$Q = C_d \left[\frac{A_2}{\sqrt{1 - (A_2/A_1)^2}} \sqrt{\frac{2g(p_1 - p_2)}{\gamma}} \right]$$

where C_d is the coefficient of discharge, which takes into account the frictional effects and is determined experimentally or from handbook tabulations.

5.17. Water flows through a horizontal bend at a rate of 2 m³/s, discharging into the atmosphere. $D_1 = 50$ cm and $D_2 = 35$ cm, as shown in Fig. P5.17. Neglecting the effects of viscosity, calculate the x component of force (through the flange bolts) required to hold the bend in place.

5.18. A disk, which weighs 3 lbf, is held stable by a wire and is free to move in the vertical direction, as shown in Fig. P5.18. A jet of water issues from an orifice such that the initial velocity is 40 ft/s and the initial jet diameter is 1 in. Find the equilibrium height to which the disk will rise due to the jet of water striking it from below. For this problem, you should assume that the wire has no effect on the flow.

5.19. A jet of water exhausts to the atmosphere through a pipe, as shown in Fig. P5.19. If the velocity at point B is 20 m/s, what is the pressure at point A? What is the mass flow rate of water through the pipe? Neglect all losses.

5.20. Air flows through a converging pipe section, as shown in Fig. P5.20. Since the centerline of the duct is horizontal, the change in potential energy is zero. The pitot probe at the upstream station provides a measure of the total pressure (or stagnation pressure). The downstream end of the U-tube provides a measure of the static pressure at the second station. Assuming the density of air to be 1.225 kg/m³ and neglecting the effects of viscosity, compute the flow rate in m³/s. The manometer fluid is unity weight oil ($\sigma = 1.0$).

5.21. Compute the mass flow rate of ethyl alcohol through the pipe system shown in Fig. P5.21. Neglect all losses.

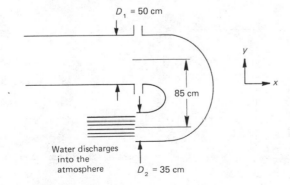

Figure P5.17 Sketch for Prob. 5.17.

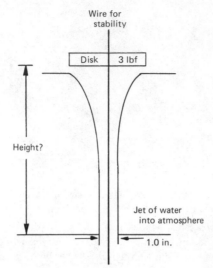

Wire for stability

Disk   3 lbf

Height?

Jet of water into atmosphere

1.0 in.

Figure P5.18   Sketch for Prob. 5.18.

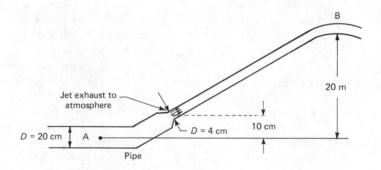

B

Jet exhaust to atmosphere

20 m

$D = 20$ cm   A

$D = 4$ cm   10 cm

Pipe

Figure P5.19   Sketch for Prob. 5.19.

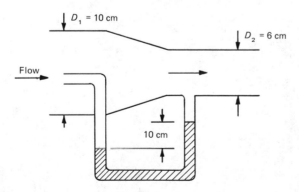

$D_1 = 10$ cm

$D_2 = 6$ cm

Flow

10 cm

Figure P5.20   Sketch for Prob. 5.20.

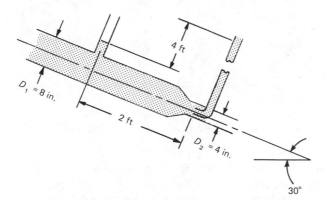

Figure P5.21 Sketch for Prob. 5.21.

5.22. Water supplied by a large reservoir is used to drive a turbine, as shown in Fig. P5.22. Neglecting the effects of friction, compute the horsepower developed by the turbine.

5.23. Water in a large tank is pumped through a pipe, as shown in Fig. P5.23. The pressure at the free surface in the tank is 5 psig. For the dimensions given, what is the horsepower required by the pump?

5.24. The cylindrical tank in Fig. P5.24 is partially filled with oil whose density is 1.65 slugs/ft^3. The diameter of the tank is 10 ft. Initially, the pressure of the air above the free surface of the oil is 50 psig. The air space is 1.0 ft high. The initial depth of the oil above the drain is 10 ft (i.e., $h_0 = 10$ ft). The oil drains through a pipe that is 4.0 in. in diameter. The air behaves as a perfect gas whose temperature is constant during the expansion. The flow may be assumed to be quasi-steady, inviscid, and incompressible, so we can use Bernoulli's equation.

    (a) Develop an expression for the exhaust velocity (V_{ex}) of oil at the drain in terms of the *parameters* of the problem; that is, do not substitute numerical values for this part.

    (b) What is the value of h for which $V_{ex} = 0$?

5.25. Consider the steady, incompressible flow around the airfoil shown in Fig. P5.25. The airfoil moves at 120 m/s at an altitude of 5 km. The free-stream conditions at 5 km are

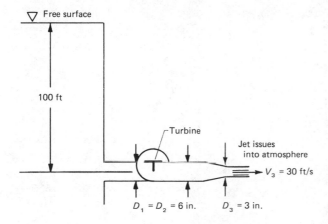

Figure P5.22 Sketch for Prob. 5.22.

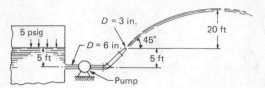

Figure P5.23   Sketch for Prob. 5.23.

$$\rho_\infty = 0.7364 \text{ kg/m}^3, \qquad p_\infty = 405.4 \text{ mm Hg}, \qquad T_\infty = 255.7 \text{ K}$$

Complete Table P5.25. The values of the local velocity are to be given with respect to an earth-fixed coordinate system (just as the velocity of 120 m/s is given).

5.26. You are working as a flight-test engineer at the Dryden Research Center. During the low-speed phase of the test program for the F-22, you know the following information.

$$p_\infty = 1000 \text{ psf} \quad \text{and} \quad \rho_\infty = 0.00128 \text{ slugs/ft}^3$$

The pressure at gage 1 is $+50.2$ psf, gage; the pressure at gage 2 is -125.5 psf, gage.
   (a) If gage 1 is known to be at the stagnation point, what is the velocity of the airplane?
   (b) What is the free-stream dynamic pressure for this test condition?
   (c) What is the velocity of the air at the edge of the boundary layer at the second point relative to the airplane? What is this velocity relative to the ground? What is C_p for this gage?

5.27. The potential function for a source is given by Eq. (5.35) as $\phi = (K/2\pi) \ln r$.
   (a) Show that the resultant velocity field satisfies the condition that the flow is irrotational.
   (b) Show that the resultant velocity field satisfies the continuity equation for constant-density flow.
   (c) What is the corresponding stream function?

5.28. Consider the superposition of a uniform flow and a line source of strength K that is located at the origin. If the distance from the source to the stagnation point is R, calculate the strength of the source in terms of U_∞ and R. Determine the equation of the streamline that passes through the stagnation point. The streamline of interest is that shown in Fig. P5.28. Let this

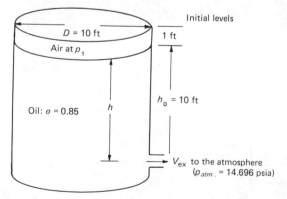

Figure P5.24   Sketch for Prob. 5.24.

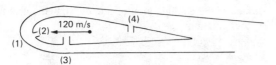

Figure P5.25 Sketch for Prob. 5.25.

TABLE P5.25

	p_1 (N/m²)	C_p	V_{local} (m/s)
(1) At the stagnation point outside any viscous layer	?	?	?
(2) At the stagnation point at the surface of the airfoil	?	?	?
(3) At a point just outside the boundary layer where $C_p = -1.0$	?	−1.0	?
(4) At a point at the surface where $C_p = -1.0$	?	−1.0	?

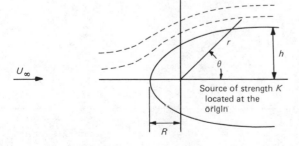

Figure P5.28 Sketch for the flow around a Rankine half-body (Probs. 5.28 and 5.29).

streamline represent the surface of the configuration of interest and complete the following table for the surface of the configuration:

θ	$\dfrac{r}{R}$	$\dfrac{U}{U_\infty}$	C_p
30°			
45°			
90°			
135°			
150°			
180°			

This configuration is known as a Rankine half-body.

5.29. A source (Fig. P5.28) whose strength K is 50 ft²/s is located at the origin and is combined with a uniform stream from left to right for which U_∞ is 25 ft/s. For the resultant Rankine half-body, find (a) the coordinates of the stagnation point, (b) the body height as it crosses the y axis, (c) the body height as $x \to \infty$ (i.e., h), and (d) the r, θ coordinates of the maximum surface velocity.

5.30. A perfect, incompressible, irrotational fluid is flowing past a wall with a two-dimensional sink of strength K per unit length that is located at the origin, as shown in Fig. P5.30. At infinity the flow is parallel to the wall and of uniform velocity U_∞. Determine the location of the stagnation point x_0 in terms of U_∞ and K. Find the pressure distribution along the wall as a function of x. Taking the free-stream static pressure to be p_∞, express the pressure coefficient as a function of x/x_0. Sketch the resulting pressure distribution.

5.31. A line source is located at the origin of the coordinate system in a uniform flow from right to left, as shown in Fig. P5.31. A plate is parallel to the free-stream flow and is situated such that the source only affects the flow above the plate. The plate is 1.0 m long (symmetric about the origin) and the free-stream velocity U_∞ is 20 m/s.
   (a) What is the strength of the source if the stagnation point is to be at the leading edge of the plate?
   (b) Develop an expression for the pressure distribution above the plate. Leave the resulting expression in terms of general parameters.

5.32. Consider the flow field generated by a two-dimensional source of strength K ($= 10$ m²/s) located a distance a ($= 2$ m) above a horizontal wall, as shown in Fig. P5.32.
   (a) Because of the presence of the wall, $v = 0$ when $y = -a$. How is this boundary condition satisfied?

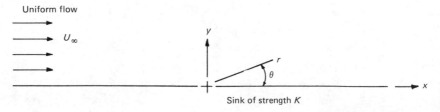

Figure P5.30   Uniform flow past a wall containing a sink of strength K at the origin.

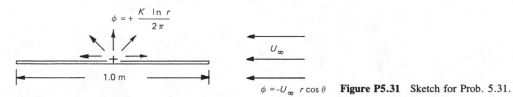

$$\phi = +\frac{K \ln r}{2\pi}$$

1.0 m

$\phi = -U_\infty \, r \cos \theta$ **Figure P5.31** Sketch for Prob. 5.31.

(b) Develop the expression for the general velocity distribution along the plate. Your expression should contain the parameters K and a. *Note*: Since you only want the velocity along the plate, your analysis need not be too general.

(c) What is the maximum velocity along the plate? Where does it occur?

5.33. The potential function for a doublet that is located at the origin and oriented such that the flow proceeds out from the origin in the negative direction is $\phi = (B/r) \cos \theta$.

(a) Show that the resultant velocity field satisfies the continuity equation for constant-density flow.

(b) Show that the resultant velocity field satisfies the condition that the flow is irrotational.

(c) What is the corresponding stream function.

5.34. Consider the velocity field induced by a potential vortex, as given by Eq. (5.41):

$$\vec{V} = -\frac{\Gamma}{2\pi r}\hat{e}_\theta$$

Calculate the circulation around the closed curve C_1, the circle of Fig. P5.34a, which encloses the origin. Calculate the circulation around the closed curve C_2 of Fig. P5.34b, which does not enclose the origin. Does the result violate Stokes's theorem, Eq. (5.47)? Justify your answer.

Problems 5.35 and 5.36 represent flows obtained by adding a potential vortex and a sink. Note the similarity between the results obtained in these two problems and a natural flow as shown in Fig. P5.35.

5.35. Consider the flow field where the velocity is

$$\vec{V} = -\frac{K}{2\pi r}\hat{e}_r + \frac{\Gamma}{2\pi r}\hat{e}_\theta$$

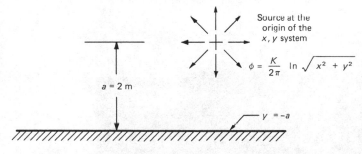

Source at the origin of the x, y system

$$\phi = \frac{K}{2\pi} \ln \sqrt{x^2 + y^2}$$

$a = 2$ m

$y = -a$

Figure P5.32 Sketch for Prob. 5.32.

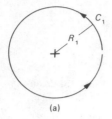 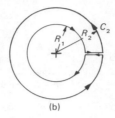

(a)   (b)

Figure P5.34 Curves for Prob. 5.34: (a) C_1, curve that encloses the origin; (b) C_2, curve that does not enclose the origin.

Figure P5.35 Photograph of water spout. (Printed with the permission of J. H. Golden, NOAA/ERL.)

where K and Γ are constants. Develop the expression for the total acceleration at any point r, θ. Calculate the circulation around a closed circular curve C_1 (the same as that of Fig. P5.34a). Compare the results for this velocity field with those for the velocity field of Prob. 5.34.

5.36. The velocity field of a stationary hurricane can be approximated by adding a counterclockwise vortex and a line sink. Thus,

$$\phi = +\frac{\Gamma\theta}{2\pi} - \frac{K}{2\pi}\ln r$$

where the $+$ sign for the potential vortex function indicates counterclockwise circulation. As shown in Fig. P5.36, this potential function can be used to represent the flow, for $r \geqslant 40$ m (i.e., except near the core). Assume that the pressure at $r = 40$ m is -1500 Pa gage (i.e., relative to the atmosphere far from the storm) and that the density is constant at 1.2 kg/m³. Assume also that the influx of air across the (invisible) cylinder at $r = 40$ m is 5000 m³/s per meter of depth into the paper. Calculate (a) the total wind speed at $r = 40$ m, (b) the strength of the sink (K) in m²/s, (c) the gage pressure at $r = 100$ m, and (d) the angle ϕ at which the streamlines cross the cylinder at $r = 40$ m.

5.37. Consider the velocity field given by

$$\vec{V} = 2x^2y\hat{i} - 2xy^2\hat{j}$$

Is the flow rotational or irrotational? Calculate the circulation around the right triangle shown in the sketch of Fig. P5.37. That is,

$$\oint \vec{V} \cdot \vec{dr} = ?$$

What is the integral of the curl $\vec{V}$ over the surface of the triangle? That is,

$$\iint (\nabla \times \vec{V}) \cdot \vec{dA} = ?$$

5.38. The velocity field is given by

$$\vec{V} = (\cos\theta + 2\sin\theta)\hat{e}_r + (2\cos\theta - \sin\theta)\hat{e}_\theta$$

(a) Calculate the contribution to circulation for each segment of the closed path and in the direction indicated, as shown in Fig. P5.38.

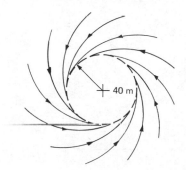

+ 40 m

Figure P5.36   Hurricane model for Prob. 5.36.

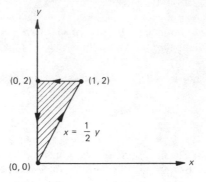

Figure P5.37   Curve for Prob. 5.37.

Segment 1: A straight line from the origin along the x axis to the point $r = 1$.
Segment 2: The arc of a circle of unit radius.
Segment 3: A straight line along the y axis from $r = 1$ back to the origin.
(b) Does a potential function exist for this flow? Why? Note that in cylindrical coordinates

$$\vec{dr} = \hat{e}_r\, dr + \hat{e}_\theta r\, d\theta$$

5.39. The velocity field for fully developed, viscous flow between two infinitely long, parallel plates (that are a distance h apart) is

$$u = \frac{1}{2\mu}\frac{dp}{dx}\left(y^2 - \frac{h^2}{4}\right)$$

$$v = 0$$

$$w = 0$$

Is the flow rotational or irrotational? Why?

5.40. Find the integral along the path $\vec{r}$ between the two points $(0, 0)$ and $(1, 2)$ of the component of $\vec{V}$ in the direction of $\vec{r}$ for the following three cases:
(a) $\vec{r}$ is a straight line.
(b) $\vec{r}$ is a parabola with the vertex at the origin and opening to the right.

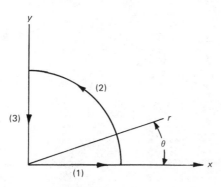

Figure P5.38   Curve for Prob. 5.38.

(c) $\vec{r}$ is a two-segment curve, with one segment along the x axis from (0, 0) to (1, 0) and the second segment perpendicular to it from (1, 0) to (1, 2).

The components of $\vec{V}$ are given by

$$u = x^2 + y^2, \qquad v = 2xy^2$$

5.41. What is the strength of the doublet B (in ft³/s) required to simulate the inviscid flow around a cylinder without circulation if the free-stream velocity is 25 ft/s and the cylinder is 1 ft in diameter. If the fluid is water at 20°C, what is the pressure at the stagnation point of the cylinder if the free stream pressure is 4000 lbf/ft²? What is the pressure at the shoulder (i.e., at $\theta = 90°$)? What are the pressure and velocity at $\theta = 135°$?

5.42. Consider an incompressible flow around a semicylinder as shown in Fig. P5.42. Assume that velocity distribution for the windward surface of the cylinder is given by the inviscid solution

$$\vec{V} = -2U_\infty \sin\theta \, \hat{e}_\theta$$

Calculate the lift and drag coefficients if the base pressure (i.e., the pressure on the flat, or leeward, surface) is equal to the pressure at the separation point, p_{corner}.

5.43. A semicylindrical tube, as shown in Fig. P5.42, is submerged in a stream of air where $p_\infty = 1.22$ kg/m³ and $U_\infty = 75$ m/s. The radius is 0.3 m. What are the lift and drag forces acting on the tube using the equations developed in Prob. 5.42.

5.44. You are to design quonset huts for a military base in the mid-East. The design wind speed is 100 ft/s. The static free-stream properties are those for standard sea-level conditions:

$$\rho_\infty = 0.00238 \text{ slugs/ft}^3 \quad \text{and} \quad p_\infty = 2116 \text{ lbf/ft}^2$$

The quonset hut may be considered to be a closed (no leaks) semicylinder, whose radius is 15 ft, mounted on tie-down blocks, as shown in Fig. P5.44. The flow is such that the velocity distribution and, thus, the pressure distribution over the top of the hut (the semicircle of the sketch) is represented by the potential function

$$\phi = U_\infty r \cos\theta + \frac{B}{r}\cos\theta$$

When calculating the flow over the hut, neglect the presence of the air space under the hut. The air under the hut is at rest and the pressure is equal to the stagnation pressure, p_t (= $p_\infty + \frac{1}{2}\rho_\infty U_\infty^2$).

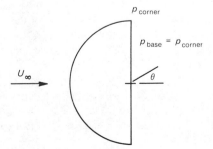

Figure P5.42 Semicylinder for Probs. 5.42 and 5.43.

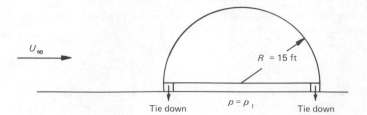

(a) What is the value of B for the 15-ft-radius (R) quonset hut?

(b) What is the net lift force acting on the quonset hut?

(c) What is the net drag force acting on the quonset hut?

5.45. Consider the flow around the quonset hut of Fig. P5.45 to be represented by superimposing a uniform flow and a doublet. Assume steady, incompressible, potential flow. The ground plane is represented by the plane of symmetry and the hut by the upper half of the cylinder. The free-stream velocity is 175 km/h; the radius R_0 of the hut is 6 m. The door is not well sealed and the static pressure inside the hut is equal to that on the outer surface of the hut, where the door is located.

(a) If the door to the hut is located at ground level (i.e., at the stagnation point), what is the net lift acting on the hut? What is the lift coefficient?

(b) Where should the door be located (i.e., at what angle θ_0 relative to the ground) so that the net force on the hut will vanish?

5.46. You are the consulting engineer on the design of the high-rise headquarters of the Pie-in-the-Sky Political Party. The building is pie shaped (of course) with an included angle of $60°$. The wind speed is 75 mph at standard sea-level conditions. As shown in Fig. P5.46, the pressure on the two flat surfaces is equal to the pressure at the corners of the curved surface (p_c). If the velocity on the curved surface varies as $v_\theta = -2U_\infty \sin \theta$, what is the section drag force (i.e., per unit height) acting on the building?

5.47. An infinite-span cylinder (two-dimensional) serves as a plug between the two airstreams, as shown in Fig. P5.47. Both air flows may be considered to be steady, inviscid, and incompressible. Neglecting the body forces in the air and the weight of the cylinder, in which direction does the plug move (i.e., due to the air flow)?

5.48. The velocity at the surface of the cylinder for inviscid, incompressible flow past a fixed cylinder is given by the expression

$$\vec{V} = -2U_\infty \sin \theta \, \hat{e}_\theta$$

Make a coordinate transformation and consider the case of the cylinder moving through a still fluid, as shown in Fig. P5.48. Sketch the velocity vector at points spaced every $15°$ around the cylinder. (Note that part of the solution is given: the velocity at $\theta = 90°$ is U_∞ to the right.)

5.49. Using the data of Fig. 5.26, calculate the force and the overturning moment exerted by a 4 m/s wind on a cylindrical smokestack that has a diameter of 3 m and a height of 50 m. Neglect variations in the velocity of the wind over the height of the smokestack. The temperature of the air is 30°C; its pressure is 99 kPa. What is the Reynolds number for this flow?

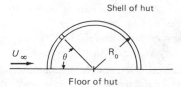

Figure P5.45 Sketch for Prob. 5.45.

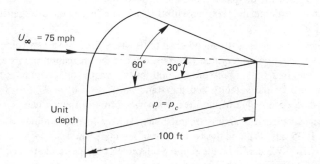

Figure P5.46 Sketch for Prob. 5.46.

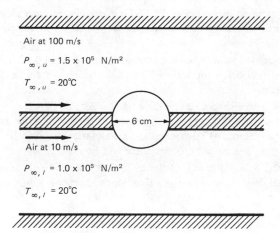

Figure P5.47 Sketch for Prob. 5.47.

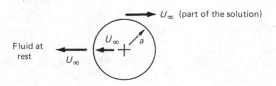

Figure P5.48 Sketch for Prob. 5.48.

5.50. Calculate the force and the overturning moment exerted by a 45-mph wind on a cylindrical flagpole that has a diameter of 6 in. and a height of 15 ft. Neglect variations in the velocity of the wind over the height of the flagpole. The temperature of the air is 85°F; its pressure is 14.4 psi. What is the Reynolds number of this flow?

5.51. A flagpole, 10 cm in diameter, is found to have a minimum drag coefficient at a wind speed of 10 m/s. Is the surface of the flagpole rough or smooth?

5.52. There were early attempts in the development of the airplane to use rotating cylinders as airfoils. Consider such a cylinder having a diameter of 1 m and a length of 10 m. If this cylinder is rotated at 100 rpm while the plane moves at a speed of 100 km/h through the air at 2-km standard atmosphere, estimate the maximum lift that could be developed, disregarding end effects.

5.53. A cylinder 3 ft in diameter is placed in a stream of air at 68°F where the free-stream velocity is 120 ft/s. What is the vortex strength required in order to place the stagnation points at $\theta = 30°$ and $\theta = 150°$? If the free-stream pressure is 2000 lbf/ft^2, what is the pressure at the stagnation points? What will be the velocity and the static pressure at $\theta = 90°$? at $\theta = 270°$? What will be the theoretical value of the lift per spanwise foot of the cylinder?

5.54. A cylinder 2 m in diameter is placed in an air stream at standard sea-level conditions where the free-stream velocity is 35 m/s. What is the vortex strength required in order to place the stagnation point at $\theta = 270°$? What will be the theoretical value of lift per unit span of the cylinder? What is the lift coefficient for these conditions?

5.55. Integrate the pressure distribution for flow around a cylinder with circulation, Eq. (5.55), to show that the lift force per unit span of the cylinder is $l = \rho U_\infty \Gamma$, Eq. (5.69).

5.56. Consider the pressure distribution shown in Fig. P5.56 for the windward and leeward surfaces of a thick disk whose axis is parallel to the free-stream flow. What is the corresponding drag coefficient?

5.57. What drag force will be exerted on a thick disk similar to that of Prob. 5.56 if it is towed through water at a depth 10 m below the surface? The disk, which is 1 cm in diameter, is moving at a speed of 5 m/s.

5.58. Consider air flowing past a hemisphere resting on a flat surface, as shown in Fig. P5.58. Neglecting the effects of viscosity, if the internal pressure is p_i, find an expression for the pressure force on the hemisphere. At what angular location should a hole be cut in the surface of the hemisphere so that the net pressure force will be zero?

5.59. A sphere, 1 m in diameter, is towed in fresh water at 20°C at a speed U_∞, as shown in Fig. P5.59. Assuming inviscid flow, estimate the speed at which cavitation will first appear on

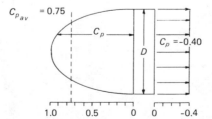

Figure P5.56   Sketch for Prob. 5.56.

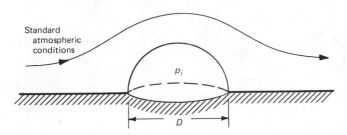

Figure P5.58   Sketch for Prob. 5.58.

the surface of the sphere. At what point will cavitation appear? The vapor pressure of water at 20°C is 2.35 kPa.

5.60. Calculate the steady-state velocity at which small metal spheres, 0.1 in. in diameter, fall through water. The specific gravity of the metal sphere is 8.0. For water, $\rho = 1.937$ slugs/ft³; $\mu = 2.088 \times 10^{-5}$ lbf s/ft². What is the Reynolds number of this flow?

5.61. A spherical rock, 30 cm in diameter, has a specific gravity of 2.5. What is its terminal velocity in seawater?

5.62. A spherical rock weighs 45 N in air and 25 N in water. What is its terminal velocity in water?

5.63. A major league pitcher is accused of hiding sandpaper in his belt in order to scuff up an otherwise "smooth" baseball. Why would he do this? To estimate the Reynolds number of the baseball, assume its speed to be 90 mph and its diameter, 2.75 in.

5.64. Consider a dumbbell-type mechanism rotating in a horizontal plane (neglect gravity) on a frictionless bearing (neglect friction in the mechanical system) in a wind stream of U_∞, as shown in Fig. P5.64. The mechanism spins at 60 rpm. Spheres 4.0 in. in diameter are located 2.0 ft from the axis. You are to consider two different freestream velocities: (a) $U_\infty = 130$ ft/s, and (b) $U_\infty = 160$ ft/s. Recall that the $\mathrm{Re}_{\mathrm{crit}} = 350{,}000$, $C_{D,\mathrm{Lam}} \simeq 0.4$, and $C_{D,\mathrm{turb}} \simeq 0.14$. For the configuration shown in Fig. P5.64, state whether the rotation is enhanced, retarded, or unaffected by the free-stream flow. That is, do the aerodynamic forces on the spheres (i) aid the rotating motion, (ii) retard the rotating motion (slow it down), or (iii) not affect it at all? Answer the question for both velocities.

5.65. Your golf partner in the best-ball golf match is Slice Woods. Despite lessons from Arnold Palmer, Jack Nicklaus, and Tom Watson, Slice rarely breaks 200. Then you notice he is using smooth golf balls. Tell him what he is doing wrong and why? Your answer should

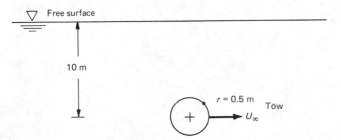

Figure P5.59   Sketch for Prob. 5.59.

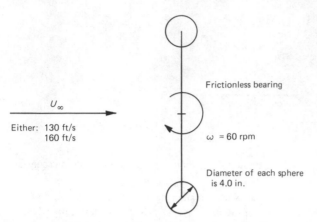

Frictionless bearing

U_∞

Either: 130 ft/s
160 ft/s

ω = 60 rpm

Diameter of each sphere
is 4.0 in.

Figure P5.64 Rotating dumbbell-type
mechanism for Prob. 5.64.

include the terms Reynolds number, boundary layer (laminar or turbulent), pressure gradient, separation, form drag, and the like.

5.66. A spherical probe with three radially drilled orifices, as shown in Fig. P5.66, can be used as a flow-direction indicator. Whenever the pressure on the two side holes is equal, the pressure at the center hole is the stagnation pressure. The instrument is called a direction-finding pitot tube or a spherical yaw probe.

(a) If the orifices of the direction-finding pitot tube are to be used to measure the free-stream static pressure, where would they have to be located if we use the theory for inviscid flow around the sphere?

(b) For a direction-finding pitot tube with orifices located as calculated in part (a), what is the sensitivity? Let the sensitivity be defined as the pressure change per unit angular change (i.e., $\partial p/\partial \theta$).

5.67. With increased fuel costs, automobile designers are very aware of aerodynamic drag. Contemporary designs have drag coefficients from 0.3 for the best designs to greater than 0.5 for the worst design. What horsepower is required to overcome the aerodynamic drag force for a car going 55 mph for each of these two drag coefficients? Note that the required horsepower is equal to the force times distance/time, that 1 hp = 550 ft · lbf/s, and that the drag coefficient is based on the frontal area. The frontal area is 22 ft².

5.68. The rear-deck of the LN7 from Lincoln-Mercury is slanted away from the horizontal approximately by 22°. Using the data of Fig. 5.31, what is the base drag coefficient for this configuration? If the total drag coefficient for the LN7 is 0.36, what fraction of the total drag is base drag?

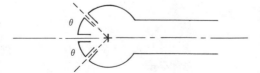

θ

θ

Figure P5.66 Sketch for Prob. 5.66.

REFERENCES

5.1. I. H. Shames, *Mechanics of Fluids,* McGraw-Hill Book Company, New York, 1962.

5.2. E. Achenbach, "Distribution of Local Pressure and Skin Friction around a Circular Cylinder in Cross-flow up to Re $= 5 \times 10^6$," *Journal of Fluid Mechanics,* vol. 34, pt. 4, 1968, 625–639.

5.3. H. Schlichting, *Boundary-Layer Theory,* 7th ed., McGraw-Hill Book Company, New York, 1979.

5.4. T. Morel, "Aerodynamic Drag of Bluff Body Shapes Characteristic of Hatch-Back Cars," SAE Technical Paper 780267, 1978.

5.5. J. Dunne, "How Designers Build More MPG into New Low-Drag Cars," *Popular Science,* vol. 219, no. 3 (Sept. 1981), 74–76.

CHAPTER SIX

Dynamics of an Incompressible, Viscous Flow

The equation for the conservation of linear momentum was developed in Chapter 4 by applying Newton's law, which states that the net force acting on a fluid particle is equal to the time rate of change of the linear momentum of the fluid particle. The principal forces considered were those that act directly on the mass of the fluid element (i.e., the body forces) and those that act on its surface (i.e., the pressure forces and shear forces). The resultant equations are known as the Navier–Stokes equations. Even though there are no general solutions for the complete Navier–Stokes equations, exact solutions can be obtained for special flows and approximate engineering solutions can be obtained for many other flows when reasonable simplifying assumptions are introduced.

The steady, fully developed flow fields discussed in Chapter 4 are examples of exact solutions to the Navier–Stokes equations. Because of the fully developed character of the flow, many of the velocity gradients are zero. Infinitely long, bounding surfaces constrain the flow so that the streamlines are parallel. As a result, two of the three velocity components are identically zero. The exact solutions were obtained for viscous flows between parallel plates and in constant-diameter pipes.

In Chapters 2 and 5, solutions were generated for flow fields in which the effects of viscosity were negligible. Since the fluid is at rest in the applications of Chapter 2, the velocity gradients that produce shear forces are absent. Thus, it is clear that viscosity can be neglected in a static medium. Although the fluid is not at rest for the applications of Chapter 5, solutions were obtained assuming that the flow was "inviscid"; that is, the product of the coefficient of viscosity times the velocity gradients was negligible relative to the inertia forces and pressure forces acting on the fluid particles. For many applications, the solutions obtained with this inviscid assumption provide a reasonable approximation to the major part of the flow field around an object. However, one cannot neglect the

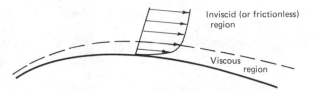

Figure 6.1 Two-layer model for viscous flow near a solid boundary.

viscous forces throughout the flow field. They must be considered in the thin, boundary layer near the surface where the velocity of the fluid particles increases from a value of zero (in a vehicle-fixed coordinate system) at the wall to the value that corresponds to the external "frictionless" flow outside the boundary layer, such as shown in Fig. 6.1. In these cases, the Reynolds number is relatively large, and the viscous forces are significant only in the thin boundary layer. For many high Reynolds number flows, the flow field may be divided into two regions: (1) the viscous boundary layer adjacent to the solid boundary and (2) the essentially inviscid flow outside the boundary layer.

There are many high Reynolds number flows in which, although the coefficient of viscosity is relatively small, the viscosity has a dramatic effect on the flow field. Such is the case for incompressible flows around blunt configurations, where the combined effect of a large adverse pressure gradient acting on fluid particles retarded by viscous forces produces a region of separated flow. In such cases, the flow field cannot be divided into two regions as discussed in the previous paragraph. The flow around a cylinder immersed in a uniform stream (as discussed in Chapter 5) is an example of a high Reynolds number flow where the viscous effects cannot be neglected. Note also that two distinctly different flow fields were observed depending on whether the Reynolds number is subcritical or supercritical.

LOSSES IN PIPE SYSTEMS

When we derived Bernoulli's equation in Chapter 5, it was assumed that we could neglect friction, heat transfer, and all work except that due to the pressure forces. Since each term of Eq. (5.9) has the dimensions of velocity squared or, equivalently, of energy per unit mass, the value of the Bernoulli constant between two points in the flow indicates that there is no net change in energy between the two points. However, there are many flows for which energy is added to or taken from the system. The work done by a pump would add energy to the system. Energy can be removed from the system as the output of a turbine. As will be discussed in Chapter 8, a governing equation for such flows can be developed from the first law of thermodynamics. Examples are presented in Chapter 8 where the energy equation is applied to a flow for which Eq. (5.9) is applicable as well as to systems involving pumps and turbines. Recall that in working Example 5.4, Bernoulli's equation was applied separately to points in the flow upstream of the turbine and then to downstream points. The energy equation was used to determine the change in the Bernoulli constant, Eq. (5.16). That flow will be reexamined in Example 8.2 using the first law of thermodynamics.

In a similar fashion, the work lost due to friction in a pipe system can be modeled using the energy equation, as will be discussed in Example 8.3. However, irreversible losses that occur in all real flows as a result of viscous dissipation converting mechanical energy into nonrecoverable internal energy can also be represented as a change in the Bernoulli constant. To calculate the flow in a pipe system, we will use

$$\frac{V_1^2}{2g} + z_1 + \frac{p_1}{\rho g} = \frac{V_2^2}{2g} + z_2 + \frac{p_2}{\rho g} + h_f \tag{6.1}$$

which we will call the "modified Bernoulli's equation." Equation (6.1) is a form of the energy equation representing the first law of thermodynamics, wherein h_f represents the head loss due to friction. It is represented graphically in Fig. 6.2. The second law of thermodynamics requires that h_f be positive in a real fluid flow.

In this equation, we are assuming that the density remains constant even though there are changes in the internal energy and there is heat transfer. We must ask ourselves, "Is the constant-density model useful in modeling the actual flow?" Consider a pipeline carrying liquids such as water or oil over comparatively long distances. Although the heat-transfer rate may be small over any small section of pipe, the total heat transfer from a unit mass of fluid as it moves over a long distance may be significant. However, the difference between the temperature of the fluid and that of the surroundings may be small. Thus, the temperature of the fluid tends to remain constant and, consequently, even though significant pressure changes occur, the density of the liquid remains essentially constant. Furthermore, changes in the internal energy due to pressure change and

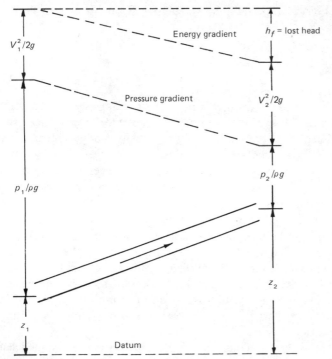

Figure 6.2 Representation of the terms in Eq. (6.1).

whatever small differences in temperature may exist are taken into account by the head loss term. As a result, the head loss may be relatively large, even though the density is constant.

The head loss in a pipe (or duct) depends on (1) the type of fluid, its density and viscosity; (2) the velocity of the liquid and the velocity profile; (3) the geometry of the duct, its size and length; and (4) the roughness of the interior surface. Pressure has practically no effect on the loss of head, since the viscosity of liquids varies only slightly with pressure in the ranges ordinarily occurring in practice. Let us now develop procedures for calculating the head loss, given the flow parameters.

Just as there is a dramatic change in the external flow field around a cylinder when a critical Reynolds number is reached, there is a similar change for the internal flow in a pipe (or duct) when the transition Reynolds number is exceeded. Below the critical Reynolds number, the flow is smooth and steady, as shown in Fig. 6.3a. Above the critical Reynolds number, considerable mixing occurs with significant fine-scale fluctuations in the flow, as shown in Fig. 6.3b. In turbulent flows, rapid fluctuations occur in the velocity components even though the average flow properties may be steady (not time dependent). Transition depends on many effects, such as fluctuations in the flow at the inlet, the geometry of the inlet, surface roughness, and the Reynolds number. References such as Refs. 6.2 and 6.3 contain further discussions of the transition process in pipe flows.

Darcy–Weisbach Equation

Let us represent the head loss in terms of the product of (1) the kinetic energy per unit mass (based on the average velocity) divided by g, (2) the ratio of the distance between stations relative to the diameter of the pipe (L/D), and (3) a parameter that we shall call the friction factor (f). Thus, by definition

$$h_f = \frac{V_{av}^2}{2g} \frac{L}{D} f \qquad (6.2)$$

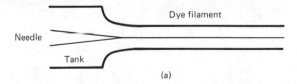

(a)

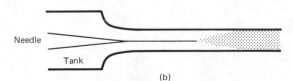

(b)

Figure 6.3 Reynolds's sketches of pipe-flow transition: (a) subcritical Reynolds number (laminar flow); (b) supercritical Reynolds number (turbulent flow). (From O. Reynolds, *Philosophical Transactions of the Royal Society,* vol. 174, 1883, 935–982.)

Equation (6.2) is known as the Darcy–Weisbach equation as applied to circular ducts and pipes. Note that h_f has the units of $V^2/2g$. Thus, the equation is valid either for metric units or English units, as long as the quantities are consistently expressed. It also applies either for laminar flow or turbulent flow. The equation can be applied to a duct of general cross section if we use the hydraulic radius R_h instead of the diameter D. Thus, for a general duct

$$h_f = \frac{V_{av}^2}{2g} \frac{L}{4R_h} f \tag{6.3}$$

where $R_h = A/P$, i.e., the ratio of the cross-sectional area of the duct divided by its perimeter.

Head Loss for Laminar Flow in a Pipe

In Example 4.3, we developed a relation between the streamwise pressure gradient and the characteristic flow parameters for a steady, fully developed flow where the velocity profile is given by

$$u = U_o \left[1 - \left(\frac{r}{R} \right)^2 \right]$$

The streamwise pressure gradient for this flow was found to be

$$\frac{dp}{dx} = - \frac{4\mu U_o}{R^2} \tag{4.21}$$

Experimental data indicate that this result is valid when the Reynolds number based on the average velocity and the pipe diameter is 2300, or less. Thus, this relation is valid when the flow in the pipe is laminar.

The volumetric flow rate (Q) across a station is

$$Q = \int_o^R U_o \left[1 - \left(\frac{r}{R} \right)^2 \right] 2\pi r \, dr = \frac{\pi U_o R^2}{2} = \frac{\pi U_o D^2}{8} \tag{6.4a}$$

But, by definition,

$$Q = V_{av} \frac{\pi D^2}{4} \tag{6.4b}$$

where V_{av} is the average velocity across the cross section. Comparing Eqs. (6.4a) and (6.4b), we can see that the average velocity is

$$V_{av} = 0.5 U_o$$

Thus, Eq. (4.21) can be written as

$$\frac{dp}{dx} = - \frac{128\mu Q}{\pi D^4} = - \frac{32\mu V_{av}}{D^2} \tag{6.5}$$

However, to use this relation in Eq. (6.1), we note that h_f represents the change in pressure due to friction that takes place from station 1 to station 2. If we designate the distance between these two stations as L, we can rewrite Eq. (6.5) as

$$h_f = \frac{\Delta p}{\rho g} = \frac{32\mu V_{av}L}{\rho g D^2} \tag{6.6}$$

The minus sign has been eliminated since the decrease in pressure due to skin friction, as given by Eq. (6.5), represents the magnitude of the head loss for Eq. (6.1). Furthermore, Δp has been divided by ρg so that the units are consistent with those of Eq. (6.1).

Comparing Eqs. (6.2) and (6.6), we see that, for a laminar flow,

$$f = \frac{64}{(\rho V_{av}\, D)/\mu} = \frac{64}{\mathrm{Re}_D} \tag{6.7}$$

As was stated in Chapter 4 when discussing similarity parameters for the momentum equation, the Reynolds number is an important similarity parameter for flows in which we account for the effects of viscosity.

Example 6.1

SAE 10W-30 oil at 17°C flows upward through a constant-diameter pipe that is inclined 40° to the horizontal, as shown in Fig. 6.4. The flow is fully developed and steady. The static pressure at station 1 is 350 kPa; that at station 2 is 250 kPa. The stations are 10 m apart. The pipe is 7 cm in diameter.

(a) Verify that the flow goes from station 1 to station 2.

(b) Compute h_f between the two stations.

(c) What is the volumetric flow rate?

(d) Calculate the average velocity.

Solution. The viscosity of SAE 10W-30 oil at 17°C can be determined from Fig. 1.5. It is 2.0×10^{-1} N · s/m². The density of the oil can be estimated using the specific gravity information presented in Table 1.3. Assuming that the specific gravity is approximately 0.92, ρ of the oil is 920 kg/m³.

The flow goes in the direction of decreasing hydraulic grade line (HGL). Thus, using the gage pressures at the two stations in Eq. (5.18),

$$\mathrm{HGL}_1 = z_1 + \frac{p_1}{\rho g} = 0 + \frac{2.49 \times 10^5 \text{ N/m}^2}{(920 \text{ kg/m}^3)\,(9.8066 \text{ m/s}^2)}$$

$$= 27.60 \text{ m}$$

$$\mathrm{HGL}_2 = z_2 + \frac{p_2}{\rho g} = (10)\sin 40° + \frac{1.49 \times 10^5}{(920)(9.8066)}$$

$$= 22.95 \text{ m}$$

Since the value of HGL at station 1 is greater than that at station 2, we have verified that the flow is from 1 to 2.

Since the flow in the pipe is fully developed, the velocity at station 1 is equal to that at station 2. Thus, using Eq. (6.1), we see that

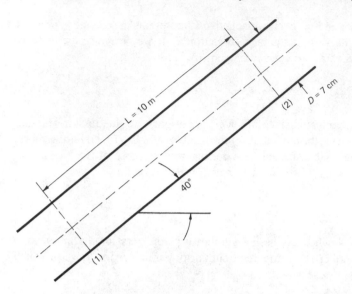

Figure 6.4   Sketch for Example 6.1.

$$h_f = (z_1 + \frac{p_1}{\rho g}) - (z_2 + \frac{p_2}{\rho g}) = \text{HGL}_1 - \text{HGL}_2 = 4.65 \text{ m}$$

To calculate either the volumetric flow rate or the average velocity, we can use either Eq. (6.2) or (6.6). Recall that Eq. (6.6) is based on the fact the flow is laminar; that is, the Reynolds number is less than (or equal to) 2300. Thus, once we have calculated the average velocity, we need to verify that the flow is laminar as assumed. Using Eq. (6.6),

$$V_{av} = \frac{\rho g D^2 h_f}{32 \mu L} = \frac{(920 \text{ kg/m}^3)(9.8066 \text{ m/s}^2)(0.0049 \text{ m}^2)(4.65 \text{ m})}{32(0.2 \text{ N} \cdot \text{s/m}^2)(10 \text{ m})}$$

$$= 3.21 \text{ m/s}$$

Let us now calculate the Reynolds number:

$$\text{Re}_D = \frac{\rho V_{av} D}{\mu} = \frac{(920 \text{ kg/m}^3)(3.21 \text{ m/s})(0.07 \text{ m})}{0.2 \text{ N} \cdot \text{s/m}^2} = 1033.62$$

Since the Reynolds number is well below the critical value of 2300, the flow in the pipe is laminar. Thus, the relations we used are valid for this application.

Finally, using Eq. (6.4b),

$$Q = V_{av} \frac{\pi D^2}{4} = 0.0124 \text{ m}^3/\text{s}$$

Head Loss for Turbulent Flow in a Pipe

If the Reynolds number (based on the average velocity and the diameter of the pipe) is above the critical value, the laminar-flow relations developed in the previous section are no longer valid. As noted, the accepted value for the transition criterion for commercial pipes is usually taken to be

$$\mathrm{Re}_{D,\mathrm{crit}} = 2300$$

Although transition can be delayed to significantly higher Reynolds numbers if special care is used to provide a rounded entrance to the pipe, smooth walls, vibration isolation from the surroundings, and a very low turbulence flow at the pipe inlet, 2300 is a reasonable value for practical applications.

As illustrated in Fig. 6.5, the velocity profile for turbulent flow in the pipe is markedly different than that for laminar flow. The two profiles are for the same volumetric flow rate. In comparing the two types of flows, we see that the parabolic profile of laminar flow has a larger value for the maximum velocity (U_0), the velocity at the centerline, but relatively less shear at the wall, that is, a lower velocity gradient at the wall. Conversely, for turbulent flow, the velocity increases rapidly with distance from the wall from the no-slip value at the wall (i.e., $u_{r=R} = 0$). Thus, a turbulent pipe flow produces relatively large shear. However, the centerline value for the velocity (U_0), which is also the maximum value, is not much greater than the average value (V_{av}). For turbulent flow, the relatively high shear is caused by macroscopic mixing within the liquid. Individual fluid particles no longer follow the well-defined paths of laminar flow. As a result of the mixing process superimposed on the rectilinear motion, the radial distribution of the time-averaged velocity is much more uniform, except very near the wall, where the large velocity gradient produces relatively large shear forces and a correspondingly large head loss.

For turbulent flow in a smooth-walled pipe, the velocity distribution will be assumed to be given by the relation

$$\frac{u}{u^*} \simeq \frac{1}{\kappa} \ln \frac{(R - r)u^*}{\nu} + B \tag{6.8}$$

where ν is the kinematic viscosity and u^* is the friction velocity and is given by the expression

$$u^* = \left(\frac{\tau_w}{\rho}\right)^{0.5} \tag{6.9}$$

The dimensionless constants, κ and B, are found to have the approximate values

$$\kappa \simeq 0.41 \quad \text{and} \quad B \simeq 5.0 \tag{6.10}$$

The derivation of turbulent velocity profiles of the form given by Eq. (6.8) will be discussed in Chapter 7.

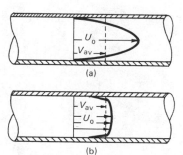

(a)

(b)

Figure 6.5 Comparison of laminar and turbulent pipe-flow velocity profiles for the same volumetric flow rate: (a) laminar flow; (b) turbulent flow.

Before developing additional relations involving this particular velocity profile for turbulent flow in a smooth pipe, let us reexamine Eq. (4.20):

$$\frac{dp}{dx} = -\frac{2\,|\tau_w|}{R}$$

This equation can be used to define the pressure drop for fully developed flow in a constant-diameter pipe, whether the flow is turbulent or laminar. Rearranging and again eliminating the minus sign as discussed earlier in this chapter,

$$\tau_w = \frac{\Delta p}{L}\frac{D}{4} \tag{6.11}$$

Using Eq. (6.2), one can obtain an expression for the pressure drop (Δp) in terms of the friction factor (f):

$$\Delta p = \rho\,\frac{V_{av}^2}{2}\frac{L}{D}f \tag{6.12}$$

Substituting Eq. (6.12) into Eq. (6.11), we find that

$$\tau_w = \rho V_{av}^2\,\frac{f}{8} \tag{6.13}$$

Using the definition of the friction velocity, as given in Eq. (6.9), we can write that

$$\frac{V_{av}}{u^*} = \left(\frac{8}{f}\right)^{0.5} \tag{6.14}$$

Thus, the nondimensionalized value for the average velocity is related directly to the Darcy friction factor. Now we can use our assumed velocity profile to determine the average value of the velocity.

Let us now calculate the average velocity for the turbulent profile given by Eq. (6.8). Using the definition for the average velocity,

$$V_{av} = \frac{Q}{A} = \frac{u^*}{\pi R^2}\int_0^R \left[\frac{1}{\kappa}\ln\frac{(R-r)u^*}{\nu} + B\right]2\pi r\,dr$$

$$= \frac{1}{2}u^*\left[\frac{2}{\kappa}\ln\frac{Ru^*}{\nu} + 2B - \frac{3}{\kappa}\right]$$

Substituting the approximate values for B and κ into this expression, we obtain

$$\frac{V_{av}}{u^*} = 2.439\ln\frac{Ru^*}{\nu} + 1.341 \tag{6.15}$$

The argument of the logarithm in Eq. (6.15) can be rewritten

$$\frac{Ru^*}{\nu} = \frac{\dfrac{1}{2}D\left(\dfrac{f}{8}\right)^{0.5}V_{av}}{\nu} = \frac{1}{2}\,\text{Re}_D\left(\frac{f}{8}\right)^{0.5} \tag{6.16}$$

Combining Eqs. (6.14) through (6.16) and changing to a base-10 logarithm, we obtain

$$\frac{1}{f^{0.5}} = 1.99 \log (\text{Re}_D \, f^{0.5}) - 1.02 \tag{6.17}$$

Many alternative relations for the friction factor are available in the literature. One such approximation from which f can be readily computed if Re_D is known is that of Blasius:

$$f = \frac{0.316}{(\text{Re}_D)^{0.25}} = \frac{0.316}{(\rho V_{\text{av}} \, D/\mu)^{0.25}} \tag{6.18}$$

which is valid for Reynolds numbers in the range from 4×10^3 to 10^5. Using this relation in Eq. (6.12), we obtain the relation for the pressure drop:

$$\Delta p = \rho \frac{V_{\text{av}}^2}{2} \frac{L}{D} f = 0.158 \frac{\rho^{0.75} \mu^{0.25} V_{\text{av}}^{1.75} L}{D^{1.25}} \tag{6.19}$$

Thus, it has been determined that the pressure decrease caused by turbulent flow in a constant-diameter pipe depends on the following factors:

1. D, the pipe diameter.
2. ρ, the density of the fluid.
3. μ, the coefficient of viscosity of the fluid.
4. V_{av}, the mean-time average of the velocity, averaged over the cross section.
5. L, the length of the pipe over which the pressure drop takes place.

Because we have developed the relations using the velocity profile for turbulent flow in a smooth pipe, there exists another significant parameter that has not yet appeared in our analysis:

6. ε, the wall roughness height.

The pressure drop (or head loss) for turbulent flow in a constant-diameter pipe depends on these six parameters. Note that the pressure level does not appear in the preceding discussion. Thus, we will conclude that the head loss is independent of the pressure intensity.

Effect of Roughness on the Turbulent-Flow Head Loss

The roughness of the interior pipe surface does not affect the pressure loss providing the pipe flow remains laminar, as indicated by the equation for the friction factor, Eq. (6.7). However, turbulent flow is strongly affected by surface roughness. As described in the previous section and as will be discussed in more detail in Chapter 7, there is considerable mixing in a turbulent flow. The velocity can be represented as the sum of a time-averaged component and a fluctuating component. (The equations in this chapter are expressed in terms of the time-averaged component.) The turbulent fluctuations in the flow are damped very near the wall. Thus, even for a turbulent flow, there is a thin *laminar sublayer* immediately adjacent to the wall. If the roughness elements of the wall surface remain submerged in this laminar sublayer, they do not affect the friction factor and the flow is known as *smooth pipe flow*.

When the roughness elements protrude through the laminar sublayer and become exposed to the turbulent motion, they affect it. If the Reynolds number is sufficiently high that the thickness of the laminar sublayer becomes small compared to the height of the roughness elements, the flow is considered to be *completely turbulent*. An equation for the friction factor for completely turbulent flow is

$$\frac{1}{f^{0.5}} = -2.0 \log \frac{\varepsilon/D}{3.7} \tag{6.20}$$

Note that the friction factor for turbulent flow in a very rough pipe is independent of Reynolds number. Thus, for fully turbulent flow, the pressure loss does not depend on the viscosity. The correlation between the relative roughness (ε/D) and the minimum Reynolds number for fully turbulent flow is indicated by the broken line presented in Fig. 6.6. Thus, for ε/D of 0.01, the flow in the pipe is fully turbulent if Re_D exceeds 10^5. Above this Reynolds number, the friction factor correlation is essentially horizontal, since the friction factor is independent of the Reynolds number, as indicated by Eq. (6.20). Common values of ε for typical commercial pipe surfaces are presented in Table 6.1. The values are taken from Ref. 6.4.

Conditions between laminar flow and fully turbulent flow are known as *transitionally rough*. In this range, the friction factor depends on both the Reynolds number and the relative roughness. The friction factor for such transitionally rough flows can be calculated using the correlation developed by Colebrook (Ref. 6.5):

$$\frac{1}{f^{0.5}} = -2.0 \log \left[\frac{2.51}{\mathrm{Re}_D \, f^{0.5}} + \frac{\varepsilon/D}{3.7} \right] \tag{6.21}$$

The friction factors based on this equation are presented in Fig. 6.6. This graphical presentation was done by Moody (Ref. 6.6) in 1944 and is, therefore, known as the Moody chart (or Moody diagram) for pipe friction.

There are three types of elementary pipe-flow problems that are basic to the solution of more complex problems. They are as follows:

1. Given Q, L, D, and ε; solve for h_f, the head loss.
2. Given h_f, L, D, and ε; solve for Q, the flow rate.
3. Given h_f, Q, L, and ε; solve for D, the diameter.

In each of these cases, the Darcy–Weisbach equation, the continuity equation, and the Moody diagram are used to determine the unknown quantity.

For the first type, the Reynolds number and the relative roughness are readily calculated from the data given. We can determine f using the Moody diagram and then

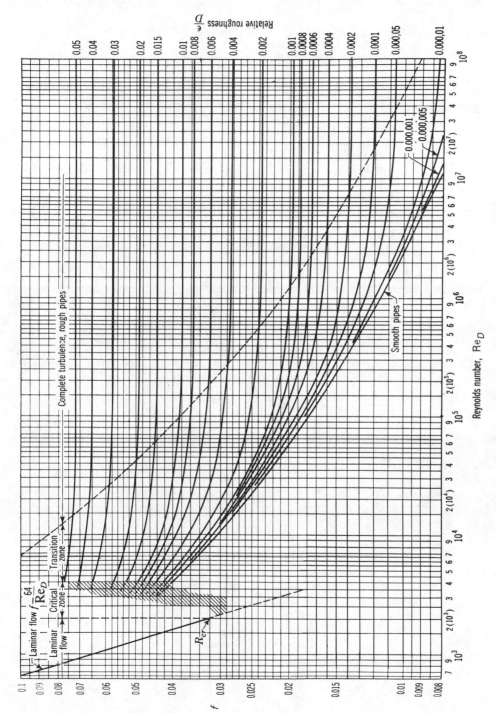

Figure 6.6 Friction factors for flow in pipes, the Moody diagram. (From L. F. Moody, "Friction Factors for Pipe Flow," *ASME Transactions*, vol. 66, 1944.)

TABLE 6.1   AVERAGE ROUGHNESS HEIGHT (ε) FOR NEW PIPE SURFACES

	Average roughness, ε	
	cm	ft
Riveted steel	0.09–0.9	0.003–0.03
Concrete	0.03–0.3	0.001–0.01
Wooden stave	0.018–0.09	0.0006–0.003
Cast iron	0.026	0.00085
Galvanized iron	0.015	0.0005
Asphalted cast iron	0.012	0.0004
Wrought iron, steel	0.0046	0.00015
Glass, drawn brass, copper, lead	Smooth	Smooth

Source: T. Baumeister and L. S. Marks, eds., *Standard Handbook for Mechanical Engineers*, 7th ed. New York: McGraw-Hill Book Company, 1967. Used with permission.

substitute f into the Darcy–Weisbach equation to solve for h_f and consequently the pressure loss.

Example 6.2

Crude oil with a specific gravity of 0.86 and a kinematic viscosity (ν) of 1×10^{-5} m²/s flows through a cast-iron pipe that is 300 m long and 20 cm in diameter. The flow rate is 0.126 m³/s. *Note:* 1 gal/min is equal to 6.309×10^{-5} m³/s. Thus,

$$Q = 0.126 \text{ m}^3\text{/s} \, \frac{1.585 \times 10^4 \text{ gal/min}}{1.0 \text{ m}^3\text{/s}} = 1997 \text{ gal/min}$$

Thus, the volumetric flow rate is approximately 2000 gal/min. Calculate the head loss.

Solution.   The average velocity is

$$V_{av} = \frac{Q}{\pi D^2/4} = \frac{0.126}{[\pi(0.2)^2]/4} = 4.01 \text{ m/s}$$

and the Reynolds number is therefore

$$Re_D = \frac{V_{av} \, D}{\nu} = \frac{(4.01)(0.2)}{1 \times 10^{-5}} = 8.02 \times 10^4$$

At this Reynolds number, the flow in the pipe is transitionally rough.

Using Table 6.1, $\varepsilon = 0.026$ cm and, therefore, the relative roughness (ε/D) is 0.0013. Using the Moody diagram (Fig. 6.6),

$$f \approx 0.0235$$

Hence, using Eq. 6.2, we obtain the expression for the head loss:

$$\Delta p = \rho \, \frac{V_{av}^2}{2} \frac{L}{D} f$$

$$= (860 \text{ kg/m}^3) \, \frac{(4.01 \text{ m/s})^2}{2} \frac{300 \text{ m}}{0.2 \text{ m}} \, 0.0235 = 2.437 \times 10^5 \text{ N/m}^2$$

Thus, the pressure decreases 2.437×10^5 N/m^2 over 300 m of pipe length. This is equivalent to a pressure drop of 35.35 psi over 984 ft of pipe.

Since the flow rate is not known in the second type of problem, we also do not know the velocity or the friction factor. Therefore, we must develop a procedure to satisfy the Darcy–Weisbach equation and the Moody diagram simultaneously in order to obtain the appropriate values of these two parameters.

Example 6.3

Water at 20°C flows through a smooth plastic pipe that is 6 cm in diameter. If there is a head loss (h_f) of 10 m over a length of 500 m of pipe, what is the volumetric flow rate?

Solution.   (a) Using Fig. 1.5, the viscosity of water is 1×10^{-3} N · s/m^2. For simplicity, we will use 1000 kg/m^3 for the density of water. Thus, the Reynolds number is

$$\text{Re}_D = \frac{\rho D V_{av}}{\mu} = 6.0 \times 10^4 \, V_{av}$$

(b) For a smooth plastic pipe, we will assume ε/D is approximately zero. Thus, we will use the curve for smooth pipes, the lowest curve in the Moody diagram (Fig. 6.6).
 (c) Rearranging the Darcy–Weisbach equation, Eq. (6.2), we find that

$$V_{av} = \left[h_f \frac{2gD}{Lf} \right]^{0.5}$$

(i) First iteration: Let us assume $V_{av} = 5$ m/s. Thus, (a) $\text{Re}_D = 3.0 \times 10^5$. (b) For a smooth-pipe flow at this Reynolds number, we use the Moody diagram to find that $f = 0.0142$. (c) Using the Darcy–Weisbach equation,

$$V_{av} = \left[10 \, \frac{2(9.8066)0.06}{(500)(0.0142)} \right]^{0.5} = 1.287 \text{ m/s}$$

(ii) Second iteration: Let us assume $V_{av} = 0.8$ m/s. (a) Thus, $\text{Re}_D = 4.8 \times 10^4$. (b) Using the Moody diagram, $f = 0.021$. (c) $V_{av} = 1.059$ m/s.
 (iii) Third iteration: Clearly the variation in the average velocity is relatively insensitive to the variation in f. Thus, let us assume that $V_{av} = 1.11$ m/s. (a) $\text{Re}_D = 6.66 \times 10^4$. (b) $f = 0.0194$. (c) $V_{av} = 1.10$ m/s. Since the calculated value of the average velocity is equal to the assumed value, we have completed the iterative procedure. To calculate the volumetric flow rate,

$$Q = V_{av} \frac{\pi D^2}{4} = 1.10 \, \frac{\pi (0.06)^2}{4} = 0.00311 \text{ m}^3/\text{s} = 49.3 \text{ gal/min}$$

Since D is unknown for the third type of elementary pipe-flow problem, we also do not know V_{av}, Re_D, or f. The relative roughness is also unknown. Therefore, we must develop an iterative procedure to obtain the appropriate values of these parameters.

Example 6.4

Crude oil with a specific gravity of 0.86 and a kinematic viscosity (ν) of 1×10^{-5} m^2/s flows through a wrought-iron pipe. Determine the diameter of the pipe that is 3000 m long if we are to move 0.25 m³/s of oil through the pipe while limiting the head loss (h_f) to 25 m.

Solution.   Using Table 6.1, $\varepsilon = 0.0046$ cm. Since we know the volumetric flow rate, we will use Q instead of V_{av}:

$$V_{av} = \frac{4Q}{\pi D^2}$$

Thus, the Darcy–Weisbach equation can be rewritten:

$$\text{(a)}\quad D^5 = \frac{8Q^2 L}{\pi^2 g h_f} f = 0.62 f$$

Furthermore, the Reynolds number is

$$\text{(b)}\quad \mathrm{Re}_D = \frac{V_{av} D}{\nu} = \frac{4Q}{\pi D \nu} = \frac{3.183 \times 10^4}{D}$$

(i) First iteration: Let us assume that $f = 0.02$. Using equation (a), $D = 0.4156$ m. From (b), $\mathrm{Re}_D = 7.659 \times 10^4$ and $\varepsilon/D = 0.00011$. Using the values for these two parameters, we can find the corresponding value of f using the Moody diagram; $f = 0.0198$. This value is reasonably close to our initial guess, so we will not iterate.

Thus, the diameter of the required pipe is 0.4156 m.

MINOR LOSSES

The head losses that occur in pipelines due to valves, fittings, and the like, are called minor losses. For many applications (e.g., a partially closed valve), these losses may be relatively large. Thus, even though they are called minor losses, there are many situations in which they are more important than the head losses due to friction that are described in the previous sections. Minor losses include pressure losses that are due to the presence of the following:

1. Entrance or exit of the pipe.
2. Expansions or contractions of the pipe cross section.
3. Bends, elbows, tees, and other fittings.
4. Valves.

Since the flow patterns associated with these configurations are usually quite complex, in most cases the minor head losses are determined experimentally and presented as correlations in terms of the pipe-flow parameters. Experience has shown that the experimentally determined values may depend on the particular manufacturer's design. Thus, the values presented herein should be taken as nominal values for developing solution techniques.

The correlation for minor head loss can be represented as

$$h_{f_m} = \frac{\Delta p}{\rho g} = K \frac{V_{av}^2}{2g} \tag{6.22}$$

where K is a dimensionless head-loss factor. The values of K presented in the literature are usually given in terms of the dimensions of the fitting, but not in terms of the Reynolds number or roughness ratio. Furthermore, the values are usually for turbulent flow into the device.

Minor head loss can also be expressed in terms of the equivalent length of pipe (L_e) that causes the same head loss at the same volumetric flow rate. Thus,

$$f \frac{L_e}{D} \frac{V_{av}^2}{2g} = K \frac{V_{av}^2}{2g}$$

in which K may refer to the minor head loss due to a single element or due to a combination of pipe fittings. Solving for L_e gives

$$L_e = \frac{KD}{f} \tag{6.23}$$

Thus, if the sum of the minor losses in a 25-cm pipe is equivalent to a K of 20 and if f = 0.02 for the line, the effective length of the pipe line is the actual length of the pipe line plus 250 m, which is determined using Eq. (6.23).

Entrance or the Exit of the Pipe. Head losses at the entrance are highly dependent on the entrance geometry; losses at the exit are not. Sharp edges or protusions at the entrance produce large zones of separated flow and, therefore, relatively large head losses. Rounding the entrance can reduce the head loss dramatically. Thus, the value of K for a well-rounded entrance (i.e., one for which the corner radius is 0.2D) is only 0.05. At the exit, however, the flow simply passes out of the pipe into the large downstream reservoir and loses its complete velocity head due to viscous dissipation. Therefore, K = 1.0 for all exit configurations, no matter how well they are designed. Values of K for various entrances and for the exit are presented in Table 6.2.

Expansions or Contractions of the Pipe Cross Section. The head-loss factor for an abrupt change in cross-sectional area is presented in Fig. 6.7. For both the sudden expansion and sudden contraction, the head loss is based on the average velocity for the smaller pipe.

For a sudden expansion, the head-loss factor is

$$K = \left(1 - \frac{d^2}{D^2}\right)^2 \tag{6.24}$$

where d is the diameter of the smaller pipe and D is that of the larger pipe. Note that if there is a sudden expansion from a pipe (of diameter d) to a reservoir (i.e., if $d/D = 0$), K = 1. This is consistent with the value presented in Table 6.2. Thus, the complete kinetic energy is lost due to viscous dissipation.

For a sudden contraction, flow separation in the downstream pipe causes the fluid

TABLE 6.2 REPRESENTATIVE VALUES OF THE HEAD-LOSS
FACTOR FOR ENTRANCES AND FOR THE EXIT

Entrance		K
Projecting inward (or reentrant)		0.78
Sharp edged		0.40–0.50
Slightly rounded		0.23
Well rounded		0.05
Exit		
Projecting, sharp edged, well rounded		1.00

to contract to a minimum diameter that is smaller than the diameter of the smaller pipe (d). The minimum diameter is called the *vena contracta*. The values for the head-loss presented in Fig. 6.7 are given by the approximation

$$K = 0.40\left(1 - \frac{d^2}{D^2}\right)^2 \tag{6.25}$$

If the change in cross-sectional area is gradual, the losses are quite different. The head-loss factor for a gradual conical expansion (often called a *diffuser*) is presented in Fig. 6.8. Based on the correlations presented, the minimum head loss occurs when the included conical angle is approximately 5°. There is a large friction-related (Moody-type) head loss due to the long diffuser length required to attain a given increase in diameter if the conical angle is smaller than 5°. If the cone angle is much larger, the flow separates from the wall and produces a large head loss, and it would actually be better to use a sudden expansion. The divergence angle is of prime importance in the design of the

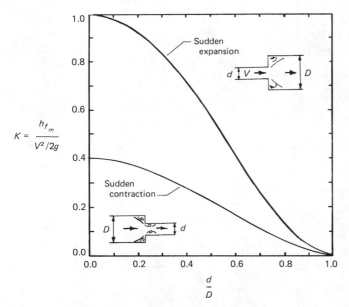

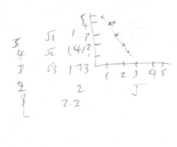

Figure 6.7 Head-loss factor (K) for an abrupt change in cross section.

diffuser. The designer must often account for other parameters, such as the Reynolds number, viscous layer thickness, and surface roughness.

For a gradual contraction, the head loss is relatively small. Representative values of the head-loss factor are presented in Table 6.3.

Bends, Elbows, and Tees. The head-loss factors for representative elbows and tees are presented in Table 6.4. Small fittings usually use internal screw connections, while larger fittings are connected by flanges. Note that K generally decreases with the size of the connected pipe. This is consistent with our previous experience that head-loss factors decrease as the Reynolds numbers increase and as the relative roughness decreases.

Valves. The valve loss coefficients presented in Table 6.4 are for the fully open condition. The pressure loss is much greater when the valve is only partially open. The

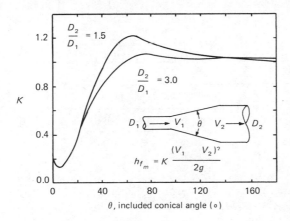

Figure 6.8 Head-loss factors for gradual conical expansions.

TABLE 6.3 REPRESENTATIVE VALUES OF
THE HEAD-LOSS FACTOR FOR A GRADUAL
CONICAL CONTRACTION

Contraction cone-angle (degrees)	K
30	0.02
45	0.04
60	0.07

TABLE 6.4 DIMENSIONLESS HEAD-LOSS FACTORS (*K*) FOR OPEN VALVES, ELBOWS, AND TEES

Nominal diameter, in.	Screwed				Flanged				
	$\frac{1}{2}$	1	2	4	1	2	4	8	20
Valves (fully open)									
Globe	14	8.2	6.9	5.7	13	8.5	6.0	5.8	5.5
Gate	0.30	0.24	0.16	0.11	0.80	0.35	0.16	0.07	0.03
Swing check	5.1	2.9	2.1	2.0	2.0	2.0	2.0	2.0	2.0
Angle	9.0	4.7	2.0	1.0	4.5	2.4	2.0	2.0	2.0
Elbows									
45° regular	0.39	0.32	0.30	0.29					
45° long radius					0.21	0.20	0.19	0.16	0.14
90° regular	2.0	1.5	0.95	0.64	0.50	0.39	0.30	0.26	0.21
90° long radius	1.0	0.72	0.41	0.23	0.40	0.30	0.19	0.15	0.10
180° regular	2.0	1.5	0.95	0.64	0.41	0.35	0.30	0.25	0.20
180° long radius					0.40	0.30	0.21	0.15	0.10
Tees									
Line flow	0.90	0.90	0.90	0.90	0.24	0.19	0.14	0.10	0.07
Branch flow	2.4	1.8	1.4	1.1	1.0	0.80	0.64	0.58	0.41

Source: From *Fluid Mechanics* by F. M. White. Copyright © 1979 by McGraw-Hill Book Company. Used with the permission of McGraw-Hill Book Company.

TABLE 6.5 INCREASED LOSSES OF
PARTIALLY OPEN VALVES

Condition	Ratio *K* / *K*(open condition)	
	Gate valve	Globe valve
Open	1.0	1.0
Closed, 25%	3.0–5.0	1.5–2.0
50%	12–22	2.0–3.0
75%	70–120	6.0–8.0

Source: White, *Fluid Mechanics*.

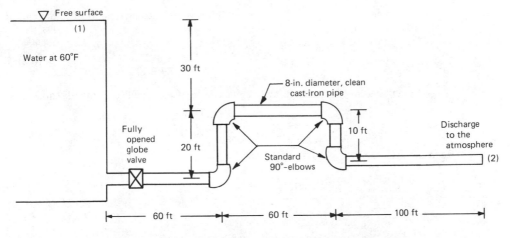

Figure 6.9 Pipeline system for Example 6.5.

approximate increases in the head-loss factors for partially open valves are indicated in Table 6.5. Because of the complex geometry of the valves, the head-loss factors are very sensitive to the manufacturer's design details. If accurate values are required, the manufacturer's data should always be consulted.

Example 6.5

Water flows from a large, open tank (1), through a pipeline system, and discharges to the atmosphere (2), as shown in Fig. 6.9. The density of water is 1.938 slugs/ft³; the viscosity is 2.088×10^{-5} lbf · s/ft². Find the volumetric flow rate through the pipeline.

Solution. Applying the modified Bernoulli's equation to the flow between points 1 and 2,

$$\frac{V_1^2}{2g} + z_1 + \frac{p_1}{\rho g} = \frac{V_2^2}{2g} + z_2 + \frac{p_2}{\rho g} + h_f \tag{6.1}$$

Using station 2 as our reference height, $z_1 = 40$ ft and $z_2 = 0$. The pressure both for the free surface at (1) and for the pipe discharge at (2) is atmospheric. Furthermore, since the tank is large, $V_1 \simeq 0$. Thus, we can reduce Eq. (6.1) to the conditions of this flow:

$$40 = \frac{V_2^2}{2g} + h_f \tag{6.26}$$

Because the pipe and fittings are of constant diameter, the velocity will be constant throughout. Thus, we need to determine the minor losses for each of the elements. Let us list the elements and their head-loss factors.

Element	K
(a) Sharp-edged entrance	0.50
(b) Fully opened globe valve	5.8
(c) Four standard 90° elbows	4×0.26
Total	7.34

We must also consider the head loss in the 250 ft of pipe in the system. To evaluate h_f for the friction in the pipe,

$$h_f = \frac{V_{av}^2}{2g}\frac{L}{D}f = \frac{V_2^2}{2g}\frac{L}{D}f \tag{6.2}$$

Combining this information, the resultant form of the modified Bernoulli equation is

$$40 = \frac{V_2^2}{2g} + K\frac{V_2^2}{2g} + \frac{V_2^2}{2g}\frac{L}{D}f$$

Rearranging,

$$80g = V_2^2(1 + K + \frac{L}{D}f)$$

Finally,

$$2.574 \times 10^3 = V_2^2(8.34 + 375f) \tag{6.27}$$

We have two unknowns that must satisfy one explicit equation and the relations of the Moody diagram. Therefore, we must develop an iterative procedure to determine the value of f that is consistent with V_2. To calculate f, we need to know ε/D and Re_D. For an 8-in. cast-iron pipe,

$$\frac{\varepsilon}{D} = \frac{0.00085}{8/12} = 0.001275$$

The Reynolds number

$$Re_D = \frac{\rho V_2 D}{\mu} = \frac{(1.938 \text{ lbf s}^2/\text{ft}^4) V_2}{2.088 \times 10^{-5} \text{ lbf s/ft}^2}\left(\frac{8}{12}\right) \text{ ft} = 6.188 \times 10^4 V_2$$

Let us now calculate V_2 by an iterative procedure.

First iteration: Let us assume $f = 0.02$. Solving Eq. (6.27) for the velocity, $V_2 = 12.75$ ft/s. Thus, the Reynolds number would be 7.89×10^5. For this value of the Reynolds number and for $\varepsilon/D = 0.001275$, we use the Moody diagram to find f.

$$f = 0.021$$

Second iteration: Let us assume $f = 0.021$. Following the same procedure as the first iteration,

$$V_2 = 12.60 \text{ ft/s}$$

$$Re_D = 7.80 \times 10^5$$

Note that there is no significant difference between the value of f that we would obtain from the Moody diagram and the assumed value. Thus, $V_2 = 12.60$ ft/s.

The volumetric flow rate that we seek is

$$Q = VA = 12.60\left[\frac{\pi}{4}\left(\frac{8}{12}\right)^2\right] = 4.398 \text{ ft}^3/\text{s}$$

Since 1 gal/min = 0.002228 ft³/s, this volumetric flow rate may also be written as 1974.1 gal/min.

Hydraulic Grade Line and Energy Grade Line

The concept of the hydraulic grade line (HGL) and the energy grade line (EGL) that were developed in Chapter 5 are useful in analyzing more complex flow problems. Recall that the energy grade line corresponds to a graph of the total energy of the flow as a function of the distance along the pipe; that is,

$$\text{EGL} = \frac{V^2}{2g} + z + \frac{p}{\rho g} \qquad (5.17)$$

Furthermore, the hydraulic grade line corresponds to the locus of heights to which the liquid would rise in vertical glass tubes connected to piezometer openings in the line; that is,

$$\text{HGL} = z + \frac{p}{\rho g} \qquad (5.18)$$

In these two equations, the pressure is the gage value. Thus, if the pressure in the pipeline were less than atmospheric, $p/\rho g$ would be negative. By definition, the energy grade line is vertically above the hydraulic grade line by a distance of $V^2/2g$.

The hydraulic grade line and the energy grade line for a simple pipeline that contains a square-edged entrance, a valve, and a nozzle at the end of the pipeline are presented in Fig. 6.10. To construct these lines when the reservoir surface is given, it is necessary to apply the modified Bernoulli's equation from the reservoir to the exit, accounting for minor losses and skin friction, in order to calculate the velocity head, $V^2/2g$. Then, to find the elevation of the hydraulic grade line at any point, the modified Bernoulli's equation is applied between the reservoir and that point, accounting for all the losses between the two points.

As shown in Fig. 6.10, the free surface of the reservoir is the initial point on both the hydraulic grade line and energy grade line. Assuming that $K = 0.5$ for the sharp-edged entrance of pipe, the energy grade line drops by $0.5 (V^2/2g)$ because of this loss. The hydraulic grade line drops by $1.5 (V^2/2g)$. To see this more clearly, let us apply the modified Bernoulli equation between the free surface and a point just downstream of the square-edged reference:

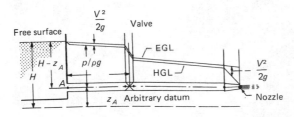

Figure 6.10 The HGL and EGL for a simple pipeline flow.

$$H + \frac{p_{\text{atm}}}{\rho g} + 0 = z_A + \frac{p_A}{\rho g} + \frac{V_A^2}{2g} + 0.5\frac{V_A^2}{2g}$$

where the $0.5\ (V_A^2/2g)$ is the head loss at the entrance. Rearranging, we find

$$z_A + \frac{p_A - p_{\text{atm}}}{\rho g} = H - 1.5\frac{V_A^2}{2g} \qquad (6.28)$$

The left-hand side of this equation is by definition the hydraulic grade line at A. Although it is customary to portray the energy loss due to the sharp-edged entrance as occurring at the entrance, it does not actually occur at the entrance itself but over a distance of ten or more diameters into the pipe. One can construct the complete energy grade line and hydraulic grade line in this matter.

The hydraulic gradient is the slope of the hydraulic grade line. For constant area pipelines, it is h_f/L, which can be determined from the Darcy–Weisbach equation. Thus,

$$\frac{h_f}{L} = \frac{f}{D}\frac{V^2}{2g}$$

The energy gradient is the slope of the energy grade line. With the exception of flow through a pump, the flow is always in the direction of decreasing energy grade line. The energy that is added to the flow by a pump can be expressed in the modified Bernoulli equation as a negative loss or by representing the energy per unit weight added as a positive term on the upstream side of the equation. The hydraulic grade line rises sharply at a pump. This will be discussed further in Chapter 8 where the role of these parameters will be more correctly defined using the energy equation.

Example 6.6

Water is pumped from a large reservoir to a device through the pipeline system, as shown in Fig. 6.11. The pump has a shaft input of 150 hp and an efficiency of 80%. What pressure will be available at the inlet of the device (i.e., at 3), if the volumetric flow is 10 ft³/s. For water at 60°F, $\gamma = 62.35$ lbf/ft³.

Solution.   Since we know the volumetric flow rate and since the pipe diameter is constant throughout the system, we can calculate the average velocity in the pipe:

$$V_{\text{av}} = V_3 = \frac{Q}{\pi D^2/4} = 28.648 \text{ ft/s}$$

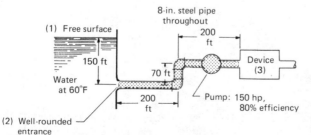

Figure 6.11   Sketch for Example 6.6.

Since the pump has a shaft input of 150 hp at an 80% efficiency, 120 hp are input into the water. The pump produces a sharp increase in the hydraulic grade line and will be represented in the modified Bernoulli equation as the negative of the energy added per unit weight. Since 1 hp = 550 ft · lbf/s, the effect of the pump is

$$-\frac{\dot{W}_s}{\dot{m}g} = -\frac{\dot{W}_s}{\gamma Q} = -\frac{66000}{(62.35)(10)} = -105.9 \text{ ft}$$

Let us apply the modified Bernoulli equation, accounting for the energy added by the pump and the minor losses between the free surface at the reservoir (1) and a point in the pipe just upstream of the inlet of the device (3).

$$\frac{V_1^2}{2g} + z_1 + \frac{p_1}{\rho g} = \frac{V_3^2}{2g} + z_3 + \frac{p_3}{\rho g} + K\frac{V_{av}^2}{2g} + \frac{V_{av}^2}{2g}\frac{L}{D}f - \frac{\dot{W}}{\dot{m}g} \qquad (6.29)$$

The reader may be interested in comparing this equation, which describes a system with losses and with a pump that puts energy into the system, and Eq. (5.16), which describes a system with no losses and with a turbine that extracts energy from the system. See also the examples in Chapter 8.

In this equation, $K [V_{av}^2/(2g)]$ is the summation of the minor losses and $(V_{av}^2/2g)(L/D)f$ is the Darcy–Weisbach expression for the head loss due to friction. Let us tabulate the head-loss factors for each of the elements of the pipeline system.

Element		K
Well-rounded entrance		0.05
Two standard 90°-elbows		0.52
	Total	0.57

To calculate the head loss due to friction, we must first determine the friction factor f. To determine f from the Moody diagram, we need ε/D and Re_D. For an 8-in. steel pipe,

$$\frac{\varepsilon}{D} = \frac{0.0018}{8.0} = 0.000225$$

and, referring to Example 6.5, the Reynolds number is

$$Re_D = 6.188 \times 10^4 \ V_{av} = 1.773 \times 10^6$$

Thus, $f = 0.0146$.

Using the elevation of the entrance to the device as the reference level, $z_3 = 0$ and $z_1 = 80$ ft. Thus, Eq. (6.29) can be written as

$$80 \text{ ft} + \frac{p_{atm}}{\rho g} = \frac{p_3}{\rho g} + \left[1 + K + f\frac{L}{D}\right]\frac{V_3^2}{2g} - \frac{\dot{W}}{\gamma Q}$$

$$p_3 - p_{atm} = (62.35) [80 - (1.0 + 0.57 + 10.293)12.754 - (-105.9)]$$

$$= 2157.3 \text{ lbf/ft}^2 = 15.0 \text{ lbf/in.}^2$$

Thus, the pressure at the inlet to the device (point 3) is 15.0 psi, gage, or 103.3 kPa, gage.

MULTIPLE-PIPE SYSTEMS

Having developed techniques to solve for the flow in a general single-pipe system, we can apply them to solve more complex systems. When a system contains two or more pipes, certain basic rules can be used to simplify the calculation procedure. We will consider three types of multiple-pipe systems: (1) pipes in series, (2) pipes in parallel, and (3) a branching-pipe, or interconnected reservoir, system. Sketches illustrating these three types of multiple-pipe systems are presented in Fig. 6.12.

Pipes in Series

When pipes of different size and different roughness are connected so that the fluid flows through each pipe in the sequence, they are said to be connected in series. For three pipes in series, the continuity equation yields

$$Q_1 = Q_2 = Q_3 = \text{constant} \tag{6.30}$$

Furthermore, the total head loss through the system equals the sum of the head loss in each pipe:

$$h_{f_{AB}} = h_{f_1} + h_{f_2} + h_{f_3} \tag{6.31}$$

Example 6.7

Water flows from a reservoir through three pipes in series, as shown in Fig. 6.13. Pipe 1 is 20 m long, 20 cm in diameter; pipe 2 is 30 m long, 15 cm in diameter; and pipe 3 is 30

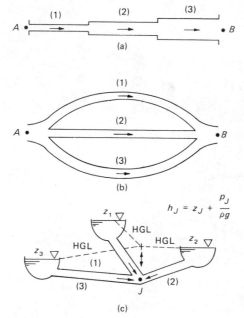

Figure 6.12 Multiple-pipe systems: (a) pipes in series; (b) pipes in parallel; (c) interconnected reservoir system.

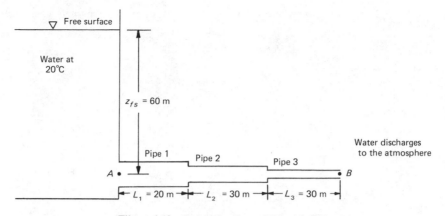

Figure 6.13 Series-pipe flow of Example 6.7.

m long, 10 cm in diameter. All three pipes are cast iron. If the pipe system is in a horizontal plane, located 60 m below the free surface of the reservoir, what is the flow rate?

Solution. Let us apply the modified Bernoulli equation between the free surface of the reservoir and the existing flow:

$$z_{fs} + \frac{p_{\text{atm}}}{\rho g} = \frac{V_3^2}{2g} + \frac{p_{\text{atm}}}{\rho g} + h_{f_{AB}} \tag{6.32}$$

To simplify the solution procedure, we will express the flow in each pipe in terms of the velocity in the third pipe. Thus, using the continuity equation,

$$V_1 = \left(\frac{d_3}{d_1}\right)^2 V_3 = 0.25V_3, \qquad V_2 = \left(\frac{d_3}{d_2}\right)^2 V_3 = 0.444V_3$$

Let us now evaluate the minor head losses associated with the transition from one section to the next. The minor head loss at the sharp-edged entrance from the reservoir to the pipe system is

$$h_f = 0.5 \frac{V_1^2}{2g} = 0.0313 \frac{V_3^2}{2g}$$

Since $d/D = 0.75$, the minor head loss at the sudden contraction from pipe 1 to 2 is

$$h_f = 0.0766 \frac{V_2^2}{2g} = 0.0151 \frac{V_3^2}{2g}$$

where we use V_2, since (as noted in the text) the head loss is based on the velocity in the smaller pipe. Since $d/D = 0.667$, the minor head loss at the sudden contraction from pipe 2 to 3 is

$$h_f = 0.1235 \frac{V_3^2}{2g}$$

Let us now calculate the skin friction losses. For the three pipes, they are

$$h_f = \frac{V_1^2}{2g}(100)f_1 = 6.25f_1\frac{V_3^2}{2g}$$

$$h_f = \frac{V_2^2}{2g}(200)f_2 = 39.51f_2\frac{V_3^2}{2g}$$

and

$$h_f = \frac{V_3^2}{2g}(300)f_3 = 300.00f_3\frac{V_3^2}{2g}$$

Thus, substituting these equations into Eq. (6.32), we obtain

$$z_{fs} = 60 \text{ m} = \frac{V_3^2}{2g} + \frac{V_3^2}{2g}(0.0313 + 0.0151 + 0.1235)$$

$$+ \frac{V_3^2}{2g}(6.25f_1 + 39.51f_2 + 300.00f_3)$$

Thus,

$$1176.8 = V_3^2(1.1699 + 6.25f_1 + 39.51f_2 + 300.00f_3) \tag{6.33}$$

To calculate the skin friction factors, we need the appropriate values of ε/D and Re_D for each of the three pipes. The relative roughnesses are

$$\frac{\varepsilon_1}{D_1} = 0.0013, \qquad \frac{\varepsilon_2}{D_2} = 0.00173, \qquad \frac{\varepsilon_3}{D_3} = 0.0026$$

The Reynolds numbers are

$$\text{Re}_D = \frac{\rho V_i D_i}{\mu} \approx 10^6 V_i D_i$$

Thus,

$$\text{Re}_{D_1} = 0.5 \times 10^5\, V_3, \qquad \text{Re}_{D_2} = 0.667 \times 10^5\, V_3, \qquad \text{Re}_{D_3} = 1.0 \times 10^5\, V_3$$

Let us use an iterative procedure to solve for the flow through the pipe system. (i) First iteration: Let us assume $V_3 = 2.0$ m/s. Then

$$\text{Re}_{D_1} = 1.0 \times 10^5, \qquad \text{Re}_{D_2} = 1.334 \times 10^5, \qquad \text{Re}_{D_3} = 2.0 \times 10^5$$

Using the Moody diagram, we find that

$$f_1 = 0.023, \qquad f_2 = 0.024, \qquad f_3 = 0.0262$$

Substituting these values into Eq. (6.33), we obtain

$$V_3 = 10.782 \text{ m/s}$$

(ii) Second iteration: Let us assume $V_3 = 10$ m/s. Then

$$\text{Re}_{D_1} = 5.0 \times 10^5, \qquad \text{Re}_{D_2} = 6.667 \times 10^5, \qquad \text{Re}_{D_3} = 10.0 \times 10^5$$

Using the Moody diagram, we find that

$$f_1 = 0.0213, \quad f_2 = 0.023, \quad f_3 = 0.026$$

Substituting these values into Eq. (6.33), we obtain

$$V_3 = 10.841 \text{ m/s}$$

(iii) Third iteration: Let us assume $V_3 = 10.84$ m/s. Then

$$\text{Re}_{D_1} = 5.42 \times 10^5, \quad \text{Re}_{D_2} = 7.23 \times 10^5, \quad \text{Re}_{D_3} = 10.84 \times 10^5$$

Using the Moody diagram, we find that

$$f_1 = 0.0212, \quad f_2 = 0.023, \quad f_3 = 0.026$$

Substituting these values into Eq. (6.33), we obtain

$$V_3 = 10.842 \text{ m/s}$$

Thus, we have found the desired velocity,

$$V_3 = 10.84 \text{ m/s}$$

and, therefore, the volumetric flow rate is 0.085 m³/s.

Pipes in Parallel

A combination of two or more pipes connected as in Fig. 6.12b, so that the flow is divided among the pipes and then flows together again, is called a parallel-pipe system. For pipes in parallel, the mechanical energy (i.e., the head loss) is the same for each line and the volumetric flow rates are cumulative. Thus,

$$h_{f_{AB}} = h_{f_1} = h_{f_2} = h_{f_3} \tag{6.34}$$

and

$$Q_{AB} = Q_1 + Q_2 + Q_3 \tag{6.35}$$

There are two types of flow problems common to parallel-pipe flows: (1) given the elevation of the hydraulic grade line at A and B, find the volumetric flow rate, and (2) given the volumetric flow rate Q, find the distribution of flow and the head loss. For both types of flow problems, the pipe material and dimensions, the pipeline elements, and the fluid properties are known. If the total head loss is known, it is a relatively straightforward exercise to solve for each Q_i and to add them up to determine the total flow rate. The second type of problem is more difficult, since neither the head loss nor the discharge for any one pipe is known. A possible solution procedure is as follows.

1. Assume a discharge for pipe 1.
2. Using the assumed flow rate, solve for the head loss in this pipeline, h_{f_1}.
3. Using h_{f_1}, determine Q_2 and Q_3.

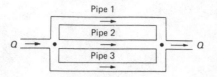

Figure 6.14   Three pipes in parallel for Example 6.8

4. Having calculated the three component flow rates for the common head loss, sum them to determine $\Sigma \, Q_i$. If the summation is incorrect (i.e., if $\Sigma \, Q_i \neq Q$), the original value of Q_1 should be scaled in proportion. Thus, if $\Sigma \, Q_i = 1.22Q$, $Q_{1,\text{new}} = Q_{1,\text{old}}/1.22$, and repeat the iterative process until it converges.

Example 6.8

Assume that three pipes are in parallel in a horizontal plane as shown in Fig. 6.14. The pipe data are as follows.

Pipe	L (m)	D (cm)	ε (mm)
1	120	10	0.26
2	100	20	0.26
3	120	10	0.046

The head loss for each pipe in the system is 10 m. Neglecting the minor losses (but not the friction losses), calculate the total flow rate of water flowing through the pipe network.

Solution

$$\frac{\varepsilon_1}{D_1} = 0.0026, \qquad \frac{\varepsilon_2}{D_2} = 0.0013, \qquad \frac{\varepsilon_3}{D_3} = 0.00046$$

Using the Darcy–Weisbach equation to calculate the head loss due to skin friction,

$$h_f = 10.0 = \frac{V_1^2}{2g} 1200f_1 = \frac{V_2^2}{2g} 500f_2 = \frac{V_3^2}{2g} 1200f_3 \tag{6.36}$$

Assume that the flow in pipe 1 is completely turbulent. Thus, since f_1 would be independent of Reynolds number, $f_1 = 0.026$. Solving Eq. (6.36) for V_1, we find that

$$V_1 = 2.507 \text{ m/s}$$

Thus, the Reynolds number would be

$$\text{Re}_{D_1} = \frac{\rho V_1 D_1}{\mu} = 10^5 \, V_1 = 2.507 \times 10^5$$

Using the Moody diagram, $f_1 = 0.0262$. Solving Eq. (6.36) again,

$$V_1 = 2.498 \text{ m/s}$$

and $Q_1 = 0.0196 \text{ m}^3/\text{s}$.

Assume that the flow in pipe 2 is completely turbulent. Thus, $f_2 = 0.021$. Solving Eq. (6.36),

$$V_2 = 4.322 \text{ m/s}$$

Thus, the Reynolds number would be

$$\text{Re}_{D_2} = 2.0 \times 10^5 \; V_2 = 8.644 \times 10^5$$

Using the Moody diagram, $f_2 = 0.0213$. For this value of f_2,

$$V_2 = 4.291 \text{ m/s}$$

which is essentially the value used to calculate the Reynolds number and is, therefore, the desired value. Thus,

$$Q_2 = 0.1348 \text{ m}^3/\text{s}$$

For pipe 3, let us assume that $f_3 = 0.0165$. Thus,

$$V_3 = 3.147 \text{ m/s}$$

For which $\text{Re}_{D_3} = 3.147 \times 10^5$. Using the Moody diagram,

$$f_3 = 0.0182$$

Thus,

$$V_3 = 2.997 \text{ m/s}$$

for which $\text{Re}_{D_3} = 2.997 \times 10^5$. Using the Moody diagram,

$$f_3 = 0.0184$$

and

$$V_3 = 2.980 \text{ m/s, which is basically unchanged}$$

Thus,

$$Q_3 = 0.0234 \text{ m}^3/\text{s}$$

The total flow rate is

$$Q = Q_1 + Q_2 + Q_3 = 0.1778 \text{ m}^3/\text{s}$$

Interconnected-Reservoir System

A simple three-reservoir pipe system is shown in Fig. 6.12c. For this type of flow, the sizes and materials of the pipes are known, the fluid and its properties are known, and the reservoir elevations are known. The Darcy–Weisbach equation must be satisfied for each pipe, and the continuity equation must be satisfied. Thus, the flow into the junction J must equal the flow out of the junction. Flow must be out of the highest reservoir and into the lowest reservoir. However, flow may be either into or out of the intermediate reservoir.

The elevation of the hydraulic grade line at the junction J is $h_J = z_J + p_J/(\rho g)$, where p_J is the gage pressure. If h_J is above the elevation of the free surface of the intermediate reservoir, flow is into it. The continuity equation is

$$Q_1 = Q_2 + Q_3 \tag{6.37a}$$

However, if the elevation of the hydraulic grade line at J is below the free surface of the intermediate reservoir, the liquid flows out of the reservoir. The continuity equation is

$$Q_1 + Q_2 = Q_3 \tag{6.37b}$$

If each reservoir is open to the atmosphere, as has been assumed in the previous paragraph, then $p_1 = p_2 = p_3 = p_{atm} = 0$, gage pressure at the surface of each reservoir. The head loss through each pipe must be such that

$$\Delta h_1 = \frac{V_1^2 L_1}{2g D_1} f_1 = z_1 - h_J \tag{6.38a}$$

$$\Delta h_2 = \frac{V_2^2 L_2}{2g D_2} f_2 = z_2 - h_J \tag{6.38b}$$

$$\Delta h_3 = \frac{V_3^2 L_3}{2g D_3} f_3 = z_3 - h_J \tag{6.38c}$$

Rearranging, we obtain a general expression for V_1, V_2, and V_3:

$$V_i^2 = \frac{(z_i - h_J)2g}{(L_i/D_i)f_i} \tag{6.39}$$

Note f_i and V_i are related through the Moody diagram and the Reynolds number.

In our iterative procedure, we will assume a value of h_J and solve Eq. (6.39) for V_i and hence the flow rates, Q_i. We will iterate until the flow rates into the junction balance.

Example 6.9

Three reservoirs containing crude oil are interconnected, as shown in Fig. 6.12c. Crude oil has a specific gravity of 0.86 and a kinematic viscosity of 1.0×10^{-5} m²/s. The elevations of the free surfaces of the reservoirs are

$$z_1 = 100 \text{ m}, \qquad z_2 = 40 \text{ m}, \qquad z_3 = 20 \text{ m}$$

The reservoirs are connected by steel pipes, 12 cm in diameter. $L_1 = 100$ m; $L_2 = L_3 = 50$ m. For purposes of illustration, we will neglect the minor losses in the pipes. Calculate the flow rate for each pipe.

Solution. For all three pipes, $\varepsilon/D = 0.000383$ and $\text{Re}_{D_i} = 1.2 \times 10^4 V_i$. For the first iteration, we will assume that $h_J = 40$ m. Since $h_J = z_2$ for this assumption, there will be no flow into or out of the second reservoir.

Reservoir	$z_i - h_J$	L_i/D_i	f_i	V_i (m/s)	Q_i (m³/s)
1	+60	833.33	0.02	8.45	+0.0956
2	0	416.67	–	0	0
3	−20	416.67	0.0205	6.78	−0.0767
				Net	+0.0189

Note that an iterative procedure is required to determine the compatible values of f_i and V_i that satisfy both Eq. (6.39) and the Moody diagram. The values of the flow rates assume that flow into the junction J is positive. Since we have a "surplus" of flow into the junction, the assumed value of h_J was too low.

For the second iteration, let us assume $h_J = 44$ m.

Reservoir	$z_i - h_J$	L_i/D_i	f_i	V_i (m/s)	Q_i (m³/s)
1	+56	833.33	0.020	8.12	+0.092
2	−4	416.67	0.024	2.80	−0.032
3	−24	416.67	0.0205	7.42	−0.084
				Net	−0.024

Comparing the results from the first two iterations, let us assume that $h_J = 41.4$ m. The corresponding values are shown below.

Reservoir	$z_i - h_J$	L_i/D_i	f_i	V_i (m/s)	Q_i (m³/s)
1	+58.6	833.33	0.020	8.30	+0.0939
2	−1.4	416.67	0.0268	1.57	−0.0178
3	−21.4	416.67	0.0205	7.01	−0.0793
				Net	−0.0032

The net flow is relatively close to balanced, so we will assume that the third iteration has produced the desired solution.

Example 6.10

Let us consider another situation involving three interconnected reservoirs, similar to those of Example 6.9. However, in this case, there is a pump in the line connecting the lowest reservoir (reservoir 3) to J. This situation may exist at a seaport–refinery complex where the lowest reservoir serves as temporary storage for the crude oil as it is transferred from the tanker and then to the other two reservoirs. We will use the same nomenclature and dimensions that were used in Example 6.9. Thus,

$$z_1 = 100 \text{ m}, \quad z_2 = 40 \text{ m}, \quad z_3 = 20 \text{ m}$$

Furthermore,

$$\frac{\varepsilon_i}{D_i} = 0.000383 \quad \text{and} \quad Re_{D_i} = 1.2 \times 10^4 \, V_i, \quad \text{for all three lines}$$

As shown in Fig. 6.15, a pump is installed in line 3 so that the crude oil can be transferred from reservoir 3 to the other reservoirs. The pump raises the HGL in the line by 150 m. Neglecting the minor losses in the pipelines, calculate the flow rate for each pipe.

Solution. Since there is a pump in line 3, we cannot use Eq. (6.38c) in our analysis. The appropriate equation for relating the conditions at the free surface of reservoir 3 to those at J is

$$z_3 + \frac{p_{\text{atm}}}{\rho g} + \Delta h_p = z_J + \frac{p_J}{\rho g} + \frac{V_3^2}{2g} \frac{L_3}{D_3} f_3$$

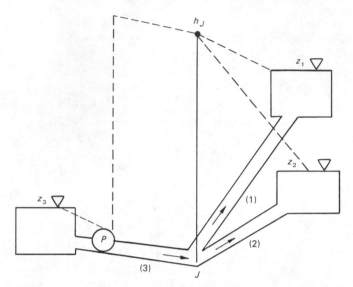

Figure 6.15 Interconnected reservoir system for Example 6.10.

where Δh_p, the change in head produced by the pump, is 150 m. Rearranging and noting that $h_J = z_J + (p_J - p_{atm})/(\rho g)$, we obtain

$$(z_3 - h_J) + \Delta h_p = \frac{V_3^2 L_3}{2g D_3} f_3 \tag{6.40}$$

The expressions for $(z_1 - h_J)$ and for $(z_2 - h_J)$ do not change; they are those given by Eq. (6.38) or (6.39).

To obtain the desired solution, we will repeat the procedure of the previous example. For the first iteration, let us assume $h_J = 110$ m.

Reservoir	$z_i - h_J$	L_i/D_i	f_i	V_i (m/s)	Q_i (m³/s)
1	-10	833.33	0.0220	4.626	-0.0523
2	-70	416.67	0.0187	13.274	-0.1501
3	-90	416.67	0.0190	12.192	$+0.1379$
				Net	-0.0645

Since the equation governing the flow in line 3 satisfies Eq. (6.40), we must add Δh_p to the value of $(z_3 - h_J)$ to determine V_3. The flow in lines 2 and 3 must satisfy Eq. (6.39), as before. Again, note that an iterative procedure is needed to obtain the values of f_i and V_i that satisfy both the Moody diagram and the governing equations, Eqs. (6.39) and (6.40). As before, a positive value of velocity indicates flow from a reservoir into the junction J. For the second iteration, let us assume that $h_J = 103$ m.

Reservoir	$z_i - h_J$	L_i/D_i	f_i	V_i (m/s)	Q_i (m³/s)
1	-3	833.33	0.027	1.617	-0.0183
2	-63	416.67	0.019	12.419	-0.1413
3	-83	416.67	0.0186	13.057	$+0.1477$
				Net	-0.0119

For the third iteration, we will assume that $h_J = 101.5$ m.

Reservoir	$z_i - h_J$	L_i/D_i	f_i	V_i (m/s)	Q_i (m³/s)
1	−1.5	833.33	0.0292	1.100	−0.0124
2	−61.5	416.67	0.019	12.344	−0.1396
3	−81.5	416.67	0.0185	13.202	+0.1493
				Net	−0.0027

Since the net flow is relatively small, we will use these last values as the solution we seek. Note that, although $z_3 - h_J = -81.5$, $(z_3 - h_J) + \Delta h_p = +68.5$, which provides the pressure head to drive the fluid into reservoirs 1 and 2.

NETWORK OF PIPES

Interconnected pipes through which the flow to a given outlet may come from several circuits are called a network of pipes, such as shown in Fig. 6.16. This might represent the water-supply system for an apartment or a subdivision. To solve the flow in the network, we must use a relatively complex, iterative procedure. However, the procedure must satisfy the following basic conditions.

1. The net flow into any junction must be zero.
2. The net head loss around any closed loop must be zero. In other words, the HGL at each junction must have one and only one elevation.
3. All head losses must satisfy the Moody and minor-loss friction correlations.

By applying these rules to each junction and independent loop in the network, one obtains a set of simultaneous algebraic equations for the flow rates in each pipe leg and the HGL at each junction. Since the equations are not linear, the solution is obtained by numerical iteration.

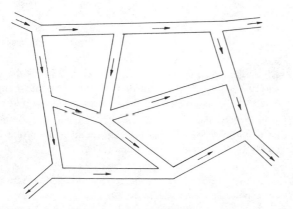

Figure 6.16 Network of pipes.

CONDUITS WITH NONCIRCULAR CROSS SECTIONS

In this chapter so far, only circular pipes have been considered. For cross sections that are noncircular, the Darcy–Weisbach equation may be applied if the term D can be interpreted in terms of the cross section. The concept of the hydraulic radius R_h permits noncircular cross sections to be treated in the same manner. The hydraulic radius is defined as the cross-sectional area divided by the wetted perimeter. (In a partially filled tube use only the perimeter in contact with fluid.) Hence, for a circular cross section,

$$R_h = \frac{\text{area}}{\text{perimeter}} = \frac{\pi D^2/4}{\pi D} = \frac{D}{4} \tag{6.41}$$

and the diameter is equivalent to $4R_h$. Assuming that the diameter may be replaced by $4R_h$ in the Darcy–Weisbach equation and in expressions for the Reynolds number and for the relative roughness,

$$h_f = f\frac{L}{4R_h}\frac{V^2}{2g}, \qquad \mathrm{Re}_D = \frac{\rho V(4R_h)}{\mu}, \qquad \frac{\varepsilon}{D} = \frac{\varepsilon}{4R_h} \tag{6.42}$$

A variety of noncircular cross sections may be handled in this manner. The Moody diagram applies as before. The assumptions in Eq. (6.42) cannot be expected to hold for odd-shaped sections but should give reasonable values for square, oval, triangular, and similar types of cross sections.

SUMMARY

Note that, in all the example problems of this chapter, we calculated the Reynolds number as part of the solution procedure. However, in those problems of Chapter 5 where we neglected the viscous effects, the Reynolds number was not calculated. Recall that, in Chapter 4, we noted that Reynolds number is important for all flows in which we account for viscosity. Conversely, when we can use the inviscid flow approximations, the value of the Reynolds number is immaterial.

PROBLEMS

6.1. SAE 30 oil at 20°C flows through a pipe that is 5 cm in diameter. What is the maximum value of the average velocity that still yields laminar flow? What is the maximum laminar flow rate in gallons per minute? What is the corresponding pressure loss in $N/m^2/m$?

6.2. For water at 20°C flowing in a pipe that is 4 in. in diameter, for what flow rate (in ft^3/s) would we expect transition to turbulence? What is the corresponding flow rate in gallons per minute? What is the corresponding pressure loss in $lbf/ft^2/ft$?

6.3. Water at 100°C is flowing in a pipe that is 4 in. in diameter. For what flow rate (in ft^3/s) would we expect transition to turbulence? What is the corresponding flow rate in gallons per minute? What is the corresponding pressure loss in $lbf/ft^2/ft$?

6.4. Water at 20°C flows through a smooth plastic pipe that is 21 cm in diameter. If the average velocity is 3 m/s, what is the head loss per meter of length of the pipe?

6.5. Water at 100°C flows through a smooth plastic pipe that is 21 cm in diameter. If the average velocity is 3 m/s, what is the head loss per meter of length of the pipe?

6.6. SAE 30 oil at 20°C flows through a smooth plastic pipe that is 20 cm in diameter. If the average velocity is 10 m/s, what is the head loss per meter of the pipe?

6.7. Gasoline at 20°C has a specific gravity of 0.68 and a viscosity of 3×10^{-4} N · s/m². What is the head loss per unit length if it flows through a steel pipe at a flow rate of 20 gal/min?

6.8. SAE 30 oil at 20°C flows through a steel pipe that is 10 cm in diameter. If there is a head loss (h_f) of 30 m over a length of 500 m of pipe, what is the volumetric flow rate?

6.9. Room temperature water (20°C) flows through a steel pipe at the rate of 1 ft³/s. The density of water is 1.937 slugs/ft³; the viscosity is 2.088×10^{-5} lbf · s/ft². If the allowable head loss (h_f) is 10 ft per 100-ft length of pipe, what is the diameter of the pipe?

6.10. Repeat Prob. 6.9 for SAE 30 oil.

6.11. Repeat Prob. 6.9 for glycerine.

6.12. Repeat Prob. 6.9 for methane.

6.13. Oil with a specific gravity of 0.85 drains from a tank through a steel pipe, as shown in Fig. P6.13. If the flow rate is 35 ft³/h, what is the kinematic viscosity of oil in ft²/s? Neglect minor losses. Is the flow laminar or turbulent?

6.14. For the configuration of Fig. P6.13, what is the flow rate of water at 20°C if we neglect minor losses? What is the flow rate if we account for the minor losses? The entrance is sharp edged.

6.15. If kerosene at 20°C is to be pumped through 60 m of drawn tubing at a volumetric flow rate of 20 m³/h with a head loss of 30 m, what is the proper tube diameter in centimeters?

6.16. Gasoline at 20°C is pumped at a flow rate of 0.3 m³/s through a cast-iron pipe that is 25 km long and 30 cm in diameter. If the viscosity is 3×10^{-4} N · s/m², compute the head loss in meters. What is the power required in kilowatts if the pumps are 75% efficient?

6.17. Oil whose properties are $\gamma = 50$ lbf/ft³ and $\mu = 5.0 \times 10^{-4}$ lbf · s/ft² flows through a 4-in.-diameter pipe. If the flow rate is 400 gal/min, what is the pressure loss in lbf/ft² per foot as a function of pipe roughness? Present your results as a graph of $\Delta p/L$ versus ε/D.

6.18. Water at 20°C flows from a large open tank through a pipeline system and discharges to the atmosphere, as shown in Fig. P6.18. The density of water is 1.937 slugs/ft³, the viscosity is 2.088×10^{-5} lbf · s/ft², and $z_1 = 15$ ft. The cast-iron pipe is 2 in. in diameter and 12 ft long (L_1). The fittings are screw type with a gate valve. The entrance is sharp edged. Calculate the flow rate in gallons per minute, neglecting any losses.

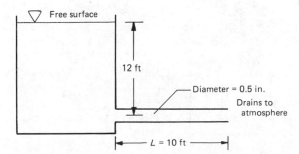

Figure P6.13 Sketch for Probs. 6.13 and 6.14.

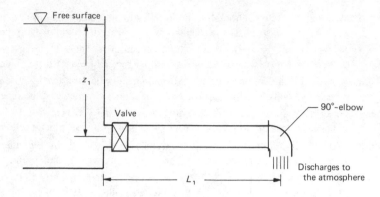

Figure P6.18   Sketch for Probs. 6.18 through 6.23.

6.19. Calculate the flow rate in gallons per minute for the pipeline system of Prob. 6.18 considering only the viscous losses in the pipe, that is, neglecting minor losses.

6.20. Calculate the flow rate in gallons per minute for the pipeline system of Prob. 6.18 accounting for all losses. Sketch the energy grade line and the hydraulic grade line for this flow.

6.21. SAE 30 oil at 20°C flows from a large open tank through a pipeline system and discharges to the atmosphere, as shown in Fig. P6.18. The steel pipe is 10.16 cm in diameter and 5 m long (L_1). The fittings are flange type with a globe valve. The entrance is well rounded. If the height z_1 is 8 m, calculate the flow rate in cubic meters per second, neglecting any losses.

6.22. Calculate the flow rate in cubic meters per second for the pipeline system of Prob. 6.21 considering only the viscous losses in the pipe, that is, neglecting minor losses.

6.23. Calculate the flow rate in cubic meters per second for the pipeline system of Prob. 6.21 accounting for all losses. Sketch the energy grade line and the hydraulic grade line for this flow.

6.24. The reservoirs of Fig. P6.24 contain water at 20°C. If the pipe is smooth, $L = 2000$ m, and $D = 5.08$ cm, what will be the flow rate in cubic meters per hour for $\Delta z = 100$ m? The entrance and exit to the pipe system are sharp edged.

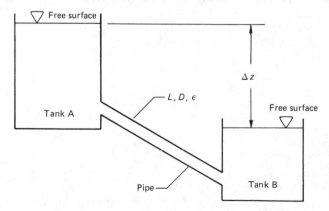

Figure P6.24   Sketch for Prob. 6.24 through 6.26.

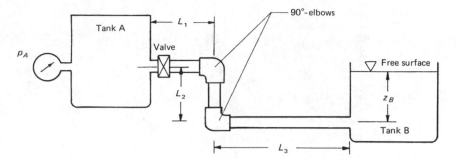

Figure P6.27   Sketch for Prob. 6.27.

6.25. The reservoirs of Fig. P6.24 again contain water at 20°C. Again $\Delta z = 100$ m, $L = 2000$ m, and $D = 5.08$ cm. What will be the flow rate in cubic meters per hour if $\varepsilon = 0.026$ cm? The entrance and exit to the pipe system are sharp edged.

6.26. The reservoirs of Fig. P6.24 contain oil at room temperature. The oil properties are $\mu = 5.0 \times 10^{-4}$ lbf · s/ft^2 and $\gamma = 50$ lbf/ft^3. The length of the steel pipe is 300 ft; $\Delta z = 30$ ft. The entrance to the pipe system is slightly rounded. If we are to deliver a minimum of 200 gal/min of oil, what should be the diameter of the pipe?

6.27. Water at 200°F flows through the pipeline system shown in Fig. P6.27. The pressure in tank A (i.e., P_A) is 70 psig. The entrance to the pipe system is sharp edged. The lengths are $L_1 = 100$ ft, $L_2 = 15$ ft, $L_3 = 100$ ft, and $z_B = 30$ ft. The fittings are flange type with a globe valve. What diameter of cast-iron pipe would deliver 1 cfs of water? Sketch the energy grade line and hydraulic grade line.

6.28. Consider room-temperature water in the tank–pipeline system shown in Fig. P6.28. The parameters are $p_A = 1.0 \times 10^6$ N/m^2, $z_A = 5$ m, $p_B = 8.0 \times 10^5$ N/m^2, $z_B = 5$ m, and $z_2 = 15$ m. The lengths of the cast-iron pipe, 10.16 cm in diameter, with flanged fittings,

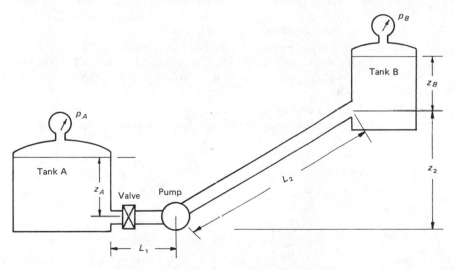

Figure P6.28   Sketch for Probs. 6.28 and 6.29.

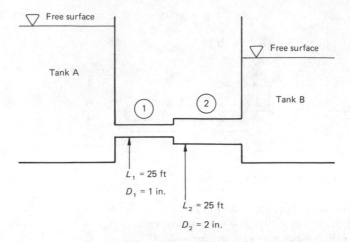

Figure P6.30 Sketch for Probs. 6.30 and 6.31.

are $L_1 = 10$ m and $L_2 = 50$ m. The entrance and exit are sharp edged. The valve is a globe valve. What is the power required to deliver 100 m³/h of water?

6.29. Repeating the conditions of Prob. 6.28, what is the power required to deliver 500 m³/h of water?

6.30. Room-temperature water flows between two reservoirs through two cast-iron pipes that are connected in series, as shown in Fig. P6.30. The entrance, exit, and pipe interface are sharp edged. Including minor losses, calculate the flow rate in cubic feet per second if the free surface of the water in tank A is 65 ft higher than that of tank B.

6.31. Repeat Prob. 6.30 for the case where the free-surface of the water in tank B is 65 ft higher than that of tank A. Note that the only difference between the two problems is the direction of the flow through the cross-section change. How much does the flow rate change?

6.32. Room-temperature water flows through two parallel concrete pipes, as shown in Fig. P6.32. Calculate the total flow rate if the pressure drop from point 1 to 2 is 20 kPa and $D_1 = 10$ cm, $L_1 = 100$ m, $D_2 = 15$ cm, and $L_2 = 120$ m.

6.33. What is the total flow rate for the two-pipe system of Fig. P6.32 if the fluid is oil with a specific weight of 50 lbf/ft³ and a viscosity of 5.0×10^{-4} lbf · s/ft². The pipes are steel, $D_1 = 2$ in., $L_1 = 100$ ft, $D_2 = 4$ in., and $L_2 = 150$ ft. The pressure drop from point 1 to 2 is 2 lbf/in.².

6.34. Consider two steel pipes in parallel carrying oil as in the previous problem. If the total flow rate is 50 gal/min, calculate the pressure drop between points 1 and 2.

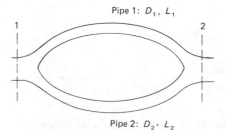

Figure P6.32 Parallel pipe system for Probs. 6.32 through 6.35.

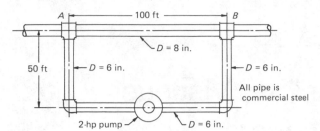

Figure P6.36   Sketch for Prob. 6.36.

6.35. A second cast-iron pipe is to be added to a pipeline system creating a pair of parallel pipes, such as shown in Fig. P6.32. For the original pipe, D_1 = 6 in. and L_1 = 200 ft. Prepare a graph of the D_2, L_2 dimensions of the second pipe that would provide a total flow rate of 1500 gal/min with a total pressure loss of 3 lbf/in.^{2}.

6.36. Consider a pair of steel pipes in parallel in a horizontal plane, as shown in Fig. P6.36. There is a 2-hp pump in the 6-in. line. If 10 ft^3/s flows into the pipe system at point A (the upper left-side tee), where the pressure is 40 psig, what is the pressure at point B (the upper right-side tee)?

6.37. Consider three interconnected reservoirs, such as shown in Fig. 6.12c, that contain crude oil. The crude oil has a specific gravity of 0.86 and a kinematic viscosity of 1.0×10^{-5} m^2/s. The elevations of the free surfaces are

$$z_1 = 110 \text{ m}, \qquad z_2 = 50 \text{ m}, \qquad z_3 = 10 \text{ m}$$

The reservoirs are connected by steel pipes that are 15 cm in diameter. L_1 = 120 m, L_2 = 60 m, and L_3 = 75 m. Neglecting the minor losses in the system, calculate the flow rate for each pipe.

6.38. Consider the pipeline configuration that was discussed in Prob. 6.37. Calculate the flow rates for each pipe if we put a pump in line 1 that raises the hydraulic grade line in line 1 by 140 m.

REFERENCES

6.1. O. Reynolds, "An Experimental Investigation of the Circumstances Which Determine Whether the Motion of Water Shall Be Direct or Sinuous and of the Law of Resistance in Parallel Channels," *Philosophical Transactions of the Royal Society,* vol. 174, 1883, 935–982.

6.2. J. O. Hinze, *Turbulence,* 2nd ed., McGraw-Hill Book Company, New York, 1975.

6.3. H. Schlichting, *Boundary Layer Theory,* 7th ed., McGraw-Hill Book Company, New York, 1979.

6.4. T. Baumeister and L. S. Marks, eds., *Standard Handbook for Mechanical Engineers,* 7th ed., McGraw-Hill Book Company, New York, 1967.

6.5. C. F. Colebrook, "Turbulent Flow in Pipes with Particular Reference to the Transition between the Smooth and Rough Pipe Laws," *Journal of the Institute of Civil Engineering London,* vol. 11, 1938–1939, 133–156.

6.6. L. F. Moody, "Friction Factors for Pipe Flow," *ASME Transactions,* vol. 66, 1944, 671–684.

6.7. F. M. White, *Fluid Mechanics,* McGraw-Hill Book Company, New York, 1979.

CHAPTER SEVEN

Incompressible, Viscous Boundary Layers

The equation for the conservation of linear momentum was developed in Chapter 4 by applying Newton's law, which states that the net force acting on a fluid particle is equal to the time rate of change of the linear momentum of the fluid particle. The principal forces considered were those that act directly on the mass of the fluid element (i.e., the body forces) and those that act on its surface (i.e., the pressure forces and shear forces). The resultant equations are known as the Navier–Stokes equations. Exact solutions were obtained for specific flow conditions in Chapter 4. However, even today, there are no general solutions for the complete Navier–Stokes equations. Nevertheless, reasonable approximations can be introduced to describe the motion of a viscous fluid if the viscosity is either very large or very small. This latter case is of special interest to us, since two important fluids, water and air, have very small viscosities. Not only is the viscosity of these fluids very small, but the velocity for many of the practical applications relevant to this text is such that the Reynolds number is very large.

Even in the limiting case where the Reynolds number is large, it is not permissible simply to omit the viscous terms completely, because the solution of the simplified equation could not be made to satisfy the complete boundary conditions. However, for many Reynolds number flows, the flow field may be divided into two regions: (1) a viscous boundary layer adjacent to the surface of the vehicle and (2) the essentially inviscid flow outside the boundary layer. The velocity of the fluid particles increases from a value of zero (in a vehicle-fixed coordinate system) at the wall to the value that corresponds to the external "frictionless" flow outside the boundary layer, as shown in Fig. 6.1.

Outside the boundary layer, the transverse velocity gradients become so small that the shear stresses acting on a fluid element are negligibly small. Thus, the effect of the viscous terms may be ignored when solving for the flow field external to the boundary layer. The solution for the inviscid portion of the flow field must satisfy the boundary conditions, that the velocity of the fluid particles far from the body be equal to the free-stream value and that the velocity of the fluid particles adjacent to the body be parallel to the "surface" (but not necessarily of zero magnitude). This latter condition represents the physical requirement that there is no flow through a solid surface. When using the two-region flow model to solve for the flow field, the first step is to calculate the inviscid flow field subject to the boundary condition that the flow be parallel to the actual surface of the body. The second step is to calculate the resultant boundary layer and its displacement thickness (which will be defined in this chapter). Then the inviscid flow field is recalculated using the effective surface as the boundary condition. The geometry of the effective surface is determined by adding the displacement thickness to the surface co-ordinate of the actual configuration. As discussed in Ref. 7.1, the iterative procedure required to converge to a solution requires an understanding of each region of the flow field and their interactions. In Chapter 5, we generated solutions for the inviscid flow field for a variety of configurations. In Chapter 6, we generated solutions for viscous flows without concerning ourselves with the details of the viscous region. In this chapter, we shall examine the viscous region in detail, assuming that the inviscid flow field is known.

EQUATIONS GOVERNING THE BOUNDARY LAYER FOR A STEADY, TWO-DIMENSIONAL, INCOMPRESSIBLE FLOW

In this chapter we shall discuss techniques by which we can obtain engineering solutions when the boundary layer is either laminar or turbulent. Thus, for the purposes of this text, we shall assume that we know whether the boundary layer is laminar or turbulent. The transition process is quite complex and depends on many parameters (e.g., surface roughness, surface temperature, pressure gradient, and Mach number). A brief summary of the factors affecting transition is presented later in this chapter. For a more detailed discussion of the parameters that affect transition, the reader is referred to Refs. 7.2 and 7.3.

To simplify the development of the solution techniques, we will consider the flow to be steady, two dimensional, and constant property (or, equivalently, incompressible for a gas flow). By restricting ourselves to such flows, we can concentrate on the development of the solution techniques themselves. As shown in Fig. 7.1, the coordinate system is fixed to the surface of the body. The x coordinate is measured in the streamwise

Figure 7.1 Body-oriented coordinate system.

direction along the surface of the configuration. The stagnation point (or the leading edge if the configuration is a sharp object) is at $x = 0$. The y coordinate is perpendicular to the surface. This coordinate system is used throughout this chapter.

Referring to Eq. (3.8), the differential form of the continuity equation for this flow is

$$\frac{\partial u}{\partial x} + \frac{\partial v}{\partial y} = 0 \tag{7.1}$$

Referring to Eq. (4.11), the x component of momentum is

$$\rho u \frac{\partial u}{\partial x} + \rho v \frac{\partial u}{\partial y} = -\frac{\partial p}{\partial x} + \mu \frac{\partial^2 u}{\partial x^2} + \mu \frac{\partial^2 u}{\partial y^2} \tag{7.2}$$

Similarly, the y component of momentum is

$$\rho u \frac{\partial v}{\partial x} + \rho v \frac{\partial v}{\partial y} = -\frac{\partial p}{\partial y} + \mu \frac{\partial^2 v}{\partial x^2} + \mu \frac{\partial^2 v}{\partial y^2} \tag{7.3}$$

Note that, if the boundary layer is thin and the streamlines are not highly curved, then $u \gg v$. Thus, if we compare each term in Eq. (7.3) with the corresponding term in Eq. (7.2), we conclude that

$$\rho u \frac{\partial u}{\partial x} > \rho u \frac{\partial v}{\partial x}, \qquad \rho v \frac{\partial u}{\partial y} > \rho v \frac{\partial v}{\partial y}, \qquad \mu \frac{\partial^2 u}{\partial x^2} > \mu \frac{\partial^2 v}{\partial x^2}, \qquad \mu \frac{\partial^2 u}{\partial y^2} > \mu \frac{\partial^2 v}{\partial y^2}$$

As a result,

$$\frac{\partial p}{\partial x} > \frac{\partial p}{\partial y}$$

The essential information supplied by the y component of the momentum equation is that the pressure variation in the y direction may be neglected for most boundary layer flows. This is true whether the boundary layer is laminar, transitional, or turbulent. It is not true in wake flows, that is, separated regions in the lee side of blunt bodies such as those behind cylinders, which were discussed in Chapter 5. The assumption that the pressure variation across a thin boundary layer is negligible only breaks down for turbulent boundary layers at very high Mach numbers. The common assumption for thin boundary layers also may be written as

$$\frac{\partial p}{\partial y} \approx 0 \tag{7.4}$$

Thus, the local static pressure is a function of x only and is determined from the solution of the inviscid portion of the flow field. As a result, Euler's equation for a steady flow with negligible body forces, which relates the streamwise pressure gradient to the velocity gradient for the inviscid flow, can be used to evaluate the pressure gradient in the viscous region, also.

$$-\frac{\partial p}{\partial x} = -\frac{dp}{dx} = \rho_e u_e \frac{du_e}{dx} \tag{7.5}$$

Substituting Eq. (7.5) into Eq. (7.2) and noting that $\mu \, (\partial^2 u/\partial x^2) < \mu \, (\partial^2 u/\partial y^2)$, we obtain

$$\rho u \frac{\partial u}{\partial x} + \rho v \frac{\partial u}{\partial y} = \rho_e u_e \frac{du_e}{dx} + \mu \frac{\partial^2 u}{\partial y^2} \tag{7.6}$$

Let us examine Eqs. (7.1) and (7.6). The assumption that the flow is constant property (or incompressible) implies that fluid properties, such as density ρ and viscosity μ, are constants. For low-speed flows of gases, the changes in pressure and temperature through the flow field are sufficiently small that ρ and μ are essentially constant. By limiting ourselves to incompressible flows, it is not necessary to include the energy equation in the formulation of our solution. For compressible (or high-speed) flows, the temperature changes in the flow field are sufficiently large that the temperature dependence of the viscosity and density must be included. As a result, the analysis of a compressible boundary layer involves the simultaneous solution of the continuity equation, the x momentum equation, and the energy equation. Compressible boundary layers are beyond the scope of this text. For a treatment of them, the reader is referred to other sources (e.g., Refs. 7.2 and 7.4).

When the boundary layer is laminar, the transverse exchange of momentum (i.e., the momentum transfer in a direction perpendicular to the principal flow direction) takes place on a microscopic scale. As a result of the molecular movement, slower moving fluid particles from the lower layer (or lamina) of fluid move upward, slowing the particles in the upper layer. Conversely, when the faster moving fluid particles from the upper layer migrate downward, they tend to accelerate the fluid particles in that layer. This molecular interchange of momentum for a laminar flow is depicted in Fig. 7.2a. Thus, the shear stress at a point in a Newtonian fluid is that given by Eq. (1.4) or by Eqs. (4.10a) through (4.10c).

For a turbulent boundary layer, there is a macroscopic transport of fluid particles, as shown in Fig. 7.2b. Thus, in addition to the laminar shear stress described in the previous paragraph, there is an effective, *turbulent shear stress* that is due to the transverse transport of momentum and that is very large. Because slower moving fluid particles near the wall are transported well upward, the turbulent boundary layer is relatively thick. Because faster moving fluid particles (which are normally located near the edge of the boundary layer) are transported toward the wall, they produce relatively high velocities for the fluid particles near the surface. Thus, the shear stress at the wall for a turbulent boundary layer is larger than that for a laminar boundary layer. Because the macroscopic transport of fluid introduces large localized variations in the flow at any instant, the values of the fluid properties and the velocity components are (in general) the sum of the "average" value and a fluctuating component.

We could introduce the fluctuating characteristics of turbulent flow at this point and treat both laminar and turbulent boundary layers in a unified fashion. For a laminar boundary layer the fluctuating components of the flow would be zero. However, to simplify

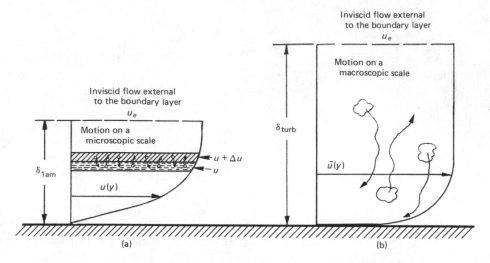

Figure 7.2 Momentum-transport models: (a) laminar boundary layer; (b) turbulent boundary layer.

the discussion, we will first discuss laminar flows and their analysis and then turbulent boundary layers and their analysis.

BOUNDARY CONDITIONS

Let us now consider the boundary conditions that we must apply in order to obtain the desired solutions. Since we are considering that portion of the flow field where the viscous forces are important, the condition of no slip on the solid boundaries must be satisfied. That is, at $y = 0$:

$$u(x, 0) = 0 \qquad (7.7a)$$

At a solid wall, the normal component of velocity must be zero. Thus,

$$v(x, 0) = 0 \qquad (7.7b)$$

Porous walls through which fluid can flow are treated in the problems at the end of the chapter. Furthermore, as we reach the edge of the boundary layer (i.e., at $y = \delta$, where δ is the local thickness of the boundary layer), the streamwise component of the velocity equals that given by the inviscid solution. In equation form,

$$u(x, \delta) = u_e(x) \qquad (7.8)$$

Note that throughout this chapter, the subscript e will be used to denote parameters evaluated at the edge of the boundary layer (i.e., those for the inviscid solution).

INCOMPRESSIBLE, LAMINAR BOUNDARY LAYER

In this section we shall analyze the boundary layer in the region from the stagnation point (or from the leading edge of a sharp object) to the onset of transition (i.e., that "point" at which the boundary layer becomes turbulent). The reader should note that, in reality, the boundary layer does not go from a laminar state to a turbulent state at a point but that the transition process takes place over a distance. The length of the transition zone may be as long as the laminar region. Typical velocity profiles for the laminar boundary layer are presented in Fig. 7.3. The streamwise (or x) component of velocity is presented as a function of distance from the wall (the y coordinate). Instead of presenting the dimensional parameter u, which is a function both of x and y, let us seek a dimensionless velocity parameter that perhaps can be written as a function of a single variable. Note that, at each station, the velocity varies from zero at $y = 0$ (i.e., at the wall) to u_e at $y = \delta$ (i.e., at the edge of the boundary layer). The local velocity at the edge of the boundary layer u_e is a function of x only. Thus, a logical dimensionless velocity parameter is u/u_e.

Instead of using the dimensional y coordinate, we will use a dimensionless coor-

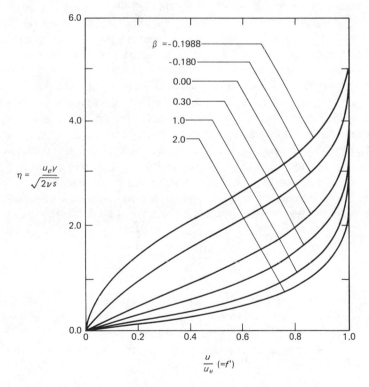

Figure 7.3 Solutions for the dimensionless streamwise velocity for the Falkner–Skan, laminar, similarity flows.

dinate η, which is proportional to y/δ for these incompressible, laminar boundary layers. The boundary-layer thickness δ at any x station depends not only on the magnitude of x but on the kinematic viscosity, the local velocity at the edge of the boundary layer, and the velocity variation from the origin to the point of interest. Thus, we will introduce the coordinate transformation for η:

$$\eta = \frac{u_e y}{\sqrt{2vs}} \tag{7.9a}$$

where v is the kinematic viscosity, as defined in Chapter 1, and where

$$s = \int u_e \, dx \tag{7.9b}$$

Note that for flow past a flat plate, where u_e is a constant (independent of x),

$$\eta = y\sqrt{\frac{u_e}{2vx}} \tag{7.10}$$

Those readers who are familiar with the transformations used in more complete treatments of boundary layers will recognize that this definition for η is consistent with that commonly used to transform the incompressible laminar boundary layer on a flat plate (Ref. 7.3). The flat-plate solution is the classical Blasius solution. This transformation is also consistent with more general forms used in the analysis of a compressible laminar flow (Ref. 7.4). By using this definition of s as the transformed x coordinate, we can account for the effect of the variation in u_e on the streamwise growth of the boundary layer.

Note that we have two equations, Eqs. (7.1) and (7.6), with two unknowns, the velocity components: u and v. (The reader should note that the typeset is such that v represents both the y-component of velocity and the kinematic viscosity. If the reader follows the text carefully, the meaning should be clear.) Since the flow is two-dimensional and the density is constant, the necessary and sufficient conditions for the existence of a stream function are satisfied. (*Note:* Because of viscosity, the boundary-layer flow cannot be considered as irrotational. Therefore, potential functions cannot be used to describe the flow in the boundary layer.) We shall define the stream function such that

$$u = \left(\frac{\partial\psi}{\partial y}\right)_x \quad \text{and} \quad v = -\left(\frac{\partial\psi}{\partial x}\right)_y$$

By introducing the stream function, the continuity equation, Eq. (7.1), is automatically satisfied. Thus, we need to solve only one equation, the x component of the momentum equation, in terms of only one unknown, the stream function.

Let us now transform our equations from the x, y coordinate system to the s, η coordinate system. To do this, note that

$$\left(\frac{\partial}{\partial y}\right)_x = \left(\frac{\partial\eta}{\partial y}\right)_x \left(\frac{\partial}{\partial\eta}\right)_s = \frac{u_e}{\sqrt{2vs}}\left(\frac{\partial}{\partial\eta}\right)_s \tag{7.11a}$$

$$\left(\frac{\partial}{\partial x}\right)_y = \left(\frac{\partial s}{\partial x}\right)_y \left[\left(\frac{\partial \eta}{\partial s}\right)_y \left(\frac{\partial}{\partial \eta}\right)_s + \left(\frac{\partial}{\partial s}\right)_\eta\right] \tag{7.11b}$$

Thus, the streamwise component of velocity may be written in terms of the stream function as

$$u = \left(\frac{\partial \psi}{\partial y}\right)_x = \frac{u_e}{\sqrt{2vs}} \left(\frac{\partial \psi}{\partial \eta}\right)_s \tag{7.12a}$$

Let us introduce a transformed stream function f, which we define so that

$$u = u_e \left(\frac{\partial f}{\partial \eta}\right)_s \tag{7.12b}$$

Comparing Eqs. (7.12a) and (7.12b), we see that

$$f = \frac{1}{\sqrt{2vs}} \psi \tag{7.13}$$

Similarly, we can develop an expression for the transverse component of velocity:

$$v = -\left(\frac{\partial \psi}{\partial x}\right)_y$$

$$= -u_e \sqrt{2vs} \left[\left(\frac{\partial \eta}{\partial s}\right)_y \left(\frac{\partial f}{\partial \eta}\right)_s + \left(\frac{\partial f}{\partial s}\right)_\eta + \left(\frac{f}{2s}\right)\right] \tag{7.14}$$

In Eqs. (7.12b) and (7.14), we have written the two velocity components, which were the unknowns in the original formulation of the problem, in terms of the transformed stream function. We can rewrite Eq. (7.6) using the differentials of the variables in the s, η coordinate system; for example,

$$\frac{\partial^2 u}{\partial y^2} = \frac{\partial}{\partial y}\left[\frac{\partial \eta}{\partial y}\frac{\partial(u_e f')}{\partial \eta}\right] = \left(\frac{\partial \eta}{\partial y}\right)^2 u_e \frac{\partial^2 f'}{\partial \eta^2}$$

$$= \frac{u_e^2}{2vs} u_e f'''$$

where the prime (′) denotes differentiation with respect to η. Using these substitutions, the momentum equation becomes:

$$ff'' + f''' + [1 - (f')^2]\frac{2s}{u_e}\frac{du_e}{ds} = 2s\left[f'\left(\frac{\partial f'}{\partial s}\right)_y - f''\left(\frac{\partial f}{\partial s}\right)_y\right] \tag{7.15}$$

As discussed earlier, by using a stream function we automatically satisfy the continuity equation. Thus, we have reduced the formulation to one equation with one unknown.

For many problems, the parameter $(2s/u_e)(du_e/ds)$, which is represented by the symbol β, is assumed to be constant. The assumption that β is a constant implies that the s derivatives of f and f' are zero. As a result, the transformed stream function and its derivatives are functions of η only, and Eq. (7.15) becomes the ordinary differential equation:

$$ff'' + f''' + [1 - (f')^2]\beta = 0 \qquad (7.16)$$

Because the dimensionless velocity function f' is a function of η only, the velocity profiles at one s station are the same as those at another. Thus, the solutions are called *similar solutions*. Note that the Reynolds number does not appear as a parameter when the momentum equation is written in the transformed coordinates. It will appear when our solutions are transformed back into the x, y coordinate system. There are no analytical solutions to this third-order equation, which is known as the *Falkner–Skan equation*. Nevertheless, there are a variety of well-documented numerical techniques available to solve it.

Let us examine the three boundary conditions necessary to solve the equation. Substituting the definition that

$$f' = \frac{u}{u_e}$$

into the boundary conditions given by Eqs. (7.7) and (7.8),

$$f'(s, 0) = 0 \qquad (7.17a)$$

and

$$f'(s, \eta_e) = 1.0 \qquad (7.17b)$$

where η_e is given by

$$\eta_e = \frac{u_e\delta}{\sqrt{2vs}}$$

Using Eqs. (7.14) and (7.7), the boundary condition that the transverse velocity be zero at the wall becomes

$$f(s, 0) = 0 \qquad (7.17c)$$

Since f is the transformed stream function, this third boundary condition states that the stream function is constant along the wall (i.e., the surface is a streamline). This is consistent with the requirement that $v(x, 0) = 0$ results because the component of velocity normal to a streamline is zero.

Numerical Solutions for the Falkner–Skan Problem

Numerical solutions of Eq. (7.16) that satisfy the boundary conditions represented by Eq. (7.17) have been generated for $-0.1988 \leq \beta \leq +2.0$. The resultant velocity profiles are presented in Fig. 7.3 and Table 7.1. Since

$$\beta = \frac{2s}{u_e}\frac{du_e}{ds}$$

TABLE 7.1. NUMERICAL VALUES OF THE DIMENSIONLESS STREAMWISE VELOCITY $f'(\eta)$ FOR THE FALKNER–SKAN, LAMIN SIMILARITY FLOWS

η	β					
	-0.1988	-0.180	0.000	0.300	1.000	
0.0	0.0000	0.0000	0.0000	0.0000	0.0000	0.0000
0.1	0.0010	0.0138	0.0470	0.0760	0.1183	0.1588
0.2	0.0040	0.0293	0.0939	0.1489	0.2266	0.2979
0.3	0.0089	0.0467	0.1408	0.2188	0.3252	0.4185
0.4	0.0159	0.0658	0.1876	0.2857	0.4145	0.5219
0.5	0.0248	0.0867	0.2342	0.3494	0.4946	0.6096
0.6	0.0358	0.1094	0.2806	0.4099	0.5663	0.6834
0.7	0.0487	0.1337	0.3265	0.4671	0.6299	0.7450
0.8	0.0636	0.1597	0.3720	0.5211	0.6859	0.7959
0.9	0.0804	0.1874	0.4167	0.5717	0.7351	0.8377
1.0	0.0991	0.2165	0.4606	0.6189	0.7779	0.8717
1.2	0.1423	0.2790	0.5452	0.7032	0.8467	0.9214
1.4	0.1927	0.3462	0.6244	0.7742	0.8968	0.9531
1.6	0.2498	0.4169	0.6967	0.8325	0.9323	0.9727
1.8	0.3127	0.4895	0.7611	0.8791	0.9568	0.9845
2.0	0.3802	0.5620	0.8167	0.9151	0.9732	0.9915
2.2	0.4510	0.6327	0.8633	0.9421	0.9839	0.9955
2.4	0.5231	0.6994	0.9011	0.9617	0.9906	
2.6	0.5946	0.7605	0.9306	0.9755	0.9946	
2.8	0.6635	0.8145	0.9529	0.9848		
3.0	0.7277	0.8606	0.9691	0.9909		
3.2	0.7858	0.8985	0.9804	0.9947		
3.4	0.8363	0.9285	0.9880			
3.6	0.8788	0.9514	0.9929			
3.8	0.9131	0.9681	0.9959			
4.0	0.9398	0.9798				
4.2	0.9597	0.9876				
4.4	0.9740	0.9927				
4.6	0.9838	0.9959				
4.8	0.9903					
5.0	0.9944					

these solutions represent a variety of inviscid flow fields and, therefore, represent the flow around different configurations. Note that when $\beta = 0$, $u_e = $ constant, and the solution is that for flow past a flat plate (known as the Blasius solution). Negative values of β correspond to cases where the inviscid flow is decelerating, which corresponds to an adverse pressure gradient [i.e., $(dp/dx) > 0$]. The positive values of β correspond to an accelerating inviscid flow, which results from a favorable pressure gradient [i.e., $(dp/dx) < 0$].

As noted in the discussion of flow around a cylinder in Chapter 5, when the air particles in the boundary layer encounter a relatively large adverse pressure gradient, boundary-layer separation may occur. Separation results because the fluid particles in the viscous layer have been slowed to the point that they cannot overcome the adverse pressure gradient. The effect of an adverse pressure gradient is evident in the velocity profiles presented in Fig. 7.3. When $\beta = -0.1988$, not only is the streamwise velocity zero at the wall, but the velocity gradient $\partial u/\partial y$ is also zero at the wall. If the adverse pressure gradient were any larger, the laminar boundary layer would separate from the surface, and flow reversal would occur.

For the accelerating flows (i.e., positive β), the velocity increases rapidly with distance from the wall. Thus, $\partial u/\partial y$ at the wall is relatively large. Referring to Eq. (1.4), one would expect that the shear force at the wall would be relatively large. To calculate the shear force at the wall,

$$\tau = \left(\mu \, \frac{\partial u}{\partial y} \right)_{y \, = \, 0} \tag{7.18}$$

let us introduce the transformation presented in Eq. (7.11a). Thus, the shear is

$$\tau = \frac{\mu u_e^2}{\sqrt{2\nu s}} f''(0) \tag{7.19}$$

Because of its use in Eq. (7.19), we will call f'' the *transformed shear function*. Theoretical values of $f''(0)$ are presented in Fig. 7.4 and in Table 7.2. Note that $f''(0)$ is a unique function of β for these incompressible, laminar boundary layers. The value does not depend on the stream conditions, such as velocity or Reynolds number.

When $\beta = 0, f''(0) = 0.4696$. Thus, for the laminar boundary layer on a flat plate,

$$\tau = 0.332 \sqrt{\frac{\rho \mu u_e^3}{x}} \tag{7.20}$$

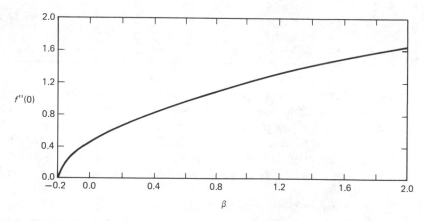

Figure 7.4   Transformed shear function at the wall for laminar boundary layers as a function of β.

TABLE 7.2 THEORETICAL VALUES OF THE TRANSFORMED SHEAR FUNCTION AT THE WALL FOR LAMINAR BOUNDARY LAYERS AS A FUNCTION OF β

β	−0.1988	−0.180	0.000	0.300	1.000	2.000
$f''(0)$	0.0000	0.1286	0.4696	0.7748	1.2326	1.6872

For flow past a flat plate, the velocity at the edge of the boundary layer (u_e) is equal to the free-stream value (U_∞). We can express the shear in terms of the dimensionless skin-friction coefficient:

$$C_f = \frac{\tau}{\frac{1}{2}\rho_\infty U_\infty^2} = \frac{0.664}{\sqrt{Re_x}} \tag{7.21}$$

where

$$Re_x = \frac{\rho u_e x}{\mu} = \frac{\rho U_\infty x}{\mu} \tag{7.22}$$

Mentally substituting the values of $f''(0)$ presented in Fig. 7.4, we see that the shear is zero when $\beta = -0.1988$. Thus, this value of β corresponds to the onset of separation. Conversely, when the inviscid flow is accelerating, the shear is greater than that for a zero pressure gradient flow.

The transformed stream function (f), the dimensionless streamwise velocity (f'), and the shear function (f'') are presented as a function of η for a laminar boundary layer on a flat plate in Table 7.3. Note that as η increases (i.e., as y increases) the shear goes to zero and the function f' tends asymptotically to 1.0. If we define the boundary-layer thickness as that distance from the wall for which $u = 0.99u_e$, we see that

$$\eta_e \simeq 3.5$$

independent of the specific flow properties of the free stream. Converting this to a physical distance, the corresponding boundary-layer thickness (δ) is

$$\delta = y_e = \eta_e \sqrt{\frac{2\nu x}{u_e}}$$

or

$$\frac{\delta}{x} = \frac{5.0}{\sqrt{Re_x}} \tag{7.23}$$

Thus, the thickness of a laminar boundary layer is proportional to $\sqrt{x}$ and is inversely proportional to the square root of the Reynolds number.

TABLE 7.3 SOLUTION FOR THE
LAMINAR BOUNDARY LAYER ON A
FLAT PLATE

η	f	f'	f''
0.0	0.0000	0.0000	0.4696
0.1	0.0023	0.0470	0.4696
0.2	0.0094	0.0939	0.4693
0.3	0.0211	0.1408	0.4686
0.4	0.0375	0.1876	0.4673
0.5	0.0586	0.2342	0.4650
0.6	0.0844	0.2806	0.4617
0.7	0.1147	0.3265	0.4572
0.8	0.1497	0.3720	0.4512
0.9	0.1891	0.4167	0.4436
1.0	0.2330	0.4606	0.4344
1.2	0.3336	0.5452	0.4106
1.4	0.4507	0.6244	0.3797
1.6	0.5829	0.6967	0.3425
1.8	0.7288	0.7610	0.3005
2.0	0.8868	0.8167	0.2557
2.2	1.0549	0.8633	0.2106
2.4	1.2315	0.9010	0.1676
2.6	1.4148	0.9306	0.1286
2.8	1.6032	0.9529	0.0951
3.0	1.7955	0.9691	0.0677
3.2	1.9905	0.9804	0.0464
3.4	2.1874	0.9880	0.0305
3.5	2.2863	0.9907	0.0244
4.0	2.7838	0.9978	0.0069
4.5	3.2832	0.9994	0.0015

Although the transverse component of velocity at the wall is zero, it is not zero at the edge of the boundary layer. Referring to Eq. (7.14), we can see that

$$\frac{v_e}{u_e} = \frac{1}{\sqrt{2}} \sqrt{\frac{\nu}{u_e x}} \left[\eta_e (f')_e - f_e \right] \tag{7.24}$$

Using the values given in Table 7.3,

$$\frac{v_e}{u_e} = \frac{0.84}{\sqrt{\text{Re}_x}} \tag{7.25}$$

This means that at the outer edge there is an outward flow, which is due to the fact that the increasing boundary-layer thickness causes the fluid to be displaced from the wall as it flows along it. There is no boundary-layer separation for flow past a flat plate, since the streamwise pressure gradient is zero.

Since the streamwise component of the velocity in the boundary layer asymptotically approaches the local free-stream value, the magnitude of δ is very sensitive to the ratio of u/u_e, which is chosen as the criterion for the edge of the boundary layer [e.g., 0.99 was the value used to develop Eq. (7.23)]. A more significant measure of the boundary layer is the displacement thickness δ^*, which is the distance by which the external streamlines are shifted due to the presence of the boundary layer. Referring to Fig. 7.5,

$$\rho_e u_e \delta^* = \int_0^\delta \rho(u_e - u)\, dy$$

Thus, for any incompressible boundary layer,

$$\delta^* = \int_0^\delta \left(1 - \frac{u}{u_e}\right) dy \tag{7.26}$$

Note that, since the integrand is zero for any point beyond δ, the upper limit for the integration does not matter providing it is equal to (or greater than) δ. Substituting the transformation of Eq. (7.10) for the laminar boundary layer on a flat plate,

$$\delta^* = \sqrt{\frac{2\nu x}{u_e}} \int_0^\infty (1 - f')\, d\eta$$

Using the values presented in Table 7.3,

$$\frac{\delta^*}{x} = \frac{\sqrt{2}(\eta_e - f_e)}{\sqrt{\text{Re}_x}} = \frac{1.72}{\sqrt{\text{Re}_x}} \tag{7.27}$$

Thus, for a flat plate at zero incidence in a uniform stream, the displacement thickness δ^* is on the order of one-third the boundary-layer thickness δ.

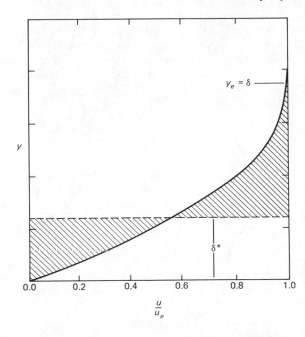

Figure 7.5 Velocity profile for a laminar boundary layer on a flat plate illustrating the boundary-layer thickness δ and the displacement thickness δ^*.

Example 7.1

A rectangular plate, whose streamwise dimension (or chord c) is 0.2 m and whose width (or span b) is 1.8 m, is mounted in a wind tunnel. The free-stream velocity is 40 m/s. The density of the air is 1.2250 kg/m^3, and the absolute viscosity is 1.7894×10^{-5} kg/m $\cdot$ s. Graph the velocity profiles at $x = 0.0$ m, $x = 0.05$ m, $x = 0.10$ m, and $x = 0.20$ m. Calculate the chordwise distribution of the skin friction coefficient and the displacement thickness. What is the drag coefficient for the plate?

Solution.   Since the span (or width) of the plate is 9.0 times the chord (or streamwise dimension), let us assume that the flow is two-dimensional (i.e., it is independent of the spanwise coordinate). The maximum value of the local Reynolds number, which occurs when $x = c$, is

$$\text{Re}_c = \frac{(1.225 \text{ kg/m}^3)(40 \text{ m/s})(0.2 \text{ m})}{1.7894 \times 10^{-5} \text{ (kg/m} \cdot \text{s)}} = 5.477 \times 10^5$$

This Reynolds number is close enough to the transition criteria for a flat plate that we will assume that the boundary layer is laminar for its entire length. Thus, we will use the relations developed in this section to calculate the required parameters.

Noting that

$$y = \sqrt{\frac{2\nu x}{u_e}}\, \eta = 8.546 \times 10^{-4}\, \sqrt{x}\, \eta$$

we can use the results presented in Table 7.3 to calculate the velocity profiles. The resultant profiles are presented in Fig. 7.6. At the leading edge of the flat plate (i.e., at $x = 0$), the velocity is constant (independent of y). The profiles at the other stations illustrate the growth of the boundary layer with distance from the leading edge. Note that the scale of the y coordinate is greatly expanded relative to that for the x coordinate. Even though the streamwise velocity at the edge of the boundary layer (u_e) is the same at all stations, the velocity within the boundary layer is a function of x and y. However, if the dimensionless velocity (u/u_e) is presented as a function of η, the profile is the same at all stations. Specifically, the profile is that for $\beta = 0.0$ in Fig. 7.3. Since the dimensionless profiles are similar at all x stations, the solutions are termed *similarity solutions*.

The displacement thickness in meters is

$$\delta^* = \frac{1.72x}{\sqrt{\text{Re}_x}} = 1.0394 \times 10^{-3}\, \sqrt{x}$$

The chordwise (or streamwise) distribution of the displacement thickness is presented in Fig. 7.6. These calculations verify the validity of the common assumption that the boundary layer is thin. Therefore, the inviscid solution obtained neglecting the boundary layer altogether and that obtained for the effective geometry (the actual surface plus the displacement thickness) are essentially the same.

The skin-friction coefficient is

$$C_f = \frac{0.664}{\sqrt{\text{Re}_x}} = \frac{4.013 \times 10^{-4}}{\sqrt{x}}$$

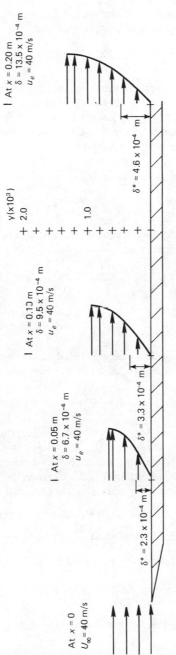

At $x = 0$
$U_\infty = 40$ m/s

At $x = 0.05$ m
$\delta = 6.7 \times 10^{-4}$ m
$u_e = 40$ m/s

$\delta^* = 2.3 \times 10^{-4}$ m

At $x = 0.13$ m
$\delta = 9.5 \times 10^{-4}$ m
$u_e = 40$ m/s

$\delta^* = 3.3 \times 10^{-4}$ m

At $x = 0.20$ m
$\delta = 13.5 \times 10^{-4}$ m
$u_e = 40$ m/s

$\delta^* = 4.6 \times 10^{-4}$ m

$y(\times 10^3)$
2.0

1.0

Figure 7.6 Velocity profiles for the flat plate laminar boundary layer $\mathbf{Re}_c = 5.477 \times 10^5$.

Let us now calculate the drag coefficient for the plate. Obviously, the pressure contributes nothing to the drag. Therefore, the drag force acting on the flat plate is due only to skin friction. Using general notation, we see that

$$D = 2b \int_0^c \tau \, dx \tag{7.28}$$

We need integrate only in the x direction, since by assuming the flow to be two-dimensional, we have assumed that there is no spanwise variation in the flow. In Eq. (7.28), the integral, which represents the drag per unit width (or span) of the plate, is multiplied by b (the span) and by 2 (since friction acts on both the top and bottom surfaces of the plate). Substituting the expression for the laminar shear forces, given in Eq. (7.20),

$$D = 0.664b \sqrt{\rho\mu u_e^3} \int_0^c \frac{dx}{\sqrt{x}} \tag{7.29}$$

$$= 1.328b \sqrt{c\rho\mu u_e^3}$$

Since the edge velocity (u_e) is equal to the free stream velocity (U_∞), the drag coefficient for the plate is, therefore,

$$C_D = \frac{D}{q_\infty cb} = \frac{2.656}{\sqrt{Re_c}} \tag{7.30}$$

For the present problem, $C_D = 3.589 \times 10^{-3}$.

Example 7.2

In several example problems presented in the earlier chapters, the streamwise velocity component for a laminar boundary layer was assumed to be given by the linear relation

$$u = \frac{y}{\delta} u_e$$

where $\delta = 1.25 \times 10^{-2} \sqrt{x}$. Assume that we are trying to approximate the flow of air at standard sea-level conditions past a flat plate where $u_e = 2.337$ m/s. Calculate the streamwise distribution of the displacement thickness (δ^*), the velocity at the edge of the boundary layer (v_e), and the skin-friction coefficient (C_f). Compare the values obtained assuming a linear velocity profile with the more exact solutions presented in this chapter.

Solution.   As given in Table 1.1, the standard atmospheric conditions at sea level include

$$\rho_\infty = 1.2250 \text{ kg/m}^3 \quad \text{and} \quad \mu_\infty = 1.7894 \times 10^{-5} \text{ kg/s} \cdot \text{m}$$

Thus, for constant-property flow past a flat plate,

$$Re_x = \frac{\rho_\infty u_e x}{\mu_\infty} = 1.60 \times 10^5 \, x$$

Using the definition for the displacement thickness of an incompressible boundary layer, Eq. (7.26),

$$\delta^* = \int_0^\delta \left(1 - \frac{u}{u_e}\right) \, dy = \delta \int_0^1 \left(1 - \frac{u}{u_e}\right) d\left(\frac{y}{\delta}\right)$$

Notice that, since we have u/u_e in terms of y/δ, we have changed our independent variable from y to y/δ. We must also change the upper limit on our integral from δ to 1. Thus, since

$$\frac{u}{u_e} = \frac{y}{\delta} \quad \text{and} \quad \delta = 1.25 \times 10^{-2} \sqrt{x}$$

then

$$\delta^* = 1.25 \times 10^{-2} \sqrt{x} \int_0^1 \left(1 - \frac{y}{\delta}\right) d\left(\frac{y}{\delta}\right) = 0.625 \times 10^{-2} \sqrt{x}$$

for the linear profile.

Using the equation for the more exact formulation, Eq. (7.27), and noting that $Re_x = 1.60 \times 10^5 x$, we find that

$$\delta^* = 0.430 \times 10^{-2} \sqrt{x}$$

Recall from Example 3.2 that the linear approximation gave a value for v_e of

$$v_e = \frac{3.125 \times 10^{-3}}{\sqrt{x}} u_e$$

Using the more exact formulation of Eq. (7.25),

$$v_e = \frac{0.84}{\sqrt{Re_x}} u_e = \frac{2.10 \times 10^{-3}}{\sqrt{x}} u_e$$

Finally, we find that the skin friction for the linear velocity approximation is given by

$$\tau = \mu \left(\frac{\partial u}{\partial y}\right)_{y=0} = \frac{\mu u_e}{\delta}$$

Thus, the skin friction coefficient is

$$C_f = \frac{\tau}{\frac{1}{2}\rho_\infty u_e^2} = \frac{2\mu_\infty}{\rho_\infty u_e \delta} = \frac{2}{1.60 \times 10^5 (1.25 \times 10^{-2} \sqrt{x})}$$

$$= \frac{1.00 \times 10^{-3}}{\sqrt{x}}$$

For the more exact formulation:

$$C_f = \frac{0.664}{\sqrt{Re_x}} = \frac{1.66 \times 10^{-3}}{\sqrt{x}}$$

Summarizing these calculations provides the following comparison:

	Linear approximation	More exact solution
δ^*	$0.625 \times 10^{-2} \sqrt{x}$	$0.430 \times 10^{-2} \sqrt{x}$
v_e	$(3.125 \times 10^{-3} u_e)/\sqrt{x}$	$(2.10 \times 10^{-3} u_e)/\sqrt{x}$
C_f	$(1.00 \times 10^{-3})/\sqrt{x}$	$(1.66 \times 10^{-3})/\sqrt{x}$

Comparing the velocity profiles, which are presented in Fig. 7.7, the reader should be able to use physical reasoning to determine that these relationships are intuitively correct. That is, if one uses a linear profile, the shear would be less than that for the exact solution, whereas δ^* and v_e would be greater for the linear profile.

In this example, we assumed that the boundary-layer thickness δ was $1.25 \times 10^{-2} \sqrt{x}$, which is the value obtained using the more exact formulation, i.e., Eq. (7.23). However, if we had used the integral approach to determine the value of δ for a linear profile, we would have obtained

$$\delta = \frac{3.464x}{\sqrt{Re_x}} = 0.866 \times 10^{-2} \sqrt{x}$$

Although this is considerably less than the assumed (more correct) value, the values of the other parameters, e.g., δ^* and C_f, would be in closer agreement with those given by the more exact solution. See Problem 7.13.

Although the linear profile for the streamwise velocity component was a convenient approximation to use when demonstrating points about the continuity equation or about Kelvin's theorem in the earlier chapters, it clearly does not provide reasonable values for engineering parameters, such as δ^* and C_f. A more realistic approximation for the streamwise velocity component in a laminar boundary layer would be

$$\frac{u}{u_e} = \frac{3}{2}\left(\frac{y}{\delta}\right) - \frac{1}{2}\left(\frac{y}{\delta}\right)^3 \tag{7.31}$$

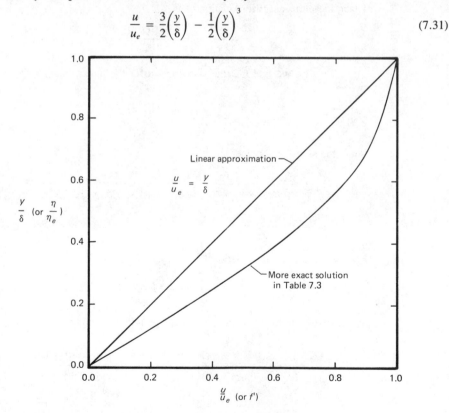

Figure 7.7   Comparison of velocity profiles for a laminar boundary layer on a flat plate.

Example 7.3

Calculate the velocity gradient parameter β, which appears in the Falkner–Skan form of the momentum equation, Eq. (7.16), for the NACA 65-006 airfoil. The coordinates of this airfoil section, which are given in Table 7.4, are given in terms of the coordinate system used in Fig. 7.8. Note that the maximum thickness is located relatively far aft in order to maintain a favorable pressure gradient, which tends to delay transition. The β distribution is required as an input to obtain the local similarity solutions for a laminar boundary layer.

Solution. Using the definition for β,

$$\beta = \frac{2s}{u_e} \frac{du_e}{ds} = \frac{2\int u_e \, dx}{u_e} \frac{du_e}{dx} \frac{dx}{ds}$$

But

$$\frac{dx}{ds} = \frac{1}{u_e}$$

$$\frac{u_e}{U_\infty} = (1 - C_p)^{0.5}$$

TABLE 7.4 PRESSURE DISTRIBUTION FOR THE NACA 65-006

$\bar{x} \, (= \tilde{x}/c)$	$\bar{y} \, (= \tilde{y}/c)$	C_p
0.000	0.0000	1.000
0.005	0.0048	−0.044
0.025	0.0096	−0.081
0.050	0.0131	−0.100
0.100	0.0182	−0.120
0.150	0.0220	−0.134
0.200	0.0248	−0.143
0.250	0.0270	−0.149
0.300	0.0285	−0.155
0.350	0.0295	−0.159
0.400	0.0300	−0.163
0.450	0.0298	−0.166
0.500	0.0290	−0.165
0.550	0.0274	−0.145
0.600	0.0252	−0.124
0.650	0.0225	−0.100
0.700	0.0194	−0.073
0.750	0.0159	−0.044
0.800	0.0123	−0.013
0.850	0.0087	+0.019
0.900	0.0051	+0.056
0.950	0.0020	+0.098
1.000	0.0000	+0.142

Source: I. H. Abbott and A. E. von Doenhoff, *Theory of Wing Sections*. New York: Dover Publications, 1949.

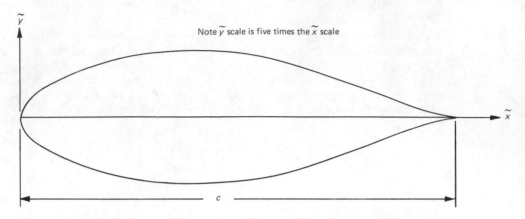

Note $\tilde{y}$ scale is five times the $\tilde{x}$ scale

Figure 7.8 Cross section for a symmetric NACA 65-006 airfoil of Example 7.3.

Therefore, at any chordwise location

$$\beta = -\frac{\int_0^{\bar{x}} (1 - C_p)^{0.5}\, d\bar{x}}{(1 - C_p)^{1.5}} \frac{dC_p}{d\bar{x}}$$

where $\bar{x} = \tilde{x}/c$.

The resultant β distribution is presented in Fig. 7.9. Note that a favorable pressure gradient acts over the first half of the airfoil. For $\bar{x} \geq 0.6$, the negative values of β exceed that required for separation of a similar laminar boundary layer. Because of the large streamwise variations in β, the nonsimilar character of the boundary layer should be taken into

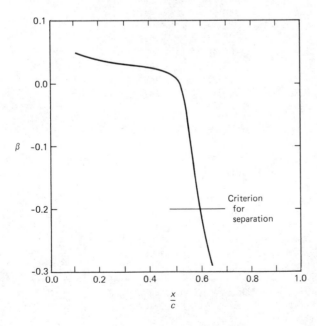

Figure 7.9 The distribution for a NACA 65-006 airfoil (assuming that the boundary layer does not separate).

account when establishing a separation criteria. Nevertheless, these calculations indicate that, if the boundary layer were laminar along its entire length, it would separate, even for this airfoil at zero angle of attack. Boundary-layer separation would result in significant changes in the flow field. However, the experimental measurements of the pressure distribution indicate that the actual flow field corresponds closely to the inviscid flow field. Thus, boundary-layer separation apparently does not occur at zero angle of attack. The reason that separation does not occur is as follows. At the relatively high Reynolds numbers associated with airplane flight, the boundary layer is turbulent over a considerable portion of the airfoil. As discussed previously, a turbulent boundary layer can overcome an adverse pressure gradient longer, and separation is not as likely to occur.

BOUNDARY-LAYER TRANSITION

As the boundary layer develops in the streamwise direction, it is subjected to numerous disturbances. The disturbances may be due to surface roughness, temperature irregularities, background noise, and so on. For some flows, these disturbances are damped and the flow remains laminar. For other flows, the disturbances amplify and the boundary layer becomes turbulent. The onset of transition from a laminar boundary layer to a turbulent layer (if it occurs at all) depends on many parameters, such as the following:

1. Pressure gradient
2. Surface roughness
3. Compressibility effects (usually related to the Mach number)
4. Surface temperature
5. Suction or blowing at the surface
6. Free-stream turbulence

Obviously, no single criterion for the onset of transition can be applied to a wide variety of flow conditions. However, as a rule of thumb, adverse pressure gradients, surface roughness, blowing at the surface, and free-stream turbulence promote transition, that is, cause it to occur early. Conversely, favorable pressure gradients, increased Mach numbers, suction at the surface, and surface cooling delay transition. Although the parameters used and the correlation formula for the onset of transition depend on the details of the application, transition criteria incorporate a Reynolds number. For incompressible flow past a flat plate, a typical transition criteria

$$\mathrm{Re}_{x,tr} = 500{,}000 \tag{7.32}$$

Thus, the location for the onset of boundary-layer transition would occur at

$$x_{tr} = \frac{\mathrm{Re}_{x,tr}}{\left(\dfrac{\rho u_e}{\mu}\right)} \tag{7.33}$$

Once the critical Reynolds number is exceeded, the flat-plate boundary layer would contain regions with the following characteristics as it transitioned from the laminar state to a fully turbulent flow:

1. Stable, laminar flow near the leading edge.
2. Unstable flow containing two-dimensional Tollmien–Schlichting (T-S) waves.
3. A region where three-dimensional unstable waves and hairpin eddies develop.
4. A region where vortex breakdown produces locally high shear.
5. Fluctuating, three-dimensional flow due to cascading vortex breakdown.
6. A region where turbulent spots form.
7. Fully turbulent flow.

A sketch of the idealized transition process is presented in Fig. 7.10.

Stability theory predicts and experiment verifies that the initial instability is in the form of two-dimensional T-S waves that travel in the mean flow direction. Even though the mean flow is two-dimensional, three-dimensional unstable waves and hairpin eddies soon develop as the T-S waves begin to show spanwise variations. The experimental verification of the transition process is illustrated in the photograph of Fig. 7.11. A vibrating ribbon perturbs the low-speed flow upstream of the left margin of the photograph. Smoke accumulation in the small recirculation regions associated with the T-S waves can be seen at the left edge of the photograph. The sudden appearance of three dimensionality is associated with the nonlinear growth region of the laminar instability. In the advanced stages of the transition process, intense local fluctuations occur at various times and locations in the viscous layer. From these local intensities, true turbulence bursts forth

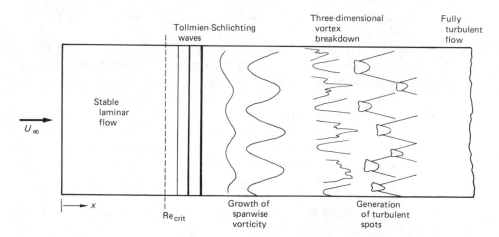

Figure 7.10 Idealized sketch of the transition process on a flat plate. (Based on the sketch from *Viscous Fluid Flow* by F. M. White. Copyright © 1974 by McGraw-Hill Book Company. Used with the permission of McGraw-Hill Book Company.)

U_∞

Figure 7.11   Flow visualization of the transition process on a flat plate. (Photograph supplied by the Lockheed-Georgia Company.)

and grows into a turbulent spot. Downstream of the region where the spots first form, the flow becomes fully turbulent.

Transition-promoting phenomena, such as an adverse pressure gradient and finite surface roughness, may short circuit the transition process, eliminating one or more of the five transitional regions described previously.

INCOMPRESSIBLE TURBULENT BOUNDARY LAYER

Let us now consider flows where transition has occurred and the boundary layer is fully turbulent. A turbulent flow is one in which irregular fluctuations (mixing or eddying motions) are superimposed on the mean flow. Thus, the velocity at any point in a turbulent boundary layer is a function of time. The fluctuations occur in the direction of the mean flow and at right angles to it, and they affect macroscopic lumps of fluid. Thus, whereas momentum transport occurs on a microscopic (or molecular) scale in a laminar boundary layer, it occurs on a macroscopic scale in a turbulent boundary layer. It should be noted that, although the velocity fluctuations may be only several percent of the local streamwise values, they have a decisive effect on the overall motion. The size of these macroscopic lumps determines the scale of turbulence.

The effects caused by the fluctuations are as if the viscosity were increased by a factor of 10 or more. As a result, the shear forces at the wall and the skin-friction component of the drag are much larger when the boundary layer is turbulent. However, since a turbulent boundary layer can negotiate an adverse pressure gradient for a longer distance, boundary layer separation may be delayed or even avoided altogether. Delaying (or avoiding) the onset of separation reduces the pressure component of the drag (i.e., the form drag). For a blunt body or for a slender body at angle of attack, the reduction in form drag usually dominates the increase in skin friction drag. Thus, it may be desirable to use local surface roughness to trip the boundary layer. In such cases, one might use vortex generators or other forms of surface roughness.

When describing a turbulent flow, it is convenient to express the local velocity components as the sum of a mean motion plus a fluctuating, or eddying, motion. For example, as illustrated in Fig. 7.12,

$$u = \bar{u} + u' \tag{7.34}$$

where $\bar{u}$ is the time-averaged value of the u component of velocity, and u' is the velocity of fluctuation. The time-averaged value at a given point in space is calculated as

$$\bar{u} = \frac{1}{\Delta t} \int_{t_0}^{t_0 + \Delta t} u \, dt \tag{7.35}$$

The integration interval Δt should be much larger than any significant period of the fluctuation velocity u'. Thus, the mean value is independent of time. The integration interval depends on the physics and geometry of the problem. Referring to Eq. (7.35), we see that $\overline{u'} = 0$, by definition. The time average of any fluctuating parameter or its derivative is zero. The time average of products of fluctuating parameters and their derivatives is not zero. For example, $\overline{v'} = 0$, $[\partial(\overline{v'})]/\partial x = 0$; but $\overline{u'v'} \neq 0$. Of fundamental importance to turbulent motion is the way in which the fluctuations u', v', and w' influence the mean motion $\bar{u}$, $\bar{v}$, and $\bar{w}$.

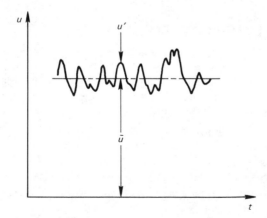

Figure 7.12 Histories of the mean component ($\bar{u}$) and the fluctuating component (u') of the streamwise velocity u for a turbulent boundary layer.

Derivation of the Momentum Equation for Turbulent Boundary Layer

Let us now derive the x (or streamwise) momentum equation for a steady, constant-property, two-dimensional, turbulent boundary layer. Since the density is constant, the continuity equation is

$$\frac{\partial(\overline{u} + u')}{\partial x} + \frac{\partial(\overline{v} + v')}{\partial y} = 0 \tag{7.36}$$

Expanding,

$$\frac{\partial \overline{u}}{\partial x} + \frac{\partial \overline{v}}{\partial y} + \frac{\partial u'}{\partial x} + \frac{\partial v'}{\partial y} = 0 \tag{7.37}$$

Let us take the time-averaged value for each of these terms. The first two terms already are time-averaged values. As noted when discussing Eq. (7.35), the time-averaged value of a fluctuating component is zero; that is,

$$\frac{\overline{\partial u'}}{\partial x} = \frac{\overline{\partial v'}}{\partial y} = 0$$

Thus, for a turbulent flow, we learn from the continuity equation that

$$\frac{\partial \overline{u}}{\partial x} + \frac{\partial \overline{v}}{\partial y} = 0 \tag{7.38a}$$

and that

$$\frac{\partial u'}{\partial x} + \frac{\partial v'}{\partial y} = 0 \tag{7.38b}$$

Substituting the fluctuating descriptions for the velocity components into the x momentum equation, Eq. (7.6),

$$\rho(\overline{u} + u')\frac{\partial(\overline{u} + u')}{\partial x} + \rho(\overline{v} + v')\frac{\partial(\overline{u} + u')}{\partial y} = \rho_e u_e \frac{du_e}{dx} + \mu \frac{\partial^2(\overline{u} + u')}{\partial y^2}$$

Expanding,

$$\rho\overline{u}\frac{\partial \overline{u}}{\partial x} + \rho\overline{v}\frac{\partial \overline{u}}{\partial y} + \rho u'\frac{\partial \overline{u}}{\partial x} + \rho v'\frac{\partial \overline{u}}{\partial y} + \rho u'\frac{\partial u'}{\partial x} + \rho v'\frac{\partial u'}{\partial y} + \rho\overline{u}\frac{\partial u'}{\partial x} + \rho\overline{v}\frac{\partial u'}{\partial y}$$

$$= \rho_e u_e \frac{du_e}{dx} + \mu \frac{\partial^2 \overline{u}}{\partial y^2} + \mu \frac{\partial^2 u'}{\partial y}$$

Taking the time average of the terms in this equation, the terms that contain only one fluctuating parameter vanish, since their time-averaged value is zero. However, the time average of terms involving the product of fluctuating terms is not zero. Thus, we obtain

$$\rho\bar{u}\,\frac{\partial\bar{u}}{\partial x} + \rho\bar{v}\,\frac{\partial\bar{u}}{\partial y} + \overline{\rho u'\,\frac{\partial u'}{\partial x}} + \overline{\rho v'\,\frac{\partial u'}{\partial y}} = \rho_e u_e\,\frac{du_e}{dx} + \mu\,\frac{\partial^2\bar{u}}{\partial y^2} \tag{7.39}$$

Let us now multiply the fluctuating portion of the continuity equation, Eq. (7.38b) by $\rho(\bar{u} + u')$. We obtain

$$\rho\bar{u}\,\frac{\partial u'}{\partial x} + \rho u'\,\frac{\partial u'}{\partial x} + \rho\bar{u}\,\frac{\partial v'}{\partial y} + \rho u'\,\frac{\partial v'}{\partial y} = 0$$

Taking the time average of these terms, we find that

$$\overline{\rho u'\,\frac{\partial u'}{\partial x}} + \overline{\rho u'\,\frac{\partial v'}{\partial y}} = 0 \tag{7.40}$$

Adding Eq. (7.40) to Eq. (7.39) and rearranging the terms, we obtain

$$\rho\bar{u}\,\frac{\partial\bar{u}}{\partial x} + \rho\bar{v}\,\frac{\partial\bar{u}}{\partial y} = \rho_e u_e\,\frac{du_e}{dx} + \mu\,\frac{\partial^2\bar{u}}{\partial y^2} - \rho\,\frac{\partial}{\partial y}\,(\overline{u'v'}) - \rho\,\frac{\partial}{\partial x}\,(\overline{u'})^2 \tag{7.41}$$

We will neglect the streamwise gradient of the time-averaged value of the square of the fluctuating velocity component, that is, $(\partial/\partial x)(\overline{u'})^2$ as compared to the transverse gradient. Thus, the momentum equation becomes

$$\rho\bar{u}\,\frac{\partial\bar{u}}{\partial x} + \rho\bar{v}\,\frac{\partial\bar{u}}{\partial y} = \rho_e u_e\,\frac{du_e}{dx} + \mu\,\frac{\partial^2\bar{u}}{\partial y^2} - \rho\,\frac{\partial}{\partial y}(\overline{u'v'}) \tag{7.42}$$

Let us further examine the last two terms,

$$\frac{\partial}{\partial y}\left(\mu\,\frac{\partial\bar{u}}{\partial y} - \rho\overline{u'v'}\right) \tag{7.43}$$

Recall that the first term is the laminar shear stress. To evaluate the second term, let us consider a differential area dA such that the normal to dA is parallel to the y axis, and the directions x and z are in the plane of dA. The mass of fluid passing through this area in time dt is given by the product $(\rho v)(dA)(dt)$. The flux of momentum in the x direction is given by the product $(u)(\rho v)(dA)(dt)$. For a constant density flow, the time-averaged flux of momentum per unit time is

$$\overline{\rho uv}\,dA = \rho(\overline{uv} + \overline{u'v'})\,dA$$

Since the flux of momentum per unit time through an area is equivalent to an equal-and-opposite force exerted on the area by the surroundings, we can treat the term $-\rho\overline{u'v'}$ as equivalent to a "turbulent" shear stress. This "apparent," or Reynolds, stress can be added to the stresses associated with the mean flow. Thus, we can write

$$\tau_{xy} = \mu\left(\frac{\partial u}{\partial y}\right) - \rho\overline{u'v'} \tag{7.44}$$

Mathematically, then, the turbulent inertia terms behave as if the total stress on the system were composed of the Newtonian viscous stress plus an apparent turbulent stress.

The term $-\rho\overline{u'v'}$ is the source of considerable difficulties in the analysis of a turbulent boundary layer because its analytical form is not known a priori. It is related not only to physical properties of the fluid but also to the local flow conditions (velocity, geometry, surface roughness, upstream history, etc.). Furthermore, the magnitude of $-\rho\overline{u'v'}$ depends on the distance from the wall. Because the wall is a streamline, there is no flow through it. Thus, $\overline{v}$ and v' go to zero at the wall, and the flow for $y < 0.02\delta$ is basically laminar. At points away from the wall, $-\rho\overline{u'v'}$ is the dominant term and is called the *turbulent shear*. Experimental programs provide the information necessary to develop correlations for this stress.

The development of correlations in terms of known parameters is usually termed the *closure problem*. Closure procedures can be placed into one of three categories: (1) simple (or zeroth-order) methods, (2) first-order (or mean-field) closure methods, and (3) second-order (or mean-turbulence-field) closure methods. Zeroth-order techniques are characterized by a substantial amount of empiricism. For the mean-field closure approach, the turbulent-flux terms are related to mean-flow quantities. For the mean-turbulence-field closure technique, differential equations are derived from the Navier–Stokes equations, introducing additional unknowns and the need for additional information about the structure of the turbulent flow. There are numerous references providing detailed reviews (e.g., Ref. 7.6) for the reader who seeks additional information. The present discussion will be limited to simple methods.

Turbulent Boundary Layer for a Flat Plate

Since u_e is a constant for flat plate, the pressure gradient term is zero. Even with this simplification, there is no exact solution for the turbulent boundary layer. Very near the wall, the viscous shear dominates. Ludwig Prandtl deduced that the mean velocity in this region must depend on the wall shear stress, the fluid's physical properties, and the distance y from the wall. Thus, $\overline{u}$ is a function of (τ_w, ρ, μ, y). To a first order, the velocity profile is linear; that is, $\overline{u}$ is proportional to y. Thus,

$$\tau_w = \mu \frac{\partial \overline{u}}{\partial y} = \mu \frac{\overline{u}}{y} \tag{7.45}$$

Let us define

$$u^+ = \frac{\overline{u}}{u^*} \tag{7.46a}$$

and

$$y^+ = \frac{yu^*}{\nu} \tag{7.46b}$$

where u^* is called the *wall-friction velocity* and is defined as

$$u^* = \sqrt{\frac{\tau_w}{\rho}} \tag{7.46c}$$

Note that y^+ has the form of a Reynolds number.

Substituting these definitions into Eq. (7.45), we obtain

$$\tau_w = \mu \frac{u^+ u^*}{(y^+ \nu)/u^*} = (u^+/y^+) \rho u^{*2}$$

Introducing the definition of the wall-friction velocity, it is clear that

$$u^+ = y^+ \tag{7.47}$$

for the laminar sublayer. In the laminar sublayer, the velocities are so small that viscous forces dominate and there is no turbulence. The edge of the laminar sublayer corresponds to a y^+ of 5 to 10.

In 1930, Theodor von Karman deduced that, in the outer region of a turbulent boundary-layer, the mean velocity $\bar{u}$ is reduced below the free-stream value (u_e) in a manner that is independent of the viscosity but is dependent on the wall shear stress and the distance y over which its effect has diffused. Thus, the velocity defect ($u_e - \bar{u}$) for the outer region is a function of (τ_w, ρ, y, δ). For the outer region, the velocity-defect law is given by

$$\frac{u_e - \bar{u}}{u^*} = g\left(\frac{y}{\delta}\right) \tag{7.48}$$

The outer region of a turbulent boundary layer contains 80% to 90% of the boundary-layer thickness δ.

In 1933, Prandtl deduced that the mean velocity in the inner region must depend on the wall shear stress, the fluid physical properties, and the distance y from the wall. Thus, $\bar{u}$ is a function of (τ_w, ρ, μ, y). Specifically,

$$\frac{\bar{u}}{u^*} = f\left[\left(\frac{y}{\delta}\right)\left(\frac{\delta u^*}{\nu}\right)\right] \tag{7.49}$$

for the inner region.

Since the velocities of the two regions must match at their interface,

$$\frac{\bar{u}}{u^*} = f\left[\left(\frac{y}{\delta}\right)\left(\frac{\delta u^*}{\nu}\right)\right] = \frac{u_e}{u^*} - g\left(\frac{y}{\delta}\right)$$

As a result, the velocity in the inner region is given by

$$\frac{\bar{u}}{u^*} = \frac{1}{\kappa} \ln \frac{yu^*}{\nu} + B \tag{7.50a}$$

or, in terms of u^+, y^+, the equation can be written as

$$u^+ = \frac{1}{\kappa} \ln y^+ + B \tag{7.50b}$$

This velocity correlation is valid only in regions where the laminar shear stress can be neglected in comparison with the turbulent stress. Thus, the flow in this region (i.e., $70 < y^+ < 400$), is fully turbulent.

The velocity in the outer region is given by

$$\frac{u_e - \overline{u}}{u^*} = -\frac{1}{\kappa} \ln \frac{y}{\delta} + A \qquad (7.51)$$

where κ, A, and B are dimensionless parameters. For incompressible flow past a flat plate,

$$\kappa \simeq 0.40 \text{ or } 0.41$$

$$A \simeq 2.35$$

$$B \simeq 5.0 \text{ to } 5.5$$

The resultant velocity profile is presented in Fig. 7.13.

Although the logarithmic friction law provides a realistic description of the velocity profile, following a suggestion by Prandtl, the turbulent velocity profile can be represented by a power-law approximation. We will use the integral approach to study the power-law approximation for the turbulent boundary layer.

Integral Equations for a Flat-plate Boundary Layer

We shall use the mean-flow properties in the integral form of the equation of motion to develop engineering correlations for the skin-friction coefficient and the boundary-layer thickness for an incompressible, turbulent boundary layer on a flat plate. Since we will use only the time-averaged (or mean-flow) properties in this section, we will drop the overbar notation. Consider the control volume shown in Fig. 7.14. The wall (which is, of course, a streamline) is the inner boundary of the control volume. A streamline outside the boundary layer is the outer boundary. Any streamline that is outside the boundary layer (and, therefore, has zero shear force acting across it) will do. Because the viscous

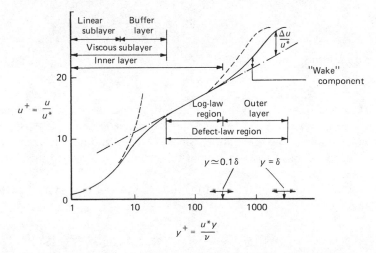

Figure 7.13 Turbulent boundary layer illustrating wall-layer nomenclature.

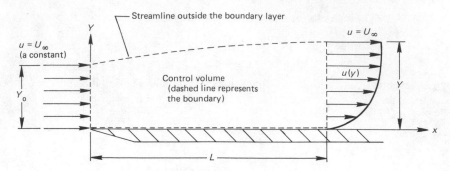

Figure 7.14   Control volume used to analyze the boundary layer on a flat plate.

action retards the flow near the surface, the outer boundary is not parallel to the wall. Thus, the streamline is a distance Y_0 away from the wall at the initial station and is a distance Y away from the wall at the downstream station, with $Y > Y_0$. Since $\vec{V} \cdot \vec{dA}$ is zero for both boundary streamlines, the continuity equation, Eq. (3.19), yields:

$$\int_0^Y u \, dy - u_e Y_0 = 0 \tag{7.52}$$

But also

$$\int_0^Y u \, dy = \int_0^Y [u_e + (u - u_e)] \, dy$$

$$= u_e Y + \int_0^Y (u - u_e) \, dy \tag{7.53}$$

Combining these two equations and introducing the definition for the displacement thickness,

$$\delta^* = \int_0^\delta \left(1 - \frac{u}{u_e} \right) dy$$

we find that

$$Y - Y_0 = \delta^* \tag{7.54}$$

Thus, we have derived the expected result that the outer streamline is deflected by the transverse distance δ^*. In developing this relation, we have used both δ and Y as the upper limit for the integration. Since the integrand goes to zero for $y \geqslant \delta$, the integral is independent of the upper limit of integration, provided that it is at, or beyond, the edge of the boundary layer.

Similarly, application of the integral form of the momentum equation, Eq. (4.19), yields

$$-d = \int_0^Y u(\rho u \, dy) - \int_0^{Y_0} u_e(\rho u_e \, dy)$$

Note we are using the same nomenclature as in Chapter 5 in that the lowercase letter designates the drag per unit span (d). Thus,

$$d = \rho u_e^2 Y_0 - \int_0^Y (\rho u^2 \, dy) \tag{7.55}$$

Using Eq. (7.52), we find that

$$d = \rho u_e \int_0^Y u \, dy - \int_0^Y \rho u^2 \, dy$$

This equation can be rewritten in terms of the section drag coefficient as

$$C_d = \frac{d}{\frac{1}{2} \rho_\infty U_\infty^2 L}$$

$$= \frac{2}{L} \left[\int_0^Y \frac{u}{u_e} \, dy - \int_0^Y \frac{u^2}{u_e^2} \, dy \right] \tag{7.56}$$

Let us introduce the definition for the momentum thickness of an incompressible flow:

$$\theta = \int_0^\delta \frac{u}{u_e} \left(1 - \frac{u}{u_e} \right) dy \tag{7.57}$$

Note that the result is independent of the upper limit of integration provided that the upper limit is equal to or greater than the boundary-layer thickness. Thus, the drag coefficient (for one side of a flat plate of length L) is

$$C_d = \frac{2\theta}{L} \tag{7.58}$$

The equations developed in this section are valid for incompressible flow past a flat plate whether the boundary layer is laminar or turbulent. The value of the integral technique is that it requires only a "reasonable" approximation for the velocity profile [i.e., $u(y)$] in order to achieve "fairly accurate" drag predictions, because the integration often averages out positive and negative deviations in the assumed velocity function.

Application of the Integral Equations to a Turbulent, Flat-Plate Boundary Layer

Now let us apply these equations to develop correlations for a turbulent boundary layer on a flat plate. As discussed earlier, an analytical form for the turbulent shear is not known a priori. Therefore, we need some experimental information. Experimental measurements have shown that the time-averaged velocity may be represented by the power law

$$\frac{u}{u_e} = \left(\frac{y}{\delta} \right)^{1/7} \tag{7.59}$$

when the local Reynolds number Re_x is in the range from 5×10^5 to 1×10^7. However, note that the velocity gradient for this profile,

$$\frac{\partial u}{\partial y} = \frac{u_e}{7} \frac{1}{\delta^{1/7}} \frac{1}{y^{6/7}}$$

goes to infinity at the wall. Thus, although the correlation given in Eq. (7.59) provides a reasonable representation of the actual velocity profile, we need another piece of experimental data: a correlation for the shear at the wall. Blasius found that the skin friction coefficient for a turbulent boundary layer on a flat plate where the local Reynolds number is in the range of 5×10^5 to 1×10^7 is given by

$$C_f = \frac{\tau}{\frac{1}{2} \rho u_e^2} = 0.0456 \left(\frac{\nu}{u_e \delta}\right)^{0.25} \tag{7.60}$$

Differentiating Eq. (7.56),

$$C_f = -2 \frac{d}{dx} \left[\delta \int_0^1 \frac{u}{u_e} \left(\frac{u}{u_e} - 1\right) d\left(\frac{y}{\delta}\right) \right] \tag{7.61}$$

Substituting Eqs. (7.59) and (7.60) into Eq. (7.61), we obtain

$$0.0456 \left(\frac{\nu}{u_e \delta}\right)^{0.25} = -2 \frac{d}{dx} \left\{ \delta \int_0^1 \left[\left(\frac{y}{\delta}\right)^{2/7} - \left(\frac{y}{\delta}\right)^{1/7} \right] d\left(\frac{y}{\delta}\right) \right\}$$

which becomes

$$\delta^{0.25} \, d\delta = 0.2345 \left(\frac{\nu}{u_e}\right)^{0.25} dx$$

If we assume that the boundary-layer thickness is zero when $x = 0$, we find that

$$\delta = 0.3747 \left(\frac{\nu}{u_e}\right)^{0.2} (x)^{0.8}$$

Rearranging, the thickness of a turbulent boundary layer on a flat plate is given by

$$\frac{\delta}{x} = \frac{0.3747}{(Re_x)^{0.2}} \tag{7.62}$$

Comparing the turbulent correlation given by Eq. (7.62) with the laminar correlation given by Eq. (7.23), we see that a turbulent boundary layer grows at a faster rate than a laminar boundary layer subject to the same conditions. Furthermore, at a given x station, a turbulent boundary layer is thicker than a laminar boundary layer for the same stream conditions.

Substitution of Eq. (7.62) into Eq. (7.60) yields

$$C_f = \frac{0.0583}{(Re_x)^{0.2}} \tag{7.63}$$

The skin-friction coefficient correlations for laminar boundary layers and for turbulent boundary layers are compared in Fig. 7.15. Included is an approximate transition criteria for flat-plate boundary layers,

$$Re_{x,tr} \approx 500,000$$

When the local Reynolds number is significantly above this value, the boundary layer is probably turbulent.

Example 7.4

Air at atmospheric pressure and 5°C flows at 200 km/h across a flat plate. For comparison purposes, present a graph of the velocity distribution for a laminar boundary layer and for a turbulent boundary layer at the transition point, assuming that the transition process is completed instantaneously at that location.

Solution. For air which is at atmospheric pressure and 5°C,

$$\rho_\infty = \frac{1.01325 \times 10^5 \ N/m^2}{(287.05 \ N \cdot m/kg \cdot K)(278.15 \ K)} = 1.2691 \ kg/m^3$$

$$\mu_\infty = 1.458 \times 10^{-6} \frac{(278.15)^{1.5}}{278.15 + 110.4} = 1.7407 \times 10^{-5} \ kg/s \cdot m$$

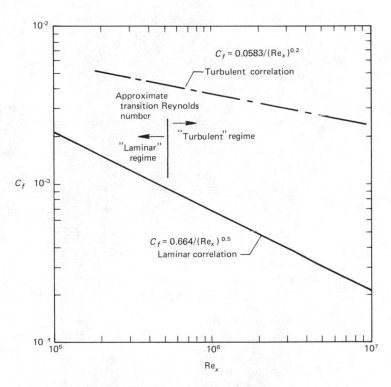

Figure 7.15 Skin-friction correlations for flat-plate boundary layers.

and

$$U_\infty = \frac{(200 \text{ km/h})(1000 \text{ m/km})}{3600 \text{ s/h}} = 55.556 \text{ m/s}$$

We will assume that the transition Reynolds number for this incompressible flow past a flat plate is 500,000. Thus,

$$x_{tr} = \frac{\text{Re}_{x,tr}}{(\rho u_e / \mu)} = 0.12344 \text{ m}$$

The thickness of a laminar boundary layer at this point is

$$\delta_{1am} = \frac{5.0x}{\sqrt{\text{Re}_x}} = 8.729 \times 10^{-4} \text{ m}$$

For comparison, we will calculate the thickness of the turbulent boundary layer at this point for this Reynolds number, assuming the boundary layer is turbulent all the way from the leading edge. Thus,

$$\delta_{turb} = \frac{0.3747x}{(\text{Re}_x)^{0.2}} = 3.353 \times 10^{-3} \text{ m}$$

In reality, the flow is continuous at the transition location and the boundary layer thickness does not change instantaneously. Furthermore, since we are at the transition location, it is not realistic to use the assumption that the boundary layer is turbulent all the way from the leading edge. (This assumption would be reasonable far downstream of the transition location so that $x \gg x_{tr}$.) Nevertheless, the objective of these calculations is to illustrate the characteristics of the turbulent boundary layer relative to a laminar boundary layer at the same conditions.

The resultant velocity profiles are compared in Table 7.5 and Fig. 7.16. Note that the streamwise velocity component u increases much more rapidly with y near the wall for the turbulent boundary layer. Thus, the shear at the wall is greater for the turbulent boundary

TABLE 7.5   VELOCITY PROFILES
FOR EXAMPLE 7.4

y (m)	u_{1am} (m/s)	u_{turb} (m/s)
0.00000	0.00	0.00
0.00017	17.78	36.21
0.00034	33.33	39.98
0.00067	52.50	44.14
0.00101	Inviscid flow	46.78
0.00134		48.74
0.00168		50.32
0.00201		51.64
0.00235		52.79
0.00268		53.81
0.00302		54.71
0.00335		55.56

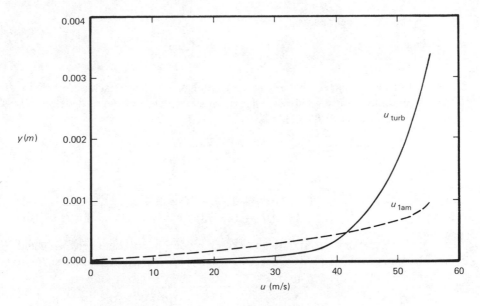

Figure 7.16 Velocity profiles for Example 7.4.

layer even though this layer is much thicker than the laminar boundary layer for the same conditions at a given x station. The macroscopic transport of fluid in the y direction causes both increased shear and increased thickness of the boundary layer.

Integral Solutions for a Turbulent Boundary Layer with a Pressure Gradient

If we apply the integral equations of motion to a flow with a velocity gradient external to the boundary layer, we obtain

$$\frac{d\theta}{dx} + (2 + H) \frac{\theta}{u_e} \frac{du_e}{dx} = \frac{C_f}{2} \tag{7.64}$$

where θ, the momentum thickness, was defined in Eq. (7.57). H, the momentum shape factor, is defined as

$$H = \frac{\delta^*}{\theta} \tag{7.65}$$

where δ^*, the displacement thickness, is defined in Eq. (7.26). Equation (7.64) contains three unknown parameters, θ, H, and C_f, for a given external velocity distribution. For a turbulent boundary layer, these parameters are interrelated in a complex way. Head (Ref. 7.7) assumed that the rate of entrainment is given by

$$\frac{d}{dx}(u_e \theta H_1) = u_e F \tag{7.66}$$

where H_1 is defined as

$$H_1 = \frac{\delta - \delta^*}{\theta} \tag{7.67}$$

Head also assumed that H_1 is a function of the shape factor H, that is, $H_1 = G(H)$. Correlations of several sets of experimental data that were developed by Cebeci and Bradshaw (Ref. 7.8) yielded

$$F = 0.0306 \, (H_1 - 3.0)^{-0.6169} \tag{7.68}$$

and

$$G = \begin{cases} 0.8234(H - 1.1)^{-1.287} + 3.3, & \text{for } H \leqslant 1.6 \\ 1.5501(H - 0.6778)^{-3.064} + 3.3, & \text{for } H \geqslant 1.6 \end{cases} \tag{7.69}$$

Equations (7.66) through (7.69) provide a relationship between θ and H. A relation between C_f, θ, and H is needed to complete our system of equations. A curve-fit formula given in Ref. 7.3 is

$$C_f = \frac{0.3 e^{-1.33H}}{(\log \text{Re}_\theta)^{(1.74 \, + \, 0.31H)}} \tag{7.70}$$

where Re_θ is the Reynolds number based on the momentum thickness:

$$\text{Re}_\theta = \frac{\rho u_e \theta}{\mu} \tag{7.71}$$

We can numerically solve this system of equations for a given inviscid flow field. To start the calculations at some initial streamwise station, such as the transition location, values for two of the three parameters, θ, H, and C_f, must be specified at this station. The third parameter is then calculated using Eq. (7.70). Using this method, the shape factor H can be used as a criteria for separation. Although it is not possible to define an exact value of H corresponding to the separation, the value of H for separation is usually in the range from 1.8 to 2.8.

ATMOSPHERIC BOUNDARY LAYER

As discussed in Chapter 4, the unaccelerated straight-line horizontal motion of the air relative to the earth's surface in the absence of viscous effects (i.e., at sufficiently great heights) is determined by the balance between the pressure gradient and the Coriolis force. The inviscid flow is perpendicular to the pressure gradient. Thus, if a person stands with his back to the wind in the Northern Hemisphere, the high pressure will be on his right and the low pressure will be on his left. The reverse is true in the Southern Hemisphere.

The earth's surface exerts a horizontal drag force on the moving air. The effect of this force decreases as the height above the ground increases, becoming negligible at sufficiently large heights. The height at which viscous effects become negligible is the *gradient height*, which is a function of surface roughness. Typical values of the gradient height are 275 m for flat, open country, 400 m for suburban terrain, and 500 m for an urban area. Above the gradient height, the frictionless wind balance is established, and the air moves at the gradient wind velocity along isobars.

Within the atmospheric boundary layer, the wind crosses the isobars. In the case of a cyclonic flow (flow around a center of low pressure), the wind moves across isobars toward the center, as shown in Fig. 7.17. The air moving toward the center will slowly converge and ascend. The ascending air cools, possibly causing the moisture in the air to condense. In the case of an anticyclone, the wind near the ground crosses the isobars, moving away from the center of high pressure.

Accordingly, the atmospheric motions of importance to engineers are strongly affected by the complex boundary conditions associated with specific sites, including nonuniform temperature distributions, nonuniform roughness, nonplanar topography, and a variety of climatological factors. As a result, the mean motion may be three-dimensional, and the turbulence structure may be nonhomogeneous in planes parallel to the surface.

Nevertheless, for many applications, simplifying assumptions are introduced into the analysis of the flow or into the experimental simulation. Because of the scale of the atmospheric motion, it is often assumed that the flow is horizontally homogeneous within a region where there is uniform roughness over a sufficiently long fetch. The existence of horizontal homogeneous atmospheric flows is supported by observations and distinguishes the atmospheric boundary layer from "conventional" boundary layers that develop (or grow) along various surfaces.

The variation of mean velocity with distance from the ground is usually modeled using one of two approaches: (1) the logarithmic law or (2) the power law. The logarithmic law can be written as

$$\frac{u}{u^*} = \frac{1}{\kappa} \ln \frac{z - z_d}{z_0} \tag{7.72}$$

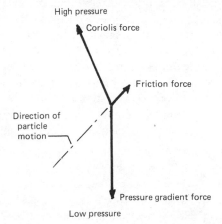

Figure 7.17 Balance of forces in the atmospheric boundary layer.

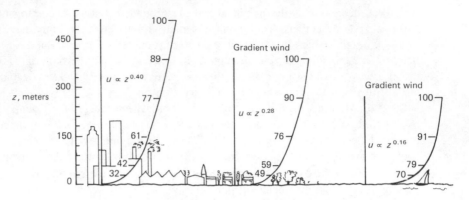

Figure 7.18 Representative empirical power-law profiles over different terrain. (From A. G. Davenport, *Proceedings of the Symposium on Wind Effects on Buildings and Structures,* Vol. 1, National Physics Laboratory, Teddington. London: H. M. Stationery Office, 1965.)

where $\kappa \approx 0.4$, z is the height above the ground, z_d is a length known as the zero plane displacement, and z_0 is a surface roughness length. The parameters z_0 and z_d are determined experimentally and are functions of the nature, height, and distribution of the surface roughness elements. For additional information, the reader is referred to references such as 7.9 and 7.10.

The mean velocity profile for a horizontally homogeneous terrain can also be described in terms of a power-law profile:

$$\frac{u}{u_{\text{ref}}} = \left(\frac{z}{z_{\text{ref}}}\right)^a \tag{7.73}$$

where a is an exponent that depends on the roughness of the terrain and the subscript ref denotes reference conditions. Typical values of a are 0.16 for flat, open country, 0.28 for woodland forest or suburban terrain, and 0.40 for urban areas or centers of large cities. Typical power-law profiles for different terrain are presented in Fig. 7.18. Such values, although representative, are not universal. Counihan (Ref. 7.9) recommends that the value of a for urban areas should be about 0.28 to 0.30, citing data for London, Louisville, Minneapolis, Montreal, New Orleans, Philadelphia, St. Louis, and Tokyo. Cermak (Ref. 7.12) discusses factors that affect the power-law velocity profiles.

The choice of which approach should be used is often predicated on the user's background and experience. The lower 30 to 50 m of the earth's boundary layer is better represented by the log law. However, the power law provides a suitable representation of the mean velocity over a relatively large range of heights at high wind conditions.

VELOCITY MEASUREMENTS

It is clear that there are many situations when it is necessary to obtain experimental information about the velocity field. Many techniques can be used to "measure" velocity. If we are interested in the average velocity over a cross-sectional area, we can use techniques such as a venturi meter or an orifice in a reservoir. Sample problems involving the use of such devices were presented in Chapter 4. However, if we are interested in determining the local velocity at different points in the flow field, we would use instruments such as a pitot-static probe, a hot-wire or hot-film anemometer, or a laser velocimeter or laser anemometer system.

Pitot-Static Probes

A pitot-static probe, such as illustrated in Fig. 7.19, can be used to obtain a measure of the local velocity. The pitot tube has no internal flow velocity, and the pressure therein is equal to the total pressure of the airstream. The purpose of the static ports is to sense the static pressure of the local free stream. Using Bernoulli's equation, Eq. (5.19), these two measurements can be used to calculate the local velocity when changes in elevation are negligible:

$$U_l = \sqrt{\frac{2(p_t - p_l)}{\rho_l}} \qquad (7.74)$$

As indicated in the sketch of Fig. 7.19, measurements of local static pressure are often made using an orifice flush mounted at the vehicle's surface. Although the orifice opening is located on the surface beneath the viscous boundary layer, the static pressure measurement is used to calculate the velocity at the (outside) edge of the boundary layer (i.e., the velocity of the inviscid stream). Nevertheless, the use of Bernoulli's equation, which is valid only for an inviscid flow, is appropriate. It is appropriate because (as discussed earlier in this chapter) the analysis of the y momentum equation reveals that the pressure is essentially constant across a thin boundary layer. As a result, the value of the static pressure measured at the wall is essentially equal to the value of the static pressure in the inviscid stream (immediately outside the boundary layer). Problem 7.18 illustrates a situation where a pitot-static probe is used to determine the velocity field.

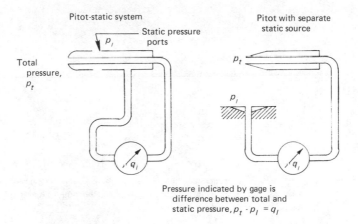

Figure 7.19 Pitot-static system used to measure velocity.

Hot-Wire and Hot-Film Anemometers

Hot-wire and hot-film anemometers are widely used sensors for measuring the velocity field in liquid or gas flows. The sensing elements of a hot-wire or hot-film anemometer are relatively small and hence afford high spatial resolution with a relatively short response time due to small system mass. The small dimensions of the sensing element can be seen in the photographs of Fig. 7.20, which provide a close-up of the sensor as well as a view of the complete probe, which includes the sensor, probe body, and electrical connection.

In many situations, the flow is unsteady as well as three-dimensional, with periodic as well as random components present. The flows in the wakes of turbomachine blades, such as those in compressors, turbines, propellors, and fans, are typical examples of such unsteady, three-dimensional flows. Three-sensor probes have been used to obtain simultaneous measurement of the three components of velocity and of six components of Reynolds stresses for such flows.

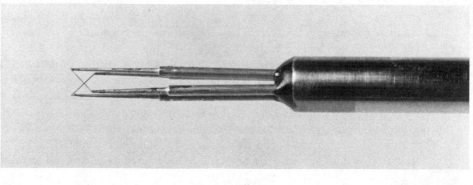

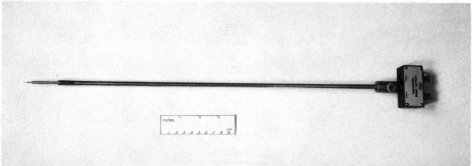

Figure 7.20   Two component hot-film anemometer: (top) close-up of sensor: (bottom) view of complete sensor, probe, and electrical connection. (Photographs from the collection of the author and E. Zihlman.)

Laser Velocimeters

In laser velocimeters, particles (either natural or added) that move with the fluid are illuminated with a focused laser beam and become a source of scattered light. The velocity of these particles is then determined from the change in frequency (Doppler shift) of the scattered light due to the movement of particles when observed by a stationary detector. From the particle velocity, the fluid velocity is inferred. Since only light beams enter the flow, there is no probe in the fluid that would perturb the flow that it was intended to measure or that would be damaged by a corrosive fluid.

A photograph of a two-component LV system is presented in Fig. 7.21. Velocity

Figure 7.21   Two-component LV system in operation. (Photograph supplied by Lockheed-Georgia Company.)

profiles in the near wake of a wing are being measured. A rake consisting of five-hole hemispherical probes can be seen in the wake of the wing in the lower corner of the photograph.

PROBLEMS

7.1. Room-temperature water flows over a flat plate. What is the maximum value for the edge velocity that will still maintain laminar flow at $x = 1$ ft. What is the shear at the wall at this point? What is the boundary-layer thickness at this point? What is the displacement thickness?

7.2. Repeat the previous problem for oil whose specific gravity is 0.86 and whose kinematic viscosity is 1.0×10^{-5} m²/s.

7.3. Air at 50 kPa and 200°C flows past a flat plate at 50 m/s. Assuming the properties of the air are constant and equal to the perfect-gas values, calculate the transition location. What is the boundary-layer displacement thickness at this point? Prepare graphs of the laminar values of u and v as functions of y at this point.

7.4. A very thin, "flat-plate" wing of a model airplane moves through the air at standard sea-level conditions at a velocity of 15 m/s. The dimensions of the plate are such that its chord (streamwise dimension) is 0.5 m and its span (length perpendicular to the flow direction) is 5 m. What is the Reynolds number at the trailing edge ($x = 0.5$ m)? Assume that the boundary layer is laminar in answering the remaining questions. What are the boundary-layer thickness and the displacement thickness at the trailing edge? What are the local shear at the wall and the skin-friction coefficient at $x = 0.5$ m? Calculate the total drag on the wing (both sides). Prepare a graph of $\bar{u}$ as a function of y, where $\bar{u}$ designates the x component of velocity relative to a point on the ground, at $x = 0.5$ m.

7.5. Assume that the inviscid external flow over a configuration is given by

$$u_e = Ax$$

Thus, the stagnation point occurs at the leading edge of the configuration (i.e., at $x = 0$). Obtain the expression for β. Using Fig. 7.4 and assuming that the boundary layer is laminar, determine the value of $f''(0)$, that is, the value of the shear function at the wall. What is the relation between the shear at a given value of x for this flow and that for a flat plate?

7.6. Consider two-dimensional, incompressible flow over a cylinder. For ease of use with the nomenclature of the current chapter, we will assume that the windward plane of symmetry (i.e., the stagnation point) is $\theta = 0$ and that θ increases in the streamwise direction. Thus,

$$u_e = 2U_\infty \sin \theta \quad \text{and} \quad x = R\theta$$

Determine the values of β at $\theta = 30°$, at $\theta = 45°$, and at $\theta = 90°$.

7.7. Consider a steady laminar boundary layer in the presence of a pressure gradient. Given $s = 12$ m²/s, $u_e = 10$ m/s, $\rho = 0.66$ kg/m³, and $\mu = 1.595 \times 10^{-5}$ kg/s · m. What are the values of δ, that point at which $u = 0.99u_e$, for β of -0.1988, 0.0, 0.3, and 2.0?

7.8. Calculate the shear at the wall and the corresponding skin friction coefficient for the flow conditions of Prob. 7.7 and for the four values of β.

7.9. Assume that the wall is porous so that there can be flow through the wall; that is, $v(x, 0) = v_w \neq 0$. Using Eq. (7.14), show that

$$\frac{v_w}{u_e} = -\frac{f(0)}{\sqrt{2Re_x}}$$

in order to have similarity solutions; that is $(\partial f/\partial s)_\eta = 0$ for steady, incompressible flow past a flat plate.

7.10. We plan to use suction through a porous wall as a means of boundary-layer control. Using the equation developed in Prob. 7.9, determine $f(0)$ if $v_w = -0.001u_e$ for steady flow past a flat plate where $u_e = 10$ m/s at standard sea-level conditions. What are the remaining two boundary conditions?

7.11. Transpiration (or injecting gas through a porous wall into the boundary layer) is to be used to reduce the skin-friction drag for steady, laminar flow past a flat plate. Using the equation developed in Prob. 7.9, determine v_w if $f(0) = -0.25$. The inviscid velocity (u_e) is 50 ft/s with standard atmospheric conditions.

7.12. Use the integral momentum analysis and the assumed velocity profile for a laminar boundary layer,

$$\frac{u}{u_e} = \frac{3}{2}\left(\frac{y}{\delta}\right) \quad \frac{1}{2}\left(\frac{y}{\delta}\right)^3$$

where δ is the boundary-layer thickness, to describe the incompressible, viscous flow past a flat plate. For this profile, calculate (a) $(\delta/x)\sqrt{Re_x}$, (b) $(\delta^*/x)\sqrt{Re_x}$, (c) $(v_e/u_e)\sqrt{Re_x}$, (d) $C_f\sqrt{Re_x}$, and (e) $C_d\sqrt{Re_x}$. Compare these values with those presented in the chapter that were obtained using the more exact differential technique [e.g., $(\delta/x)\sqrt{Re_x} = 5.0$]. Prepare a graph comparing this approximate velocity profile and that given in Table 7.3. For the differential solution, use $\eta_e = 3.5$ to define δ when calculating y/δ.

7.13. Use the integral momentum analysis and a linear velocity profile for a laminar boundary layer,

$$\frac{u}{u_e} = \frac{y}{\delta}$$

where δ is the boundary layer thickness. If the viscous flow is incompressible, calculate $(\delta/x)\sqrt{Re_x}$, $(\delta^*/x)\sqrt{Re_x}$, and $C_f\sqrt{Re_x}$. Compare these values with those presented in the chapter that were obtained using the more exact differential technique, e.g., $(\delta/x)\sqrt{Re_x} = 5.0$.

7.14. Nitrogen at 250 kPa and 20°C flows past a flat plate at 100 m/s. Calculate the boundary-layer thickness and the shear at the wall at a point 1.0 m from the leading edge. What is the corresponding value of u^*?

7.15. Room-temperature water flows past a plate 100 cm by 15 cm. If the free-stream velocity is 20 m/s, calculate the drag coefficient for the plate assuming that the streamwise dimension is 15 cm.

7.16. Repeat Prob. 7.15 assuming that 100 cm is the streamwise dimension.

7.17. Let us represent the wing of an airplane by a flat plate. The airplane is flying at standard sea-level conditions at 170 mph. The dimensions of the wing are chord = 4 ft and span = 28 ft. What is the total friction drag acting on the wing? What is the drag coefficient?

7.18. A flat plate at zero angle of attack (see Fig. P7.18) is mounted in a wind tunnel where

$$p_\infty = 1.01325 \times 10^5 \text{ N/m}^2 \qquad\qquad U_\infty = 100 \text{ m/s}$$

$$\mu_\infty = 1.7894 \times 10^{-5} \text{ kg/m} \cdot \text{s}, \qquad\qquad \rho_\infty = 1.2250 \text{ kg/m}^3$$

A pitot probe is used to determine the velocity profile at a station 1.0 m from the leading edge.

(a) Using a transition criterion that $\mathrm{Re}_{x,tr} = 500{,}000$, where does transition occur?

(b) Use Eq. (7.62) to calculate the thickness of the turbulent boundary layer at a point 1.00 m from the leading edge.

(c) If the streamwise velocity varies as the $\frac{1}{7}$ power law [i.e., $u/u_e = (y/\delta)^{1/7}$, calculate the pressure you should expect to measure with the pitot probe (p_t) as a function of y. Present the predicted values as follows:

  (1) The difference between that sensed by the pitot probe and that sensed by the static port in the wall [i.e., y versus $p_t(y) - p_{\text{static}}$].

  (2) The pressure coefficient, that is,

$$y \text{ versus } C_p(y) = \frac{p_t(y) - p_\infty}{\frac{1}{2}\rho_\infty U_\infty^2}$$

Note that for part (c) we can use Bernoulli's equation to relate the static pressure and the velocity on the streamline just ahead of the probe and the stagnation pressure sensed by the probe. Even though this is in the boundary layer, we can use Bernoulli's equation, since we relate properties on a streamline and since we calculate these properties at a "point," not letting viscous forces affect the properties.

(d) Is the flow described by this velocity function rotational or irrotational?

7.19. The velocity variation in the earth's boundary layer is often given in terms of a power-law profile,

$$\frac{u}{u_{\text{ref}}} = \left(\frac{y}{y_{\text{ref}}}\right)^a$$

where the reference velocity is that at 30 ft ($= y_{\text{ref}}$). For a suburban environment, $a = 0.28$. If the reference velocity is 20 mph, what is the velocity at 100 ft? What is the total pressure at 100 ft? What is the dynamic pressure at 30 ft?

7.20. You are going to place a 10-story office building in a suburban industrial park. Using the velocity profile of Prob. 7.19, calculate the variation of the total pressure up the face of the

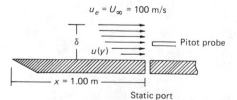

$u_e = U_\infty = 100$ m/s

δ

$u(y)$

Pitot probe

$x = 1.00$ m

Static port

Figure P7.18   Sketch for Prob. 7.18.

building if the reference velocity is 75 mph (i.e., minimum hurricane strength). Assume that there are 10 ft per floor of the building.

7.21. A wind tunnel has a 1-m^2, 6-m-long test section in which air at standard sea-level conditions moves at 70 m/s. It is planned to let the walls diverge slightly (slant outward) to compensate for the growth in boundary-layer displacement thickness and, thus, maintain a constant area for the inviscid flow. This allows the free-stream velocity to remain constant. At what angle should the walls diverge to maintain a constant velocity between $x = 1.5$ m and $x = 6$ m?

REFERENCES

7.1. G. W. Brune, P. W. Rubbert, and T. C. Nark, Jr., "A New Approach to Inviscid Flow/ Boundary Layer Matching," *AIAA Paper 74-601*, presented at the 7th Fluid and Plasma Dynamics Conference, Palo Alto, Calif., 1974.

7.2. H. Schlichting, *Boundary Layer Theory*, 7th ed., McGraw-Hill Book Company, New York, 1979.

7.3. F. M. White, *Viscous Fluid Flow*, McGraw-Hill Book Company, New York, 1974.

7.4. W. H. Dorrance, *Viscous Hypersonic Flow*, McGraw-Hill Book Company, New York, 1962.

7.5. I. H. Abbott and A. E. von Doenhoff, *Theory of Wing Sections*, Dover Publications, New York, 1949.

7.6. D. M. Bushnell, A. M. Cary, Jr., and J. E. Harris, "Calculation Methods for Compressible Turbulent Boundary Layers—1976," SP-422, NASA. Langley Research Center, 1977.

7.7. M. R. Head, "Cambridge Work on Entrainment," in *Proceedings, Computation of Turbulent Boundary Layers—1968 AFOSR-IFP-Stanford Conference*, vol. 1, Stanford University Press, Stanford, Calif., 1969.

7.8. T. Cebeci, and P. Bradshaw, *Momentum Transfer in Boundary Layers*, McGraw-Hill Book Company, New York, 1979.

7.9. J. Counihan, "Adiabatic Atmospheric Boundary Layers: A Review and Analysis of Data from the Period 1880–1972," *Atmospheric Environment*, vol. 9, 1975, 871–905.

7.10. E. Simiu and R. H. Scanlan, *Wind Effects on Structures: An Introduction to Wind Engineering*, John Wiley & Sons, New York, 1978.

7.11. A. G. Davenport, "The Relationship of Wind Structure to Wind Loading," in *Proceedings of the Symposium on Wind Effects on Buildings and Structures*, vol. 1, National Physics Laboratory, Teddington, U.K., Her Majesty's Stationery Office, London, 1965, pp. 53–102.

7.12. J. E. Cermak, "Applications of Fluid Mechanics to Wind Engineering—A Freeman Scholar Lecture," *Journal of Fluids Engineering*, Transactions of the ASME, March 1975, 9–38.

CHAPTER EIGHT

The Conservation of Energy

When we developed the equations describing the conservation of mass and the conservation of linear momentum, we considered fluids whose temperature could vary in space and/or in time. Variations in temperature would, of course, produce corresponding changes in the density and viscosity. However, in all the problems for which we have obtained solutions in the previous chapters, temperature variations were sufficiently small that we could assume that the density and viscosity were essentially constant. Thus, the number of variables was reduced, and we could obtain flow-field solutions for these constant-property flows using only the continuity equation and the momentum equation. There are many flows that involve sufficient temperature variations so that convective heat transfer is important, but for which the constant-property assumption is reasonable. An example is flow in a heat exchanger. For such flows, the temperature field is obtained by solving the energy equation after the velocity field has been determined by solving the continuity equation and the momentum equation. One such solution is known as the Pohlhausen solution for a laminar boundary layer, which will be discussed later in this chapter.

The reader will recall that we have already used the energy equation. It was introduced in Chapters 5 and 6 to solve flows involving shaft work put into or taken from the system. For example, Eq. (6.29) was introduced into Example 6.6 in order to obtain a solution to a flow with a pump in the system. The energy equation was also introduced into Example 5.4, as Eq. (5.16), to account for the output of a turbine. Thus, even for constant-property flows, there are many applications in which we need to include the energy equation into our solution procedure.

We must also include the energy equation in the solution algorithm for compressible flows. Compressible flows are those in which the pressure and temperature variations are sufficiently large that we must account for changes in the other fluid properties (e.g., density and viscosity). Recall the discussion relating to Eqs. (4.11a) through (4.11c).

In this chapter, we will derive the energy equation and discuss its application to various flows.

FIRST LAW OF THERMODYNAMICS

Consider a system of fluid particles. Everything outside the group of particles is called the *surroundings* of the system. The *first law of thermodynamics* results from the fundamental experiments of James Joule. Joule found that, for a cyclic process, that is, one in which the initial state and the final state of the fluid are identical,

$$\oint \delta q - \oint \delta w = 0 \tag{8.1}$$

Thus, Joule has shown that the heat transferred from the surroundings to the system less the work done by system on its surroundings during a cyclic process is zero. In Eq. (8.1), we have adopted the convention that heat transfer to the system is positive and that work done by the system is positive. The use of lowercase symbols to represent the parameters means that we are considering the magnitude of the parameter per unit mass of the fluid. We use the symbols δq and δw to designate that the incremental heat transfer to the system and the work done by the system are not exact differentials but depend on the process used in going from state 1 to state 2. Equation (8.1) is true for any and all cyclic processes. Thus, if we apply it to a process that takes place between any two states (1 and 2), then

$$\delta q - \delta w = de = e_2 - e_1 \tag{8.2}$$

Note that de is an exact differential and the energy is, therefore, a property of the fluid. The energy is usually divided into three components: (1) kinetic energy, (2) potential energy, and (3) all other energy. The internal energy of the fluid is part of the third component. Since we are normally only concerned with changes in energy rather than its absolute value, an arbitrary zero energy (or datum) state can be assigned.

In terms of the three energy components, Eq. (8.2) becomes

$$\delta q - \delta w = dke + dpe + du_e \tag{8.3}$$

Note that u_e is the symbol used for specific internal energy (i.e., the internal energy per unit mass).

Work

In mechanics, work is defined as the effect that is produced by a system on its surroundings when the system moves the surroundings in the direction of the force exerted by the system on its surroundings. The magnitude of the effect is measured by the product of

Figure 8.1 Incremental work done by the pressure force.

the displacement times the component of the force in the direction of the motion. Thermodynamics deals with phenomena considerably more complex than covered by this definition from mechanics. Thus, we may say that work is done by a system on its surroundings if we can postulate a process in which the system passes through the same series of states as in the original process, but in which the sole effect on the surroundings is the raising of a weight.

In an inviscid flow, the only forces acting on a fluid system (providing we neglect gravity) are the pressure forces. Consider a small element of the surface dA of a fluid system, as shown in Fig. 8.1. The force acting on dA due to the fluid in the system is $p\,dA$. If this force displaces the surface a differential distance ds in the direction of the force, the work done is $p\,dA\,ds$. Differential displacements are assumed so that the process is reversible; that is, there are no dissipative factors such as friction and/or heat transfer. But the product of dA times ds is just $d(\text{vol})$, the change in volume of the system. Thus, the work per unit mass is

$$\delta w = + p\,dv \qquad (8.4a)$$

where v is the volume per unit mass (or specific volume). It is, therefore, the reciprocal of the density. The reader should not confuse this use of the symbol v with the y component of velocity. Equivalently,

$$w = + \int_1^2 p\,dv \qquad (8.4b)$$

where the work done by the system on its surroundings in going from state 1 to state 2 (a finite process), as given by Eq. (8.4b), is positive when dv represents an increase in volume.

DERIVATION OF THE ENERGY EQUATION

Having discussed the first law and its implications, we are now ready to derive the differential form of the energy equation for a viscous, heat-conducting compressible flow. Consider the fluid particles shown in Fig. 8.2. Differentiating Eq. (8.3) with respect to time, we can describe the energy balance on the particle as it moves along in the flow:

$$\rho\dot{q} - \rho\dot{w} = \rho\frac{d}{dt}(e) = \rho\frac{d}{dt}(ke) + \rho\frac{d}{dt}(pe) + \rho\frac{d}{dt}(u_e) \qquad (8.5)$$

where the overdot notation denotes differentiation with respect to time. Recall that the substantial (or total) derivative is

$$\frac{d}{dt} = \frac{\partial}{\partial t} + \vec{V} \cdot \nabla \tag{8.6}$$

and, therefore, represents the local, time-dependent changes, as well as those due to convection through space.

To simplify the illustration of the energy balance on the fluid particle, we shall

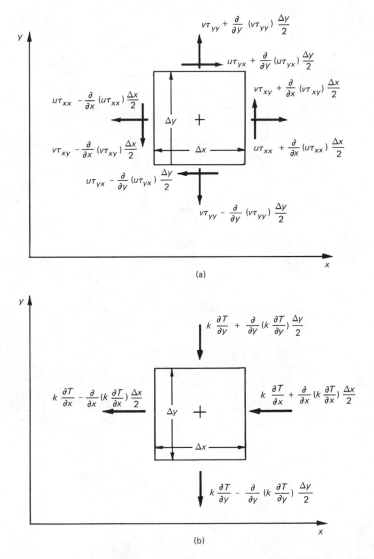

(a)

(b)

Figure 8.2 Heat-transfer and flow-work terms for the energy equation for a two-dimensional fluid element: (a) work done by stresses acting on a two-dimensional element; (b) heat transfer to a two-dimensional element.

again consider a two-dimensional flow, as shown in the sketches of Fig. 8.2. The rate at which work is done by the system on its surrounding is equal to the negative of the product of the forces acting on a boundary surface times the flow velocity (i.e., the displacement per unit time) at that surface. Thus, as shown in Fig. 8.2a,

$$-\dot{w} = \frac{\partial}{\partial x}(u\tau_{xx})\,\Delta x\,\Delta y + \frac{\partial}{\partial x}(v\tau_{xy})\,\Delta x\,\Delta y$$

$$+ \frac{\partial}{\partial y}(u\tau_{yx})\,\Delta y\,\Delta x + \frac{\partial}{\partial y}(v\tau_{yy})\,\Delta y\,\Delta x$$

Using the definitions for τ_{xx}, τ_{xy}, τ_{yx}, and τ_{yy} given in Chapter 4 and dividing by $\Delta x\,\Delta y$, one obtains

$$-\rho\dot{w} = 2\mu\left[\left(\frac{\partial u}{\partial x}\right)^2 + \left(\frac{\partial v}{\partial y}\right)^2\right] - p\left(\frac{\partial u}{\partial x} + \frac{\partial v}{\partial y}\right)$$

$$-\frac{2}{3}\mu(\nabla \cdot \vec{V})^2 + \mu\left[\left(\frac{\partial u}{\partial y} + \frac{\partial v}{\partial x}\right)^2\right] + u\frac{\partial \tau_{xx}}{\partial x} + v\frac{\partial \tau_{yy}}{\partial y}$$

$$+ v\frac{\partial \tau_{xy}}{\partial x} + u\frac{\partial \tau_{yx}}{\partial y} \tag{8.7a}$$

From the component momentum equations, Eq. (4.8),

$$u\frac{\partial \tau_{xx}}{\partial x} + u\frac{\partial \tau_{yx}}{\partial y} = u\rho\frac{du}{dt} - u\rho f_x \tag{8.7b}$$

$$v\frac{\partial \tau_{xy}}{\partial x} + v\frac{\partial \tau_{yy}}{\partial y} = v\rho\frac{dv}{dt} - v\rho f_y \tag{8.7c}$$

From Fourier's law of heat conduction,

$$\dot{Q} = -k\vec{A} \cdot \nabla T$$

we can evaluate the rate at which heat is added to the system. Note that the symbol T will be used to denote temperature and the symbol t, time. Referring to Fig. 8.2b and noting that, if the temperature is increasing in the outward direction, heat is added to the particle (which is positive by our convention),

$$\dot{Q} = +\frac{\partial}{\partial x}\left(k\frac{\partial T}{\partial x}\right)\Delta x\,\Delta y + \frac{\partial}{\partial y}\left(k\frac{\partial T}{\partial y}\right)\Delta y\,\Delta x$$

Therefore,

$$\rho\dot{q} = \frac{\partial}{\partial x}\left(k\frac{\partial T}{\partial x}\right) + \frac{\partial}{\partial y}\left(k\frac{\partial T}{\partial y}\right) \tag{8.7d}$$

Substituting Eqs. (8.7) into Eq. (8.5), we obtain

$$\frac{\partial}{\partial x}\left(k\frac{\partial T}{\partial x}\right) + \frac{\partial}{\partial y}\left(k\frac{\partial T}{\partial y}\right) + 2\mu\left[\left(\frac{\partial u}{\partial x}\right)^2 + \left(\frac{\partial v}{\partial y}\right)^2\right] - p\nabla \cdot \vec{V}$$

$$-\frac{2}{3}\mu\,(\nabla \cdot \vec{V})^2 + \mu\left[\left(\frac{\partial u}{\partial y} + \frac{\partial v}{\partial x}\right)^2\right] + \rho u\frac{du}{dt} - \rho u f_x$$

$$+ \rho v\frac{dv}{dt} - \rho v f_x = \rho\frac{d[(u^2 + v^2)/2]}{dt} + \rho\frac{d(pe)}{dt} + \rho\frac{d(u_e)}{dt} \tag{8.8}$$

From the continuity equation,

$$\nabla \cdot \vec{V} = -\frac{1}{\rho}\frac{d\rho}{dt}$$

and by definition

$$\rho\frac{d(p/\rho)}{dt} = \frac{dp}{dt} - \frac{p}{\rho}\frac{d\rho}{dt}$$

Thus,

$$-p\nabla \cdot \vec{V} = -\rho\frac{d(p/\rho)}{dt} + \frac{dp}{dt} \tag{8.9a}$$

For a conservation force field,

$$\rho\frac{d(pe)}{dt} = \rho\vec{V} \cdot \nabla F = -\rho u f_x - \rho v f_y \tag{8.9b}$$

Substituting Eqs. (8.9) into Eq. (8.8), we obtain

$$\frac{\partial}{\partial x}\left(k\frac{\partial T}{\partial x}\right) + \frac{\partial}{\partial y}\left(k\frac{\partial T}{\partial y}\right) + 2\mu\left[\left(\frac{\partial u}{\partial x}\right)^2 + \left(\frac{\partial v}{\partial y}\right)^2\right]$$

$$-\frac{2}{3}\mu\,(\nabla \cdot \vec{V})^2 + \mu\left[\left(\frac{\partial u}{\partial y} + \frac{\partial v}{\partial x}\right)^2\right] - \rho\frac{d(p/\rho)}{dt} + \frac{dp}{dt}$$

$$+ \rho u\frac{du}{dt} + \rho v\frac{\partial v}{\partial t} - \rho u f_x - \rho v f_y$$

$$= \rho u\frac{du}{dt} + \rho v\frac{dv}{dt} - \rho u f_x - \rho v f_y + \rho\frac{d(u_e)}{dt} \tag{8.10}$$

Since the terms u_e and p/ρ appear as a sum in many flow applications, it is convenient to introduce a symbol for this sum. Let us introduce the definition that

$$h = u_e + \frac{p}{\rho} \tag{8.11}$$

where h is called the *specific enthalpy*. Using Eq. (8.11) and combining terms, we can write Eq. (8.10) as

$$
\frac{\partial}{\partial x}\left(k\frac{\partial T}{\partial x}\right) + \frac{\partial}{\partial y}\left(k\frac{\partial T}{\partial y}\right) + 2\mu\left[\left(\frac{\partial u}{\partial x}\right)^2 + \left(\frac{\partial v}{\partial y}\right)^2\right]
$$

$$
-\frac{2}{3}\mu(\nabla\cdot\vec{V})^2 + \mu\left[\left(\frac{\partial u}{\partial y} + \frac{\partial v}{\partial x}\right)^2\right] = \rho\frac{dh}{dt} - \frac{dp}{dt} \tag{8.12}
$$

This is the energy equation for a general, compressible flow in two dimensions. The process can be extended to a three-dimensional flow field to yield

$$
\rho\frac{dh}{dt} - \frac{dp}{dt} = \nabla\cdot(k\,\nabla\,T) + \phi \tag{8.13a}
$$

where

$$
\phi = -\frac{2}{3}\mu(\nabla\cdot\vec{V})^2 + 2\mu\left[\left(\frac{\partial u}{\partial x}\right)^2 + \left(\frac{\partial v}{\partial y}\right)^2 + \left(\frac{\partial w}{\partial z}\right)^2\right]
$$

$$
+ \mu\left[\left(\frac{\partial u}{\partial y} + \frac{\partial v}{\partial x}\right)^2 + \left(\frac{\partial v}{\partial z} + \frac{\partial w}{\partial y}\right)^2 + \left(\frac{\partial w}{\partial x} + \frac{\partial u}{\partial z}\right)^2\right] \tag{8.13b}
$$

Equation (8.13b) defines the dissipation function ϕ.

Integral Form of the Energy Equation

The integral form of the energy equation is

$$
\dot{Q} - \dot{W} = \iiint\limits_{vol} \frac{\partial}{\partial t}(\rho e)\,d(vol) + \oiint\limits_{A} e\rho\vec{V}\cdot d\vec{A} \tag{8.14}
$$

That is, the net heat added to the system less the work done by the system is equal to the time rate of change of energy within the control volume plus the net efflux of energy across the system boundary. Note that the heat added to the system is positive. So too is the work done by the system. Conversely, heat transferred from the system or work done on the system is negative.

Energy of the System

The energy of the system can take a variety of forms. They are usually grouped as follows:

1. Kinetic energy (ke), the energy associated with the directed motion of the mass.
2. Potential energy (pe), the energy associated with the position of the mass in the external field.

3. Internal energy (u_e), the molecular and atomic energy associated with the internal fields of the mass.

Thus, the energy of the system may be written as

$$e = ke + pe + u_e \tag{8.15a}$$

Let us further examine the terms that comprise the energy of the system. The kinetic energy per unit mass is given by

$$ke = \tfrac{1}{2} V^2 \tag{8.15b}$$

Note that the change in kinetic energy during a process clearly depends only on the initial velocity and final velocity of the system of fluid particles. Assuming that the external force field is that of gravity, the potential energy per unit mass is given by

$$pe = gz \tag{8.15c}$$

Note that the change in the potential energy depends only on the initial and final elevations. Furthermore, the change in internal energy is a function of the values at the end points only.

Substituting Eqs. (8.15a) through (8.15c) into Eq. (8.14), we obtain

$$\dot{Q} - \dot{W} = \frac{\partial}{\partial t} \iiint \rho \left(\frac{V^2}{2} + gz + u_e \right) d(\text{vol})$$

$$+ \oiint \rho \left(\frac{V^2}{2} + gz + u_e \right) \vec{V} \cdot d\vec{A} \tag{8.16}$$

It should be noted that, whereas the changes in the energy components are a function of the states, the amount of heat transferred and the amount of work done during a process are path dependent. That is, the changes depend not only on the initial and final states but on the process that takes place between these states.

Let us consider further the work term, $\dot{W}$. For convenience, the work is divided into flow work ($\dot{W}_f$) and shaft work ($\dot{W}_s$).

Flow Work

Flow work is the work done by the pressure forces on the surroundings as the fluid moves through space. Consider flow through the streamtube shown in Fig. 8.3. The pressure p_2 acts over the differential area $d\vec{A}_2$ at the right end (i.e., the downstream end) of the control volume. Recall that the pressure is a compressive force acting on the system of particles. Thus, the force acting on the right end surface is $-p_2 d\vec{A}_2$. In moving the surrounding fluid through the distance $\vec{V}_2 \, \Delta t$ for the velocity shown in Fig. 8.3, the system does work on the surroundings (which is positive by our sign convention). Thus, the work done is the dot product of the force times the distance:

$$p_2 \, d\vec{A}_2 \cdot \vec{V}_2 \, \Delta t$$

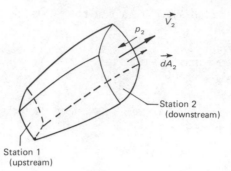

Station 1
(upstream)

Figure 8.3 Streamtube for derivation of
Eq. (8.17).

The rate at which work is done on this area is obtained by dividing through by Δt:

$$\dot{W}_{f,2} = p_2 \vec{V}_2 \cdot \vec{dA}_2 = \frac{p_2}{\rho_2} \rho_2 \vec{V}_2 \cdot \vec{dA}_2 \qquad (8.17a)$$

The positive sign is consistent with the assumed directions of Fig. 8.3, that is, the velocity and the area vectors are in the same direction, and with the convention that work done by the system on the surroundings is positive.

In a similar manner, it can be shown that the flow work done on the surrounding fluid at the upstream end (station 1) is

$$\dot{W}_{f,1} = - \frac{p_1}{\rho_1} \rho_1 \vec{V}_1 \cdot \vec{dA}_1 \qquad (8.17b)$$

The negative sign results because the pressure force is compressive (acts on the system of particles), and the assumed velocity represents movement of the fluid particles in that direction. Thus, since work is done by the surroundings on the system at the upstream end, it is negative by our sign convention.

Shaft Work

Shaft work is defined as any other work done by the system other than the flow work. This usually enters or leaves the system through the action of a shaft (from which the term originates), which either takes energy out of or puts energy into the system. Since a turbine extracts energy from the system, the system does work on the surroundings and $\dot{W}_s$ is positive. In the case where the shaft is that of a pump, the surroundings are doing work on the system and $\dot{W}_s$ is negative.

Thus, the energy equation can be written:

$$\dot{Q} - \dot{W}_s = \frac{\partial}{\partial t} \iiint \rho \left(\frac{V^2}{2} + gz + u_e \right) d(\text{vol})$$

$$+ \oiint \rho \left(\frac{V^2}{2} + gz + u_e + \frac{p}{\rho} \right) \vec{V} \cdot \vec{dA} \qquad (8.18)$$

Note that the flow work, as represented by Eqs. (8.17a) and (8.17b), has been incorporated into the second integral of the right-hand side of Eq. (8.18).

Example 8.1

Consider the steady, inviscid, one-dimensional flow of water in the curved pipe shown in Fig. 8.4. If water drains to the atmosphere at station 2 at the rate of 0.001π m³/s, what is the static pressure at station 1? There is no shaft work or heat transfer, and there are no perceptible changes in the internal energy.

Solution. We will apply Eq. (8.18) to the control volume that encloses the fluid in the pipes between stations 1 and 2. Applying the conditions and assumptions in the problem statement,

$$\text{No heat transfer: } \dot{Q} = 0$$

$$\text{No shaft work: } \dot{W}_s = 0$$

$$\text{Steady flow: } \frac{\partial}{\partial t} = 0$$

Thus,

$$\oiint \left(\frac{V^2}{2} + gz + u_e + \frac{p}{\rho} \right) \rho \vec{V} \cdot \vec{dA} = 0$$

Since the properties for the inviscid, one-dimensional flow are uniform over the plane of each station and since the velocities are perpendicular to the cross-sectional area, the integral can readily be evaluated. It is

$$\left(\frac{V_1^2}{2} + gz_1 + u_{e1} + \frac{p_1}{\rho_1} \right) \rho_1 V_1 A_1 = \left(\frac{V_2^2}{2} + gz_2 + u_{e2} + \frac{p_2}{\rho_2} \right) \rho_2 V_2 A_2$$

By continuity, $\rho_1 V_1 A_1 = \rho_2 V_2 A_2$. Since water is incompressible, $\rho_1 = \rho_2$. Furthermore, we are told that there are no perceptible changes in the internal energy (i.e., $u_{e1} = u_{e2}$). Thus,

$$\frac{V_1^2}{2} + gz_1 + \frac{p_1}{\rho} = \frac{V_2^2}{2} + gz_2 + \frac{p_2}{\rho}$$

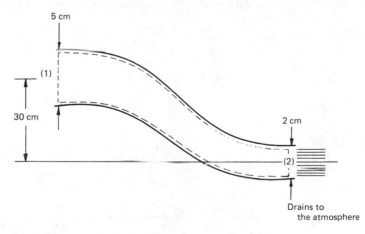

Figure 8.4 Pipe flow for Example 8.1.

Note that the resultant form of the energy equation for this flow is Bernoulli's equation. Refer to Eq. (5.9). This should not be altogether surprising since the conditions set forth in the statement of the problem are consistent with those required in order to apply Bernoulli's equation. Thus, Bernoulli's equation may also be interpreted in terms of the conservation of energy.

$$V_2 = \frac{Q}{A_2} = \frac{0.001\pi}{[\pi(0.02)^2]/4} = 10 \text{ m/s}$$

$$V_1 = \left(\frac{D_2}{D_1}\right)^2 V_2 = 0.16(10) = 1.6 \text{ m/s}$$

Thus,

$$\frac{(1.6)^2}{2} + 9.8066(0.3) + \frac{p_1}{1000} = \frac{10^2}{2} + \frac{p_{atm}}{1000}$$

$$p_1 = p_{atm} + (50 - 1.28 - 2.94)1000$$

$$= 4.58 \times 10^4 \text{ N/m}^2, \text{ gage}$$

Example 8.2

Water flows steadily in a pipeline system containing a turbine, as shown in Fig. 8.5. Neglecting friction in the pipe system and assuming the density is constant, develop the equation for determining the output of the turbine.

Solution. As in Example 8.1, we will neglect heat transfer and changes in the internal energy. Recall that, since the water is driving the turbine, the fluid in the system does shaft work on its surroundings and is, therefore, positive. Thus, applying Eq. (8.18) to the flow,

$$-\dot{W}_s = -\rho_2 A_2 V_2 \left(\frac{V_2^2}{2} + \frac{p_2}{\rho}\right) + \rho_3 A_3 V_3 \left(\frac{V_3^2}{2} + \frac{p_3}{\rho}\right)$$

Since $\rho_2 A_2 V_2 = \rho_3 A_3 V_3 = \dot{m}$, we can rearrange the equation to obtain

$$\frac{V_2^2}{2} + \frac{p_2}{\rho} = \frac{V_3^2}{2} + \frac{p_3}{\rho} + \frac{\dot{W}_s}{\dot{m}} \qquad (8.19)$$

This equation is identical to Eq. (5.16).

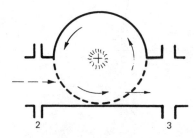

Figure 8.5 Flow through turbine for Example 8.2.

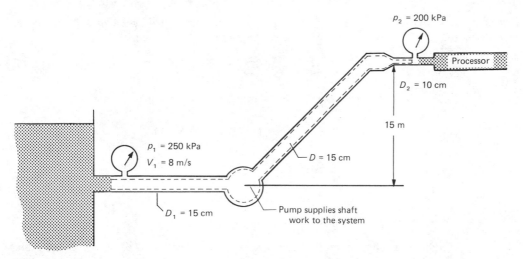

Figure 8.6 Sketch for Example 8.3.

Example 8.3

Consider the steady, one-dimensional flow of water in the piping system shown in Fig. 8.6. A pump is used to supply water to the processor. The conditions at stations 1 and 2, as well as the relevant dimensions, are shown in the sketch. Neglecting any losses in the system, what is the power requirement of the pump? What is the power requirement if the losses in the system can be approximated by a K of 2.5 based on the velocity at station 1?

Solution. Let us use the integral form of the energy equation, Eq. (8.18). We can quickly eliminate several terms by noting that the flow is steady, by neglecting heat transfer to or from the system, and by assuming that the internal energy remains constant through the control volume. The one-dimensional assumption implies that the flow properties are constant across a cross section. Thus, neglecting any losses in the system, we obtain

$$-\dot{W}_s = -\rho_1 V_1 A_1 \left(\frac{V_1^2}{2} + gz_1 + \frac{p_1}{\rho}\right) + \rho_2 V_2 A_2 \left(\frac{V_2^2}{2} + gz_2 + \frac{p_2}{\rho}\right)$$

Using the integral form of the continuity equation,

$$V_2 = V_1 \left(\frac{D_1^2}{D_2^2}\right) = 8 \left(\frac{15}{10}\right)^2 = 18 \text{ m/s}$$

Furthermore,

$$\dot{m} = \rho_1 V_1 A_1 = \rho_2 V_2 A_2 = (1000 \text{ kg/m}^3)(8 \text{ m/s})(0.01767 \text{ m}^2) = 141.4 \text{ kg/s}$$

Since the pump is doing work on the fluid in the system, the shaft work is negative. Thus,

$$\dot{W}_s = -141.4 \left(\frac{64}{2} + \frac{2.50 \times 10^5}{1000}\right) + 141.4 \left(\frac{324}{2} + 9.8066 (15) + \frac{2.00 \times 10^5}{1000}\right)$$

$$= 32112 \text{ N} \cdot \text{m/s} = 32.112 \text{ kW}$$

If there are losses in the system that can be represented by a K of 2.5 based on the velocity at station 1, we refer to the relations of Chapter 6. The head loss is

$$h_f = (\textstyle\sum K) \frac{V_1^2}{2g}$$

Since the head loss must be added to work supplied by the pump,

$$\dot{W}_s = -\dot{m} \left(\frac{V_1^2}{2} + \frac{p_1}{\rho} \right) + \dot{m} \left(\frac{V_2^2}{2} + gz_2 + \frac{p_2}{\rho} \right)$$

$$+ \dot{m} (\textstyle\sum K) \frac{V_1^2}{2}$$

$$= -141.4(282) + 141.4(509.1) + 141.4(80)$$

$$= 43{,}424 \ \text{N} \cdot \text{m/s} = 43.424 \ \text{kW}$$

Note that the application of the energy equation to the flows illustrated in Examples 8.1 through 8.3 yielded equations identical to those used in previous chapters. This occurred because the changes in the temperature were sufficiently small that we could neglect heat transfer and changes in the internal energy. Let us now consider applications in which the heat transfer is important to us.

SPECIFIC HEATS

For simplicity (and without loss of generality), let us consider a system in which there are no changes in the kinetic and potential energies. We can combine Eqs. (8.3) and (8.4a) to obtain

$$\delta q - p \, dv = du_e \tag{8.20}$$

As an extension of our discussion of fluid properties in Chapter 1, we note that, for any simple substance, the specific internal energy is a function of any other two independent fluid properties. Thus, consider $u_e = u_e(v, T)$. Then, by the chain rule of differentiation,

$$du_e = \left(\frac{\partial u_e}{\partial T} \right)_v dT + \left(\frac{\partial u_e}{\partial v} \right)_T dv \tag{8.21}$$

where the subscript is used to designate which variable is constant during the differentiation process.

From the principles of thermodynamics, it may be shown that for a thermally perfect gas, that is, one obeying Eq. (1.3), we can write

$$\left(\frac{\partial u_e}{\partial v} \right)_T = 0$$

which is equivalent to saying that the internal energy of a perfect gas does not depend on the specific volume, or equivalently the density, and hence depends on the temperature alone. Thus, Eq. (8.21) becomes

$$du_e = \left(\frac{\partial u_e}{\partial T}\right)_v dT = c_v \, dT \qquad (8.22)$$

In Eq. (8.22) we have introduced the definition that

$$c_v \equiv \left(\frac{\partial u_e}{\partial T}\right)_v$$

which is the specific heat at constant volume. It follows that

$$\Delta u_e = u_{e2} - u_{e1} = \int_1^2 c_v \, dT \qquad (8.23)$$

Experimental evidence indicates that for most gases c_v is constant over a wide range of conditions. For air below a temperature of approximately 850 K and over a wide range of pressure, c_v can be treated as a constant. The value for air is

$$c_v = 717.6 \, \frac{\text{N} \cdot \text{m}}{\text{kg} \cdot \text{K}} \qquad \left(\text{or} \, \frac{\text{J}}{\text{kg} \cdot \text{K}}\right)$$

Note that since the change in temperature in K is equal to the change in °C, the units of specific heat also may be written as J/kg · °C. The assumption that c_v is constant is contained within the more general assumption that the gas is a perfect gas. Thus, for a perfect gas

$$\Delta u_e = c_v \, \Delta T \qquad (8.24)$$

Since c_v and T are both properties of the fluid and since the change in a property between any two given states is independent of the process used in going between the two states, Eq. (8.24) is valid even if the process is not one of constant volume. Thus, Eq. (8.24) is valid for any simple substance undergoing any process where c_v can be treated as a constant.

Substituting Eq. (8.21) into Eq. (8.20), one sees that c_v is only directly related to the heat transfer if the process is one in which the volume remains constant (i.e., $dv = 0$). Thus, the name "specific heat" can be misleading. Physically, c_v is the proportionality constant between the amount of heat transferred to a substance and the temperature rise in the substance held at constant volume.

Since it is often more convenient to analyze certain flows using the enthalpy,

$$h \equiv u_e + \frac{p}{\rho} \qquad (8.11)$$

let us develop the corresponding relations for it. Substituting the differential form of Eq. (8.11) into Eq. (8.20) and collecting terms yields

$$\delta q + v \, dp = dh \qquad (8.25)$$

which is the first law of thermodynamics expressed in terms of the enthalpy rather than the internal energy.

Since any property of a pure substance can be written as a function of any two other properties, we can write

$$h = h(p, T) \tag{8.26}$$

Thus,

$$dh = \left(\frac{\partial h}{\partial p}\right)_T dp + \left(\frac{\partial h}{\partial T}\right)_p dT \tag{8.27}$$

From the definition of the enthalpy, it follows that h is also a function of temperature only for a thermally perfect gas, since both u_e and p/ρ are functions of the temperature only. Thus,

$$\left(\frac{\partial h}{\partial p}\right)_T = 0$$

and Eq. (8.27) becomes

$$dh = \left(\frac{\partial h}{\partial T}\right)_p dT = c_p dT \tag{8.28}$$

We have introduced the definition

$$c_p \equiv \left(\frac{\partial h}{\partial T}\right)_p \tag{8.29}$$

which is the specific heat at constant pressure. In general, c_p depends on the composition of the substance and its pressure and temperature. It follows that

$$\Delta h = h_2 - h_1 = \int_1^2 c_p dT \tag{8.30}$$

Experimental evidence indicates that for most gases c_p is essentially independent of temperature and pressure over a wide range of conditions. Again, we conclude that, provided that the temperature extremes in a flow field are not too widely separated, c_p can be treated as a constant so that

$$\Delta h = c_p \Delta T \tag{8.31}$$

For air below a temperature of approximately 850 K, the value of c_p is 1004.7 N $\cdot$ m/ kg $\cdot$ K (or J/kg $\cdot$ K).

An argument parallel to that used for c_v shows that Eq. (8.31) is valid for any simple substance undergoing any process where c_p can be treated as a constant. Again, we note that the term "specific heat" is somewhat misleading, since c_p is only directly related to the heat transfer if the process is isobaric.

Additional Relations

A perfect gas is one that obeys Eqs. (8.24) and (8.31). In such a case, there is a simple relation between c_p, c_v, and R. From the definitions of c_p and h, the perfect-gas law, and the knowledge that h depends upon T alone, we write

$$c_p \equiv \left(\frac{\partial h}{\partial T}\right)_p = \frac{dh}{dT} = \frac{du_e}{dT} + \frac{d}{dT}\left(\frac{p}{\rho}\right) = c_v + R \qquad (8.32)$$

Let us introduce another definition, one for the ratio of specific heats:

$$k \equiv \frac{c_p}{c_v} \qquad (8.33)$$

For the most simple molecular model, the kinetic theory of gases shows that

$$k = \frac{n + 2}{n}$$

where n is the number of degrees of freedom for the molecule. Thus, for a monatomic gas, such as helium, $n = 3$ and $k = 1.667$. For a diatomic gas such as nitrogen, oxygen, and air, $n = 5$ and $k = 1.400$. Extremely complex molecules, such as Freon or tetrafluoromethane, have large values of n and values of k that approach unity.

Combining Eqs. (8.32) and (8.33), we can write

$$c_p = \frac{kR}{k - 1} \quad \text{and} \quad c_v = \frac{R}{k - 1} \qquad (8.34)$$

Perfect-gas values for c_p, c_v, and k for gases other than air are presented in Table 8.1.

Example 8.4

A closed-circuit wind tunnel with a test section that is $1.3 \text{ m} \times 2.0 \text{ m}$ contains a total volume of air of 115 m^3, as shown in Fig. 8.7. The fan that drives the air in the tunnel (so that the air speed in the test section is a steady 40 m/s) does 40 kW of work on the air. If

TABLE 8.1 PERFECT-GAS VALUES OF c_p, c_v, AND k

	c_p (Btu/lbm · °R)	c_p (N · m/kg · K)	c_v (N · m/kg · K)	k
Air	0.2404	1,004.7	717.6	1.40
Carbon dioxide	0.203	849.9	661.5	1.285
Carbon monoxide	0.249	1,042.5	745.2	1.40
Helium	1.25	5,233.4	3,147.0	1.67
Hydrogen	3.43	14,360.5	10,215.6	1.404
Methane	0.533	2,227.3	1,687.3	1.32
Nitrogen	0.248	1,038.3	741.1	1.40
Oxygen	0.219	916.9	657.0	1.40

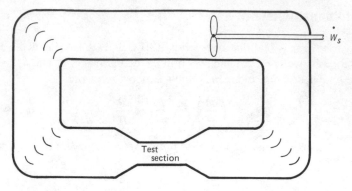

Figure 8.7   Closed-circuit wind tunnel for Example 8.4.

the density of the air is assumed to be constant at 1.225 kg/m³ and if the air is assumed to behave as a perfect gas, what is the rate at which the temperature of the air increases?

Solution.   Applying Eq. (8.18) to the air contained in the wind tunnel, we see that there is no fluid entering or leaving the system. Thus, the last term in the equation is zero. Let us assume that there is no heat transferred to or from the system. For these conditions, Eq. (8.18) yields

$$-\dot{W}_s = \frac{\partial}{\partial t} \iiint \rho u_e \, d(\text{vol})$$

The fan does work on the air contained within the control volume. Thus, the shaft work is negative.

$$40 \text{ kW} = 40{,}000 \text{ N} \cdot \text{m/s} = 1.225 \text{ kg/m}^3 \left(717.6 \text{ N} \cdot \text{m/kg} \cdot \text{K} \right) \frac{dT}{dt} \left(115 \text{ m}^3 \right)$$

Solving for dt/dt, we obtain

$$\frac{dT}{dt} = 0.396 \text{ K/s} \quad \text{or} \quad 0.396 \text{ °C/s}$$

STEADY, ONE-DIMENSIONAL FLOW

Consider a steady, one-dimensional flow as indicated in Fig. 8.8. Flow enters the control volume at station 1 and exits at station 2. Both heat transfer and shaft work are a factor in the flow. One possible example of this flow is a steam turbine where the control volume has been selected to represent the inside volume of the turbine casing and stations 1 and 2 correspond to the inlet and outlet pipes of the turbine.

Since the flow properties are constant over sections 1 and 2 and since the fluid velocity is normal to the cross-sectional areas at the inlet and outlet, the integrations of Eq. (8.18) can be carried out with ease.

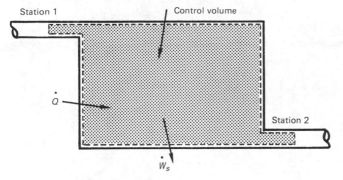

Figure 8.8 plus labels: Station 1, Control volume, Station 2, $\dot{Q}$, $\dot{W}_s$

Figure 8.8 One-dimensional flow used in the derivation of Eq. (8.35).

$$\dot{Q} - \dot{W}_s = -\rho_1 V_1 A_1 \left(\frac{V_1^2}{2} + gz_1 + h_1\right) + \rho_2 V_2 A_2 \left(\frac{V_2^2}{2} + gz_2 + h_2\right) \quad (8.35)$$

In this formulation, the flow can be either compressible or incompressible. However, it must be one-dimensional. Using the integral form of the continuity equation for this control volume, we note that

$$\rho_1 V_1 A_1 = \rho_2 V_2 A_2 = \dot{m}$$

Dividing each term in Eq. (8.35) by $\dot{m}$ and rearranging, we obtain

$$\frac{\dot{Q}}{\dot{m}} + \frac{V_1^2}{2} + gz_1 + h_1 = \frac{\dot{W}_s}{\dot{m}} + \frac{V_2^2}{2} + gz_2 + h_2 \quad (8.36)$$

Note that $\dot{Q}/\dot{m}$ is simply the heat added to the system per unit mass of the flow, while $\dot{W}_s/\dot{m}$ is the net shaft work done by the system per unit mass of the flow.

Example 8.5.

A steam turbine uses 4500 kg/h of steam while delivering 750 kW of power to the turbine shaft. The inlet velocity to the turbine is 70 m/s, while the outlet velocity is 300 m/s. The enthalpy at the inlet is 9×10^6 J/kg; that at the outlet is 6.8×10^6 J/kg. Using the control volume shown in Fig. 8.9, calculate the rate at which heat is lost from the turbine casing and bearings.

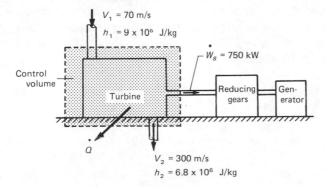

Labels: $V_1 = 70$ m/s, $h_1 = 9 \times 10^6$ J/kg, $\dot{W}_s = 750$ kW, Control volume, Turbine, Reducing gears, Generator, $\dot{Q}$, $V_2 = 300$ m/s, $h_2 = 6.8 \times 10^6$ J/kg

Figure 8.9 Turbine for Example 8.5.

Solution. Let us apply Eq. (8.35) to the control volume shown in the sketch. We will neglect the changes in potential energy for this flow. Furthermore, since the shaft work is the output of a turbine, the fluid does work on the surrounding. Thus, $\dot{W}_s$ is positive. Rearranging,

$$\dot{Q} = \dot{W}_s + \dot{m}\left(\frac{V_2^2}{2} + h_2\right) - \dot{m}\left(\frac{V_1^2}{2} + h_1\right)$$

$$= 750 \times 10^3 \text{ J/s} + 1.25 \text{ kg/s} \left[\frac{(300)^2}{2} \text{ m}^2/\text{s}^2 + 6.8 \times 10^6 \text{ J/kg}\right]$$

$$- 1.25 \text{ kg/s} \left[\frac{(70)^2}{2} \text{ m}^2/\text{s}^2 + 9 \times 10^6 \text{ J/kg}\right]$$

Noting that $1 \text{ m}^2/\text{s}^2 = 1 \text{ N} \cdot \text{m/kg} = 1 \text{ J/kg}$, we find that

$$\dot{Q} = 0.750 \times 10^6 \text{ J/s} + 1.25(0.045 \times 10^6 + 6.8 \times 10^6) \text{ J/s}$$

$$- 1.25(0.00245 \times 10^6 + 9.0 \times 10^6) \text{ J/s}$$

$$= -1.95 \times 10^6 \text{ J/s}$$

The negative sign indicates that we are dealing with heat transfer from the fluid to the surroundings. This is consistent with the problem statement.

THERMAL BOUNDARY LAYER FOR CONSTANT-PROPERTY FLOWS

As noted earlier, there are many constant-property flows for which we are interested in calculating the convective heat transfer. Thus, the temperature variations in the flow field are sufficiently large so that there is heat transfer to or from a body in the flow but are small enough that the corresponding variations in density and viscosity can be neglected. Let us examine one such flow, the thermal boundary layer for a steady, low-speed flow past a flat plate. We will consider flows where the boundary layer is laminar. The solution for the velocity field for this flow was described in Chapter 7; see Eqs. (7.6) through (7.27).

We will now solve the energy equation, Eq. (8.13), in order to determine the temperature distribution. For a low-speed, constant-property, laminar boundary layer, the viscous dissipation is negligible (i.e., $\phi = 0$). For flow past a flat plate, $dp/dt = 0$. Thus, for a perfect gas, Eq. (8.13) becomes

$$\rho u c_p \frac{\partial T}{\partial x} + \rho v c_p \frac{\partial T}{\partial y} = k \frac{\partial^2 T}{\partial y^2} \qquad (8.37)$$

Note that we have already neglected $k\,(\partial^2 T/\partial x^2)$ since it is small compared to $k\,(\partial^2 T/\partial y^2)$. We made a similar assumption about the corresponding velocity gradients when working with the momentum equation; see Eq. (7.6).

Let us now change the dependent variable from T to the dimensionless parameter θ, where

$$\theta = \frac{T - T_w}{T_e - T_w}$$

Note that $\theta = 0$ at the wall (i.e., at $y = 0$), and $\theta = 1$ at the edge of the thermal boundary layer. Using θ as the dependent variable, the energy equation becomes

$$\rho u \frac{\partial \theta}{\partial x} + \rho v \frac{\partial \theta}{\partial y} = \frac{k}{c_p} \frac{\partial^2 \theta}{\partial y^2} \qquad (8.38)$$

Since the pressure is constant along the flat plate, the velocity at the edge of the boundary layer (u_e) is constant, and the momentum equation becomes

$$\rho u \frac{\partial u}{\partial x} + \rho v \frac{\partial u}{\partial y} = \mu \frac{\partial^2 u}{\partial y^2} \qquad (8.39)$$

Let us replace u in the derivatives by the dimensionless parameter, u^*, where

$$u^* = \frac{u}{u_e}$$

Thus, Eq. (8.39) becomes

$$\rho u \frac{\partial u^*}{\partial x} + \rho v \frac{\partial u^*}{\partial y} = \mu \frac{\partial^2 u^*}{\partial y^2} \qquad (8.40)$$

Note that $u^* = 0$ at the wall (i.e., at $y = 0$), and $u^* = 1$ at the edge of the velocity boundary layer.

Compare Eq. (8.38) and Eq. (8.40). Note that the equations are identical if $k/c_p = \mu$. Furthermore, the boundary conditions are identical: $\theta = 0$ and $u^* = 0$ at the wall, and $\theta = 1$ and $u^* = 1$ at the edge of the boundary layer. Thus, if

$$\frac{\mu c_p}{k} = 1$$

the velocity and the thermal boundary layers are identical. This ratio is called the Prandtl number (Pr) in honor of the German scientist:

$$\mathrm{Pr} = \frac{\mu c_p}{k} \qquad (8.41)$$

The Prandtl number is an important dimensionless parameter for problems involving convective heat transfer where one encounters both fluid motion and heat conduction.

Reynolds Analogy

The shear at the wall is defined as

$$\tau = \left(\mu \frac{\partial u}{\partial y} \right)_{y = 0}$$

Therefore, the skin-friction coefficient for a flat plate is

$$C_f = \frac{\tau}{\frac{1}{2}\rho u_e^2} = \frac{2\mu}{\rho u_e} \frac{\partial u^*}{\partial y} \qquad (8.42)$$

The rate at which heat is transferred to the surface ($\dot{q}$) is defined as

$$\dot{q} = \left(k \frac{\partial T}{\partial y} \right)_{y=0} \qquad (8.43)$$

The Stanton number (designated by the symbols St or C_h), which is a dimensionless heat-transfer coefficient, is defined as

$$\text{St} \equiv C_h = \frac{\dot{q}}{\rho u_e c_p (T_e - T_w)} \qquad (8.44)$$

Combining these last two expressions, we find that the Stanton number is

$$\text{St} = \frac{k}{\rho u_e c_p} \frac{\partial \theta}{\partial y} \qquad (8.45)$$

Relating the Stanton number, as given by Eq. (8.45), to the skin-friction coefficient, as defined by Eq. (8.42), we obtain the ratio

$$\frac{C_f}{\text{St}} = \frac{2\mu c_p}{k} \frac{\partial u^*/\partial y}{\partial \theta/\partial y} \qquad (8.46)$$

Note that if $\mu c_p / k \equiv \text{Pr} = 1$, then

$$\frac{\partial u^*}{\partial y} = \frac{\partial \theta}{\partial y}$$

Thus, if the Prandtl number is 1,

$$\text{St} = \frac{C_f}{2} \qquad (8.47)$$

This relation between the heat-transfer coefficient and the skin-friction coefficient is known as the Reynolds analogy.

Example 8.6

The thermal conductivity of air can be calculated using the relation

$$k = 4.76 \times 10^{-6} \frac{T^{1.5}}{T + 112} \text{ cal/cm} \cdot \text{s} \cdot \text{K} \qquad (8.48)$$

over the range of temperatures below those for which oxygen dissociates, that is, approximately 2000 K at atmospheric pressure. What is the Prandtl number for air at 15°C, that is, at 288.15 K?

Solution. Using the results from Example 1.4, the viscosity is 1.7894×10^{-5} kg/s · m. The specific heat is 1004.7 J/kg · K. Using the equation to calculate the thermal conductivity,

$$k = 4.76 \times 10^{-6} \frac{(288.15)^{1.5}}{400.15} = 5.819 \times 10^{-5} \text{ cal/cm} \cdot \text{s} \cdot \text{K}$$

Noting that there are 4.187 J/cal, the thermal conductivity is

$$k = 2.436 \times 10^{-2} \text{ J/m} \cdot \text{s} \cdot \text{K}$$

Thus,

$$\text{Pr} = \frac{\mu c_p}{k} = \frac{(1.7894 \times 10^{-5} \text{ kg/s} \cdot \text{m}) (1004.7 \text{ J/kg} \cdot \text{K})}{2.436 \times 10^{-2} \text{ J/m} \cdot \text{s} \cdot \text{K}} = 0.738$$

Note that, as a rule of thumb, the Prandtl number for air is essentially constant (approximately 0.7) over a wide range of flow conditions.

Example 8.7

What is the Prandtl number of lubricating oil at 104°F? As given in Ref. 8.1, the thermal conductivity is 0.083 Btu/h · ft · °F, the specific heat is 0.469 Btu/lbm · °F, and the viscosity is 512 lbm/ft · h.

Solution.

$$\text{Pr} = \frac{\mu c_p}{k} = \frac{(512 \text{ lbm/ft} \cdot \text{h})(0.469 \text{ Btu/lbm} \cdot \text{°F})}{(0.083 \text{ Btu/hr} \cdot \text{ft} \cdot \text{°F})} = 2893$$

Thermal Boundary Layer for Pr ≠ 1

To solve for the temperature distribution for the laminar, flat-plate boundary layer, let us introduce the transformation of Eq. (7.10):

$$\eta = y \sqrt{\frac{u_e}{2\nu x}}$$

Using the transformed stream function f, as defined by Eq. (7.12b), Eq. (8.38) becomes

$$\theta'' + (\text{Pr}) f \, \theta' = 0 \qquad (8.49a)$$

where the ′ denotes differentiation with respect to η. But we have already obtained the solution for the stream function in Chapter 7. Referring to Eq. (7.16) for a flat plate (i.e., $\beta = 0$),

$$f = -\frac{f'''}{f''} \qquad (8.49b)$$

Combining Eqs. (8.49a) and (8.49b) and rearranging, we obtain

$$\frac{\theta''}{\theta'} = (\text{Pr})\frac{f'''}{f''}$$

Integrating twice

$$\theta = C \int_0^\eta (f'')^{\text{Pr}} \, d\eta + \theta_0 \tag{8.50}$$

where C and θ_0 are constants of integration. They can be evaluated by applying the boundary conditions (1) at $\eta = 0$, $\theta = 0$, and (2) for $\eta \to$ large, $\theta = 1$.

Thus,

$$\theta = \frac{T - T_w}{T_e - T_w} = 1 - \frac{\int_\eta^\infty (f'')^{\text{Pr}} \, d\eta}{\int_0^\infty (f'')^{\text{Pr}} \, d\eta} \tag{8.51}$$

The rate at which heat is transferred to the wall ($\dot{q}$) can be calculated using

$$\dot{q} = \left(k \frac{\partial T}{\partial y} \right)_{y=0} = k(T_e - T_w) \frac{\partial \eta}{\partial y} \left(\frac{\partial \theta}{\partial \eta} \right)_{\eta=0}$$

Using the values of Pohlhausen, we find that

$$\left(\frac{\partial \theta}{\partial \eta} \right)_{\eta=0} = 0.4696(\text{Pr})^{0.333}$$

Combining these two relations, the rate at which heat is transferred from a laminar boundary layer to the wall is given by the relation

$$\dot{q} = 0.332k(T_e - T_w)(\text{Pr})^{0.333} \sqrt{\frac{u_e}{\nu x}} \tag{8.52}$$

The heat transfer can be expressed in terms of the Stanton number using Eq. (8.44). Thus,

$$\text{St} = 0.332 \frac{k}{\mu c_p} \sqrt{\frac{\mu}{\rho u_e x}} (\text{Pr})^{0.333}$$

Using the definitions for the Reynolds number and Prandtl number, the Stanton number is

$$\text{St} = \frac{0.332}{(\text{Pr})^{0.667}(\text{Re}_x)^{0.5}} \tag{8.53}$$

Another popular dimensionless heat-transfer parameter is the Nusselt number. The Nusselt number is defined as

$$\text{Nu}_x = \frac{hx}{k} \tag{8.54a}$$

In this equation, h is the local heat-transfer coefficient, which is defined as

$$h = \frac{\dot{q}}{T_e - T_w} \qquad (8.54b)$$

Combining this definition with Eqs. (8.52) and (8.54a),

$$\mathrm{Nu}_x = 0.332(\mathrm{Re}_x)^{0.5}(\mathrm{Pr})^{0.333} \qquad (8.55)$$

By dividing the expression for the Stanton number, Eq. (8.53), by that for the skin-friction coefficient, Eq. (7.21), we obtain

$$\mathrm{St} = \frac{C_f}{2(\mathrm{Pr})^{0.667}} \qquad (8.56)$$

Because of the similarity between this equation and Eq. (8.47), we shall call this the *modified Reynolds analogy*.

Example 8.8

Using the modified Reynolds analogy, develop relations for the dimensionless heat-transfer parameters, St and Nu_x, for a turbulent flat-plate boundary layer.

Solution. Referring to the discussion of turbulent boundary layers in Chapter 7, we note that

$$C_f = \frac{0.0583}{(\mathrm{Re}_x)^{0.2}} \qquad (7.63)$$

Thus, using Eq. (8.56) for the modified Reynolds analogy, we can approximate the Stanton number as

$$\mathrm{St} = \frac{0.0292}{(\mathrm{Re}_x)^{0.2}(\mathrm{Pr})^{0.667}} \qquad (8.57)$$

Comparing Eqs. (8.53) and (8.55), we can see that the Nu_x is given as

$$\mathrm{Nu}_x = (\mathrm{St})(\mathrm{Pr})(\mathrm{Re}_x)$$

Thus, the Nusselt number for turbulent flow past a flat plate can be approximated as

$$\mathrm{Nu}_x = 0.0292(\mathrm{Re}_x)^{0.8}(\mathrm{Pr})^{0.333} \qquad (8.58)$$

Example 8.9

The radiator systems on many of the early racing aircraft were flush mounted on the external surface of the airplane. Let us assume that the local heat-transfer rate can be estimated using the flat-plate relations. What is the local heating rate for $x = 3.0$ m when the airplane is flying at 468 km/h at an altitude of 3 km? The surface temperature is 330 K.

Solution. Using Table 1.1 to find the free-stream flow properties,

$$p_\infty = 7.012 \times 10^4 \text{ N/m}^2, \qquad T_\infty = 268.659 \text{ K}$$

$$\rho_\infty = 0.9092 \text{ kg/m}^3, \qquad \mu_\infty = 1.6938 \times 10^{-5} \text{ kg/s m}$$

Since we have assumed that the flow corresponds to that for a flat plate, these values are also the local properties at the edge of the boundary layer at $x = 3.0$ m. Note that

$$u_e = U_\infty = 468 \text{ km/h} = 130 \text{ m/s}$$

To determine whether the boundary layer is laminar or turbulent, let us calculate the local Reynolds number.

$$\text{Re}_x = \frac{\rho_e u_e x}{\mu_e} = \frac{(0.9092)(130)(3.0)}{1.6938 \times 10^{-5}} = 2.093 \times 10^7$$

This is well above the transition value. In fact, if the transition Reynolds number is assumed to be 500,000, transition would occur at a point

$$x_{tr} = \frac{500,000}{(\rho_e u_e)/\mu_e} = 0.072 \text{ m}$$

from the leading edge. Thus, the calculation of the heating will be based on the assumption that the boundary layer is turbulent over its entire length.

Combining Eqs. (8.54a) and (8.54b),

$$\dot{q} = \frac{\text{Nu}_x k(T_e - T_w)}{x}$$

where the Nu_x is given by Eq. (8.58). Thus,

$$\dot{q} = \frac{0.0292(\text{Re}_x)^{0.8}(\text{Pr})^{0.333} k(T_e - T_w)}{x}$$

To calculate the thermal conductivity for air,

$$k = 4.76 \times 10^{-6} \frac{T^{1.5}}{T + 112} = 5.506 \times 10^{-5} \text{ cal/cm} \cdot \text{s} \cdot \text{K} = 2.306 \times 10^{-2} \text{ J/m} \cdot \text{s} \cdot \text{K}$$

Since $1 \text{ W} = 1 \text{ J/s}$,

$$k = 2.306 \times 10^{-2} \text{ w/m} \cdot \text{K}$$

Furthermore, the Prandtl number is

$$\text{Pr} = \frac{\mu c_p}{k} = 0.738$$

Thus,

$$\dot{q} = \frac{(0.0292)(2.093 \times 10^7)^{0.8}(0.738)^{0.333} 2.306 \times 10^{-2} \text{ w/m} \cdot \text{K} (268.659 - 330) \text{ K}}{3.0 \text{ m}}$$

$$= -8.944 \times 10^3 \text{ w/m}^2 = -8.944 \text{ kW/m}^2$$

The minus sign indicates that heat is transferred from the surface to the air flowing past the aircraft. This is as it should be, since the surface is hotter than the adjacent air. Furthermore, since the problem discusses a radiator, proper performance would produce cooling. Since there are 1.341 hp/kW, the heat transfer rate is equivalent to 1.114 hp/ft^2.

SUMMARY

In this chapter, we have analyzed systems that are involved in a process in which there is an exchange of energy between the system and its surroundings. The first law of thermodynamics requires only that, during any and all processes, one must account for all the energies. The second law of thermodynamics places restrictions on the direction of the energy transfer as well as the direction in which all real processes proceed. For instance, heat is always transferred from a higher temperature to a lower temperature (if no external influence is exerted on the process).

In the frictionless, incompressible flows that were discussed in earlier chapters, the second law of thermodynamics is automatically satisfied. In such flows, there is only the exchange of energies between the fluid elements. Because of the absence of friction and heat transfer, there are no restrictions on the manner of the interchange of these energies. The inclusion of heat transfer requires that the solution procedure be conducted to ensure the satisfaction of the second law of thermodynamics.

PROBLEMS

8.1. To illustrate the point that the two integrals in Eq. (8.1) are path dependent, consider a system consisting of air contained in a piston–cylinder arrangement (see Fig. P8.1). The system of air particles is made to undergo two cyclic processes. Note that all properties (p, T, ρ, etc.) return to their original value (i.e., undergo a net change of zero), since the processes are cyclic.

(a) Assume that both cycles are reversible and determine (1) $\oint \delta q$ and (2) $\oint \delta w$ for each cycle.

(b) Describe what occurs physically with the piston–cylinder–air configuration during each leg of each cycle.

(c) Using the answers to part (a), what is the value of ($\oint \delta q - \oint \delta w$) for each cycle?

(d) Is the first law satisfied for this system of air particles?

8.2. In Prob. 8.1 the entropy change in going from A to C directly (i.e., following process ii) is

$$s_C - s_A$$

Going via B (i.e., following process i), the entropy change is

$$s_C - s_A = (s_C - s_B) + (s_B - s_A)$$

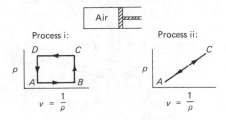

Figure P8.1 Sketch for Prob. 8.1.

(a) Is the net entropy change $(s_C - s_A)$ the same for both paths?

(b) Processes AC and ABC were specified to be reversible. What is $s_C - s_A$ if the processes are irreversible? Does $s_C - s_A$ depend on the path if the process is irreversible?

8.3. Starting with the general differential form of the energy equation, Eq. (8.13a), derive the energy equation for steady, incompressible, two-dimensional, constant-property, low-speed flow past a flat plate.

8.4. Starting with the thermodynamic relation that

$$T \, ds = dh - \frac{dp}{\rho}$$

and the general differential form of the energy equation, Eq. (8.13a), show that

$$\rho T \frac{ds}{dt} = k\nabla^2 T + \phi$$

for a Newtonian fluid for which k is a constant.

8.5. Crude oil contained in a sealed tank is stirred by a mixing device. The power input to the mixing device is 10 hp. Heat is transferred to the tank at the rate of 10,000 Btu/h. Consider the tank and the fluid in it as the system, and determine the rate of change in the internal energy.

8.6. Consider a system consisting of a stone whose mass is 10 lbm and of a bucket containing 100 lbm of water. Initially, the stone is 77.8 ft above the water, and the stone and the water are at the same temperature. The stone then falls into the water. Determine the changes in internal energy (Δu_e), kinetic energy (Δke), potential energy (Δpe), the work done (δw), and the heat transferred (δq) for each of the following cases.

(a) At the instant before the stone enters the water.

(b) Just after the stone has come to rest in the bucket.

(c) After a sufficiently long time has passed so that both the stone and the water have returned to their original temperature.

8.7. To escape the heat on an extremely sultry, summer day, an impoverished family closes off the kitchen and opens the refrigerator door. After an initial breath of cool air, the room ultimately heats up. Assuming that the room is a perfectly insulated, closed system with only the plug that carries power to the refrigerator crossing the boundary of the control volume, evaluate this situation as it relates to the first law of thermodynamics. Evaluate the situation if the room is not insulated.

8.8. Consider the hydroelectric plant shown in Fig. P8.8. Water enters the inlet conduit at the level of the lake, flows through the pipe, and delivers work through the hydraulic turbine. Assume that there is no change in the kinetic energy or internal energy in the inlet conduit and that the kinetic energy and internal energy of the water leaving the hydraulic turbine are the same as those in the inlet conduit. Calculate the power developed by the hydraulic turbine considering each of the three systems shown.

8.9. The heat exchanger of a power plant delivers 50 mW of waste heat to the water in the river, as shown in Fig. P8.9. The flow rate of the river (Q) is 2 m³/s and the temperature upstream of the power plant (T_i) is 20°C. For steady flow with negligible heat loss from the river water to the atmosphere or to the ground, what will be the water temperature at the downstream location (i.e., T_0)? The specific heat (c_p) for water is 4186.7 J/kg K.

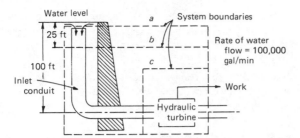

Figure P8.8   Sketch for Prob. 8.8.

8.10. For the flow situation of Fig. P8.9, what should be the flow rate through the heat exchanger if the outlet temperature is to be 30°C?

8.11. Oil flows steadily through a pipeline that is 30 in. in diameter at the rate of 500,000 barrels per day (1 barrel = 5.6146 ft³). The specific gravity of oil is 0.86. The friction head loss is 8.4 ft/1000 ft of pipe length. If a pumping station is to be placed every 12 miles, what is the pressure drop in pounds per square inch between pumping stations? What is the horsepower that must be delivered to the oil by each pump?

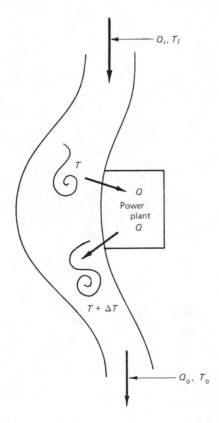

Figure P8.9   Sketch for Probs. 8.9 and 8.10.

8.12. Consider the steady flow of air through a compressor. For the air, at the inlet p_i = 100 kPa, T_i = 20°C, and V_i = 10 m/s; at the exit, p_e = 400 kPa, T_e = 120°C, and U_e = 80 m/s. If the weight flux is 5.5 N/s and if the heat transfer is negligible, what is the rate at which shaft work is done on the air?

8.13. Consider the steady flow of air through a compressor with the same conditions at the inlet and exit as given in Prob. 8.12. However, 15,000 J/kg of heat is transferred from the air while passing through the compressor. What is the rate at which shaft work is done on the air?

8.14. The average heat transfer from a person to the surroundings when he is not actively working is approximately 4.25×10^5 J/h. Suppose that there are 1000 people in an auditorium when the ventilating system fails (i.e., there is no flow of air through the auditorium).
(a) How much does the internal energy of the air in the auditorium change during the first 15 min after the ventilation system fails. If there are 6500 m³ of air in the auditorium, what is the change in air temperature?
(b) Considering the auditorium and all the people as a system and assuming that there is no heat transfer to the surroundings, how much does the internal energy of this system change?

8.15. Tank A contains 1.0 lbm of nitrogen at 200 psia and at 80°F. The valve in the system shown in Fig. P8.15 is opened slightly so that nitrogen flows slowly into cylinder B until the pressure is 30 psia. During this process, heat is transferred to the nitrogen so that its temperature remains constant at 80°F. What is the heat transferred during the process? The gas constant for nitrogen is 55.15 ft · lbf/lbm°R.

8.16. Calculate the internal energy and enthalpy of air at standard sea-level conditions. Use units of J/kg.

8.17. Calculate the internal energy and enthalpy of perfect air at 1000°F. Use units of Btu/lbm.

8.18. Calculate the internal energy and enthalpy of carbon dioxide when the pressure is 150 kPa and the temperature is 100°C. Use the perfect-gas relations.

8.19. Sea-level atmosphere air flows at 1000 m/s. What is the temperature of the perfect air if it is brought to rest adiabatically?

8.20. The mass flow rate into a steam turbine is 10,000 lbm/h. Heat is transferred from the turbine at the rate of 30,000 Btu/h. The conditions of the steam at the inlet and exit of the turbine are as follows:

Inlet: p_i = 3000 psia, T_i = 700°F, h_i = 1368.3 Btu/lbm, V_i = 200 fps, and

z_i = 16 ft

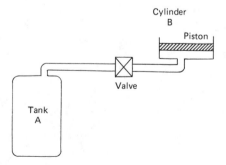

Figure P8.15 Sketch for Prob. 8.15.

Exit: $p_e = 16$ psia, $T_e = 216°F$, $h_e = 1152.0$ Btu/lbm, $V_e = 600$ fps, and

$z_e = 10$ ft

What is the power output of the turbine?

8.21. A steam turbine delivers 6.5 kW of power. Heat is transferred from the turbine at the rate of 3.25×10^7 J/h. The conditions of the steam at the inlet and exit of the turbine are as follows:

Inlet: $p_i = 2.068 \times 10^6$ N/m², $T_i = 371.4°C$, $h_i = 3.182 \times 10^6$ J/kg,

$V_i = 60$ m/s, and $z_i = 5.0$ m

Exit: $p_e = 1.103 \times 10^5$ N/m², $T_e = 102.6°C$, $h_e = 2.680 \times 10^6$ J/kg,

$V_e = 180$ m/s, and $z_e = 3.0$ m

What is the mass flow rate through the turbine?

8.22. In a refrigeration system, in which Freon-12 is the refrigerant, the Freon enters the compressor at 30 psia, 20°F, and an enthalpy of 80 Btu/lbm, and leaves the compressor at 160 psia, 200°F, and an enthalpy of 104 Btu/lbm. The mass rate of flow is 125 lbm/h and the power input to the compressor is 1 kW. What is the heat transfer rate from the compressor?

8.23. Consider the steady flow of water through a "block box," as shown in Figure P8.23. At the inlet, $D_1 = 10$ cm, $Q_1 = 0.056$ m³/s, and $p_1 = 1.7 \times 10^5$ N/m². The exit flows are $D_2 = 7.5$ cm, $Q_2 = 0.028$ m³/s, $p_2 = 2.0 \times 10^5$ N/m², $D_3 = 5$ cm, and $p_3 = 2.4 \times 10^5$ N/m². Heat transfer, temperature, and gravity effects are negligible. Compute the rate in kilowatts at which shaft work is done in the box. Is it done on or by the fluid?

8.24. Repeat Prob. 8.23 with the fluid as air at 20°C.

8.25. A well-insulated (adiabatic) tank is evacuated initially. A valve is then opened, allowing air at 500 psia and 500°R to flow into the tank. The valve is closed when the pressure in the tank reaches 500 psia. Assuming that the air behaves as a perfect gas, calculate the final equilibrium temperature of the air in the tank.

8.26. Perfect air accelerates through an adiabatic channel. At station 1, the air is at rest (i.e., $V_1 = 0$), the pressure is 5.70×10^6 N/m², and the temperature is 740 K. The pressure and

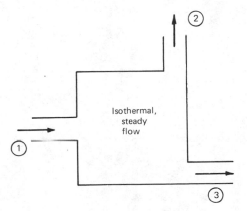

Figure P8.23   Sketch for Prob. 8.23.

temperature at station 2 are 6.0×10^2 N/m^2 and 55 K, respectively. If there is no shaft work, what is the velocity of the air at station 2? Calculate the speed of sound and the Mach number at station 2. This is a reasonable approximation of the flow in a hypersonic wind tunnel. What is the unit Reynolds number at station 2 [i.e., what is $(\rho_2 U_2)/\mu_2$]?

8.27. Using Eq. 8.48, calculate the thermal conductivity of air at 2000 K. What is the Prandtl number of perfect air at this temperature?

8.28. The boundary conditions that were used in developing the equation for the laminar thermal boundary layer were that the temperature is known at the two limits (1) $\theta = 0$ at $\eta = 0$, and (2) $\theta = 1$ at $\eta \rightarrow$ large. What would be the temperature distribution if the boundary conditions were (1) an adiabatic wall (i.e., $\theta' = 0$ at $\eta = 0$), and (2) $\theta = 1$ at $\eta \rightarrow$ large. *Hint:* from Eq. 8.50,

$$\theta' = C(f'')^{\mathrm{Pr}}$$

8.29. The lubricating oil of Example 8.7 flows past a flat steel plate. The velocity at the edge of the boundary layer is 20 ft/s. For lubricating oil, $\sigma = 0.88$. If the temperature of the metal plate is 70°F, what is the heat transfer rate (Btu/ft$^2 \cdot$ s), the Stanton number, and the Nusselt number at a point 1.0 ft from the leading edge?

8.30. A perfect insulator is placed on the back surface of the steel plate of Prob. 8.29. Thus, the plate is an adiabatic surface. What is the temperature of the plate at $x = 1.0$ ft?

8.31. Air at 50 kPa and 200°C flows past a flat plate that is at 20°C. Assuming the properties of the air are constant and equal to the perfect-gas values, what are the Stanton number and Nusselt number at the transition location? What is the heat-transfer rate (W/cm^2) at this point?

8.32. Nitrogen at 250 kPa and 20°C flows past a flat plate at 100 m/s. If the temperature of the plate is 100°C, what are the heat-transfer rate (W/cm^2), the Stanton number, and the Nusselt number at a point 1.0 m from the leading edge?

8.33. Represent the wing of an airplane by a flat plate. The airplane is flying at standard sea-level conditions at 170 mph. The dimensions of the wing are chord = 4 ft and span = 28 ft. What is the total heat transferred to the wing if the temperature of the wing is 50°F?

REFERENCE

8.1. A. J. Chapman, *Heat Transfer,* 3rd ed., Macmillan, Inc., New York, 1974.

CHAPTER NINE

Open-Channel Flows

Open-channel flows refer to those flows of a liquid that have a free surface. There are many practical examples of open-channel flows, including (1) the unsteady nonuniform flow that occurs when rain water flows over the surface of a plowed field during a driving rain storm and (2) the steady uniform flow that occurs in those regions of a very long, gradually inclined channel of constant cross section where the terminal velocity has been reached, that is, where the change in potential energy due to the decrease in elevation of the floor of the channel is equal to the head loss due to friction.

In analyzing open-channel flows, we know that the pressure along the free surface is constant and equal to the atmospheric value. However, the shape of the free surface is not known a priori. The depth profile changes with the conditions and must be determined as part of the solution. Thus, the presence of the free surface both helps and complicates the analysis.

Because of viscosity, the flow at the solid boundaries, for example, the sides and bottom of the trapezoidal channel of Fig. 9.1a, satisfies the no-slip condition. As a result, the flow is always three-dimensional. Representative velocity contours for flows in straight channels are presented in Fig. 9.1. For flow in broad, shallow channels, the maximum velocity occurs near the surface. Near the boundaries, the velocity variations are similar to those for a turbulent boundary layer. If the channel is not straight or if it meanders like a river, complex secondary flow patterns are established. Nevertheless, for many engineering applications, the flow can be modeled by assuming it to be one-dimensional with the average velocity and the cross-sectional area defined as functions of the distance along the channel.

Although most of the applications of open-channel flows relate to hydraulics, there is an interesting analogy between free surface flow and supersonic flow. This analogy

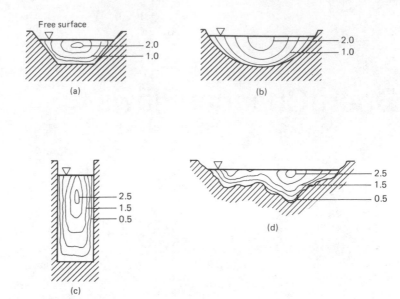

Figure 9.1 Measured isovelocity contours for representative open-channel flows: (a) trapezoidal channel; (b) shallow ditch; (c) narrow rectangular section; (d) natural irregular channel. (From *Open-Channel Hydraulics* by Ven Te Chow. Copyright © 1959 by McGraw-Hill Book Company. Used with the permission of McGraw-Hill Book Company.)

Figure 9.2 Photograph of water-table flow to simulate supersonic flow ($M = 2.5$) past a cavity. [Photograph courtesy of BPD Difesa e Spazio (Italy)].

allows engineers to use a water table to study multidimensional compressible flows in an experimental way. The photograph of Fig. 9.2 is a water-table simulation of supersonic flow past a cavity, such as occurs in the fin housings on missiles. The analysis of this flow was discussed in Ref. 9.3.

CLASSIFICATION OF OPEN-CHANNEL FLOWS

Open-channel flow may be steady or unsteady, uniform or nonuniform. *Steady uniform flow* occurs in those regions of long inclined channels of constant slope and constant cross section where the fluid has reached its terminal velocity. The terminal velocity occurs when the head loss due to viscous effects is equal to the change in potential energy. For a steady uniform flow, the depth is constant and is called the *normal depth* (y_n). As a result, the discharge (or volumetric flow rate Q) is constant along the length of the channel. The photograph of Fig. 9.3 depicts one such channel flow in an aqueduct.

Steady nonuniform flow occurs in any irregular channel in which the discharge does not change with time. It also designates those flows where the discharge is constant but the depth and, therefore, the average velocity change from one station to another. The changes in depth (or velocity) may be gradual or they may be sudden. Thus, if the slope of the channel changes, if the cross section changes, or if the flow encounters an obstruction, the depth changes and the flow is said to be varied. The flow may be *gradually varying* (GVF) or *rapidly varying* (RVF), as illustrated in Fig. 9.4. If the flow is gradually

Figure 9.3 Open-channel flow in an aqueduct in the San Joaquin Valley of California. (Photograph from the author's collection.)

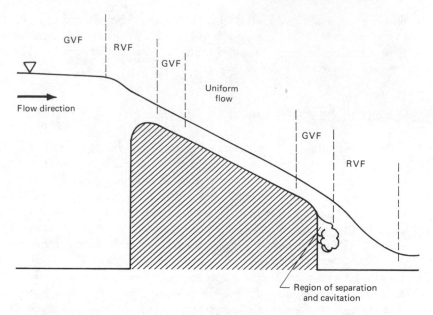

Figure 9.4 Regions of gradually varying flow (GVF) and rapidly varying flow (RVF) in an open-channel flow over an obstruction.

varying, the one-dimensional relations can be used in the engineering analysis of the flow.

Unsteady nonuniform flow can occur shortly after a sudden partial closure of a gate. A surge wave, which is a moving hydraulic jump, may occur in a channel when a gate is being opened or closed.

SIGNIFICANCE OF THE FROUDE NUMBER

In Chapter 4, we learned that the Froude number,

$$\text{Fr} = \frac{U_\infty}{(gL)^{0.50}} \tag{9.1}$$

is a dominant similarity parameter for free-surface flows. Consider a small surface wave of height ΔL propagating at a speed c into a quiescent liquid, as shown in Fig. 9.5a. Neglecting viscous effects, the water behind the wave moves with the velocity V_2 in this ground-fixed coordinate system. As we have often done in previous chapters, we will convert an unsteady flow into a steady flow by a coordinate transformation. As shown in Fig. 9.5b, we will fix the coordinate system to the wave. Thus, the flow approaches

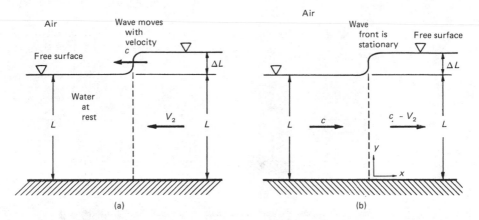

Figure 9.5 An infinitesimal wave propagating into still air: (a) ground-fixed coordinate system; (b) wave-fixed coordinate system.

the wave front (from the left) at a speed of c. In the wave-fixed coordinate system, the flow downstream of the wave moves at a speed of $c - V_2$.

Let us assume that variations in the y direction are negligible and apply the integral form of the continuity equation to the steady, constant-density flow of Fig. 9.5b. We find that

$$\rho c L = \rho(c - V_2)(L + \Delta L) \tag{9.2a}$$

Solving for V_2, we obtain

$$V_2 = c \frac{\Delta L}{L + \Delta L} \tag{9.2b}$$

To apply the integral form of the momentum equation, note that the pressure in the liquid varies as

$$p = p_{atm} + \rho g(y_s - y)$$

where the y coordinate of the free surface (y_s) is L upstream of the wave (i.e., to the left) and is $L + \Delta L$ downstream of the wave. The x-direction forces acting on our control volume are shown in Fig. 9.6. Note that, since we are neglecting viscous effects, the shear force at the bottom of the channel is neglected. Applying Eq. (4.19) to the flow of Fig. 9.6,

$$p_{atm} \, \Delta L + p_{atm}(L) + \int_0^L \rho g(L - y) \, dy$$

$$- p_{atm}(L + \Delta L) - \int_0^{L + \Delta L} \rho g(L + \Delta L - y) \, dy$$

$$= -\rho c^2 L + \rho(c - V_2)^2(L + \Delta L) \tag{9.3a}$$

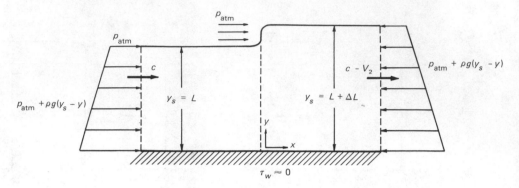

Figure 9.6 Control volume and forces for a weak wave propagating into still water.

Substituting Eq. (9.2a) into the right-hand side of this equation and combining terms, we obtain

$$\rho c L(c - V_2 - c) = \rho g \frac{L^2}{2} - \rho g \frac{(L + \Delta L)^2}{2}$$

Solving for V_2,

$$V_2 = \frac{g\,\Delta L}{c}\left[1 + \frac{\Delta L}{2L}\right] \tag{9.3b}$$

Equating the expressions for V_2, as given by Eqs. (9.2b) and (9.3b), we obtain the wave-propagation speed:

$$c^2 = gL\left(1 + \frac{\Delta L}{L}\right)\left(1 + \frac{\Delta L}{2L}\right) \tag{9.4}$$

In the limit of an infinitesimal "strength" wave whose height $\Delta L \ll L$, the wave speed becomes

$$c \approx (gL)^{0.5} \tag{9.5}$$

Thus, the Froude number becomes

$$\text{Fr} \approx \frac{U_\infty}{c} \tag{9.6}$$

which is the channel flow analogy of the Mach number in gas flows, which will be discussed in Chapter 10.

Using the Froude number to classify channel flows, we can divide the flow into three regimes:

1. $\text{Fr} < 1.0$: subcritical flow.
2. $\text{Fr} = 1.0$: critical flow.
3. $\text{Fr} > 1.0$: supercritical flow.

When flow velocities are relatively low so that a small disturbance can travel upstream and thus change the upstream conditions, the flow is said to be *tranquil*. The Froude number is less than 1.0, and the flow is controlled by the downstream conditions. When the flow velocities are sufficiently high, a small disturbance in the flow is swept downstream. Small changes in the flow at a given location do not affect the upstream flow. For these flows, the Froude number is greater than 1.0, and the flow is said to be *rapid* or *shooting*. When there is a shooting flow in a channel having an obstruction or a rapid decrease in cross section, a *hydraulic jump* can occur. Tranquil flows are analogous to subsonic flows. Rapid, or shooting, flows are analogous to supersonic flows.

CHEZY AND MANNING EQUATIONS FOR STEADY UNIFORM FLOW

As has been noted, steady uniform flow can occur in long straight channels of constant slope and constant cross section. Using the modified Bernoulli's equation, Eq. (6.1), between two points on the free surface of the open channel flow,

$$\frac{V_1^2}{2g} + z_1 + \frac{p_1}{\rho g} = \frac{V_2^2}{2g} + z_2 + \frac{p_2}{\rho g} + h_f$$

Point 2 is downstream of point 1, and h_f represents the head loss due to friction. Note that, since the points are on the free surface, $p_1 = p_2 = p_{\text{atm}}$. For steady uniform flow, $V_1 = V_2$. Thus, using the nomenclature of Fig. 9.7,

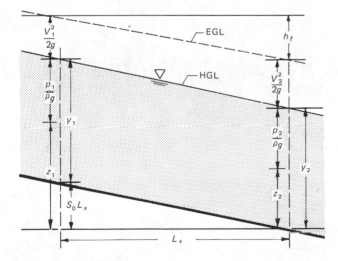

Figure 9.7 Definition sketch for flow in open channels.

$$h_f = z_1 - z_2 = L_x|\tan \theta| = L_x S_0 \tag{9.7}$$

where θ is the angle between the bottom of the channel and the horizontal, and S_0 is the slope of the channel. The head loss thus balances the loss in height along the channel.

Because the channel is very long, the flow is essentially fully developed. Thus, the Darcy–Weisbach equation, Eq. (6.2), can be used.

$$h_f = f \frac{L}{4R_h} \frac{V_{av}^2}{2g} \tag{9.8}$$

where R_h, the hydraulic radius, is equal to A/P (i.e., the ratio of the cross-sectional area to the perimeter).

Combining Eqs. (9.7) and (9.8), we find that the flow velocity for steady uniform flow is

$$V_{av} = \left(\frac{8g}{f}\right)^{0.5} (R_h S_0)^{0.5} \tag{9.9}$$

For a given channel slope and wall roughness, the quantity $(8g/f)^{0.5}$ is constant. Thus, the average velocity is given by

$$V_{av} = C(R_h S_0)^{0.5} \tag{9.10a}$$

and the discharge (or volumetric flow rate) is

$$Q = CA(R_h S_0)^{0.5} \tag{9.10b}$$

Equations (9.10a) and (9.10b) are known as the Chezy formulas, since they were first developed by the French engineer Antoine de Chezy in the eighteenth century.

The friction factor for a completely turbulent flow can be approximated by

$$f \approx 0.113 \left(\frac{\varepsilon}{R_h}\right)^{1/3} \tag{9.11}$$

This equation is a power-law approximation of the more exact approximation given by Eq. (6.20). Using Eq. (9.11), the constant C becomes

$$C \approx 8.414 g^{0.5} \left(\frac{R_h}{\varepsilon}\right)^{1/6} \tag{9.12}$$

When correlating channel resistance data in 1889, Robert Manning developed the following expression for C:

$$C = \frac{1.49}{n} [R_h(\text{ft})]^{1/6} = \frac{1.0}{n} [R_h(\text{m})]^{1/6} \tag{9.13}$$

For the first relation, R_h is in feet; for the second, meters. Manning's coefficient, n, is dimensionless and has the same value whether SI or British units are used. Comparing

Eq. (9.13) with Eq. (9.12), an approximate correlation for Manning's coefficient is obtained:

$$n \approx 0.0313[\varepsilon(\text{ft})]^{1/6} = 0.0382 \,[\varepsilon(\text{m})]^{1/6} \tag{9.14}$$

Again, the first expression uses English units; the second uses metric units. Typical values for the Manning coefficient and for the equivalent channel roughness height are presented in Table 9.1.

In applying the Manning formula, the greatest difficulty lies in the determination of the roughness coefficient n. Although we may think of a channel as having a single value of n (or a limited range of values), such as given in Table 9.1, in reality the value of n may be variable, depending upon a number of factors. The factors that exert the greatest influence upon the coefficient of roughness will be described briefly.

1. *Surface roughness:* The surface roughness is represented by the size and shape of the grains of the material forming the wetted perimeter and producing a retarding effect on the flow. Although this is often considered the only factor in selecting a roughness coefficient, other factors affect the value of n. Generally, fine grains result in a relatively low value of n and coarse grains, in a high value of n.

TABLE 9.1 EXPERIMENTAL VALUES OF MANNING'S n FACTOR

	n	Average roughness height, ε	
		ft	cm
Artificial lined channels			
Asphalt	0.016 ± 0.0003	0.018	0.54
Brickwork	0.015 ± 0.0002	0.012	0.37
Cement, finished	0.012 ± 0.0002	0.0033	0.10
Cement, unfinished	0.014 ± 0.0002	0.0079	0.24
Rubble masonry	0.025 ± 0.005	0.26	8.0
Steel, painted	0.014 ± 0.003	0.0079	0.24
Steel, riveted	0.015 ± 0.002	0.012	0.37
Steel, smooth	0.012 ± 0.002	0.0033	0.10
Evacuated earth channels			
Clean	$0.022 + 0.004$	0.12	3.7
Gravelly	0.025 ± 0.005	0.26	8.0
Weedy	0.030 ± 0.005	0.79	24.0
Natural channels			
Clean and straight	0.030 ± 0.005	0.79	24.0
Sluggish, deep pools	0.040 ± 0.010	2.95	90.0
Major rivers	0.035 ± 0.010	1.64	50.0

Source: From *Fluid Mechanics* by F. M. White. Copyright © 1979 by McGraw-Hill Book Company. Used with the permission of McGraw-Hill Book Company.

2. *Vegetation:* Vegetation may be regarded as a kind of surface roughness. It retards the flow and reduces the ability of the channel to carry fluid. This effect depends mainly on the height, density, distribution, and type of vegetation. It is very important in the design of small drainage channels.

3. *Channel alignment:* Smooth, large-radius-of-curvature changes will have a relatively low value of *n*. Sharp curvature with severe meandering will increase *n*.

4. *Stage and discharge:* The value of *n* for most streams decreases as the stage and the discharge increase. When the water is shallow, the irregularities of the channel bottom are relatively important and their effects become pronounced. However, if the banks of the channel are rough and grassy, *n* may be relatively high even when the discharge is high.

If the discharge is so high that the stream overflows its banks, a portion of the flow will be along the floodplain. The *n* value of the floodplain is generally greater than that of the channel proper, the exact value depending on surface conditions and vegetation, as illustrated in Table 9.2.

The corresponding formulas for the average velocity and the volumetric flow rate are

$$V_{av} = \frac{1.49}{n}[R_h \text{ (ft)}]^{2/3}S_0^{0.5} = \frac{1.0}{n}[R_h \text{ (m)}]^{2/3}S_0^{0.5} \tag{9.15a}$$

and

$$Q = \frac{1.49}{n}A[R_h \text{ (ft)}]^{2/3}S_0^{0.5} = \frac{1.0}{n}A[R_h \text{ (m)}]^{2/3}S_0^{0.5} \tag{9.15b}$$

respectively.

TABLE 9.2 VALUES OF *n* FOR VARIOUS STAGES OF THE NISHNABOTNA RIVER FOR THE AVERAGE GROWING SEASON

| Depth of water, ft | Channel section | Floodplain cover | | | | |
		Corn	Pasture	Meadow	Small grains	Brush and waste
Under 1	0.03	0.06	0.05	0.10	0.10	0.12
1 to 2	0.03	0.06	0.05	0.08	0.09	0.11
2 to 3	0.03	0.07	0.04	0.07	0.08	0.10
3 to 4	0.03	0.07	0.04	0.06	0.07	0.09
Over 4	0.03	0.06	0.04	0.05	0.06	0.08

Source: From *Open Channel Hydraulics* by Ven Te Chow. Copyright © 1959 by McGraw-Hill Book Company. Used with the permission of McGraw-Hill Book Company.

Example 9.1

Use both the Manning formula and the friction factor analysis to calculate the discharge for water flowing in a trapezoidal channel. Using the nomenclature of Fig. 9.8, $y_n = 3$ m, $b = 4$ m, and $\phi = 50°$. The floor of the channel slopes at 0.5°. The lining of the channel is finished concrete.

Solution. Since we are using metric units, the Manning formula for the discharge is

$$Q = \frac{1.0}{n} A[R_h]^{2/3} S_0^{0.5}$$

From Table 9.1, $n = 0.012$.

$$A = y_n \frac{b + b_0}{2} = y_n(b + y_n \cot \phi) = 3[4 + 3 \cot (50)]$$

$$= 19.552 \text{ m}^2$$

$$P = b + 2w = b + 2y_n \csc \phi = 4 + 2(3) \csc (50) = 11.832 \text{ m}$$

$$R_h = \frac{A}{P} = 1.652 \text{ m},$$

$$S_0 = \tan (0.5°) = 0.00873$$

Thus,

$$Q = \frac{1.0}{0.012} (19.552)(1.652)^{2/3}(0.00873)^{0.5} = 212.7 \text{ m}^3/\text{s}$$

Using the friction factor analysis, the discharge is given by the product of the area and V_{av}, as given by Eq. (9.9):

$$Q = \left(\frac{8g}{f}\right)^{0.5} (R_h S_0)^{0.5} A$$

From Table 9.1, $\varepsilon = 1.0 \times 10^{-3}$ m. Thus,

$$f \approx 0.113\left(\frac{\varepsilon}{R_h}\right)^{1/3} = 0.113\left(\frac{1.0 \times 10^{-3}}{1.652}\right)^{1/3} = 9.559 \times 10^{-3}$$

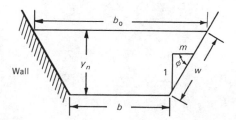

Figure 9.8 Nomenclature for a trapezoidal section.

As a result,

$$Q = \left[\frac{8(9.8066)}{9.559 \times 10^{-3}} (1.652)(0.00873) \right]^{0.5} 19.552 = 212.7 \text{ m}^3/\text{s}$$

Exact agreement between the values obtained by these two approaches will not always occur.

With the normal depth (y_n) given as in Example 9.1, the calculation of Q is straightforward. However, if Q is given (or is known from the design requirements), the calculation of the normal depth usually requires a trial-and-error procedure. This will be demonstrated in Example 9.2.

Example 9.2

A developer has been required by environmental regulatory authorities to line an open channel to prevent erosion. The channel is trapezoidal in cross section with a slope of 0.002. Referring to Fig. 9.8, $b = 10$ ft and $m = 2$. The channel is lined with rubble masonry. If the design flow rate is to be 1000 cfs, what is y_n?

Solution

$$Q = \frac{1.49}{n} A [R_h]^{2/3} S_0^{0.5}$$

From Table 9.1, $n = 0.025$. Since $m = 2$, $\phi = \tan^{-1} 0.5 = 26.57°$

$$A = y_n \frac{(2b + 2y_n \text{ ctn } \phi)}{2} = y_n(10 + 2y_n)$$

Since $R_h = A/P$,

$$Q = \frac{1.49}{n} \frac{A^{5/3}}{P^{2/3}} S_0^{0.5} \qquad (9.16)$$

where $P = b + 2y_n \csc \phi = 10 + 2\sqrt{5}y_n$.

Thus,

$$1000 = \frac{1.49 [y_n(10 + 2y_n)]^{5/3}}{0.025[10 + 2\sqrt{5}y_n]^{2/3}} (0.002)^{0.5}$$

$$375 = \frac{[y_n(10 + 2y_n)]^{5/3}}{[10 + 2\sqrt{5} \, y_n]^{2/3}}$$

By trial and error,

$$\text{If } y_n = 10 \text{ ft}, \quad rhs = 932.75$$

$$\text{If } y_n = 7 \text{ ft}, \quad rhs = 428.07$$

$$\text{If } y_n = 6.6 \text{ ft}, \quad rhs = 377.75$$

Thus, the normal depth of the water is approximately 6.6 ft.

CONVEYANCE OF A CHANNEL SECTION

The discharge of a uniform flow in a channel may be expressed as the product of the velocity, such as given by Eq. (9.9) or by Eq. (9.15a), and the cross section of the flow (i.e., $Q = VA$). It may also be given as

$$Q = KS_0^y \qquad (9.17a)$$

where

$$K = CAR_h^x \qquad (9.17b)$$

The term K is known as the conveyance of the channel section. It is a measure of the carrying capacity of the channel section, since it is proportional to Q.

Whether the Chezy formula or the Manning formula is used to determine the flow, $y = 0.5$ and Eq. (9.17a) becomes

$$Q = KS_0^{0.5} \qquad (9.18a)$$

so the conveyance is

$$K = \frac{Q}{S_0^{0.5}} \qquad (9.18b)$$

Equation (9.18b) can be used to calculate the conveyance when the discharge and slope of the channel are known.

When the Chezy formula is used, Eq. (9.17b) becomes

$$K = \left(\frac{8g}{f}\right)^{0.5} AR_h^{0.5} \qquad (9.19a)$$

Similarly, when the Manning formula is used,

$$K = \frac{1.49}{n} A[R_h \text{ (ft)}]^{2/3} = \frac{1.0}{n} A[R_h \text{ (m)}]^{2/3} \qquad (9.19b)$$

Equations (9.19a) and (9.19b) can be used to calculate the conveyance when the geometry of the water area and the resistance factor or roughness coefficient are known.

CHANNELS OF A COMPOUND SECTION

The cross section of a channel may be composed of several distinct subsections where the roughness differs for each subsection. An example of a compound section occurs when a river overflows its banks, resulting in a main channel and one or two side channels, as shown in Fig. 9.9. As indicated by the values presented in Table 9.2, the side channels are usually found to be rougher than the main channel. As a result, the mean velocity in the main channel is greater than the mean velocity in the side channel. The Manning

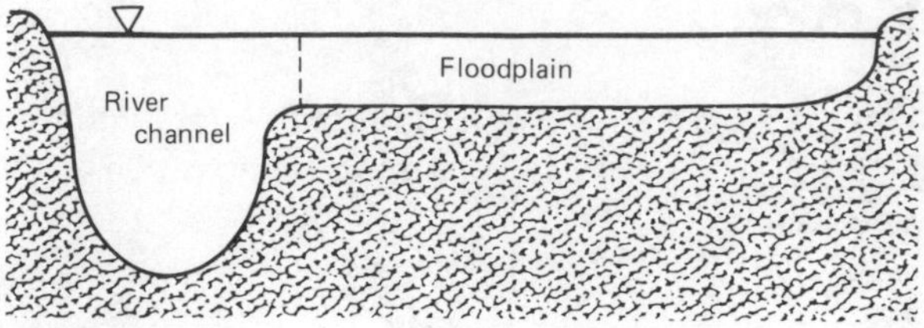

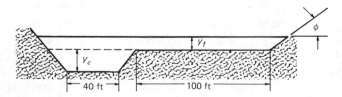

Figure 9.9 Floodplain as an example of a compound section.

formula is applied separately to each section to determine the conveyance of that section. Then the discharges of the subsections are added together to give the total discharge.

$$Q = (K_1 + K_2 + \ldots)S_0^{0.5} \tag{9.20}$$

Example 9.3

Calculate the discharge when a river overflows its banks onto a floodplain that is a meadow. Use Table 9.2 to obtain values of n. The compound-section open-channel flow can be represented by the cross section shown in Fig. 9.10, with $\phi = 45°$, $S_0 = 0.0009$, $y_c = 16$ ft, and $y_f = 8$ ft.

Solution.   We will apply the Manning formula to calculate K_1 for the river channel and K_2 for the floodplain. Since $R_h = A/P$, Eq. (9.19b) can be written

$$K_1 = \frac{1.49}{n_1} \frac{A_1^{5/3}}{P_1^{2/3}}$$

and

$$y_n = y_c + y_f$$

$$A_1 = y_n(b_1 + y_n \cot \phi) - \frac{1}{2}(y_f^2 \cot \phi) = 24(40 + 24) - \frac{1}{2}(64) = 1504 \text{ ft}^2$$

$$P_1 = \frac{y_n}{\sin \phi} + b + \frac{y_c}{\sin \phi} = 33.941 + 40 + 22.627 = 96.568 \text{ ft}$$

Note that in calculating the perimeter P_1 we have neglected the contribution of y_f at the fluid–fluid interface. In making this approximation, we have assumed that the fluid–fluid interface does not contribute to the resistance as the walls of the channel do.

$$K_1 = \frac{1.49}{0.03} \frac{(1504)^{5/3}}{(96.568)^{2/3}} = 465,861$$

Figure 9.10 Sketch for Example 9.3.

Similarly,

$$K_2 = \frac{1.49}{n_2} \frac{A_2^{5/3}}{P_2^{2/3}}$$

$$A_2 = y_f(b_2 + y_f \cot \phi) - \frac{1}{2}(y_f^2 \cot \phi) = 8(100 + 8) - \frac{1}{2}(64) = 832 \text{ ft}^2$$

$$P_2 = b_2 + \frac{y_f}{\sin \phi} = 100 + 11.314 = 111.314 \text{ ft}$$

$$K_2 = \frac{1.49}{0.05} \frac{(832)^{5/3}}{(111.314)^{2/3}} = 94,781$$

Thus,

$$Q = (K_1 + K_2)S_0^{0.5} - 16,819 \text{ ft}^3/\text{s}$$

EFFICIENT HYDRAULIC CHANNEL CROSS SECTIONS

In general, when a channel is constructed, the excavation, and possibly the lining, are important cost factors. The simplicity of Manning's relation allows us to analyze the relative efficiency of channel designs. The most common problem is that of maximizing R_h for a given flow area and discharge. Since $R_h = A/P$, maximizing R_h for a given A is equivalent to miminizing P, the wetted perimeter.

Using the equations developed in the three sample problems,

$$A = y_n(b + y_n \cot \phi) = by_n + my_n^2 \tag{9.21a}$$

$$P = b + 2y_n \csc \phi = b + 2y_n(1 + m^2)^{0.5} \tag{9.21b}$$

and, rearranging Eq. (9.16) for a given Q, S_0, and n,

$$A = CP^{0.4} \tag{9.22}$$

Eliminating b between Eqs. (9.21a) and (9.21b) yields

$$P = \frac{A}{y_n} - my_n + 2y_n(1 + m^2)^{0.5} \tag{9.23}$$

To minimize P for a given A and m, let us find dP/dy_n.

$$\frac{dP}{dy_n} = -\frac{A}{y_n^2} - m + 2(1 + m^2)^{0.5}$$

In order for $dP/dy_n = 0$,

$$A = y_n^2 [2(1 + m^2)^{0.5} - m] \tag{9.24a}$$

Also,

$$P = 2y_n [2(1 + m^2)^{0.5} - m] \tag{9.24b}$$

Note that, in general, for sections defined by Eqs. (9.21a) and (9.21b),

$$R_h = \frac{A}{P} = \frac{y_n}{2} \tag{9.25}$$

Thus, for any value of m (i.e., any angle ϕ), the most efficient cross section for uniform flow occurs when the hydraulic radius is one-half the dpeth.

Since $m = 0$ for a rectangular section, the most efficient rectangular section is such that

$$A = 2y_n^2, \qquad P = 4y_n, \qquad b = 2y_n \tag{9.26}$$

To find the best trapezoidal section, we need to find the best value of m for a given depth and area. Differentiating P, as given by Eq. (9.23), with respect to m, we find

$$\frac{dP}{dm} = -y_n + \frac{2y_n m}{(1 + m^2)^{0.5}}$$

Solving to find when this expression is zero,

$$2m = (1 + m^2)^{0.5}$$

Thus,

$$m = \sqrt{\tfrac{1}{3}} \quad \text{or} \quad \phi = 60°$$

Note that the best trapezoid section is half of a hexagon.

Similar calculations for a circular channel section that is partially full show that the best efficiency occurs for a semicircle (i.e., $y_n = 0.5D$). In fact, the semicircle is the best of all possible sections; it has the minimum wetted perimeter for a given flow area. The percentage improvement over the half-hexagon trapezoid channel is relatively small.

Example 9.4

The slope of a brick-lined channel is 0.0005. (a) What are the best dimensions for a rectangular channel, if it is to carry 40 m³/s? (b) What are the dimensions for a trapezoidal channel carrying the same flow rate?

Solution.   The volumetric flow rate is given by Eq. (9.15b):

$$Q = \frac{1.0}{n} A(R_h)^{2/3} S_0^{0.5}$$

Using Eq. (9.21), we know that, for the optimum shape,

$$R_h = \frac{y_n}{2}$$

(a) For a rectangular channel, we can use Eq. (9.26) to find that

$$A = 2y_n^2$$

For a brick-lined channel, $n = 0.015$. Thus,

$$40 = \frac{1.0}{0.015} \left[2y_n^2 \right] \left[\frac{y_n}{2} \right]^{2/3} (0.0005)^{0.5}$$

Isolating y_n,

$$y_n^{8/3} = \frac{40(0.015)(2)^{2/3}}{2(0.0005)^{0.5}}$$

Thus,

$$y_n = 3.149 \text{ m}$$

The other dimension of the channel can be calculated from Eq. (9.26):

$$b = 2y_n = 6.298$$

and

$$A = 2y_n^2 = y_n b = 19.832 \text{ m}^2$$

(b) For the optimum trapezoidal channel,

$$m = \frac{1}{\sqrt{3}}$$

and from Eq. (9.24a)

$$A = y_n^2[2(1 + m^2)^{0.5} - m] = \sqrt{3}y_n^2$$

Thus,

$$40 = \frac{1.0}{0.015} \left[\sqrt{3}y_n^2 \right] \left[\frac{y_n}{2} \right]^{2/3} (0.0005)^{0.5}$$

Isolating y_n, as was done for part (a),

$$y_n^{8/3} = \frac{40(0.015)(2)^{2/3}}{\sqrt{3}(0.0005)^{0.5}}$$

Thus,

$$y_n = 3.323 \text{ m}$$

Furthermore, we solve Eq. (9.21a) for b to find

$$b = \frac{A}{y_n} - my_n = \sqrt{3}y_n - \frac{y_n}{\sqrt{3}} = 3.837 \text{ m}$$

$$A = \sqrt{3}y_n^2 = 19.126 \text{ m}^2$$

Note that, for a given discharge, the trapezoidal channel is slightly smaller in cross section than the rectangular channel.

ENERGY RELATIONS FOR OPEN-CHANNEL FLOWS

Consider the flow in the wide rectangular channel, shown in the sketch of Fig. 9.7. Including friction in the application of Bernoulli's equation, Eq. (6.1), between two points in the flow,

$$\frac{V_1^2}{2g} + z_1 + \frac{p_1}{\rho g} = \frac{V_2^2}{2g} + z_2 + \frac{p_2}{\rho g} + h_f$$

The two points are located a distance L_x apart; point 2 is downstream of point 1, and h_f represents the head loss due to friction. The pressure and the elevation in the fluid are taken at the centroid of the flow section. Note that the free surface corresponds to the sum of $z + p/\rho g$. Therefore, the free surface is equivalent to the hydraulic grade line.

Referring to Fig. 9.7, we see that

$$\frac{p_1}{\rho g} + z_1 = y_1 + S_0 L_x \tag{9.27a}$$

and

$$\frac{p_2}{\rho g} + z_2 = y_2 \tag{9.27b}$$

where S_0 is the slope of the channel. Thus, Bernoulli's equation can be written

$$y_1 + \frac{V_1^2}{2g} + S_0 L_x = y_2 + \frac{V_2^2}{2g} + h_f \tag{9.28}$$

For (1) steady uniform flow, where $h_f = S_0 L_x$, as shown in Eq. (9.7), and for (2) the case where the bottom of the channel is horizontal (i.e., $S_0 = 0$) and the head loss (h_f) is zero, Eq. (9.28) becomes

$$y_1 + \frac{V_1^2}{2g} = y_2 + \frac{V_2^2}{2g} \tag{9.29}$$

The sum of the flow depth and the velocity head is known as the specific energy E.

Flow in Rectangular Channels

Let us define the discharge per unit width (q) of a wide rectangular channel:

$$q = \frac{Q}{b} = yV \tag{9.30}$$

Thus,

$$E = y + \frac{q^2}{2gy^2} = y_1 + \frac{q_1^2}{2gy_1^2} = y_2 + \frac{q_2^2}{2gy_2^2} \tag{9.31}$$

The relationship between E and y for a given q is illustrated in Fig. 9.11. Note that for most values of E there are two values of y: one, subcritical; the other, supercritical. There is a single value of y when the specific energy is a minimum (for a given discharge). The flow at this point is termed critical. For $E < E_{min}$, no solution exists for Eq. (9.31) and, thus, such a flow is physically impossible.

Note that critical flow occurs when the specific energy is a minimum for a given discharge. Let us determine the corresponding values of y ($= y_c$) and E ($= E_{min}$):

$$\frac{dE}{dy} = 1 - \frac{q^2}{gy^3} \qquad (9.32)$$

When $dE/dy = 0$ and $d^2E/dy^2 > 0$, E is a minimum and $y = y_c$. Thus, setting the expression given in this equation to zero, we find that

$$y_c = \left(\frac{q^2}{g}\right)^{1/3} = \left(\frac{Q^2}{b^2g}\right)^{1/3} \qquad (9.33)$$

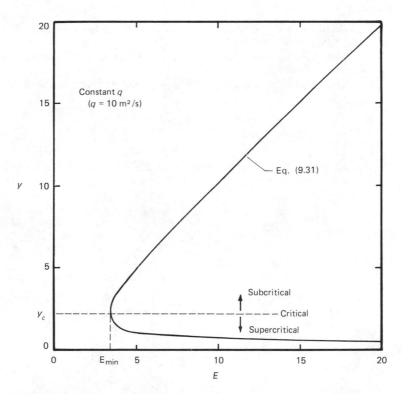

Figure 9.11 Depth as a function of specific energy (illustrating the critical depth and the minimum specific energy).

Substituting this expression into Eq. (9.31), we obtain the expression for the associated minimum energy:

$$E_{min} = \frac{3}{2} y_c \tag{9.34}$$

Combining Eqs. (9.30) and (9.33), one obtains

$$\frac{V_c^2}{gy_c} = 1 \tag{9.35}$$

Note that the left-hand side of this equation is equal to $(Fr)^2$. Hence, critical flow exists when the Froude number is unity. Observations of critical flow in open-channel flows show that the flow is often accompanied by waves and undulations in the free surface. Because of the unstable nature of critical flow, it is usually best to design canals so that the normal depth is either well above or well below the critical depth. The flows in canals and rivers are usually subcritical.

Example 9.5

Water flows in a 10-m-wide rectangular channel and has a discharge of 100 m³/s. Calculate the Froude number if the depth is 0.745 m. Classify the flow and determine the alternate depth for this specific energy. What is the critical depth for this discharge?

Solution.   Noting that $q = Q/b = 10$ m²/s, we can readily calculate the critical depth using Eq. (9.33):

$$y_c = \left(\frac{q^2}{g}\right)^{1/3} = 2.169 \text{ m}$$

Since the water is flowing at a depth of 0.745 m, which is less than y_c, the flow is supercritical. We can verify this by calculating the Froude number.

$$V = \frac{Q}{by} = \frac{100}{10(0.745)} = 13.423 \text{ m/s}$$

$$Fr = \frac{V}{(gy)^{0.5}} = \frac{13.423}{[(9.8066)(0.745)]^{0.5}} = 4.966$$

Since the Froude number is greater than 1, the flow is supercritical as we had already determined by comparing y with y_c. To calculate the alternate depth, we first calculate E for $y = 0.745$ m. Using Eq. (9.31),

$$E = y + \frac{q^2}{2gy^2} = 9.931$$

Solving for the alternate depth, we find that it is

$$y = 9.88 \text{ m}$$

HYDRAULIC JUMP

In an open-channel flow, a supercritical flow can change rapidly to a subcritical flow. This change can be caused by a sill in the channel or by the prevailing depth of the stream farther downstream. A rather abrupt change in depth and a considerable loss in energy accompany this process. Because hydraulic jumps are very effective energy dissipators, many spillways are designed so that a jump will occur on the apron of the spillway, thereby reducing the downstream velocity so that objectional scour of the river channel is reduced. Hydraulic jumps also mix fluids very efficiently and have application to sewage and water treatment facilities.

Earlier in this chapter, we used the continuity and momentum equations to develop relations for a traveling wave. A hydraulic jump is equivalent to a strong fixed wave where the change in depth ΔL is not negligible. Thus, referring to Figs. 9.5b and 9.6, we will substitute V_1 and y_1 (representing the upstream flow conditions) for c and L, respectively, and we will substitute V_2 and y_2 (the downstream flow conditions) for $c - V_2$ and $L + \Delta L$, respectively. With these changes in nomenclature, Eq. (9.4) can be applied to the hydraulic jump:

$$V_1^2 = \frac{1}{2} g y_1 \left(\frac{y_2}{y_1}\right)\left(1 + \frac{y_2}{y_1}\right) \tag{9.36}$$

Using the definition for the upstream Froude number,

$$(\text{Fr}_1)^2 = \frac{V_1^2}{g y_1}$$

we obtain

$$\left(\frac{y_2}{y_1}\right)^2 + \left(\frac{y_2}{y_1}\right) - 2\,(\text{Fr}_1)^2 = 0 \tag{9.37}$$

Using the quadratic formula, we can solve for y_2/y_1 in terms of the upstream Froude number. Obviously, only the positive value of y_2/y_1 is physically possible. Thus,

$$y_2 = \frac{y_1}{2} \{[1 + 8(\text{Fr}_1)^2]^{0.5} - 1\}$$

The depths on either side of a hydraulic jump (y_1 and y_2) are known as the *sequent depths,* in contrast to the alternate depths obtained from the specific energy concept. A hydraulic jump is approximately $6y_2$ long for a range of Froude numbers from 4 to 18.

With y_2 known, V_2 can be determined from the continuity equation for a wide channel flow:

$$V_2 = \frac{V_1 y_1}{y_2} \tag{9.39}$$

Finally, we can determine the dissipation head loss across the jump by solving Eq. (9.28) for h_f:

$$h_f = \left(y_1 + \frac{V_1^2}{2g}\right) - \left(y_2 + \frac{V_2^2}{2g}\right)$$

Using Eqs. (9.38) and (9.39) for y_2 and V_2, respectively, we find that

$$h_f = \frac{(y_2 - y_1)^3}{4y_1y_2} \tag{9.40}$$

Since the second law of thermodynamics requires that the dissipation head loss be positive, Eq. (9.40) shows that $y_2 > y_1$. As a result, Eq. (9.38) requires that $Fr_1 > 1.0$ (i.e., the upstream flow must be supercritical). Finally, from Eq. (9.39), $V_2 < V_1$. As we will see in Chapter 10, these flow phenomena for a hydraulic jump are analogous to those for a shock wave in compressible gas flows.

Example 9.6

Water flows in a rectangular channel that is 10 m wide. At station 1, the depth is 2 m and the velocity is 10 m/s. If a downstream sill causes a hydraulic jump to be formed, what will be the depth, velocity, and Froude number of the flow downstream of the jump? What is the head loss across the jump? What is the power dissipated by the jump?

Solution. Let us first calculate the upstream Froude number.

$$Fr_1 = \frac{V_1}{(gy_1)^{0.5}} = 2.258$$

We can use Eq. (9.38) to calculate y_2:

$$y_2 = \frac{y_1}{2}\{[1 + 8(Fr_1)^2]^{0.5} - 1\}$$

$$= \frac{2}{2}\{[1 + 8(2.258)^2]^{0.5} - 1\} = 5.464 \text{ m}$$

The downstream velocity is

$$V_2 = \frac{V_1y_1}{y_2} = \frac{10(2)}{5.464} = 3.660 \text{ m/s}$$

The downstream Froude number is

$$Fr_2 = \frac{V_2}{(gy_2)^{0.5}} = \frac{3.660}{[9.8066(5.464)]^{0.5}} = 0.500$$

Note that the Froude number for the upstream flow is greater than 1 and that it is less than 1 for the downstream flow.

The head loss is calculated using Eq. (9.40):

$$h_f = \frac{(y_2 - y_1)^3}{4y_1y_2} = \frac{(5.464 - 2)^3}{4(5.464)(2)} = 0.951 \text{ m}$$

The power dissipated is

$$P = Q\gamma h_f$$

Assuming that the water is 20°C,

$$\gamma = (0.9982)(9.8066 \times 10^3 \text{ N/m}^3) = 9.7889 \times 10^3 \text{ N/m}^3$$

and

$$P = 200 \text{ m}^3/\text{s} \ (9.7889 \times 10^3 \text{ N/m}^3) \ 0.951 \text{ m} = 1862 \text{ kW}$$

Example 9.7

Flow goes under a sluice gate, accelerates from subcritical to supercritical flow, and then returns to subcritical flow through a hydraulic jump, as shown in Fig. 9.12. Upstream of the sluice gate, $y_1 = 20$ ft and $V_1 = 3$ ft/s. The channel is horizontal and wide. If we neglect all losses except the dissipation in the jump, what are y_2, y_3, and h_f? What is the percentage of dissipation?

Solution. Upstream of the hydraulic jump, we can see the specific energy relations, Eq. (9.31):

$$E = y_1 + \frac{q_1^2}{2gy_1^2} = y_2 + \frac{q_2^2}{2gy_2^2}$$

where $q_1 = V_1 y_1 = 60 \text{ ft}^2/\text{s} = q_2$. Thus,

$$E = 20 + \frac{(60)^2}{2(32.174)(20)^2} = 20.140 = y_2 + \frac{55.946}{y_2^2}$$

By trial and error, we find that

$$y_2 = 1.74 \text{ ft}$$

Although it was not requested, we can calculate y_c:

$$y_c = \left(\frac{q^2}{g}\right)^{1/3} = 4.819 \text{ ft}$$

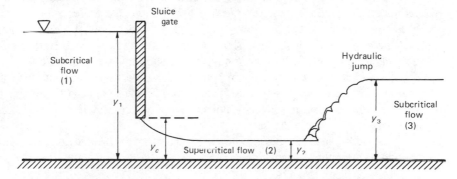

Figure 9.12 Subcritical flow accelerates under a sluice gate to supercritical flow and jumps back to subcritical flow; see Example 9.7.

Note that $y_1 > y_c$ and $y_2 < y_c$, as should be the case.

The Froude number for the supercritical flow of region 2 is

$$\text{Fr}_2 = \frac{V_2}{(gy_2)^{0.5}} = \frac{V_1 y_1}{y_2 (gy_2)^{0.5}} = \frac{20(3)}{(1.74)^{1.5}(32.174)^{0.5}} = 4.609$$

Although the supercritical flow is region 2 in the sketch of Fig. 9.12, this serves as the upstream region for the hydraulic jump. Thus, we will use the conditions in region 2 for "1" in Eq. (9.38) and those in region 3 for "2," the conditions downstream of the jump:

$$y_3 = \frac{y_2}{2}\{[1 + 8(\text{Fr}_2)^2]^{0.5} - 1\}$$

$$= \frac{1.74}{2}\{[1 + 8(4.609)^2]^{0.5} - 1\} = 10.505 \text{ ft}$$

Similarly,

$$h_f = \frac{(y_3 - y_2)^3}{4y_2 y_3} = 9.210 \text{ ft}$$

The percentage of dissipation relates h_f to the upstream energy E. Hence,

$$\text{PD} = \frac{h_f}{E_1} \times 100 = \frac{9.210}{20.140} \, 100 = 45.73\%$$

GRADUALLY VARIED FLOW

Gradually varied flow is the steady flow whose depth varies gradually along the length of the channel. This definition implies that the flow is steady so that the hydraulic characteristics of the flow remain constant for the time interval under consideration and that the streamlines are practically parallel so that the hydrostatic pressure distribution exists in the channel. The theory of gradually varied flow, which dates back to the eighteenth century, is based on the assumption that the head loss at a section for gradually varied flow is the same as that for uniform flow having the velocity and the hydraulic radius of the section. According to this assumption, the uniform-flow formula may be used to evaluate the energy slope of a gradually varied flow at a given channel section, and the corresponding coefficient of roughness developed primarily for uniform flow is applicable to the varied flow. Although this assumption has proved to be a reliable basis for design, it is undoubtedly more correct for varied flow where the velocity increases than where the velocity decreases. This is true because the head loss is due primarily to friction effects when the velocity is increasing, whereas there may be large-scale eddy losses in a flow where the velocity decreases.

In addition to the basic assumption described in the previous paragraph, the following assumptions are made:

1. The slope of the channel is small and slowly changing.
2. The water depth changes slowly (and thus there is no hydraulic jump).

3. The channel is prismatic; that is, the channel has constant alignment and shape.
4. The velocity distribution is one-dimensional.
5. The roughness coefficient is independent of the depth of the flow and is constant throughout the channel reach under consideration.

Earlier in this chapter, Bernoulli's equation was used to relate the flow properties at two sections including the head loss:

$$y_1 + \frac{V_1^2}{2g} + S_0 L_x = y_2 + \frac{V_2^2}{2g} + h_f$$

Let us consider the application of this equation between two stations that are dx apart so that

$$y_1 + \frac{V_1^2}{2g} + S_0\, dx = y_2 + \frac{V_2^2}{2g} + h_f \tag{9.41}$$

Furthermore, let us define the friction slope S as the slope of the energy grade line so that $h_f = S\, dx$. Furthermore, if we let $dy = y_2 - y_1$ and

$$\frac{d}{dx}\left(\frac{V^2}{2g}\right) dx = \frac{V_2^2}{2g} - \frac{V_1^2}{2g}$$

then Eq. (9.41) can be written

$$dy + \frac{d}{dx}\left(\frac{V^2}{2g}\right) dx = S_0\, dx - S\, dx$$

where S_0 is the slope of the channel bottom and S is the slope of the energy grade line (EGL), which drops due to wall friction losses. For continuous functions,

$$\frac{dy}{dx} = \frac{S_0 - S}{1 + \dfrac{d}{dy}\left(\dfrac{V^2}{2g}\right)} \tag{9.42}$$

Equation (9.42) is the general differential equation for gradually varied flow and can be used to describe the various types of water-surface profiles that can occur in open-channel flows. The term $(d/dy)(V^2/2g)$ represents the change in the velocity head. Note that S_0 and S are positive when sloping downward in the direction of the flow. Also, it should be recalled that y is measured from the bottom of the channel. Therefore, $dy/dx = 0$ if the slope of the water (free) surface is equal to the slope of the channel bottom, and dy/dx is positive if the water-surface slope is less than the channel slope S_0.

If we use Eq. (9.30) for flow in a wide channel, we see that:

$$\frac{d}{dy}\left(\frac{V^2}{2g}\right) = \frac{d}{dy}\left(\frac{q^2}{2gy^2}\right) = -\frac{q^2}{gy^3} = -\frac{V^2}{gy} = -\mathrm{Fr}^2$$

Thus, Eq. (9.42) can be written

$$\frac{dy}{dx} = \frac{S_0 - S}{1 - (Fr)^2} \tag{9.43}$$

Note that the denominator goes to zero as Fr goes to 1.

Since a basic assumption of gradually varied flow is that the head loss rate at any section is given by the Manning formula for the same depth and discharge, we can rearrange Eq. (9.15b) to obtain

$$S = \frac{n^2 Q^2}{2.22 A^2 R_h^{4/3}} \tag{9.44}$$

This will represent the head-loss per unit length of the channel. [Note the use of 2.22 in Eq. (9.44) implies the use of English units for this and subsequent equations.] Substituting this into Eq. (9.42) and rearranging,

$$S_0 - \frac{dy}{dx} - \frac{d}{dx}\left(\frac{V^2}{2g}\right) = \frac{n^2 Q^2}{2.22 A^2 R_h^{4/3}} \tag{9.45}$$

Differentiating the integral form of the continuity equation,

$$\frac{d}{dx}(AV) = V\frac{dA}{dx} + A\frac{dV}{dx} = 0 \tag{9.46}$$

Letting $dA = T\, dy$, where T is the free-surface width of the cross section, and combining these expressions, the differential of the velocity can be written

$$\frac{dV}{dx} = -\frac{VT}{A}\frac{dy}{dx} = -\frac{QT}{A^2}\frac{dy}{dx}$$

Substituting this into Eq. (9.45), we obtain

$$S_0 - \frac{dy}{dx} + \frac{Q^2 T}{gA^3}\frac{dy}{dx} = \frac{n^2 Q^2}{2.22 A^2 R_h^{4/3}}$$

Solving for dx,

$$dx = \frac{[1 - (Q^2 T/gA^3)]\, dy}{S_0 - [n^2 Q^2/(2.22 A^2 R_h^{4/3})]}$$

After integrating,

$$L_x = \int_{y_1}^{y_2} \frac{1 - (Q^2 T/gA^3)}{S_0 - [n^2 Q^2/(2.22 A^2 R_h^{4/3})]}\, dy \tag{9.47}$$

where L_x is the distance between two sections having depths y_1 and y_2.

For horizontal channels (i.e., $S_0 = 0$) of great width, the hydraulic radius equals the depth. Furthermore,

$$\frac{Q^2}{A^2} = V^2 = \frac{q^2}{y^2} \quad \text{and} \quad \frac{T}{A} = \frac{1}{y}$$

Thus, Eq. (9.46) can be written

$$L_x = -\int_{y_1}^{y_2} \frac{2.22 y^{10/3}}{n^2 q^2} (1 - \frac{q^2}{gy^3}) \, dy \tag{9.48}$$

Integrating,

$$L_x = -\frac{0.5123}{n^2 q^2} (y_2^{13/3} - y_1^{13/3}) + \frac{1.6650}{n^2 g} (y_2^{4/3} - y_1^{4/3}) \tag{9.49}$$

Example 9.8

After contracting under a sluice gate, water flows onto a broad horizontal plane of clean evacuated earth. If the initial velocity and the initial depth are 40 ft/s and 2 ft, respectively, what is the equation for the water-surface profile? At what point does the critical depth occur?

Solution.   Using Eq. (9.49),

$$L_x = -\frac{0.5123}{n^2 q^2} (y^{13/3} - y_1^2) + \frac{1.6650}{n^2 g} (y^{4/3} - y_1^{4/3})$$

$$y_1 = 2 \text{ ft}, \quad q = 80 \text{ ft}^2/\text{s}, \quad n = 0.022$$

$$L_x = -0.1654(y^{13/3}) + 106.9212 y^{4/3} - 266.0905$$

The critical depth is

$$y_c = \left(\frac{q^2}{g}\right)^{1/3} = 5.837 \text{ ft}$$

It occurs when

$$L_x = 511.916 \text{ ft}$$

The depth must increase in the streamwise direction, since the specific energy decreases. The depth moves toward the critical depth. The equations do not hold near the critical depth because of vertical accelerations that have been neglected in the derivation of gradually varied flow. Note that, in the formulation for dy/dx as given by Eq. (9.43), the denominator goes to zero as the Froude number approaches 1.

PROBLEMS

9.1. An infinitesimal wave travels at a speed of 12 ft/s in a pool of water having a constant depth. What is the depth of the water?

9.2. What is the speed of an infinitesimal wave that is produced in a pond that is 50 cm deep?

9.3. A shallow wave that is 3 cm high propagates into still water where the depth is 1 m. Use Eq. (9.4) to calculate the wave speed c. Compare this value of c with that calculated using Eq. (9.5). What is the velocity V_2 induced by the wave?

9.4. A wave 6 in. high propagates into still water where the depth is 5 ft. Compare the values of c as calculated using Eqs. (9.4) and (9.5).

9.5. The volumetric flow rate for water flowing in a rectangular channel is 15 m³/s. The channel is 5 m wide. Determine the Froude number and the type of flow when the depth is (a) 30 cm? (b) 97.18 cm? (c) 3.0 m?

9.6. Water at 68°F flows in a rectangular channel that is 12 ft wide and 4 ft deep. The channel is concrete lined and drops 10 ft over a length of 5000 ft. Use the Manning formula to determine the volumetric flow rate.

9.7. Repeat Prob. 9.6 using the friction factor analysis.

9.8. Repeat Example 9.2 using the two limiting values of n as given in Table 9.1.

9.9. Work Example 9.2 using the friction factor analysis.

9.10. Water at 20°C flows in a trapezoidal channel for which b is 3 m and $\phi = 60°$. If the slope of the brick-lined channel is 0.0005, what is y_n corresponding to a discharge of 40 m³/s?

9.11. A trapezoidal channel similar to that of Fig. 9.8 has $b = 10$ ft, $\phi = 25°$, and $y_n = 3.5$ ft. What is the discharge for a clean earth channel with S_0 of 0.0002?

9.12. An asphalt-lined triangular channel has sides that slope at 45°. If $S_0 = 0.0005$, what will be the normal depth when the discharge is (a) 100 ft³/s? (b) 10 ft³/s?

9.13. The parameters of a trapezoidal aqueduct, such as shown in Fig. 9.8, are $b = 6$ m and $\phi = 35°$. If $n = 0.014$ and the channel carries 50 m³/s when $y_n = 3$ m, what is the required elevation drop per kilometer?

9.14. Calculate the discharge in a painted steel, rectangular channel that is 2 ft high by 4 ft wide. Treat the channel as a compound section, where each subsection is 2 ft by 2 ft (i.e., the interface is the middle of the channel), as shown in Fig. P9.14. The slope of the channel is 3°.

9.15. Calculate the discharge when a river overflows its banks onto two floodplains. The compound-section open-channel flow can be represented by the cross section shown in Fig. P9.15. Floodplain 1 is meadow; floodplain 2 is brush and waste; $b_{f1} = b_{f2} = 50$ ft, $y_{f1} = y_{f2} = 2.5$ ft, $b_c = 40$ ft, $y_c = 15$ ft, $\phi = 45°$, and $S_0 = 0.0004$.

9.16. Calculate the discharge when a river overflows its banks onto two floodplains. The compound-section open-channel flow is represented by the cross section of Fig. P9.15. Floodplain 1 is meadow; floodplain 2 is brush and waste; $b_{f1} = 5$ m, $y_{f1} = 1.0$ m, $b_{f2} = 10$ m, $y_{f2} = 0.5$ m; $b_c = 5$ m, $y_c = 3$ m, $\phi = 60°$, and $S_0 = 0.0009$.

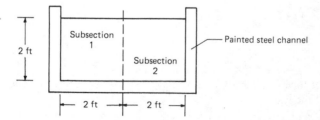

Figure P9.14 Sketch for Prob. 9.14.

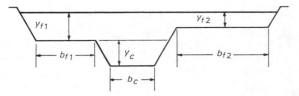

Figure P9.15 Sketch for Probs. 9.15 and
9.16.

c, designates channel; *f1*, floodplain 1; *f2*, floodplain 2.

9.17. Determine the dimensions of the most efficient trapezoidal brick-lined channel to carry 8000
cfs if S_0 is 0.0004.

9.18. A trapezoidal channel is made in the shape of a half-hexagon for maximum efficiency. If n
is 0.022 and S_0 is 0.0003, what should be the length of the side of the hexagon if the channel
is to carry 225 ft³/s of water? What is the cross-sectional area of the channel?

9.19. A semicircular channel for which $n = 0.022$ and $S_0 = 0.0003$ is designed to carry 225
ft³/s of water? What is the diameter of the channel? What is the cross-sectional area of the
channel?

9.20. Suppose that the sides of the trapezoidal channel described in Prob. 9.18 are reduced to ϕ
$= 20°$ to reduce the possibility of earth slides. If all other parameters remain the same, what
is the normal depth for this new channel? Assume that $b = 8.025$ ft. How much additional
area and wetted perimeter are needed to compare with the half-hexagon?

9.21. Show that the most efficient form of a triangular open channel is that for which the sides
slope at 45°.

9.22. Graph the specific energy curve for $q = 100$ cfs/ft of width? What are y_c and E_{min}?

9.23. Graph the specific energy curve for $q = 20$ m²/s. What are y_c and E_{min}?

9.24. What is the specific energy in ft · lbf/lbf for a flow where V is 8 ft/s and y is 3 ft? What is
the alternate depth?

9.25. Determine the alternate depths for a flow having a specific energy of 8 ft with a discharge
of 60 ft²/s.

9.26. The volumetric flow rate is 20 m³/s in a rectangular channel that is 6.5 m wide. Make a
graph of the depth as a function of specific energy for values of E from E_{min} to 10 m. What
are the alternate and the sequent depths to a y of 50 cm?

9.27. Prepare graphs of y_2/y_1 and h_f/y_1 as a function of the upstream Froude number (Fr₁) over the
range $1 \leq \text{Fr}_1 \leq 10$.

9.28. Water flows in a rectangular channel that is 30 ft wide. At station 1, the depth is 3 ft and
the velocity is 33 ft/s. If a downstream sill causes a hydraulic jump to be formed, what will
be the depth, velocity, and Froude number of the flow downstream of the jump? What is
the head loss across the jump? What is the horsepower dissipated by the jump?

9.29. Water flows in a wide channel at $q = 12$ m²/s. If $y_1 = 1.5$ m and the flow undergoes a
hydraulic jump, what are (a) y_2, (b) V_2, (c) Fr₂, (d) h_f, (e) the power dissipated per unit
width, and (f) the percentage of dissipation?

9.30. A hydraulic jump occurs in a wide rectangular channel. If the depths upstream and downstream of the jump are 30 cm and 1.2 m, respectively, what is the discharge per meter width
of the channel?

9.31. For what value of the upstream Froude number (Fr_1) is the energy dissipation across a hydraulic jump exactly 50% (according to theory)?

9.32. The discharge over the spillway of Fig. P9.32 is 10 m³/s per meter of width. Neglecting the energy loss over the spillway, what is the depth (y_2) of the supercritical flow? What is the depth (y_3) downstream of the hydraulic jump?

9.33. Water flows in a wide channel at a depth of 50 cm with a velocity of 5 m/s. An obstruction causes a hydraulic jump to be formed. What is the depth of the flow downstream of the jump? What is the head loss across the jump? What is the downstream Froude number? What is the percentage of dissipation?

9.34. After contracting under a sluice gate, water flows onto a broad horizontal plane of unfinished cement. If the initial discharge is 10 m³/s per meter of width and the initial depth is 2.5 m, what is the equation for the water surface profile?

9.35. As noted in the text, Eq. (9.44) implies the use of English units. For those flows for which we are given metric units, develop an expression equivalent to Eq. (9.44).

9.36. Apply the energy equation for gradually varying flow between two sections that are a distance ΔL apart,

$$y_1 + \frac{V_1^2}{2g} + S_0\,\Delta L = y_2 + \frac{V_2^2}{2g} + S\,\Delta L$$

to show that

$$\Delta L = \frac{(V_1^2 - V_2^2)/2g + (y_1 - y_2)}{S - S_0}$$

Using Eq. (9.44) to evaluate S, determine ΔL and y_2 for a finished-concrete lined trapezoidal channel, where $b_1 = 10$ m, $y_1 = 5$ m, $m_1 = 2$, $V_1 = 1$ m/s at station 1, $b_2 = 12$ m and $m_2 = 3$ at station 2, and $S_0 = +0.0004$.

9.37. Repeat Prob. 9.36, but for $S_0 = -0.0004$.

9.38. Develop an expression for S if we are to use the Moody approach to calculate the slope of the energy grade line.

9.39. Using the expression developed in Prob. 9.36, solve the flow in Prob. 9.36 using the Moody approach.

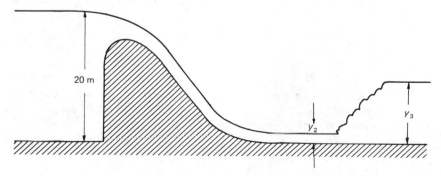

Figure P9.32 Sketch for Prob. 9.32.

REFERENCES

9.1. Ven Te Chow, *Open Channel Hydraulics,* McGraw-Hill Book Company, New York, 1959.

9.2. R. DeAmicis and S. Masullo, "Analisi Aerodinamica della Cavita' di Alloggiamento-Alette nel FIROS-25," NT GSR 11.48, Oct. 1980, *Difesa e Spazio,* Colleferro, Italy.

9.3. U. Catani, J.J. Bertin, R. DeAmicis, S. Masullo, and S.A. Bouslog, "Aerodynamic Characteristics for a Slender Missile with Wrap-Around Fins," *Journal of Spacecraft and Rockets,* Vol. 20, no. 2, 1983, 122–128.

9.4. F. M. White, *Fluid Mechanics,* McGraw-Hill Book Company, New York, 1979.

CHAPTER TEN

The Dynamics of a Compressible Flow Field

We have derived the continuity equation, momentum equation, and energy equation for general flows, that is, flows that can be steady or nonsteady, viscous or inviscid, compressible, or incompressible, and so on. Thus far, we have studied flows in which the density can be assumed to be constant. For flow fields in which the velocity is relatively low, the fluid properties are essentially constant. For such flows, we can first determine the velocity and pressure distributions by solving the continuity and momentum equations, and then determine the temperature distribution, as was done in Chapter 8 for the incompressible, thermal boundary layer. As the local velocity increases, changes in the local density of the gas affect the magnitude of the local static pressure. For our purposes, the Mach number is the parameter that determines the extent to which compressibility effects are important. The purpose of this chapter is to introduce techniques to solve compressible flows, those flows in which the density is not constant. For flow fields in which there are significant variations in the fluid properties, we must solve the three basic equations simultaneously. To do this, it will be necessary to include an equation of state (i.e., a relation between the density, pressure, and temperature) in the solution algorithm. Furthermore, if the effects of viscosity and of heat transfer are important, we must define the transport properties (viscosity and thermal conductivity) as functions of pressure and temperature.

Throughout this chapter, air will be assumed to behave as a thermally perfect gas (i.e., the gas obeys the equation of state):

$$p = \rho RT \tag{1.3}$$

We will assume that the gas is also calorically perfect; that is, the specific heats, c_p and c_v, of the gas are constant. The specific heats were discussed in Chapter 8. The term *perfect gas* will be used to describe a gas that is both thermally and calorically perfect.

364

Even though we turn our attention in this chapter to compressible flows, we may still divide the flow around the vehicle into (1) the boundary layer near the surface, where the effects of viscosity and heat conduction are important, and (2) the external flow, where the effects of viscosity and heat conduction can be neglected. As has been true in previous chapters, the inviscid flow is conservative.

SECOND LAW OF THERMODYNAMICS AND REVERSIBILITY

The first law of thermodynamics does not place any constraints regarding the types of processes that are physically possible and the types that are not, providing that Eq. (8.2) is satisfied. However, we know from experience that not all processes permitted by the first law actually occur in nature. For instance, when one rubs sandpaper across a table, both the sandpaper and the table experience a rise in temperature. The first law is satisfied because the work done on the system by the sander's arm, which is part of the surroundings and which is, therefore, negative work for Eq. (8.3), is manifested as an increase in the internal energy of the system, which consists of the sandpaper and table. Thus, the temperatures of the sandpaper and table increase. However, we do not expect that we can extract all the work back from the system and have the internal energy (and thus the temperature) decrease back to its original value, even though the first law would be satisfied. If this could occur, we would say the process was reversible, because the system and its surroundings would be restored to their original states.

The possibility of devising a reversible process, such as the type just outlined, cannot be settled by a theoretical proof. Experience shows that a truly reversible process has never been devised. This empirical observation is embodied in the *second law of thermodynamics*. For our purposes, an irreversible process is one that involves viscous (friction) effects, shock waves, or heat transfer through a finite temperature gradient. Thus, in regions outside boundary layers, viscous wakes, and planar shock waves, one can treat the flow as reversible. Note that the flow behind a curved shock wave can be treated as reversible only along a streamline.

The second law of thermodynamics provides a way to quantitatively determine the degree of reversibility (or irreversibility). Since the effects of irreversibility are dissipative and represent a loss of available energy (e.g., the kinetic energy of an aircraft wake, which is converted to internal energy by viscous stresses, is directly related to the aircraft's drag), the reversible process provides an ideal standard for comparison to real processes. Thus, the second law is a valuable tool available to the engineer.

There are several logically equivalent statements of the second law. In the remainder of this text we will usually be considering adiabatic processes, processes in which there is no heat transfer. This is not a restrictive assumption, since heat transfer in gas dynamic problems usually occurs only in the boundary layer and has a negligible effect on the flow in the inviscid region. The most convenient statement of the second law, for our purposes, is

$$ds \geq 0 \qquad (10.1)$$

for an adiabatic process. Thus, when a system is isolated from all heat exchange with its surroundings, s, the entropy of the system, either remains the same (if the process is reversible) or increases (if it is irreversible). It is not possible for a process to occur if the entropy of the system and its surroundings decreases. Thus, just as the first law led to the definition of the internal energy as a property, the second law leads to the definition of entropy as a property.

The entropy change for a reversible process can be written as

$$\delta q = T ds$$

Thus, for a reversible process in which the only work done is that done at the moving boundary of the system,

$$T ds = du_e + p dv \tag{10.2}$$

However, once we have written this equation, we see that it involves only changes in properties and does not involve any path-dependent functions. We conclude, therefore, that this equation is valid for all processes, both reversible and irreversible, and that it applies to the substance undergoing a change of state as the result of flow across the boundary of an open system (i.e., a control volume), as well as to the substance comprising a closed system (i.e., a control mass).

For a perfect gas, we can rewrite Eq. (10.2) as

$$ds = c_v \frac{dT}{T} + R \frac{dv}{v}$$

This equation can be integrated to give

$$s_2 - s_1 = c_v \ln \left\{ \left[\left(\frac{v_2}{v_1} \right)^{k-1} \right] \frac{T_2}{T_1} \right\} \tag{10.3a}$$

Applying the equation of state for a perfect gas to the two states,

$$\frac{v_2}{v_1} = \frac{\rho_1}{\rho_2} = \frac{p_1}{p_2} \frac{T_2}{T_1}$$

Eq. (10.3a) can be written

$$s_2 - s_1 = R \ln \left\{ \left[\left(\frac{T_2}{T_1} \right)^{k/(k-1)} \right] \frac{p_1}{p_2} \right\} \tag{10.3b}$$

Equivalently,

$$s_2 - s_1 = c_v \ln \left\{ \left[\left(\frac{\rho_1}{\rho_2} \right)^{k} \right] \frac{p_2}{p_1} \right\} \tag{10.3c}$$

Using the various forms of Eq. (10.3), one can calculate the entropy change in terms of the properties of the end states.

In many compressible flow problems, the flow external to the boundary layer undergoes processes that are isentropic (i.e., adiabatic and reversible). If the entropy is constant at each step of the process, it follows from Eq. (10.3) that p, ρ, and T are interrelated. The following equations describe these relations for isentropic flow:

$$\frac{p}{\rho^k} = \text{constant} \tag{10.4a}$$

$$\frac{T^{k/(k-1)}}{p} = \text{constant} \tag{10.4b}$$

and

$$Tv^{(k-1)} = \text{constant} \tag{10.4c}$$

SPEED OF SOUND

From experience, we know that the speed of sound in air is finite. To be specific, the *speed of sound* is defined as the rate at which infinitesimal disturbances are propagated from their source into an undisturbed medium. These disturbances can be thought of as small pressure pulses generated at a point and propagated in all directions. We shall learn later that finite disturbances such as shock waves propagate at a greater speed than that of sound waves.

Consider a motionless point source of disturbance in quiescent, homogeneous air (Fig. 10.1a). Small disturbances generated at the point move outward from the point in a spherically symmetric pattern. The distance between wave fronts is determined by the frequency of the disturbance. Since the disturbances are small, they leave the air behind them in the same state it was before they arrived. The radius of a given wave front is given by

$$r = at \tag{10.5}$$

where a is the speed of propagation (speed of sound) of the wave front and t is the time since the particular disturbance was generated.

Now suppose that the point source begins moving (Fig. 10.1b) from right to left at a constant speed U that is less than the speed of sound a. The wave-front pattern will now appear as shown in Fig. 10.1b. A stationary observer ahead of the source will detect an increase in frequency of the sound, while an observer behind it will note a decrease. Still, however, each wave front is separate from its neighbors.

If the speed of the source reaches the speed of sound in the undisturbed medium, the situation will appear as shown in Fig. 10.1c. We note that the individual wave fronts are still separate, except at the point where they coalesce.

A further increase in source speed, such that $U > a$, leads to the situation depicted in Fig. 10.1d. The wave fronts now form a conical envelope, known as the *Mach cone*,

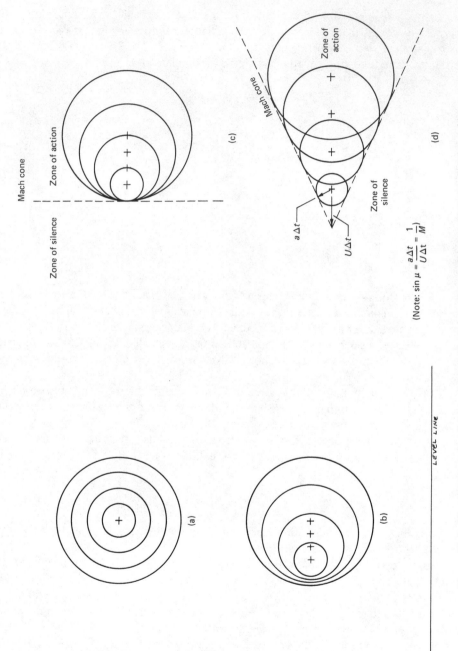

Figure 10.1 Wave pattern generated by pulsating disturbance of infinitesimal strength: (a) disturbance is stationary ($U = 0$); (b) disturbance moves to the left at subsonic speed ($U < a$); (c) disturbance moves to the left at sonic speed ($U = a$); (d) disturbance moves to the left at supersonic speeds ($U > a$).

within which the disturbances can be detected. Outside of this *zone of action* is the *zone of silence,* where the pulses have not arrived.

We see that there is a fundamental difference between subsonic ($U < a$) and supersonic ($U > a$) flow. In subsonic flow, the effect of a disturbance propagates upstream of its location, and thus the upstream flow is "warned" of the approach of the disturbance. In supersonic flow, however, no such "warning" is possible. Stating it another way: disturbances cannot propagate upstream in a supersonic flow relative to a source–fixed observer. This fundamental difference between the two types of flow has significant consequences on the flow field.

We note that the half-angle of the Mach cone dividing the zone of silence from the zone of action is given by

$$\sin \mu = \frac{1}{M} \tag{10.6}$$

where

$$M \equiv \frac{U}{a} \tag{4.17b}$$

is the Mach number. At $M = 1$ (i.e., when $U = a$), $\mu = \pi/2$, and as $M \to \infty$, $\mu \to 0$.

To determine the speed of sound a, consider the wave front in Fig. 10.1a propagating into still air. A small portion of curved wave front can be treated as planar. To an observer attached to the wave, the situation appears as shown in Fig. 10.2. A control volume is also shown attached to the wave. The boundaries of the volume are selected so that the flow is normal to faces parallel to the wave and tangent to the other faces. We make the key assumption (borne out by experiment) that, since the strength of the disturbance is infinitesimal, a fluid particle passing through the wave undergoes a process that is reversible and adiabatic (i.e., isentropic).

The integral forms of the continuity and the momentum equations for a one-dimensional, steady, inviscid flow give

$$\rho a \, dA = (\rho + d\rho)(a + dU) \, dA \tag{10.7}$$

$$p \, dA - (p + dp) \, dA = [(a + dU) - a]\rho a \, dA \tag{10.8}$$

Simplifying Eq. (10.8), dividing Eqs. (10.7) and (10.8) by dA, and combining the two relations, we see that

$$dp = a^2 d\rho \tag{10.9}$$

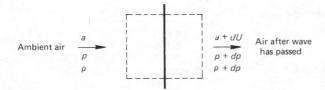

Figure 10.2 Control volume used to determine the speed of sound (a velocity of equal magnitude and opposite direction has been superimposed on a wave of Fig. 10.1a so that the sound wave is stationary in this figure).

for this wave propagation, for which the flow is isentropic. However, since this gives the same equation as the definition for the speed of sound, we can write Eq. (10.9) as

$$a^2 = \left(\frac{\partial p}{\partial \rho}\right)_s = \left(\frac{\partial p}{\partial \rho}\right)_{wp} \tag{10.10}$$

where the subscript s indicates that the derivative is taken with entropy fixed and the subscript wp denotes the wave propagation application.

For a perfect gas undergoing an isentropic process, Eq. (10.4a) gives

$$p = c\rho^k$$

where c is a constant. Thus,

$$a^2 = \left(\frac{\partial p}{\partial \rho}\right)_s = kc\rho^{(k-1)} = \frac{kp}{\rho} \tag{10.11}$$

Using the equation of state for a perfect gas, the speed of sound is

$$a = \sqrt{kRT} \tag{10.12}$$

ADIABATIC FLOWS AND ISENTROPIC STEADY FLOWS

Let us consider the one-dimensional flow of a perfect gas through a variable-area stream-tube (see Fig. 10.3). We will apply the integral form of the energy equation for steady, one-dimensional flow [i.e., Eq. (8.16)]. Let us assume that there is no heat transfer through the surface of the control volume (i.e., $\dot{Q} = 0$) and that only flow work (pressure–volume work) is done. Work is done on the system by the pressure forces acting at station 1 and is, therefore, negative. Work is done by the system at station 2. Thus,

$$+p_1U_1A_1 - p_2U_2A_2 = -\left(u_{e1}\rho_1U_1A_1 + \frac{U_1^2}{2}\rho_1U_1A_1\right) + \left(u_{e2}\rho_2U_2A_2 + \frac{U_2^2}{2}\rho_2U_2A_2\right)$$

Rearranging, noting that $\rho_1U_1A_1 = \rho_2U_2A_2$ by continuity, and using the definition for enthalpy, we obtain

$$H_t = h_1 + \frac{U_1^2}{2} = h_2 + \frac{U_2^2}{2} \tag{10.13}$$

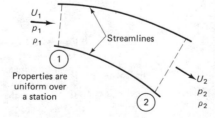

Figure 10.3   One-dimensional flow in a streamtube. (From John J. Bertin and Michael L. Smith, *Aerodynamics for Engineers*, © 1979, p. 235. Reprinted by permission of Prentice-Hall, Inc., Englewood Cliffs, N.J.)

where, as is usually the case in problems involving gas flows, changes in potential energy have been neglected. The assumption of one-dimensional flow is valid provided that the streamtube cross-sectional area varies smoothly and gradually in comparison to the axial distance along the streamtube.

For a perfect gas, Eq. (10.13) can be written

$$c_p T_1 + \frac{U_1^2}{2} = c_p T_2 + \frac{U_2^2}{2} \tag{10.14}$$

or

$$T_1 + \frac{U_1^2}{2c_p} = T_2 + \frac{U_2^2}{2c_p} \tag{10.15}$$

By definition, the stagnation temperature T_t is the temperature reached when the fluid is brought to rest adiabatically. Thus,

$$T_t = T + \frac{U^2}{2c_p} \tag{10.16}$$

Since the locations of stations 1 and 2 are arbitrary,

$$T_{t1} = T_{t2} \tag{10.17}$$

That is, the stagnation temperature is a constant for the adiabatic flow of a perfect gas and will be designated simply as T_t. Thus, for any one-dimensional adiabatic flow,

$$\frac{T_t}{T} = 1 + \frac{U^2}{2[kR/(k-1)]T} = 1 + \frac{k-1}{2} M^2 \tag{10.18}$$

Note that we have used the perfect-gas relations that $c_p = kR/(k-1)$ and that $a^2 = kRT$ in deriving Eqs. (10.14) through (10.18). Therefore, although Eq. (10.13) is valid for a general gas, Eqs. (10.14) through (10.18) are valid only for perfect-gas flows.

Isentropic Flow

If the flow is isentropic, that is, the flow is inviscid as well as adiabatic (i.e., reversible), we can use Eqs. (10.4a) through (10.4c) to relate the variables. It is particularly useful to study the isentropic flow of a perfect gas in a variable-area streamtube, since it reveals many of the general characteristics of compressible flows. In addition, the assumption of constant entropy is not too restrictive, since the flow outside the boundary layer is essentially isentropic except while crossing linear shock waves or downstream of curved shock waves.

Using Eqs. (10.4) and (10.18), we can write

$$\frac{p_{t1}}{p} = \left(1 + \frac{k-1}{2} M^2 \right)^{k/(k-1)} \tag{10.19}$$

$$\frac{\rho_{t1}}{\rho} = \left(1 + \frac{k-1}{2} M^2\right)^{1/(k-1)} \tag{10.20}$$

where p_{t1} and ρ_{t1} are the stagnation pressure and the stagnation density, respectively. Applying these equations between two streamwise stations shows that, if T_t is constant and the flow is isentropic, the stagnation pressure p_{t1} is a constant. The equation of state requires that ρ_{t1} be constant also.

Note that if the flow is isentropic there is a unique relationship between the temperature and pressure. Furthermore, Euler's equation for one-dimensional, steady flow (i.e., the inviscid-flow momentum equation) gives the same result as the energy equation. To see this, let us write Eq. (5.2) for steady, one-dimensional, inviscid flow:

$$\rho U \frac{dU}{ds} = -\frac{dp}{ds} \tag{10.21a}$$

$$\int \frac{dp}{\rho} + \int U \, dU = 0 \tag{10.21b}$$

For an isentropic process,

$$p = c\rho^k$$

Differentiating, substituting the result into Eq. (10.21b), and integrating, we obtain

$$\frac{k}{k-1} c\rho^{(k-1)} + \frac{U^2}{2} = \text{constant}$$

Thus,

$$\frac{k}{k-1}\frac{p}{\rho} + \frac{U^2}{2} = \text{constant}$$

Using the perfect-gas equation of state, we obtain

$$h + \frac{U^2}{2} = \text{constant}$$

which is Eq. (10.13).

Example 10.1

A steady one-dimensional flow of helium occurs in a duct where the static pressure is 20 psia and the static temperature is 69°F. The velocity of the helium is 600 ft/s. What are the pressure and temperature of the helium if it is brought to rest isentropically? Assume that the helium behaves as a perfect gas.

Solution. Since we seek, the pressure and temperature when the gas is brought to rest isentropically, we seek p_{t1} and T_t. From Eq. (10.16),

$$T_t = T + \frac{U^2}{2c_p}$$

Using Table 8.1,

$$c_p = 5233.4 \ \text{N} \cdot \text{m/kg} \cdot \text{K} = 1.250 \ \text{Btu/lbm°R}$$

Thus,

$$T_t = 528.6°\text{R} + \frac{36 \times 10^4 \ \text{ft}^2/\text{s}^2}{(1.250 \ \text{Btu/lbm} \cdot °\text{R}) (32.174 \ \text{ft} \cdot \text{lbm/lbf} \cdot \text{s}^2) (778 \ \text{ft} \cdot \text{lbf/Btu})}$$

$$= 540.1°\text{R} = 80.5°\text{F}$$

Using Eq. (10.4b) and noting that $k = 1.67$,

$$p_{t1} = p \left[\frac{T_t}{T} \right]^{k/(k-1)} = 20 \ \text{psia} \ (1.0551) = 21.102 \ \text{psia}$$

Example 10.2

Air at hypersonic speeds flows past a blunted cone mounted in a wind tunnel, as shown in Fig. 10.4. The pressure and temperature at point 2, which is the stagnation point behind the normal portion of the shock wave, are $4.8393 \times 10^4 \ \text{N/m}^2$ and 740 K, respectively. The static pressure at point 3 is $2.5566 \times 10^4 \ \text{N/m}^2$; that at point 4 is $5.6609 \times 10^3 \ \text{N/m}^2$. All three points are outside the boundary layer. What are the local static temperature, the local velocity, and the local Mach number at points 3 and 4?

Solution. At these conditions, air behaves as a perfect gas. Furthermore, since all three points are outside the boundary layer, we will assume that the flow expands isentropically from the stagnation point (i.e., point 2). (Note that, because the shock wave is curved, this assumption is not generally accurate. However, such considerations are beyond the scope of this text.)

To calculate the local static temperature, let us use Eq. (10.4b).

$$\frac{T_3}{T_2} = \left[\frac{p_3}{p_2} \right]^{(k-1)/k} = 0.8333, \qquad \frac{T_4}{T_2} = 0.5417$$

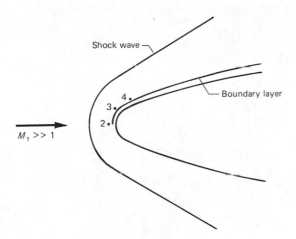

Figure 10.4 Sketch for Example 10.2.

Thus,

$$T_3 = 616.7 \text{ K} \quad \text{and} \quad T_4 = 400.9 \text{ K}$$

Since point 2 is a stagnation point, we can use Eq. (10.16) to calculate the local velocity at points 3 and 4.

$$U_3 = [2c_p(T_2 - T_3)]^{0.5} = [2(1004.7)(740 - 616.7)]^{0.5} = 497.75 \text{ m/s}$$

$$U_4 = [2c_p(T_2 - T_4)]^{0.5} = 825.46 \text{ m/s}$$

Having calculated the local velocity and local static temperature, we can calculate the Mach number directly from its definition:

$$M_3 = \frac{U_3}{a_3} = \frac{497.75}{20.047 \sqrt{616.7}} = 0.9998$$

$$M_4 = \frac{U_4}{a_4} = \frac{825.46}{20.047 \sqrt{400.9}} = 2.0565$$

The reader can verify that these same values could be obtained using Eq. (10.18). The flow accelerates from the stagnation conditions at point 2 to sonic conditions (i.e., the point where the local velocity equals the speed of sound) at point 3 to supersonic conditions at point 4.

ISENTROPIC FLOW IN A NOZZLE OR DUCT

In the previous section, relations between the pressure, temperature, density, Mach number, and so on, were derived for an isentropic flow. These relations can be applied to calculate the flow in a duct or wind tunnel, as in Example 10.1. They can also be applied to the external flow around an object, such as a turbine blade or the cone of Example 10.2. However, for isentropic flow in a nozzle, additional relations between the flow characteristics and the local area are of interest.

Consider the continuity equation for a steady, one-dimensional flow:

$$\rho U A = \text{constant}$$

Differentiating and dividing through by $\rho U A$, we obtain

$$\frac{d\rho}{\rho} + \frac{dU}{U} + \frac{dA}{A} = 0 \tag{10.22}$$

Combining Euler's equation,

$$dp = -\rho U \, dU \tag{10.23a}$$

and the fact that the change in pressure for an isentropic process is given by

$$dp = a^2 d\rho \tag{10.23b}$$

we can write

$$\frac{d\rho}{\rho} = -\frac{U^2}{a^2}\frac{dU}{U} = -M^2\frac{dU}{U} \qquad (10.23c)$$

Note that by using Eq. (10.23b) the analysis applies only to flows that are isentropic.

Substituting this relation into Eq. (10.22), we obtain the relation between the velocity change and the area change for isentropic flow in a duct:

$$\frac{dU}{U} = \frac{1}{M^2 - 1}\frac{dA}{A} \qquad (10.24)$$

If the flow is subsonic (i.e., the Mach number is less than 1), the flow accelerates in a converging section. An isentropic subsonic flow slows down as it moves through a duct of increasing area. However, an isentropic supersonic flow decelerates in a converging channel and accelerates when the area increases. Referring to Euler's equation, Eq. (10.23a), we see that the pressure increases when the velocity decreases whether the flow is subsonic or supersonic. The four combinations between changes in area, velocity, and pressure are illustrated in Fig. 10.5.

When the flow is sonic, Eq. (10.24) indicates that dU can be finite only if dA is zero. Referring to Fig. 10.5, we see that, if a flow that is initially subsonic (or at rest) is to be accelerated to supersonic speeds, the duct must be initially convergent to accelerate the subsonic flow and then divergent to accelerate the supersonic flow. This pattern implies that the duct area is a minimum when the flow is sonic. This is consistent with the

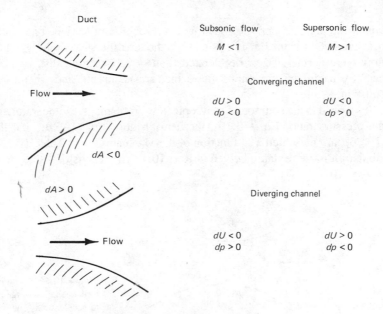

Figure 10.5 Conditions for isentropic flow in a duct.

requirement that $dA = 0$ when $M = 1$. Thus, as shown in Fig. 10.6, a convergent–divergent nozzle is required to accelerate a flow from subsonic to supersonic speeds. It should be noted that not all flows through convergent–divergent nozzles accelerate to supersonic speeds. It is possible that the flow reaches sonic speed at the throat and then decelerates in the divergent section or that the flow remains subsonic throughout, such as was the case in the flows of Chapter 3.

In deriving Eqs. (10.18) through (10.20), the respective stagnation properties have been used as references to nondimensionalize the static properties. Since the continuity equation for the one-dimensional steady flow requires that $\rho U A$ be a constant, the area becomes infinitely large as the velocity goes to zero. Instead, the area where the flow is sonic (i.e., $M = 1$) is chosen as the reference area to relate to the streamtube area at a given station. Designating the sonic conditions by a $*$ superscript, the continuity equation yields

$$\frac{A^*}{A} = \frac{\rho U}{\rho^* U^*} = \frac{\rho_{t1}\,(\rho/\rho_{t1})\,\sqrt{kRT_t}\,\sqrt{T/T_t}\,M}{\rho_{t1}\,(\rho^*/\rho_{t1})\,\sqrt{kRT_t}\,\sqrt{T^*/T_t}} \tag{10.25}$$

since $M^* = 1$. Noting that ρ^*/ρ_{t1} and T^*/T_t are to be evaluated at $M = M^* = 1$,

$$\frac{A^*}{A} = M\left\{\left[\frac{2}{k+1}\left(1 + \frac{k-1}{2}M^2\right)\right]^{\{-(k+1)/[2(k-1)]\}}\right\} \tag{10.26}$$

Given the area, A, and the Mach number, M, at any station, one could compute an A^* for that station from Eq. (10.26). A^* is the area the streamtube would have to be if the flow were accelerated or decelerated to $M = 1$ isentropically. Equation (10.26) is especially useful in streamtube flows that are isentropic and, therefore, where A^* is a constant.

To aid in the solution of isentropic flow problems, the temperature ratio, Eq. (10.18), the pressure ratio, Eq. (10.19), the density ratio, Eq. (10.20), and the area ratio, Eq. (10.26), are presented as a function of the Mach number in Table 10.1. A more complete tabulation of these data is given in Ref. 10.1. The results of Table 10.1 are summarized in Fig. 10.7.

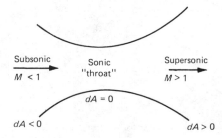

Subsonic
$M < 1$

Sonic
"throat"

Supersonic
$M > 1$

$dA = 0$

$dA < 0$ $dA > 0$

Figure 10.6 A convergent section, a throat, and a divergent section are needed to accelerate a flow from subsonic to supersonic speeds.

TABLE 10.1 CORRELATIONS FOR A ONE-DIMENSIONAL ISENTROPIC FLOW OF PERFECT AIR ($k = 1.4$)

M	$\dfrac{A}{A^*}$	$\dfrac{p}{p_{t1}}$	$\dfrac{\rho}{\rho_{t1}}$	$\dfrac{T}{T_t}$	$\dfrac{A\,p}{A^*p_{t1}}$
0	∞	1.00000	1.00000	1.00000	∞
0.05	11.592	0.99825	0.99875	0.99950	11.571
0.10	5.8218	0.99303	0.99502	0.99800	5.7812
0.15	3.9103	0.98441	0.98884	0.99552	3.8493
0.20	2.9635	0.97250	0.98027	0.99206	2.8820
0.25	2.4027	0.95745	0.96942	0.98765	2.3005
0.30	2.0351	0.93947	0.95638	0.98232	1.9119
0.35	1.7780	0.91877	0.94128	0.97608	1.6336
0.40	1.5901	0.89562	0.92428	0.96899	1.4241
0.45	1.4487	0.87027	0.90552	0.96108	1.2607
0.50	1.3398	0.84302	0.88517	0.95238	1.12951
0.55	1.2550	0.81416	0.86342	0.94295	1.02174
0.60	1.1882	0.78400	0.84045	0.93284	0.93155
0.65	1.1356	0.75283	0.81644	0.92208	0.85493
0.70	1.09437	0.72092	0.79158	0.91075	0.78896
0.75	1.06242	0.68857	0.76603	0.89888	0.73155
0.80	1.03823	0.65602	0.74000	0.88652	0.68110
0.85	1.02067	0.62351	0.71361	0.87374	0.63640
0.90	1.00886	0.59126	0.68704	0.86058	0.59650
0.95	1.00214	0.55946	0.66044	0.84710	0.56066
1.00	1.00000	0.52828	0.63394	0.83333	0.52828
1,05	1.00202	0.49787	0.60765	0.81933	0.49888
1.10	1.00793	0.46835	0.58169	0.80515	0.47206
1.15	1.01746	0.43983	0.55616	0.79083	0.44751
1.20	1.03044	0.41238	0.53114	0.77640	0.42493
1.25	1.04676	0.38606	0.50670	0.76190	0.40411
1.30	1.06631	0.36092	0.48291	0.74738	0.38484
1.35	1.08904	0.33697	0.45980	0.73287	0.36697
1.40	1.1149	0.31424	0.43742	0.71839	0.35036
1.45	1.1440	0.29272	0.41581	0.70397	0.33486
1.50	1.1762	0.27240	0.39498	0.68965	0.32039
1.55	1.2115	0.25326	0.37496	0.67545	0.30685
1.60	1.2502	0.23527	0.35573	0.66138	0.29414
1.65	1.2922	0.21839	0.33731	0.64746	0.28221
1.70	1.3376	0.20259	0.31969	0.63372	0.27099
1.75	1.3865	0.18782	0.30287	0.62016	0.26042
1.80	1.4390	0.17404	0.28682	0.60680	0.25044
1.85	1.4952	0.16120	0.27153	0.59365	0.24102
1.90	1.5555	0.14924	0.25699	0.58072	0.23211
1.95	1.6193	0.13813	0.24317	0.56802	0.22367
2.00	1.6875	0.12780	0.23005	0.55556	0.21567
2.05	1.7600	0.11823	0.21760	0.54333	0.20808
2.10	1.8369	0.10935	0.20580	0.53135	0.20087

(Continued)

TABLE 10.1 (Continued)

M	$\dfrac{A}{A^*}$	$\dfrac{p}{p_{t1}}$	$\dfrac{\rho}{\rho_{t1}}$	$\dfrac{T}{T_t}$	$\dfrac{A\,p}{A^*p_{t1}}$
2.15	1.9185	0.10113	0.19463	0.51962	0.19403
2.20	2.0050	0.09352	0.18405	0.50813	0.18751
2.25	2.0964	0.08648	0.17404	0.49689	0.18130
2.30	2.1931	0.07997	0.16458	0.48591	0.17539
2.35	2.2953	0.07396	0.15564	0.47517	0.16975
2.40	2.4031	0.06840	0.14720	0.46468	0.16437
2.45	2.5168	0.06327	0.13922	0.45444	0.15923
2.50	2.6367	0.05853	0.13169	0.44444	0.15432
2.55	2.7630	0.05415	0.12458	0.43469	0.14963
2.60	2.8960	0.05012	0.11787	0.42517	0.14513
2.65	3.0359	0.04639	0.11154	0.41589	0.14083
2.70	3.1830	0.04295	0.10557	0.40684	0.13671
2.75	3.3376	0.03977	0.09994	0.39801	0.13276
2.80	3.5001	0.03685	0.09462	0.38941	0.12897
2.85	3.6707	0.03415	0.08962	0.38102	0.12534
2.90	3.8498	0.03165	0.08489	0.37286	0.12185
2.95	4.0376	0.02935	0.08043	0.36490	0.11850
3.00	4.2346	0.02722	0.07623	0.35714	0.11528
3.50	6.7896	0.01311	0.04523	0.28986	0.08902
4.00	10.719	0.00658	0.02766	0.23810	0.07059
4.50	16.562	0.00346	0.01745	0.19802	0.05723
5.00	25.000	$189(10)^{-5}$	0.01134	0.16667	0.04725
6.00	53.189	$633(10)^{-6}$	0.00519	0.12195	0.03368
7.00	104.143	$242(10)^{-6}$	0.00261	0.09259	0.02516
8.00	190.109	$102(10)^{-6}$	0.00141	0.07246	0.01947
9.00	327.189	$474(10)^{-7}$	0.000815	0.05814	0.01550
10.00	535.938	$236(10)^{-7}$	0.000495	0.04762	0.01263
∞	∞	0	0	0	0

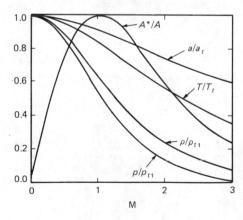

Figure 10.7 Property variations as functions of Mach number for an isentropic flow for $k = 1.4$.

To determine the mass-flow rate in a streamtube,

$$\dot{m} = \rho U A = \rho_{t1} \left(\frac{\rho}{\rho_{t1}}\right) M \sqrt{kRT_t} \sqrt{\frac{T}{T_t}} A$$

$$\frac{\dot{m}}{A} = \sqrt{\frac{k}{R}} \frac{p_{t1}}{\sqrt{T_t}} \frac{M}{\{1 + [(k-1)/2] M^2\}^{[(k+1)/2(k-1)]}} \tag{10.27}$$

Thus, the mass flow rate is proportional to the stagnation pressure and inversely proportional to the square root of the stagnation temperature. To find the condition of maximum flow per unit area, one could compute the derivative of $(\dot{m}/A)$ as given by Eq. (10.27) with respect to Mach number and set the derivative equal to zero. At this condition, one would find that $M = 1$. Thus, setting $M = 1$ in Eq. (10.27) yields

$$\left(\frac{\dot{m}}{A}\right)_{max} = \frac{\dot{m}}{A^*} = \sqrt{\frac{k}{R} \left(\frac{2}{k+1}\right)^{(k+1)/(k-1)}} \frac{p_{t1}}{\sqrt{T_t}} \tag{10.28}$$

Figure 10.7 shows that, for each value of A^*/A, there are two values of M, one subsonic, the other supersonic. Thus, from Fig. 10.7 we see that, while all static properties of the fluid monotonically decrease with Mach number, the area ratio does not.

Example 10.3

A small hole exists in the body of an airplane and serves as a convergent nozzle, as shown in Fig. 10.8. (Refer to Probs. 3.35 and 3.36.) The air in the cabin is at 0.50×10^5 N/m². Assume that the cabin volume is sufficiently large that the cabin serves essentially as a stagnation chamber and that the conditions in the cabin remain constant for a period of time, independent of the conditions outside the airplane. Furthermore, assume that the flow in the nozzle is isentropic. Sketch the pressure distribution and calculate the static pressure in the nozzle exit plane when the airplane is at the following altitudes: (a) 6 km, (b) 8 km, (c) 10 km, and (d) 12 km.

Solution. Since the air expands isentropically from constant reservoir conditions, the back pressure (i.e., the pressure outside the airplane), p_b, is an important parameter. Using Table 10.1, we see that

(a) $p_b = 354.161$ mm Hg $= 0.47218 \times 10^5$ N/m² $= 0.94435 p_{t1}$
(b) $p_b = 267.409$ mm Hg $= 0.35652 \times 10^5$ N/m² $= 0.71303 p_{t1}$
(c) $p_b = 198.765$ mm Hg $= 0.26500 \times 10^5$ N/m² $= 0.53000 p_{t1}$
(d) $p_b = 145.508$ mm Hg $= 0.19399 \times 10^5$ N/m² $= 0.38799 p_{t1}$

where $p_{t1} = p_c = 0.5 \times 10^5$ N/m².

We can calculate the Mach number to which the flow accelerates when it reaches the back pressure using Eq. (10.19):

$$M_b = \left\{\frac{2}{k-1} \left[\left(\frac{p_{t1}}{p_b}\right)^{(k-1)/k} - 1\right]\right\}^{0.5} = \left\{5.0 \left[\left(\frac{p_{t1}}{p_b}\right)^{0.2857} - 1\right]\right\}^{0.5}$$

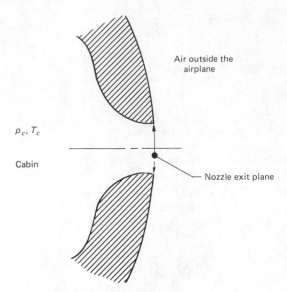

Air outside the
airplane

p_c, T_c

Cabin

Nozzle exit plane

Figure 10.8   Sketch for Examples 10.3
and 10.4.

Thus, we find that (a) $M_b = 0.2872$, (b) $M_b = 0.7122$, (c) $M_b = 0.9972$, and (d) $M_b = 1.2462$. The reader should verify these values by using Table 10.1. For conditions (a) through (c), the back pressure is such that the flow would only accelerate to subsonic speeds. Recall that we have often made use of the fact that, when flow exhausts subsonically from a duct, the static pressure in the exit plane is equal to the static pressure of the environment into which it exhausts. Thus, for conditions (a) through (c), $p_{ne} = p_b$. These results are illustrated in the pressure distributions of Fig. 10.9a and in the correlations for the nozzle exit pressure as a function of back pressure of Fig. 10.9b.

      An isentropic expansion to the back pressure of condition (d) would produce supersonic flow. However, from our discussion of duct flows, we know that the maximum speed that can be achieved in a convergent-only nozzle is the sonic value. Furthermore, that would occur at the throat (i.e., the exit plane). The existence of sonic conditions in the exit plane prevents changes in the conditions outside the nozzle from propagating upstream. Refer to the earlier discussion on the propagation of disturbances. As a result, we conclude that the flow expands to sonic conditions in the nozzle exit plane for condition (d). Further acceleration (with the corresponding decrease in pressure) takes place outside the nozzle. Any back pressure below that required for sonic flow would produce a similar "choking" of the nozzle to sonic conditions, with subsequent expansion taking place outside the airplane.

Example 10.4

If the temperature in the cabin is 22°C and the exit diameter is 0.75 cm, what is the mass flow rate through the hole of Example 10.3 when the altitude is 6 km? 12 km?

Solution.   Note that $T_t = T_c = 295.15$ K. For an altitude of 6 km, the flow is not choked. Therefore, let us use the definition

$$\dot{m} = \dot{m}_{ne} = \rho_{ne} U_{ne} A_{ne}$$

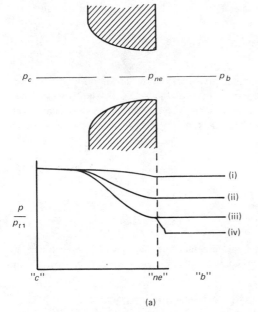

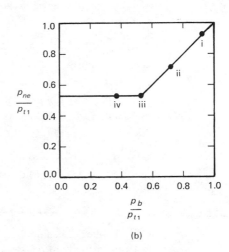

Figure 10.9 Solution for Example 10.3: (a) pressure distribution: (b) pressure ratios.

From Example 10.3,

$$p_{ne} = p_b = 0.47218 \times 10^5 \text{ N/m}^2$$

and

$$T_{ne} = \frac{T_t}{1 + [(k - 1)/2] M_{ne}^2} = \frac{295.15}{1.0165} = 290.36 \text{ K}$$

Also,

$$\rho_{ne} = \frac{0.47218 \times 10^5}{(287.05)(290.36)} = 0.56652 \text{ kg/m}^3$$

$$U_{ne} = M_{ne} a_{ne} = 0.2872(20.047\sqrt{290.36}) = 98.108 \text{ m/s}$$

Thus,

$$\dot{m} = 0.56652(98.108)(4.4179 \times 10^{-5}) = 2.4555 \times 10^{-3} \text{ kg/s}$$

For an altitude of 12 km, we know that the flow in the nozzle is choked (i.e., is sonic at the throat). Thus, we can use Eq. (10.28):

$$\dot{m} = \sqrt{\frac{k}{R}\left(\frac{2}{k + 1}\right)^{(k + 1)/(k - 1)}} \frac{p_{t1} A^*}{\sqrt{T_t}} = 0.040415 \frac{p_{t1} A^*}{\sqrt{T_t}}$$

Note that this is the equation that was given in Prob. 3.35. Using the appropriate values for the parameters,

$$\dot{m} = 5.1965 \times 10^{-3} \text{ kg/s}$$

Example 10.5

Consider the flow of air through the convergent–divergent nozzle shown in Fig. 10.10. The conditions in the stagnation chamber are $p_{t1} = 100$ psia and $T_t = 200°F$. The cross-sectional area of the test section is 2.035 times the throat area. The pressure in the test section can be varied by controlling the valve to the vacuum tank. Assuming isentropic flow in the nozzle, calculate the static pressure, static temperature, Mach number, and velocity in the test section for the following back pressures.

(a) $p_b = 100.000$ psia

(b) $p_b = 97.250$ psia

(c) $p_b = 93.947$ psia

(d) $p_b = 9.117$ psia

Solution.   Let us first convert the stagnation temperature to °R. $T_t = 659.6°R$. Since the back pressure is equal to the stagnation pressure for condition (a), there is no flow. Thus, for (a),

$$p_1 = 100.000 \text{ psia}, \quad T_1 = 659.6°R, \quad M_1 = 0, \quad U_1 = 0$$

Before proceeding with our calculations, let us find the values of the various parameters that correspond to $(A/A^*) = 2.035$ in Table 10.1. Note that for this value of the area ratio

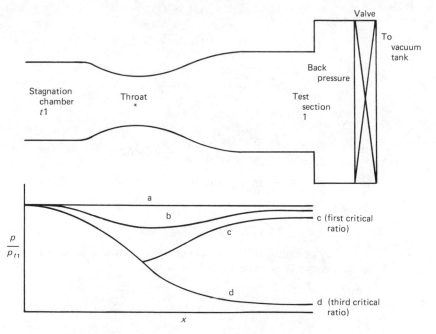

Figure 10.10   Isentropic flow in a convergent–divergent nozzle.

the Mach number can be either 0.30 or 2.23, with corresponding values for the pressure ratio (p/p_{t1}) of either 0.93947 or 0.09117. The first values correspond to the situation where the flow accelerates in the convergent section, reaches sonic speed at the throat, and then, because of the relatively high back pressure, decelerates in the divergent section. This is known as the first critical ratio. Thus, for condition (c), $p_1 = 93.947$ psia and $M_1 = 0.30$. Using Table 10.1,

$$T_1 = \left(\frac{T}{T_t}\right) T_t = 0.98232(659.6) = 647.94°\text{R}$$

The velocity is

$$U_1 = M_1 a_1 = 0.30(49.02\sqrt{T_1}) = 374.3 \text{ ft/s}$$

The second set of values from Table 10.1 corresponds to the situation where the flow accelerates in the convergent section, reaches sonic speed at the throat, and then, because of the relatively low back pressure, continues to accelerate isentropically in the divergent section. This is known as the third critical ratio. The test section Mach number is 2.23 for condition (d). Thus, $p_1 = 9.117$ psia. Furthermore,

$$T_1 = 0.50438(659.6) = 332.69°\text{R}$$

$$U_1 = 2.23(49.02\sqrt{332.69}) = 1993.88 \text{ ft/s}$$

For condition (b), the flow is subsonic throughout the nozzle. Thus,

$$p_1 = 97.250 \quad \text{and} \quad p_1 = 0.97250 \, p_{t1}$$

Therefore, using Table 10.1, $M_1 = 0.20$, $T_1 = 654.36°\text{R}$, and $U_1 = 250.79$ ft/s.

What happens to the flow when the back pressure is between 9.117 psia and 93.947 psia? To be able to define the flow field for pressures between the third critical pressure ratio and the first critical pressure ratio, we need to understand shock waves.

SHOCK WAVES

The formation of a shock wave occurs when a supersonic flow decelerates in response to a sharp increase in pressure or when a supersonic flow encounters a sudden, compressive change in direction. For flow conditions where the gas is a continuum, the shock wave is a narrow region (on the order of several molecular mean free paths thick, ~6 × 10⁻⁶ cm) across which there is an almost instantaneous change in the values of the flow parameters. Because of the large streamwise variations in velocity, pressure, and temperature, viscous and heat-conduction effects are important within the shock wave. The reader should note that a shock wave is different from a Mach wave. A Mach wave represents a surface across which some derivatives of the flow variables (such as the thermodynamic properties of the fluid and the flow velocity) may be discontinuous while the variables themselves are continuous. A shock wave represents a surface across which the thermodynamic properties and the flow velocity are essentially discontinuous.

Consider the curved shock wave illustrated in Fig. 10.11. The flow upstream of the shock wave, which is stationary in the body-fixed coordinate system, is supersonic.

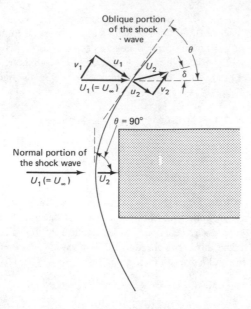

Figure 10.11 Curved shock wave illustrating nomenclature for normal shock wave and oblique shock wave. (From Bertin and Smith, *Aerodynamics for Engineers*, p. 255.)

At the plane of symmetry, the shock wave is normal (or perpendicular) to the free-stream flow, and the flow downstream of the shock wave is subsonic. Away from the plane of symmetry, the shock wave is oblique and the downstream flow is often supersonic. The velocity and thermodynamic properties upstream of the shock wave are designated by the subscript 1. Note that the subscript 1 may designate the free-stream (∞) properties for flows such as those in Fig. 10.11, or it may designate the local flow properties at some point just upstream of a second shock wave, such as for a reflected shock wave (see Example 10.8).

The downstream values are designated by the subscript 2. We will analyze oblique shock waves by writing the continuity, momentum, and energy equations for the flow through the control volume shown in Fig. 10.12. For a steady flow, the integral equations of motion yield the following relations for the flow across an oblique segment of the shock wave:

1. Continuity: $\rho_1 u_1 = \rho_2 u_2$ (10.29)
2. Normal component of momentum: $p_1 + \rho_1 u_1^2 = p_2 + \rho_2 u_2^2$ (10.30)
3. Tangential component of momentum: $\rho_1 u_1 v_1 = \rho_2 u_2 v_2$ (10.31)
4. Energy: $h_1 + \frac{1}{2}(u_1^2 + v_1^2) = h_2 + \frac{1}{2}(u_2^2 + v_2^2)$ (10.32)

In addition to describing the flow across an oblique shock wave such as shown in Fig. 10.12, these relations can be used to describe the flow across a normal shock wave, or the portion of a curved shock wave that is perpendicular to the free stream by letting $v_1 = v_2 = 0$.

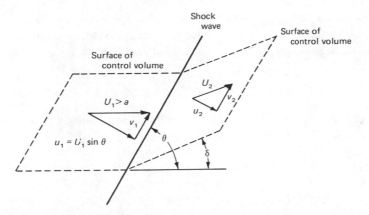

Figure 10.12 Control volume for analysis of flow through an oblique shock wave.

Comparing Eq. (10.29) with (10.31), one finds that for the oblique shock wave

$$v_1 = v_2 \qquad (10.33)$$

That is, the tangential component of the velocity is constant across the shock wave and we need consider Eq. (10.31) no further. Thus, the energy equation becomes

$$h_1 + \tfrac{1}{2}u_1^2 = h_2 + \tfrac{1}{2}u_2^2 \qquad (10.34)$$

There are four unknowns (p_2, ρ_2, u_2, h_2) in the three equations [(10.29), (10.30), and (10.34)]. Thus, we need to introduce an equation of state as the fourth equation. For hypervelocity flows where the shock waves are strong enough to cause dissociation or ionization, one can solve these equations numerically using the equation of state in tabular or in graphical form (e.g., Ref. 10.2). However, for a perfect-gas flow,

$$p = \rho R T$$

$$\text{and } h = c_p T$$

Note that Eqs. (10.29), (10.30), and (10.34) involve only the component of velocity normal to the shock wave:

$$u_1 = U_1 \sin \theta \qquad (10.35)$$

Hence, the property changes across an oblique shock wave are the same as those across a normal shock wave when they are written in terms of the upstream Mach number component perpendicular to the shock. The tangential component of the velocity is unchanged. This is the *sweepback principle,* that the oblique flow is reduced to the normal flow by a uniform translation of the axes (i.e., a Galilean transformation). Note that the tangential component of the Mach number does change, since the temperature and, therefore, the speed of sound change across the shock wave.

Since the flow through the shock wave is adiabatic, the entropy must increase as the flow passes through the shock wave. Thus, the flow must decelerate (i.e., the pressure must increase) as it passes through the shock wave. One obtains the relation between the shock-wave angle (θ) and the deflection angle (δ):

$$\cot \delta = \tan \theta \left[\frac{(k + 1)M_1^2}{2(M_1^2 \sin^2 \theta - 1)} - 1 \right] \tag{10.36}$$

From Eq. (10.36) it can be seen that the deflection angle is zero for two "shock"-wave angles. (1) The flow is not deflected when $\theta = \mu$, since the Mach wave results from an infinitesimal disturbance (i.e., a zero-strength shock wave). (2) The flow is not deflected when it passes through a normal shock wave (i.e., when $\theta = 90°$).

Solutions to Eq. (10.36) are presented in graphical form in Fig. 10.13a. Note that for a given deflection angle δ there are two possible values for the shock-wave angle θ.

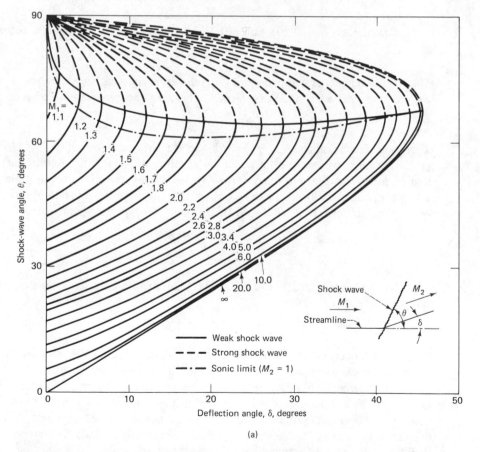

Figure 10.13 Variation of shock-wave parameters with wedge flow-detection angle for various upstream Mach numbers, $\gamma = 1.4$: (a) shock-wave angle; (b) pressure coefficient; (c) downstream Mach number.

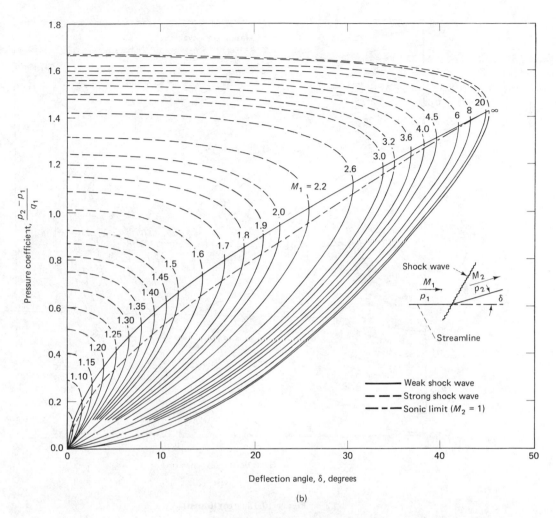

Figure 10.13 (continued)

The larger of the two values of θ is called the strong shock wave, while the smaller value is called the weak shock wave. In practice, the weak shock wave typically occurs in external aerodynamic flows. However, the strong shock wave occurs if the downstream pressure is sufficiently high. The high downstream pressure may occur in flows in wind tunnels, in engine inlets, or in other ducts.

If the deflection angle exceeds the maximum value for which it is possible that a weak shock can be generated, a strong, detached shock wave will occur. For instance, a flat plate airfoil can be inclined 34° to a Mach 3.0 stream and still generate a weak shock wave. This is the maximum deflection angle for a weak shock wave to occur. If the airfoil were to be inclined at 35° to the Mach 3.0 stream, a strong curved shock wave would occur with a complex subsonic–supersonic flow downstream of the shock wave.

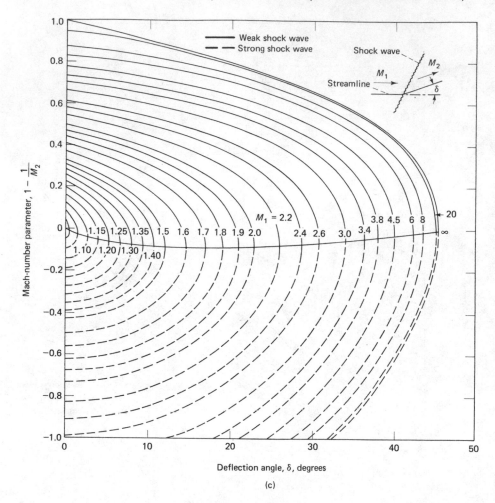

(c)

Figure 10.13   (continued)

Once the shock-wave angle θ has been found for the given values of M_1 and δ, the other downstream properties can be found using the following relations:

$$\frac{p_2}{p_1} = \frac{2kM_1^2 \sin^2 \theta - (k - 1)}{k + 1} \tag{10.37}$$

$$\frac{\rho_2}{\rho_1} = \frac{(k + 1)M_1^2 \sin^2 \theta}{(k - 1)M_1^2 \sin^2 \theta + 2} \tag{10.38}$$

$$\frac{T_2}{T_1} = \frac{[2kM_1^2 \sin^2 \theta - (k - 1)] \, [(k - 1)M_1^2 \sin^2 \theta + 2]}{(k + 1)^2 M_1^2 \sin^2 \theta} \tag{10.39}$$

$$M_2^2 = \frac{(k - 1)M_1^2 \sin^2 \theta + 2}{[2kM_1^2 \sin^2 \theta - (k - 1)] [\sin^2 (\theta - \delta)]} \tag{10.40}$$

$$\frac{p_{t2}}{p_{t1}} = e^{-\Delta s/R}$$

$$= \left[\frac{(k + 1)M_1^2 \sin^2 \theta}{(k - 1)M_1^2 \sin^2 \theta + 2}\right]^{k/(k - 1)} \left[\frac{k + 1}{2kM_1^2 \sin^2 \theta - (k - 1)}\right]^{1/(k - 1)} \tag{10.41}$$

and

$$C_p = \frac{p_2 - p_1}{q_1} = \frac{4(M_1^2 \sin^2 \theta - 1)}{(k + 1)M_1^2} \tag{10.42}$$

In developing the expression for the pressure coefficient, Eq. (10.42), we have used the fact that

$$q_1 = \frac{1}{2} \rho_1 U_1^2 = \frac{\gamma}{2} p_1 M_1^2 \tag{10.43}$$

for a perfect gas. The pressure coefficient is presented in Fig. 10.13b as a function of δ and M_1. The values for many of these ratios are presented for a normal shock wave in Table 10.2 and Fig. 10.14. The values for the pressure ratios, density ratios, and temperature ratios for an oblique shock wave can be read from Table 10.2 provided that $M_1 \sin \theta$ is used instead of M_1 in the first column. Note that since it is the tangential component of the velocity that is unchanged and not the tangential component of the Mach number, we cannot use Table 10.2 to calculate the downstream Mach number. The downstream Mach number is presented in Fig. 10.13c as a function of the deflection angle and the upstream Mach number. An alternative procedure to calculate the Mach number behind the shock wave would be to convert the value of M_2 in Table 10.2 (which is the normal component of the Mach number) to the normal component of velocity, using T_2 to calculate

TABLE 10.2 CORRELATION OF FLOW PROPERTIES ACROSS A NORMAL SHOCK WAVE AS A FUNCTION OF THE UPSTREAM MACH NUMBER FOR AIR, $k = 1.4$

M_1	M_2	$\dfrac{p_2}{p_1}$	$\dfrac{\rho_2}{\rho_1}$	$\dfrac{T_2}{T_1}$	$\dfrac{p_{t2}}{p_{t1}}$
1.00	1.00000	1.00000	1.00000	1.00000	1.00000
1.05	0.95312	1.1196	1.08398	1.03284	0.99987
1.10	0.91177	1.2450	1.1691	1.06494	0.99892
1.15	0.87502	1.3762	1.2550	1.09657	0.99669
1.20	0.84217	1.5133	1.3416	1.1280	0.99280
1.25	0.81264	1.6562	1.4286	1.1594	0.98706
1.30	0.78596	1.8050	1.5157	1.1909	0.97935

(Continued)

TABLE 10.2   (Continued)

M_1	M_2	$\dfrac{p_2}{p_1}$	$\dfrac{\rho_2}{\rho_1}$	$\dfrac{T_2}{T_1}$	$\dfrac{p_{t2}}{p_{t1}}$
1.35	0.76175	1.9596	1.6027	1.2226	0.96972
1.40	0.73971	2.1200	1.6896	1.2547	0.95819
1.45	0.71956	2.2862	1.7761	1.2872	0.94483
1.50	0.70109	2.4583	1.8621	1.3202	0.92978
1.55	0.68410	2.6363	1.9473	1.3538	0.91319
1.60	0.66844	2.8201	2.0317	1.3880	0.89520
1.65	0.65396	3.0096	2.1152	1.4228	0.87598
1.70	0.64055	3.2050	2.1977	1.4583	0.85573
1.75	0.62809	3.4062	2.2781	1.4946	0.83456
1.80	0.61650	3.6133	2.3592	1.5316	0.81268
1.85	0.60570	3.8262	2.4381	1.5694	0.79021
1.90	0.59562	4.0450	2.5157	1.6079	0.76735
1.95	0.58618	4.2696	2.5919	1.6473	0.74418
2.00	0.57735	4.5000	2.6666	1.6875	0.72088
2.05	0.56907	4.7363	2.7400	1.7286	0.69752
2.10	0.56128	4.9784	2.8119	1.7704	0.67422
2.15	0.55395	5.2262	2.8823	1.8132	0.65105
2.20	0.54706	5.4800	2.9512	1.8569	0.62812
2.25	0.54055	5.7396	3.0186	1.9014	0.60554
2.30	0.53441	6.0050	3.0846	1.9468	0.58331
2.35	0.52861	6.2762	3.1490	1.9931	0.56148
2.40	0.52312	6.5533	3.2119	2.0403	0.54015
2.45	0.51792	6.8362	3.2733	2.0885	0.51932
2.50	0.51299	7.1250	3.3333	2.1375	0.49902
2.55	0.50831	7.4196	3.3918	2.1875	0.47927
2.60	0.50387	7.7200	3.4489	2.2383	0.46012
2.65	0.49965	8.0262	3.5047	2.2901	0.44155
2.70	0.49563	8.3383	3.5590	2.3429	0.42359
2.75	0.49181	8.6562	3.6119	2.3966	0.40622
2.80	0.48817	8.9800	3.6635	2.4512	0.38946
2.85	0.48470	9.3096	3.7139	2.5067	0.37330
2.90	0.48138	9.6450	3.7629	2.5632	0.35773
2.95	0.47821	9.986	3.8106	2.6206	0.34275
3.00	0.47519	10.333	3.8571	2.6790	0.32834
3.50	0.45115	14.125	4.2608	3.3150	0.21295
4.00	0.43496	18.500	4.5714	4.0469	0.13876
4.50	0.42355	23.458	4.8119	4.8761	0.09170
5.00	0.41523	29.000	5.0000	5.8000	0.06172
6.00	0.40416	41.833	5.2683	7.941	0.02965
7.00	0.39736	57.000	5.4444	10.469	0.01535
8.00	0.39289	74.500	5.5652	13.387	0.00849
9.00	0.38980	94.333	5.6512	16.693	0.00496
10.00	0.38757	116.50	5.7143	20.388	0.00304
∞	0.37796	∞	6.000	∞	0

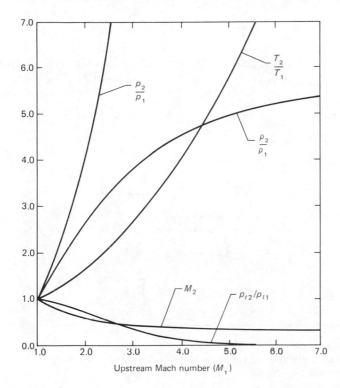

Upstream Mach number (M_1)

Figure 10.14 Property variations across a normal shock wave.

the local speed of sound. Then we can calculate the total velocity downstream of the shock wave:

$$U_2 = \sqrt{u_2^2 + v_2^2}$$

from which we can calculate the downstream Mach number.

Example 10.6

Consider the flow of air through the convergent–divergent nozzle shown in Fig. 10.15. The conditions in the stagnation chamber are $p_{t1} = 100$ psia and $T_t = 200°F$. The cross-sectional area of the test section is 2.035 times the throat area. Thus far we have repeated the conditions of Example 10.5. Calculate the static pressure, static temperature, Mach number, and velocity in the test section for the following back pressures:

(e) $p_b = 51.38$ psia

(f) $p_b = 75.86$ psia

Solution. Recall that, if the flow accelerates isentropically to the supersonic Mach number that corresponds to the area ratio of the test section (2.035), the Mach number there is 2.23. This corresponds to the third critical pressure ratio (i.e., condition (d) of Fig. 10.10). Let

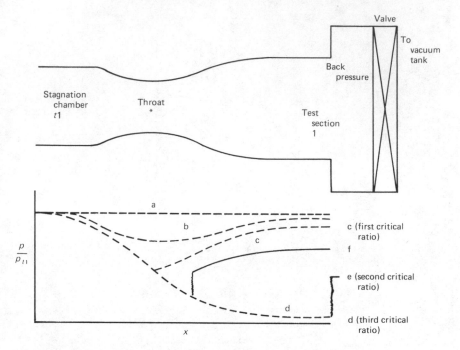

Figure 10.15 Flow in a convergent–divergent nozzle with a shock wave in the divergent section (dashed lines are from Fig. 10.10).

us assume that a normal shock wave occurs in the test section at this condition. We can use Table 10.2 to calculate the conditions downstream of the shock wave. For $M_1 = 2.23$, the pressure ratio is

$$\frac{p_2}{p_{t1}} = \left(\frac{p_2}{p_1}\right)\left(\frac{p_1}{p_{t1}}\right) = (5.6358)(0.09117) = 0.5138$$

Thus, $p_2 = 51.38$ psia. This corresponds to the value of the back pressure for condition (e). Since the thickness of the shock wave is infinitesimal, we could say that there are actually two sets of conditions in the test section for condition (e): one set upstream of the shock wave (corresponding to the condition designated 1 in the shock wave nomenclature) and a second set downstream of the shock wave (corresponding to the condition designated 2 in the shock wave nomenclature). The former set of conditions is identical to those of condition (d) in Example 10.5. The latter set of conditions (i.e., those downstream of a normal shock wave) are those of condition (e). Continuing with the parameters from Table 10.2,

$$M_2 = 0.5432$$

$$T_2 = \left(\frac{T_2}{T_1}\right) T_1 = (1.8836)332.69 = 626.65°R$$

$$U_2 = M_2 a_2 = 0.5432(49.02\sqrt{626.65}) = 666.57 \text{ ft/s}$$

The pressure downstream of a normal shock wave in the test section when written in dimensionless form as p_2/p_{t1} is known as the second critical pressure ratio.

For condition (f), a normal shock wave occurs in the divergent section of the nozzle between the throat and the test section, as shown in Fig. 10.15. Upstream of this shock wave, the flow accelerates isentropically to the supersonic speed corresponding to the area ratio at the location where the shock is located. Downstream of the shock wave, the flow is subsonic. Since subsonic flow in a divergent section decelerates, the velocity decreases as the flow proceeds in the divergent section. The static pressure increases in the streamwise direction, matching the back pressure as the downstream boundary condition.

We will use an iterative procedure to determine where the shock wave occurs such that the pressure of the subsonic flow in the test section equals the back pressure. For the first iteration, let us assume that a normal shock wave occurs in the divergent section where the area ratio (A_{sw}/A_1^*) is 1.4952. A sketch of the flow and the relevant nomenclature are presented in Fig. 10.16. Using Table 10.1, we see that the conditions ahead of the shock wave are $M_1 = 1.85$ and $(p_1/p_{t1}) = 0.16120$. We can use Table 10.2 to determine the conditions downstream of the shock wave.

$$M_2 = 0.6057 \quad \text{and} \quad \frac{p_{t2}}{p_{t1}} = 0.79021$$

Having determined the Mach number M_2, we can calculate the area ratio for a second, "imaginary" nozzle (see the broken line in Fig. 10.16) that would produce this flow by an isentropic process. From Table 10.1, the area ratio for the imaginary nozzle is $(A_{sw}/A_2^*) = 1.1819$. Let us now determine the conditions in the test section by modeling a subsonic deceleration for the test-section area ratio for the second nozzle. The corresponding area ratio is

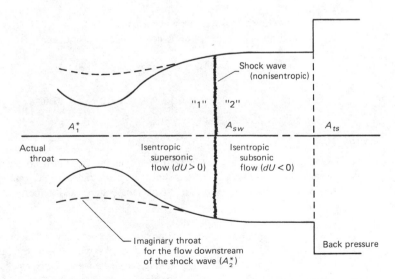

Figure 10.16 Shock wave located in the divergent portion of the nozzle (for Example 10.6).

$$\frac{A_{ts}}{A_2^*} = \frac{A_{ts}}{A_1^*} \frac{A_{sw}/A_2^*}{A_{sw}/A_1^*} = 2.035 \frac{1.1819}{1.4952} = 1.6086$$

The subsonic Mach number corresponding to this area ratio is 0.3944. For this Mach number, the pressure ratio in Table 10.1 is 0.8984. Although this ratio is defined as p/p_{t1} in the table, it is actually p_{ts}/p_{t2}, since we are considering the flow downstream of the shock wave and since the area ratio is that of the imaginary (second) nozzle. The resultant pressure ratio is

$$\frac{p_{ts}}{p_{t1}} = \frac{p_{ts}}{p_{t2}} \frac{p_{t2}}{p_{t1}} = (0.8984)(0.79021) = 0.7099$$

The pressure from this iteration is less than that specified for condition (f).

Repeat the iterative procedure until we obtain the proper value for the pressure in the test section. The appropriate values for the flow upstream of the shock wave are

$$\frac{A_{sw}}{A_1^*} = 1.3865, \quad M_1 = 1.75, \quad \text{and} \frac{p_1}{p_{t1}} = 0.18782$$

The conditions immediately downstream of the shock wave are

$$M_2 = 0.62809, \quad \frac{p_{t2}}{p_{t1}} = 0.83456, \quad \text{and} \frac{A_{sw}}{A_2^*} = 1.1571$$

For the test section,

$$\frac{A_{ts}}{A_2^*} = 1.6983, \quad M_{ts} = 0.3694 \quad \frac{p_{ts}}{p_{t1}} = 0.7594$$

Note that for this pressure ratio the pressure in the test section is essentially that prescribed for condition (f).

Since the flow across a shock wave is adiabatic, $T_{t1} = T_{t2}$. Thus, the static temperature in the test section for this condition is determined by using Table 10.1 for $M_{ts} = 0.3694$.

$$T_{ts} = \left(\frac{T_{ts}}{T_{t2}}\right) T_{t2} = (0.9733)659.6 = 642.0°R$$

$$U_{ts} = M_{ts}a_{ts} = 0.3694(49.02\sqrt{T_{ts}}) = 458.82 \text{ ft/s}$$

Example 10.7

An explosion generates a shock wave that moves through the atmosphere at 1000 m/s. The atmospheric conditions ahead of the shock wave are those of the standard sea-level atmosphere. What are the static pressure, static temperature, and velocity of the air behind the shock wave?

Solution.   Let us model a portion of the blast wave as a normal shock wave that moves to the right at 1000 m/s, as shown in Fig. 10.17a. We will convert the problem to a steady-state flow by fixing the coordinate system to the shock wave. Thus, as shown in Fig. 10.17b, the air ahead of the shock wave is "moving" to the left at 1000 m/s. Using Table 1.1, the conditions of the undisturbed air ahead of the shock wave are

$$p_1 = 1.01325 \times 10^5 \text{ N/m}^2, \quad T_1 = 288.15 \text{ K}, \quad a_1 = 340.294 \text{ m/s}$$

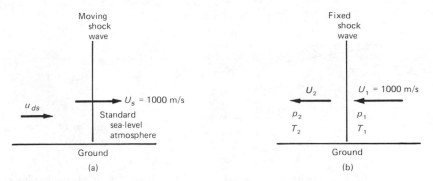

Figure 10.17   Blast wave for Example 10.7: (a) traveling blast wave; (b) transformed steady flow.

Thus, $M_1 = 2.939$. For this free-stream Mach number, we can use Table 10.2 to find that

$$\frac{p_2}{p_1} = 9.911, \quad \frac{T_2}{T_1} = 2.608, \quad \frac{\rho_2}{\rho_1} = 3.800$$

The properties of the shocked air are

$$p_2 = 9.911(1.01325 \times 10^5) = 1.00423 \times 10^6 \text{ N/m}^2$$

$$T_2 = 2.608(288.15) = 751.50 \text{ K}$$

Using the continuity equation, Eq. (10.29),

$$U_2 = \frac{\rho_1}{\rho_2} U_1 = \frac{1000}{3.800} = 263.16 \text{ m/s}$$

However, this is the velocity in the shock-wave-fixed coordinate system of Fig. 10.17b. The actual velocity of the air behind the shock wave (u_{ds} of Fig. 10.17a) is determined by returning to the ground-fixed coordinate system.

$$u_{ds} = 1000 - U_2 = 736.84 \text{ m/s}$$

The Mach number of the shock-induced motion is

$$M_{ds} = \frac{u_{ds}}{20.047\sqrt{T_2}} = 1.341$$

Note that, although the "flow" downstream of the shock wave is subsonic in the shock-wave fixed coordinate system, the air behind the shock wave actually moves at supersonic speeds. Note also that the finite disturbance created by the explosion moves significantly faster than the speed of sound.

Example 10.8   Consider the flow field at the inlet of an engine of an airplane operating at Mach 3 at an altitude of 20 km. As shown in the sketch of Fig. 10.18, the upper-surface leading edge is inclined by 10° to the oncoming flow, generating a shock wave (designated W1 in the sketch). For this example, the lower surface of the inlet is parallel to the free

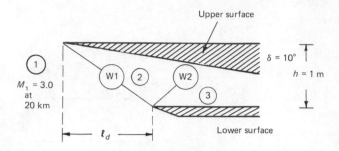

Upper surface

$\delta = 10°$

$h = 1$ m

$M_1 = 3.0$
at
20 km

W1 (2) W2

(3)

l_d

Lower surface

Figure 10.18 Jet-engine inlet for Example 10.8.

stream and is located such that the W1 shock wave intersects the leading edge of the lower surface. The shock wave W1 reflects from the lower surface as the shock wave W2. Calculate the horizontal distance (l_d) between the leading edge of the upper surface and that of the lower surface. Calculate the flow directions, the local Mach numbers, and the static pressures in regions 2 and 3. What is the ratio of the total pressure in region 3 to that in region 1?

Solution.   We must first determine the flow across the shock wave W1, which is illustrated in Fig. 10.19a. Using Fig. 10.13a, we find that the shock-wave angle θ for $M_1 = 3.0$ and $\delta = 10°$ is 27.5°. Thus,

$$l_d = \frac{h}{\tan \theta} = \frac{1.0}{0.5206} = 1.921 \text{ m}$$

The Mach number in region 2 can be determined using Fig. 10.13(c):

$$M_2 = 2.5$$

We could use Eqs. (10.37) and (10.41) to determine the pressure ratios for the shock wave. However, we will use the component of the Mach number normal to the shock wave and the pressure ratios of Table 10.2. Since $M_{n1} = M_1 \sin \theta = 1.385$,

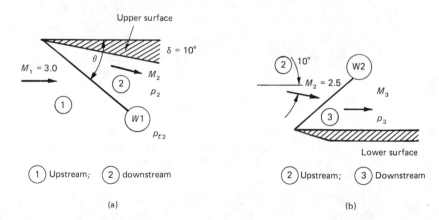

(a)

Upper surface

$\delta = 10°$

$M_1 = 3.0$

θ

M_2
p_2

(2)

(1)

W1

p_{t2}

(1) Upstream;   (2) downstream

(b)

(2) 10°   W2

$M_2 = 2.5$

M_3

(3) p_3

Lower surface

(2) Upstream;   (3) Downstream

Figure 10.19   Detailed sketches for Example 10.8: (a) leading-edge shock wave, W1; (b) reflected shock wave, W2.

$$\frac{p_2}{p_1} = 2.072 \quad \text{and} \quad \frac{p_{t2}}{p_{t1}} = 0.9618$$

Since the static pressure of the standard atmosphere at an altitude of 20 km is 5.5293 kPa,

$$p_2 = \frac{p_2}{p_1} p_1 = 2.072(5.5293) = 11.4567 \text{ kPa}$$

The flow in region 2 is parallel to the upper surface, that is, is inclined 10° downward relative to the free stream.

To determine the flow conditions in region 3, we note that the flow must turn 10° from the flow direction in region 2 in order to be parallel to the lower surface in region 3. The turning is accomplished by the shock wave W2 that appears in Fig. 10.18 and Fig. 10.19b. Note that, for this reflected wave, region 2 is upstream of the shock wave and region 3 is downstream. Thus, our subscript nomenclature must be adjusted when applying the charts and equations for shock waves.

Repeating the earlier procedures, but for an upstream Mach number of 2.5 with a turning angle of 10°,

$$M_3 = 2.083, \quad \theta = 32°, \quad M_{n2} = 1.325$$

Thus,

$$\frac{p_3}{p_2} = 1.882 \quad \text{and} \quad \frac{p_{t3}}{p_{t2}} = 0.9745$$

Since the static pressure in region 2 was found to be 11.4567 kPa,

$$p_3 = \frac{p_3}{p_2} p_2 = 1.882(11.4567) = 21.562 \text{ kPa}$$

and

$$\frac{p_{t3}}{p_{t1}} = \frac{p_{t3}}{p_{t2}} \frac{p_{t2}}{p_{t1}} = 0.9373$$

The ratio of the stagnation pressures is a measure of the entropy change (or, equivalently, of the irreversibility) of the flow process.

ADIABATIC, COMPRESSIBLE FLOW IN CONSTANT-AREA DUCTS WITH FRICTION

We have developed relations that describe a steady, compressible flow in a variable duct while neglecting friction and heat transfer. In this section we will analyze an adiabatic gas flow in a constant-area duct (or pipe) with friction. In effect, we are studying a Moody-type pipe-friction problem, but one with large changes in kinetic energy, enthalpy, and pressure. The basic assumptions are as follows:

1. Steady, one-dimensional flow
2. Perfect gas

3. Adiabatic flow (i.e., no heat transfer through the walls)
4. No shaft work added to or extracted from the flow
5. Changes in potential energy (or elevation) are negligible
6. Constant-area straight duct
7. Constant shear stress that can be correlated by a Darcy friction factor

Let us develop the integral equations of motion as they apply to a steady, one-dimensional, adiabatic flow in a constant-area duct, as shown in Fig. 10.20. The continuity equation is

$$\rho V = \text{constant}$$

which when differentiated yields

$$V\, d\rho + \rho\, dV = 0 \tag{10.44a}$$

The x component of the momentum equation

$$pA - (p + dp)A - \tau_w \pi D\, dx = \dot{m}(V + dV - V)$$

so

$$dp + \frac{4\tau_w\, dx}{D} + \rho V\, dV = 0 \tag{10.44b}$$

The energy equation for an adiabatic flow of a perfect gas is

$$h + \tfrac{1}{2} V^2 = c_p T + \tfrac{1}{2} V^2 = \text{constant}$$

which when differentiated yields

$$c_p dT + V\, dV = 0 \tag{10.44c}$$

There are five unknowns in these three equations: ρ, V, p, T, and τ_w. Therefore, we need two additional relations. One is the equation of state for a perfect gas, Eq. (1.3). Differentiating,

$$dp = RT\, d\rho + R\rho\, dT \tag{10.44d}$$

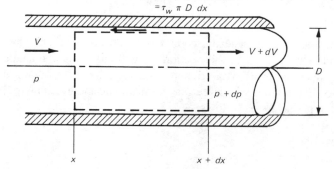

Shear force at the wall
$= \tau_w \pi D\, dx$

V

$V + dV$

D

p

$p + dp$

x

$x + dx$

Figure 10.20 Elemental control volume for flow in a constant-area duct with friction.

To eliminate τ_w as an unknown, it is assumed that the shear stress at the wall is correlated by a local Darcy friction factor, Eq. (6.13):

$$\tau_w = \rho V^2 \frac{f}{8} \tag{10.44e}$$

We now have a system of five equations with five unknowns. These equations can be combined so that we can obtain expressions for the change in a particular parameter in terms of the Mach number and the friction factor. The Mach number is defined as

$$M^2 = \frac{V^2}{kRT}$$

so

$$V \, dV = M \, dM \, (kRT) + \tfrac{1}{2} M^2 kR \, dT \tag{10.44f}$$

By eliminating variables between Eqs. (10.44a) through (10.44f), we obtain the following relations.

$$\frac{dp}{p} = -kM^2 \frac{1 + \tfrac{1}{2}(k-1)M^2}{2(1-M^2)} f \frac{dx}{D} \tag{10.45a}$$

$$\frac{d\rho}{\rho} = -\frac{kM^2}{2(1-M^2)} f \frac{dx}{D} = -\frac{dV}{V} \tag{10.45b}$$

$$\frac{dp_{t1}}{p_{t1}} = \frac{d\rho_{t1}}{\rho_{t1}} = -\tfrac{1}{2} kM^2 f \frac{dx}{D} \tag{10.45c}$$

$$\frac{dT}{T} = -\frac{k(k-1)M^4}{2(1-M^2)} f \frac{dx}{D} \tag{10.45d}$$

$$\frac{d(M^2)}{M^2} = kM^2 \frac{1 + \tfrac{1}{2}(k-1)M^2}{1-M^2} f \frac{dx}{D} \tag{10.45e}$$

All these except dp_{t1}/p_{t1} have the factor $1 - M^2$ in the denominator. As a result, subsonic and supersonic flow have opposite effects, as indicated in Table 10.3. Although there is no specific equation for the entropy, we have noted in Table 10.3 that the entropy must increase along the duct for both subsonic flow and supersonic flow. This is a consequence of the second law of thermodynamics for adiabatic flow. For the same reason, the stagnation pressure and stagnation density must both decrease.

If the pressure, density, and entropy are calculated using Eqs. (10.45a), (10.45b), and (10.3c), respectively, the result can be plotted as a function of the Mach number. The correlation for $k = 1.4$ is presented in Fig. 10.21. The maximum entropy occurs when the Mach number is 1. Thus, the second law of thermodynamics requires that, whether the inlet flow is subsonic or supersonic, the Mach number in the duct always tends toward 1. Thus, the streamwise variation in Mach number is always toward unity, since this is the path along which the entropy increases.

TABLE 10.3 STREAMWISE CHANGE IN THE
FLOW PROPERTIES FOR ADIABATIC,
COMPRESSIBLE FLOW IN A CONSTANT-
AREA DUCT WITH FRICTION

Property	Subsonic	Supersonic
p	Decreases	Increases
ρ	Decreases	Increases
V	Increases	Decreases
p_{t1}, ρ_{t1}	Decreases	Decreases
T	Decreases	Increases
M	Increases	Decreases
Entropy	Increases	Increases

Let us solve for the length of duct for which the exit Mach number becomes unity, which we will designate L^*. To do this, we rearrange Eq. (10.45e) and integrate to obtain

$$\int_0^L \frac{f\,dx}{D} = \int_{M_0^2}^{M_e^2} \frac{1 - M^2}{kM^4[1 + 0.5(k - 1)M^2]}\, d(M^2)$$

Note the subscript 0 will be used to designate the inlet conditions. The lower limit is the entrance of the duct ($x = 0$), where M_0 is the Mach number. The upper limit is the Mach number at the end of the duct (M_e and L, respectively). The result of the integration is

$$\frac{\bar{f}L}{D} = \frac{1}{k}\left(\frac{1}{M_0^2} - \frac{1}{M_e^2}\right) + \frac{k + 1}{2k} \ln\left[\left(\frac{M_0}{M_e}\right)^2 \frac{(k - 1)M_e^2 + 2}{(k - 1)M_0^2 + 2}\right] \quad (10.46)$$

When the duct is sufficiently long that the Mach number at the end of the duct is unity, the duct length is designated L^*. When the M_e is 1, the result of the integration is

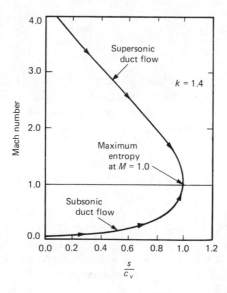

Figure 10.21 Adiabatic frictional flow in a constant-area duct always approaches $M = 1$ to satisfy the second law of thermodynamics. The computed curve is independent of the value of friction factor.

$$\frac{\bar{f}L^*}{D} = \frac{1 - M_0^2}{kM_0^2} + \frac{k + 1}{2k} \ln \left[\frac{(k + 1)M_0^2}{2 + (k - 1)M_0^2} \right] \qquad (10.47)$$

where $\bar{f}$ is the average friction factor between 0 and L. In practice an average f is always assumed, and no attempt is made to account for the slight changes in the Reynolds number along the duct. Approximate values for the friction factor $\bar{f}$ may be determined for a given Reynolds number and wall-roughness ratio using the Moody chart, Fig. 6.6. Experimental investigations indicate that the incompressible values of the friction factor presented in Fig. 6.6 are relatively accurate for compressible, subsonic flow but are up to twice the actual values for supersonic duct flow. For noncircular ducts, D is replaced by the hydraulic diameter

$$D_h = \frac{4 \times \text{area}}{\text{perimeter}}$$

Choking Due to Friction

The theoretical relations developed in this section indicate that, whether the flow is initially subsonic or supersonic, adiabatic frictional flow in a constant-area duct tends toward sonic conditions. As indicated in Eq. (10.47), there is a particular duct length L^* (which is a function of the initial Mach number) for which the exit Mach number will be exactly unity. If the actual duct is shorter than L^*, then the sonic conditions will not be reached in the exit plane. But what happens in those cases where the actual duct length is greater than the length required to reach sonic conditions in the exit plane for a given initial Mach number? There are two types of flow: one if the initial Mach number is subsonic; another if it is supersonic.

1. *Subsonic conditions at the inlet:* If the inlet Mach number is subsonic and the actual length of the tube is longer than L^* for that value of M_0, the flow adjusts itself until the inlet Mach number reaches the value that causes the tube length to equal the sonic length. Thus, the flow in the exit is sonic and the mass flow rate through the tube is reduced by choking due to friction. Recall that, if a flow is subsonic, disturbances can propagate upstream. Thus, the flow along the entire tube length adjusts until the inlet Mach number is that for the tube length for sonic flow in the exit plane.

2. *Supersonic conditions at the inlet:* If the inlet Mach number is supersonic and the actual length of the tube is longer than L^* for that value of M_0, a normal shock wave will occur at a point in the tube so that the subsequent subsonic flow will become sonic exactly at the exit.

Since p_{t1} and ρ_{t1} continually decrease along the duct due to the frictional (nonisentropic) losses, they are not useful as reference properties. Instead, the sonic properties p^*, ρ^*, T^*, and V^* are the appropriate constant reference quantitites in adiabatic duct flow. The theory then computes the ratios p/p^*, T/T^*, and so on, as a function of local Mach number and the integrated friction effect.

Formulas for other flow properties along the duct can be derived from Eqs. 10.45(a) through 10.45(e). We can eliminate $f\,dx/D$ from each of the other relations, giving, for example, dp/p as a function only of M and $(dM^2)/M^2$. For convenience in tabulating the results, each expression is then integrated all the way from (p_0, M_0) to the sonic point $(p^*, 1.0)$. The integrated results are

$$\frac{p_0}{p^*} = \frac{1}{M_0}\left[\frac{k+1}{2+(k-1)M_0^2}\right]^{1/2} \tag{10.48a}$$

$$\frac{\rho_0}{\rho^*} = \frac{V^*}{V_0} = \frac{1}{M_0}\left[\frac{2+(k-1)M_0^2}{k+1}\right]^{1/2} \tag{10.48b}$$

$$\frac{T_0}{T^*} = \frac{a_0^2}{a^{*2}} = \frac{k+1}{2+(k-1)M_0^2} \tag{10.48c}$$

Example 10.9

Consider the steady flow of air in a pipe that is 5.0 cm in diameter. The inlet conditions are $p_{t1} = 150$ kPa, $T_{t1} = 500$ K, and $V_0 = 100$ m/s. If the friction factor is 0.02, (a) what is the duct length that produces sonic conditions in the nozzle exit plane, and (b) what is the mass flow rate if the duct is 15 m long?

Solution. To calculate the duct length required for sonic conditions in the exit plane, we must first calculate the Mach number at the inlet. To do this, we first calculate the static temperature at the inlet using the energy equation for adiabatic flow, Eq. (10.16):

$$T_0 = T_{t1} - \frac{U_0^2}{2c_p} = 500 - \frac{(100)^2}{2(1004.7)} = 495.02\text{ K}$$

Using Eq. (1.9) to calculate the speed of sound,

$$a_0 = 20.047\sqrt{T} = 446.03\text{ m/s}$$

Thus, $M_0 = 0.2242$. Using Eq. (10.47), we can calculate L^*:

$$L^* = \frac{D}{f}\left\{\frac{1-M_0^2}{kM_0^2} + \frac{k+1}{2k}\ln\left[\frac{(k+1)M_0^2}{2+(k-1)M_0^2}\right]\right\} = 27.70\text{ m}$$

Note that we are to calculate the mass flow rate in a pipe that is shorter than the sonic length. We will calculate the mass flow rate at the inlet of the pipe.

$$\rho_0 = \frac{\rho_0}{\rho_{t1}}\rho_{t1} = (0.9753)\frac{150{,}000\text{ N/m}^2}{(287.05\text{ N}\cdot\text{m/kg}\cdot\text{K})(500\text{ K})} = 1.0193\text{ kg/m}^3$$

and

$$A = \frac{\pi}{4}(0.05)^2 = 0.00196\text{ m}^2$$

Thus,

$$\dot{m} = \rho_0 U_0 A = (1.0193 \text{ kg/m}^3)(100 \text{ m/s})(0.00196 \text{ m}^2) = 0.200 \text{ kg/s}$$

Example 10.10

A rocket is launched from a tube. The static pressure in the nozzle exit plane is 5.0 atm (i.e., the nozzle is underexpanded). As a result, the exhaust gases expand further as they leave the nozzle. During the expansion process, the exhaust impinges on the wall generating

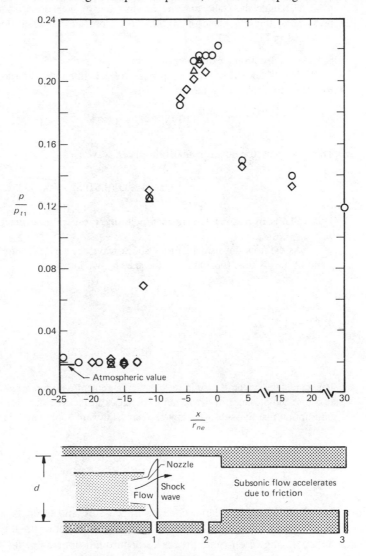

Figure 10.22 Sketch for Example 10.10.

a normal shock wave. As shown in Fig. 10.22, the downstream flow, which is subsonic, encounters a constrictive change in cross section and accelerates due to friction in the aft (small-diameter) tube. The aft tube is sufficiently long so that the flow in the exit plane is sonic.

In a scale model simulation, unheated air was exhausted through a convergent–divergent nozzle to produce the exhaust flow. Pressure data from the walls of the launch tube are presented in Fig. 10.22. To calculate pressures in the launch tube, we will assume that the flow expands isentropically to the area ratio given by $(d_{\text{tube}}/d^*)^2$, which is equal to 5.22. Calculate the static pressure downstream of the normal shock wave and the static pressure in the exit plane of the aft tube. Compare the calculated values with the data presented in Fig. 10.22.

Solution.   Isentropic expansion of air to an area ratio of 5.22 produces a Mach number of 3.22. Thus, the Mach number upstream of the impingement shock wave (M_1) is 3.22. Referring to Tables 10.1 and 10.2,

$$\frac{p_1}{p_{t1}} = 0.0196, \quad \frac{p_2}{p_1} = 11.93, \quad \frac{p_{t2}}{p_{t1}} = 0.272$$

The static pressure downstream of the shock wave is

$$\frac{p_2}{p_{t1}} = \frac{p_2}{p_1}\frac{p_1}{p_{t1}} = (11.93)(0.0196) = 0.2338$$

This value is in reasonable agreement with the pressure measurements from those orifices near $x \simeq -5r_{\text{ne}}$.

As the flow downstream of the shock wave accelerates to sonic conditions in the exit plane of the aft tube (position 3 in the sketch), we know

$$p_3 = 0.52828 p_{t2}$$

Thus,

$$\frac{p_3}{p_{t1}} = \frac{p_3}{p_{t2}}\frac{p_{t2}}{p_{t1}} = (0.52828)(0.272) = 0.144$$

This calculated value is also in reasonable agreement with the pressure measurements. Note also that the pressure in the aft tube decreases in the streamwise direction, supporting the assumption that the subsonic flow accelerates toward sonic conditions.

SUMMARY

For many flows, there are large changes in pressure and temperature and, therefore, in density. For these compressible flows, the large variations in the flow properties can occur either through isentropic processes or through nonisentropic processes. For supersonic flows, sudden increases in pressure or abrupt changes in the flow direction are accomplished by shock waves.

PROBLEMS

10.1. Consider a process that occurs between two states, such that the static pressure at station 2 is one-half that at station 1, and the temperature at station 2 is $0.75T_1$. What is the change in entropy from station 1 to station 2 if the gas is perfect helium? If the system is isolated from all heat exchange from its surroundings, does the flow go from 1 to 2 or from 2 to 1?

10.2. Consider the flow of methane in a duct. The process is such that the static pressure at station 2 is $0.5p_1$ and the static temperature at station 2 is equal to that at station 1. What is the corresponding change in entropy?

10.3. Air flows through the insulated variable-area streamtube such that it may be considered one-dimensional and steady. At one end of the streamtube, $A_1 = 5.0$ ft^2 and $M_1 = 3.0$. At the other end of the streamtube, $p_{t2} = 2116$ psfa, $p_2 = 2101$ psfa, $T_{t2} = 500°$R, and $A_2 = 5.0$ ft^2. What is the flow direction; that is, is the flow from 1 to 2 or from 2 to 1?

10.4. Consider the steady flow of perfect air in a duct that is isolated from all heat exchange with its surroundings. The static pressure and the static temperature at station 1 are 100 kPa and 300 K, respectively. At station 2, the corresponding values are 450 kPa and 503.55 K. Does the flow go from 1 to 2 or from 2 to 1?

10.5. Consider the steady, isentropic flow of perfect air in a duct. At station 1, the pressure and temperature are 500 psia and 1230°R, respectively. If the air expands to a pressure (p_2) of 0.05 psia, what is the static temperature (T_2)? What is the density at the second station?

10.6. Nitrogen is stored in a tank where the pressure is 10^6 N/m^2 and the temperature is 30°C. If the nitrogen expands isentropically, what are the pressure and density at a point where the temperature is 0°C?

10.7. Consider the flow of perfect air in a divergent channel. If the flow process is steady and isentropic, what is the expression for $\partial p/\partial \rho$ for this process? What is the speed of sound at a point where the pressure is 100 kPa and the temperature is 250°C?

10.8. Perfect helium flows in a convergent channel. If the flow process is steady and isentropic, what is the expression for $\partial p/\partial \rho$ for this process? What is the speed of sound at a point where the pressure is 100 psia and the temperature is 540°R?

10.9. Consider the flow of perfect air in a divergent channel. If the flow process is steady and constant temperature (but not isentropic), what is the expression for $\partial p/\partial \rho$ for this process? What is the speed of sound at a point where the pressure is 150 psia and the temperature is 600°R?

10.10 A source that travels in a straight, horizontal line at 200 m/s generates an infinitesimal disturbance. If the free-stream conditions are those of the atmosphere at standard sea-level conditions, make a sketch of the source location and the wave front at 1-s intervals from $t = 0$ to 5 s.

10.11. A thin piece of tape is placed on the surface of a plate in a stream where the Mach number is 2. An infinitesimal disturbance is produced by the tape. Sketch the portion of the flow field that is unaffected by the presence of the tape.

10.12. Air moves through the standard sea-level atmosphere at 100 m/s. What are the stagnation pressure and stagnation temperature if the air is brought to rest isentropically? What is the stagnation pressure that we would calculate using Bernoulli's equation (i.e., if changes in density are neglected)?

10.13. A space shuttle enters the earth's atmosphere at a speed of 7600 m/s at an altitude of 75 km. The free-stream temperature at this altitude is 200.15 K. What is the total enthalpy of the air at the stagnation point? What would be the stagnation temperature using the perfect gas relations? Note that the stagnation enthalpy as calculated will be correct, but the actual stagnation temperature is much lower. The difference is due to "real-gas" effects.

10.14. The maximum allowable skin temperature of a missile system that you are to design is 370°F. If the missile is to operate at 39,370 ft, what is the maximum Mach number at which the missile can operate? Use the perfect-gas relations for air (a reasonable assumption at these conditions) and the (relatively crude) approximation that the stagnation temperature is the maximum temperature of the skin.

10.15. Consider the steady flow of air from a reservoir where the air is at standard atmospheric conditions to a location in a convergent duct where the local static pressure is 2057.8 psfa. What is the local velocity if we use the isentropic flow relations? What is the local velocity if we use Bernoulli's equation?

10.16. Repeat Prob. 10.15 for a point in the duct where the local pressure is 82.495 kPa.

10.17. Helium is stored in a tank where the pressure is 300 kPa and the temperature is 20°C. What is the mass flow rate through a 0.5-cm-diameter hole in the tank into a room where the air is at standard atmospheric conditions? Use the relations for steady, isentropic flow through a convergent-only duct.

10.18. Derive the equation for the choked mass flow rate of air through a convergent-only nozzle, as used in Prob. 3.36.

10.19. Air flows steadily through a convergent-only nozzle. The pressure and temperature in the stagnation chamber are 25 psia and 120°F, respectively. The nozzle exhausts into a room where the pressure is 15 psia and the temperature is 80°F. What is the mass flow rate through the nozzle if the cross section of the nozzle exit plane is 1.0 ft by 1.4 ft?

10.20. What is the maximum mass flow rate for steady, isentropic flow of methane through a nozzle if the pressure and temperature in the reservoir are 250 kPa and 35°C and the throat diameter is 1 cm?

10.21. Consider the inlet duct of a jet engine as a convergent nozzle. The inlet is 0.7 m by 0.4 m. If the airplane is flying at $M_\infty = 1.6$ at an altitude of 12 km, what is the static temperature and the mass flow rate at the throat? Assume that the flow decelerates isentropically to sonic conditions at the throat.

10.22. Consider the steady, isentropic flow of air through a convergent–divergent nozzle. The conditions in the stagnation chamber are $p_{t1} = 100$ psia and $T_t = 200$°F. The cross-sectional area of the test section is $2.6367A^*$. What are the static pressure, the Mach number, and the unit Reynolds number in the test section for the first critical pressure ratio? for the third critical pressure ratio?

10.23. Consider the steady, isentropic flow of air through a convergent–divergent nozzle. The conditions in the stagnation chamber are $p_{t1} = 7.0 \times 10^5$ N/m² and 25°C. The cross-sectional area of the test section is $1.6875A^*$. What are the static pressure, the Mach number, and the unit Reynolds number in the test section for the first critical pressure ratio? for the third critical pressure ratio?

10.24. Helium accelerates through a convergent–divergent nozzle until its velocity is twice the speed of sound. What is the required area ratio for this flow?

10.25. Carbon dioxide accelerates through a convergent–divergent nozzle until its velocity is twice the speed of sound. What is the required area ratio for this flow?

10.26. Repeat Prob. 10.23 using nitrogen as the test gas.

10.27. Consider the steady, isentropic expansion of air from a stagnation chamber where the pressure is 3.5×10^6 N/m^2 and the temperature is 690 K. If the test section Mach number is 8, what is the static pressure and static temperature in the test section?

10.28. A perfect gas (not air) expands isentropically through a supersonic nozzle with an exit area that is five times its throat area. The Mach number in the exit plane is 3.8. What is the specific-heat ratio of the gas? What might this gas be? If $p_{t1} = 200$ kPa, what is the static pressure in the nozzle exit plane?

10.29. The conditions in the stagnation chamber of a small rocket are a pressure of 2500 psia and a temperature of 5000°R. The gas constant (R) is 65 ft · lbf/lbm · °R and k is 1.2. If the area ratio (A_{ne}/A^*) is 6.74, what are the pressure, temperature, and velocity in the nozzle exit plane? If the nozzle exit is 2.5 in. in diameter, what is the thrust in the sea-level atmosphere?

10.30. Consider the steady flow of air through a convergent–divergent nozzle. The conditions in the stagnation chamber are $p_{t1} = 100$ psia and $T_t = 200°$F. The cross-sectional area of the test section is $2.6367A^*$. What are the static pressure, stagnation pressure, and Mach number downstream of the normal shock wave in the test section at the second critical ratio? The flow is isentropic upstream of the shock wave.

10.31. Consider the steady flow of air through a convergent–divergent nozzle. The conditions in the stagnation chamber are $p_{t1} = 100$ psia and $T_t = 200°$F. The cross-sectional area of the test section is $2.6367A^*$. The static pressure in the test section is 65 psia. What are the Mach number, stagnation temperature, and stagnation pressure in the test section? Assume that the flow on either side of the shock wave is isentropic.

10.32. Consider the steady, isentropic flow of air through a convergent–divergent nozzle. The conditions in the stagnation chamber are $p_{t1} = 7.0 \times 10^5$ N/m^2 and 25°C. The cross-sectional area of the test section is $1.6875A^*$. What are the static pressure, stagnation pressure, and Mach number downstream of the normal shock wave in the test section at the second critical ratio? The flow is isentropic upstream of the shock wave.

10.33. An explosion generates a shock wave that moves through the atmosphere at 4000 m/s. The atmospheric conditions ahead of the shock wave are those of the standard sea-level atmosphere. What are the static pressure, static temperature, and velocity of the air behind the shock wave?

10.34. An explosion generates a shock wave that moves through the atmosphere at 10,000 ft/s. The atmospheric conditions ahead of the shock wave are those of the standard sea-level atmosphere. What are the static pressure, static temperature, and velocity of the air behind the shock wave?

10.35. Consider the airfoil of an airplane flying at $M_\infty = 0.85$ at an altitude of 12 km. A normal shock wave occurs near the midchord of the wing, as shown in Fig. P10.35. The flow is isentropic upstream of the shock wave, and the Mach number just ahead of the shock wave is 1.15. What is the Mach number and static pressure just downstream of the shock wave?

10.36. For the airfoil of Prob. 10.35, a spoiler is deployed at a point near the trailing edge of the wing. If the deployment of the spoiler does not change the location or strength of the shock wave, what changes would you expect in the flow at point A?

10.37. A space shuttle model is exposed to a Mach 8 stream of perfect air in a wind tunnel. The free-stream conditions are $p_1 = 350$ Pa and $T_1 = 50$ K. What are the static pressure, static temperature, density, stagnation pressure, and stagnation temperature downstream of the normal portion of the bow shock wave?

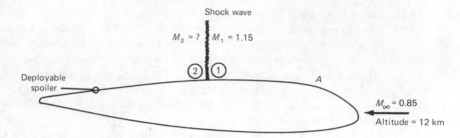

Figure P10.35 Sketch for Probs. 10.35 and 10.36.

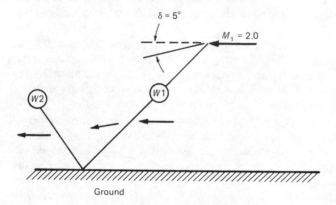

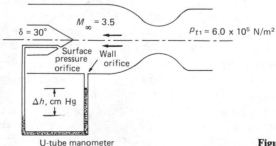

Figure P10.39 Sketch for Prob. 10.39.

10.38. During reentry, a space shuttle is flying at a speed of 7600 m/s at an altitude of 75 km. The temperature and pressure of the atmosphere at this altitude are 200.15 K and 2.49 N/m², respectively. To approximate the real-gas effects, a value of k equal to 1.12 can be used in the normal shock equations. Using this value of k, what are the static pressure and static temperature downstream of the normal portion of the bow shock wave?

10.39. The wing of an airplane flying at Mach 2 is represented by a flat plate inclined to the free stream by 5°. Let us neglect the effects of altitude and distance on the shock wave and assume that it strikes the ground and is reflected, as shown in Fig. P10.39. What is the pressure downstream of the reflected shock wave?

10.40. You are to measure the surface pressure on simple models in a supersonic wind tunnel (refer to Fig. P10.40). To evaluate the experimental accuracy, it is necessary to obtain

Figure P10.40 Sketch for Prob. 10.40.

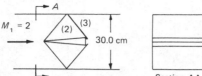

Section AA   **Figure P10.41**   Sketch for Prob. 10.41.

theoretical pressures for comparison with the data. If a 30° wedge is to be placed in a Mach 3.5 stream, calculate the following:

(a) The surface pressure in N/m^2.
(b) The pressure difference (in cm Hg) between the columns of mercury in a U-tube manometer between the pressure experienced by the surface orifice and the wall orifice (which is used to measure the static pressure in the test section).
(c) The dynamic pressure of the free-stream flow.

Other measurements are the pressure in the reservoir is 6.0×10^5 N/m^2 and the barometric pressure is 75.2 cm Hg.

10.41. The single-wedge airfoil shown in Fig. P10.41 is located on the centerline of the test section of a Mach 2.0 wind tunnel. The airfoil, which has a half-angle δ of 5°, is at zero angle of attack. When the weak, oblique shock wave generated at the leading edge of the airfoil encounters the wall, it is reflected so that the flow in region 3 is parallel to the tunnel wall. If the test section is 30.0 cm high, what is the maximum chord length (c) of the airfoil so that it is not struck by the reflected shock wave? Neglect the effects of shock-wave/boundary-layer interactions at the wall.

10.42. Air enters a pipe that is 1.0 in. in diameter and 40 ft long. The inlet conditions are $V_1 = 240$ ft/s, $p_1 = 80$ psia, and $T_1 = 600°R$. If the flow is steady and adiabatic and the friction factor is 0.022, what are V_2, p_2, and T_2 at the end of the duct? How much additional length of pipe would cause the exit flow to be sonic?

10.43. Air in a tank at $p_{t1} \doteq 100$ psia and $T_t = 520°R$ flows through a converging nozzle into a pipe that is 1.0 in. in diameter. What will be the mass flow rate through the pipe if its length is (a) 0 ft, (b) 1 ft, and (c) 10 ft? Assume $\bar{f} = 0.025$. The pressure outside the duct is negligibly small.

10.44. Air enters a square duct that is 5 cm by 5 cm at $V_1 = 900$ m/s and $T_1 = 300$ K. The friction factor is 0.018. For what duct length will the Mach number in the exit plane be exactly sonic?

REFERENCES

10.1. Staff, "Equations, Tables, and Charts for Compressible Flow," Report 1135, NACA, 1953, Ames Research Center.

10.2. W. E. Moeckel and K. C. Weston, "Composition and Thermodynamic Properties of Air in Chemical Equilibrium," TN 4265, NACA, Apr. 1958, Lewis Research Center.

10.3. D. W. Barnette and J. J. Bertin, "The Effect of Massive Blow-By on the Initial Trajectory of a Free-Flight Rocket," Aerospace Engineering Report 77003, University of Texas at Austin, May 1977.

CHAPTER ELEVEN

Computational Fluid Dynamics

In the previous chapters, the equations defining fluid motion for a wide variety of applications were developed and discussed. For many applications, relatively simple equations can be used to obtain engineering values of the design parameters. For other applications, charts and tables incorporating empirical information can be used to generate the desired values. For still other applications, experiments are conducted to measure the desired parameters using small-scale models in simulated flow fields or using full-scale models in the actual design environment. All these techniques have a valid role in engineering technology. However, because of rapid advances in computer hardware capability and software procedures, evermore use is made of computer solutions to the flow fields of interest.

Computational fluid dynamics (CFD) is certainly not pure theoretical analysis. CFD changes the fundamental nature of the analysis from calculus to arithmetic and from the continuum domain to the discrete domain so that it can be solved using a computer. The existing mathematical theory for numerical solutions of nonlinear partial differential equations is continuously being improved. In computational fluid dynamics, it is necessary to rely heavily on the mathematical analysis of simpler, linearized, formulations, and on heuristic reasoning, physical intuition, wind-tunnel experience, and trial-and-error procedures.

Solutions to the equations for a steady, incompressible, laminar boundary layer were discussed in Chapter 7. Using a coordinate transformation, the original nonlinear, partial differential equations were transformed into nonlinear, ordinary differential equations. Numerical solutions were obtained using the Runge–Kutta method for the resultant two-point boundary-value problem and the results presented in that chapter.

Although there are a variety of computational procedures and formulations, many of which are peculiar to the characteristics of the flow field for the problem of interest, in this chapter we will concentrate on the finite-difference formulation, which can be applied to a very wide range of fluid dynamic applications.

FINITE-DIFFERENCE FORMULATIONS

We seek to represent the derivatives that appear in the differential equations of motion using a finite-difference formulation. Consider the general function f, which represents a parameter that is a function of two spatial coordinates (x, y) and time (t), that is $f(x, y, t)$. The spatial coordinates are defined by a rectangular mesh, as shown in Fig. 11.1. We will use the subscript indexes i and j to represent the x and y coordinates, respectively, and the superscript index n to designate time. The mesh spacings in the x and y directions are Δx and Δy, respectively. These incremental displacements will be assumed constant throughout the flow field for the present discussion. However, advanced techniques employ variable-sized meshes that are tailored to the problem. Thus, for the two points identified in Fig. 11.1,

$$f_{i,j}^n \quad \text{represents} \quad f(x, y, t)$$

and

$$f_{i-1,j}^{n+1} \quad \text{represents} \quad f(x - \Delta x, y, t + \Delta t)$$

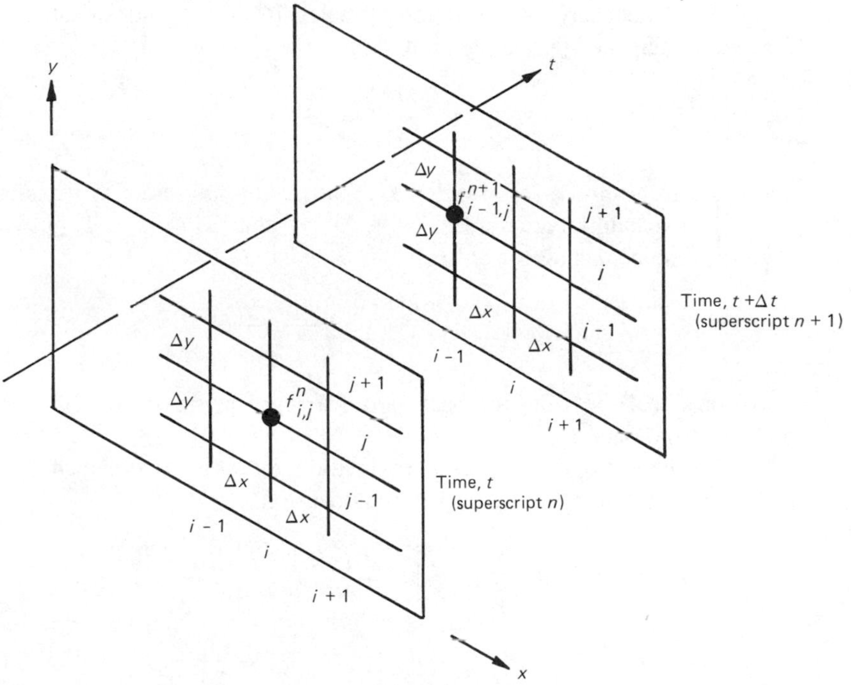

Figure 11.1 Nomenclature for space–time index.

Let us assume the function f and its derivatives are continuous. The basic finite-difference forms for the partial derivatives can be derived from Taylor-series expansions. We will first develop the spatial derivatives. For simplicity, we will omit the superscript n for the temporal variation. The Taylor series for $f_{i+1,j}$ expanded about the point (i, j) is

$$f_{i+1,j} = f_{i,j} + \left.\frac{\partial f}{\partial x}\right|_{i,j} (x_{i+1,j} - x_{i,j}) + \frac{1}{2}\left.\frac{\partial^2 f}{\partial x^2}\right|_{i,j} (x_{i+1,j} - x_{i,j})^2 + \cdots$$

$$= f_{i,j} + \left.\frac{\partial f}{\partial x}\right|_{i,j} \Delta x + \frac{1}{2}\left.\frac{\partial^2 f}{\partial x^2}\right|_{i,j} \Delta x^2 + \text{HOT} \tag{11.1}$$

where HOT is an abbreviation for higher-order terms.

Solving for $\partial f/\partial x$ gives

$$\left.\frac{\partial f}{\partial x}\right|_{i,j} = \frac{f_{i+1,j} - f_{i,j}}{\Delta x} - \frac{1}{2}\left.\frac{\partial^2 f}{\partial x^2}\right|_{i,j} \Delta x + \text{HOT}$$

$$= \frac{f_{i+1,j} - f_{i,j}}{\Delta x} + 0\,(\Delta x) \tag{11.2}$$

where $0\,(\Delta x)$ is read "terms of order Δx" and refers to additional terms with factors of Δx, Δx^2, Δx^3, and so on.

We denote any finite-difference analog of $\partial f/\partial x$ by the notation $\delta f/\delta x$. Then the forward difference approximation $\delta f/\delta x$ is

$$\left.\frac{\delta f}{\delta x}\right|_{i,j} = \frac{f_{i+1,j} - f_{i,j}}{\Delta x} \tag{11.3}$$

and has a truncation error of order Δx, that is, is a first-order approximation.

By expanding backward to $(x - \Delta x, y)$, that is, to $(i - 1, j)$, we obtain another finite-difference analog for $\delta f/\delta x$:

$$\left.\frac{\delta f}{\delta x}\right|_{i,j} = \frac{f_{i,j} - f_{i-1,j}}{\Delta x} \tag{11.4}$$

Equation (11.4) provides the backward difference approximation, which is also a first-order approximation.

The centered difference approximation for $\delta f/\delta x$ is obtained by subtracting the backward expansion from the forward expansion.

$$f_{i+1,j} = f_{i,j} + \left.\frac{\partial f}{\partial x}\right|_{i,j} \Delta x + \frac{1}{2}\left.\frac{\partial^2 f}{\partial x^2}\right|_{i,j} \Delta x^2 + \frac{1}{6}\left.\frac{\partial^3 f}{\partial x^3}\right|_{i,j} \Delta x^3$$

$$+ \frac{1}{24}\left.\frac{\partial^4 f}{\partial x^4}\right|_{i,j} \Delta x^4 + 0\,(\Delta x^5) \tag{11.5}$$

$$f_{i-1,j} = f_{i,j} - \left.\frac{\partial f}{\partial x}\right|_{i,j} \Delta x + \frac{1}{2}\left.\frac{\partial^2 f}{\partial x^2}\right|_{i,j} \Delta x^2 - \frac{1}{6}\left.\frac{\partial^3 f}{\partial x^3}\right|_{i,j} \Delta x^3$$

$$+ \frac{1}{24}\left.\frac{\partial^4 f}{\partial x^4}\right|_{i,j} \Delta x^4 + 0\,(\Delta x^5) \qquad (11.6)$$

Subtracting Eq. (11.6) from (11.5) gives

$$f_{i+1,j} - f_{i-1,j} = 2\left.\frac{\partial f}{\partial x}\right|_{i,j} \Delta x + \frac{1}{3}\left.\frac{\partial^3 f}{\partial x^3}\right|_{i,j} \Delta x^3 + \text{HOT}$$

Solving for $\partial f/\partial x$ gives

$$\left.\frac{\partial f}{\partial x}\right|_{i,j} = \frac{f_{i+1,j} - f_{i-1,j}}{2\,\Delta x} - \frac{1}{6}\left.\frac{\partial^3 f}{\partial x^3}\right|_{i,j} \Delta x^2 + \text{HOT}$$

$$= \frac{f_{i+1,j} - f_{i-1,j}}{2\,\Delta x} + 0\,(\Delta x^2) \qquad (11.7)$$

Thus, the centered difference form of $\delta f/\delta x$ is

$$\left.\frac{\delta f}{\delta x}\right|_{i,j} = \frac{f_{i+1,j} - f_{i-1,j}}{2\,\Delta x} \qquad (11.8)$$

From Eq. (11.7), we see that the centered difference expression for the derivative is a second-order approximation, that is, has a truncation error of order $(\Delta x)^2$.

Analogous expressions follow immediately for y and t derivatives. For example, the centered difference analog of $\partial f/\partial t$ is

$$\left.\frac{\delta f}{\delta t}\right|_{i,j}^{n} = \frac{f_{i,j}^{n+1} - f_{i,j}^{n-1}}{2\,\Delta t} \qquad (11.9)$$

We derive a centered difference analog of $\partial^2 f/\partial x^2$ by adding the expansions (11.5) and (11.6).

$$f_{i+1,j} + f_{i-1,j} = 2f_{i,j} + \left.\frac{\partial^2 f}{\partial x^2}\right|_{i,j} \Delta x^2 + \frac{1}{12}\left.\frac{\partial^4 f}{\partial x^4}\right|_{i,j} \Delta x^4 + \text{HOT} \qquad (11.10)$$

Solving for $\partial^2 f/\partial x^2$ gives

$$\left.\frac{\partial^2 f}{\partial x^2}\right|_{i,j} = \frac{f_{i+1,j} - 2f_{i,j} + f_{i-1,j}}{\Delta x^2} + 0\,(\Delta x^2) \qquad (11.11)$$

The centered difference form of $\delta^2 f/\delta x^2$ is

$$\left.\frac{\delta^2 f}{\delta x^2}\right|_{i,j} = \frac{f_{i+1,j} - 2f_{i,j} + f_{i-1,j}}{\Delta x^2} \qquad (11.12)$$

which is a second-order approximation.

EXPLICIT AND IMPLICIT FORMULATIONS OF UNSTEADY FLOWS

Let us apply these differencing techniques to Stokes's first problem, the suddenly accelerated plane wall. For this problem, the plate and entire fluid are at rest prior to a certain time, $t = 0$. The plate is then impulsively started from rest and moves in its own plane with a constant velocity. Selecting the x axis as coinciding with the wall and the direction of U_0, we obtain the Navier–Stokes equation:

$$\frac{\partial u}{\partial t} = \nu \frac{\partial^2 u}{\partial y^2} \qquad (11.13)$$

as discussed in Ref. 11.1. The pressure is constant throughout the flow field. The boundary conditions are

$$t < 0: u = 0 \quad \text{for all } y \qquad (11.14a)$$

$$t \geqslant 0: u = U_\text{o} \quad \text{for } y = 0$$

$$u = 0 \quad \text{for } y \to \infty \qquad (11.14b)$$

A variety of finite-difference approximations can be applied to replace the differentials in Eq. (11.13). The interested reader is referred to the discussion in Chapter 8 of Richtmyer and Morton (Ref. 11.2). Basically, two classes of methods are used in describing the time-dependent velocity distribution in the fluid: (1) explicit methods and (2) implicit methods.

Explicit Methods

Let us consider the explicit formulation where we write the time derivative of the velocity of the ith node in the forward-difference form:

$$\frac{\partial u}{\partial t} = \frac{u_i^{n+1} - u_i^n}{\Delta t} + 0(\Delta t) \qquad (11.15a)$$

and where we evaluate the spatial derivative using the values of the velocity at the nth time step:

$$\nu \frac{\partial^2 u}{\partial y^2} = \nu \frac{u_{i+1}^n - 2u_i^n + u_{i-1}^n}{(\Delta y)^2} + 0(\Delta y^2) \qquad (11.15b)$$

Note that the spatial derivative is evaluated in terms of the velocities at the time when the flow field is known (i.e., n). Thus, Eq. (11.13) can be written

$$\frac{u_i^{n+1} - u_i^n}{\Delta t} = \nu \frac{u_{i+1}^n - 2u_i^n + u_{i-1}^n}{(\Delta y)^2} + 0 \, (\Delta t, \, \Delta y^2) \qquad (11.16)$$

A sketch of this formulation is presented in Fig. 11.2. The use of the i index for the y-coordinate should not confuse the reader, since there is no fixed convention between the index notation and the coordinates.

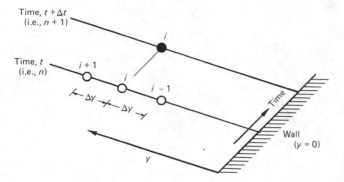

Time, $t + \Delta t$
(i.e., $n + 1$)

Time, t
(i.e., n)

$i + 1$

i

$i - 1$

Δy

Δy

Time

Wall
($y = 0$)

y

Figure 11.2 Nomenclature for explicit formulaton.

Using the explicit method, we can solve directly for the velocity at the ith node at the time $(t + \Delta t)$, that is, $(n + 1)$, as represented by the solid symbol in Fig. 11.2, since that is the only term in Eq. (11.16) that is not known.

$$u_i^{n+1} = u_i^n + \frac{\nu \, \Delta t}{(\Delta y)^2} \left[u_{i+1}^n - 2u_i^n + u_{i-1}^n \right] \tag{11.17}$$

As noted in Ref. 11.2, the method is numerically stable provided that

$$\frac{\nu \, \Delta t}{(\Delta y)^2} \leq 0.5 \tag{11.18}$$

If we take too large a time step for the mesh size, the solution procedure is unstable and oscillatory errors will grow as the solution proceeds. Furthermore, as indicated in Eq. (11.16), the accuracy of the method is $0(\Delta t)$ and $0[(\Delta y)^2]$.

Example 11.1

Let us use the explicit finite-difference representation to obtain solutions for Stokes's first problem. The plate and the entire fluid are at rest prior to a certain time, $t = 0$. The plate is then impulsively started from rest and moves in its own plane with a velocity of 10 m/s. The fluid is oil whose kinematic viscosity is 0.000217 m²/s. Using the explicit formulation described by Eq. (11.17), compute the velocity as a function of y and t for the following step sizes: $\Delta y = 0.001 \, m$ and $\Delta t = 0.010s$.

Solution. Let us first calculate the value of the stability parameter, the diffusion number (D)

$$D = \frac{\nu \, \Delta t}{(\Delta y)^2} = \frac{(0.000217)(0.010)}{(0.001)^2} = 2.17$$

Note that this value of the diffusion number exceeds the stability criterion stated in Eq. (11.18). Thus, we would expect the solution to be unstable with growing oscillatory errors.

A computer code has been written to generate a solution. We will use the nomenclature shown in Fig. 11.3. The $i = $ IMAX node is a point in the fluid "far" from the wall. The velocity at this point was assumed to be zero for all time. The wall is defined as the $i = 1$ node. The velocity $u_1^n = 10.0$ for all n zero or greater, that is, for all time t, since that is

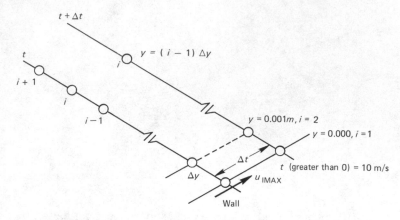

Figure 11.3 Nomenclature for the numerical solutions to Stokes's first problem of Examples 11.1 through 11.4.

a given boundary condition. Let us calculate the velocity field for the first two time steps.

Initial conditions: $t = 0$; $u_1^0 = 10.0$ m/s.

All other values of the velocity u are zero.

Flow after one time step:

$n = 1$; $t = 0.010s$; $u_1^1 = 10.0$ m/s.

Using Eq. (11.17) to calculate the velocity at the $i = 2$ node:

$$u_2^1 = u_2^0 + D(u_3^0 - 2u_2^0 + u_1^0)$$

$$u_2^1 = 0.0 + 2.17\,(0 - 0 + 10) = 21.7 \text{ m/s}$$

All other values of the velocity u are zero.

Flow after two time steps:

$$n = 2; t = 0.020s; u_1^2 = 10.0 \text{ m/s.}$$

$$u_2^2 = u_2^1 + D(u_3^1 - 2u_2^1 + u_1^1)$$

$$u_2^2 = 21.7 + 2.17\,[0 - 2(21.7) + 10] = -50.778 \text{ m/s}$$

$$u_3^2 = u_3^1 + D(u_4^1 - 2u_3^1 + u_2^1)$$

$$u_3^2 = 0.0 + 2.17\,(0 - 0 + 2.17) = 47.089 \text{ m/s}$$

All other values of the velocity u are zero.

These velocity distributions are presented graphically in Fig. 11.4. Note that except for the values at the wall, which are specified by the boundary condition, and those at points in the fluid not as yet affected by viscosity, the calculated velocities vary rapidly, changing sign with each time step. This oscillatory error growth characterizes a *dynamic instability*.

Computed solution:

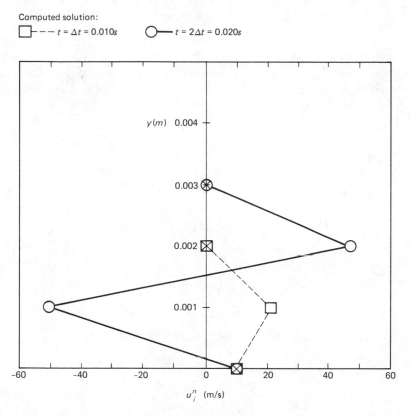

Figure 11.4 Explicit solutions for $D = 2.17$ (the boundary conditions are indicated by the symbol with the cross through them).

Additional values from the computer solution are presented in Table 11.1. It is obvious in this case that the numerical instability is entirely an analysis by-product and not related to a physical phenomenon. In more complex physical problems, however, it is not always obvious if "erratic" results are physical or numerical.

Example 11.2

Repeat Example 11.1 for the following step sizes: $\Delta y = 0.001m$, $\Delta t = 0.002s$.

Solution. Let us first calculate the diffusion number.

$$D = \frac{\nu \, \Delta t}{(\Delta y)^2} = \frac{(0.000217)(0.002)}{(0.001)^2} = 0.434$$

Note that this value is within the stability criterion stated in Eq. (11.18). Thus, we would expect the solution to be stable.

Using the established nomenclature, let us calculate the velocity distribution for the first two time steps.

TABLE 11.1   VALUES OF u(m/s)

		$t(s)$		
$y(m)$	0.000	0.010	0.020	0.030
0. (wall)	10.000	10.000	10.000	10.000
0.001	0.000	$+21.700$	-50.778	$+293.482$
0.002	0.000	0.000	$+47.089$	$-2670.$
0.003	0.000	0.000	0.000	$+102.183$
0.004	0.000	0.000	0.000	0.000
0.010	0.000	0.000	0.000	0.000
0.020	0.000	0.000	0.000	0.000

Initial conditions: $t = 0$; $n = 0$; $u_1^0 = 10.0$ m/s.

All other values of u are zero.

Flow after one time step:

$n = 1$; $t = 0.002s$; $u_1^1 = 10.0$ m/s.

$$u_2^1 = u_2^0 + D(u_3^0 - 2u_2^0 + u_1^0)$$

$$u_2^1 = 0.0 + 0.434 (0 - 0 + 10) = 4.340 \text{ m/s}$$

All other values of the velocity u are zero.

Flow after two time steps:

$n = 2$; $t = 0.004s$; $u_1^2 = 10.0$ m/s.

$$u_2^2 = u_2^1 + D(u_3^1 - 2u_2^1 + u_1^1)$$

$$u_2^2 = 4.34 + 0.434 (0 - 2(4.34) + 10) = 4.913 \text{ m/s}$$

$$u_3^2 = u_3^1 + D(u_4^1 - 2u_3^1 + u_2^1)$$

$$u_3^2 = 0.0 + 0.434(0 - 0 + 4.34) = 1.884 \text{ m/s}$$

Using these calculations and the output from the computer solution, we obtain Table 11.2. These results are presented graphically in Fig. 11.5.

TABLE 11.2   VALUES OF u(m/s)

			$t(s)$			
$y(m)$	0.000	0.002	0.004	0.008	0.240	0.480
0.0 (wall)	10.000	10.000	10.000	10.000	10.000	10.000
0.001	0.000	4.340	4.913	6.140	9.222	9.448
0.002	0.000	0.000	1.884	3.189	8.451	8.899
0.003	0.000	0.000	0.000	1.141	7.694	8.356
0.004	0.000	0.000	0.000	0.355	6.959	7.820
0.010	0.000	0.000	0.000	0.000	3.282	4.889
0.020	0.000	0.000	0.000	0.000	0.501	1.661
0.030	0.000	0.000	0.000	0.000	0.032	0.368

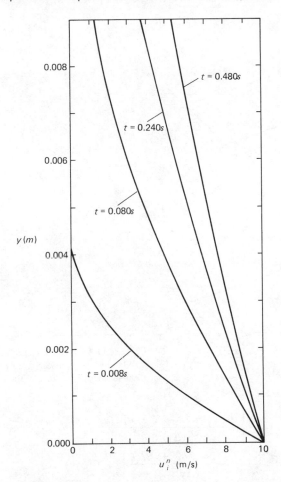

Figure 11.5 Explicit solutions for $D -$ 0.434.

Implicit Methods

For implicit methods, the gradient term is evaluated using the velocities at the end of the time step, e.g., at time $(t + \Delta t)$, or at some intermediate time $t + \Delta t/2$. The resulting expression for the second derivative at an interior node (the ith node) contains three unknown velocities: that at the ith node and those at the two adjacent nodes.

Consider the Crank–Nicolson formulation, which is illustrated in Fig. 11.6a. The time derivative of the velocity of the ith node as a centered difference about the point $n + \frac{1}{2}$ with a time increment of $\Delta t/2$ can be written

$$\left(\frac{\partial u}{\partial t}\right)_i^{n+1/2} = \frac{u_i^{n+1} - u_i^n}{2(\Delta t/2)} + 0(\Delta t^2) \tag{11.19a}$$

The centered spatial difference must also be written at time level $n + \frac{1}{2}$. This can be done by averaging the spatial difference expressions at time t and at time $t + \Delta t$. Thus,

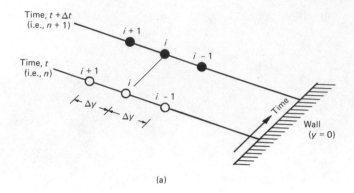

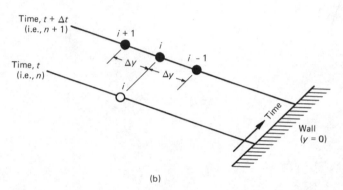

Figure 11.6 Nomenclature for implicit formulations: (a) Crank–Nicolson implicit formulation; (b) Laasonen implicit formulation.

$$\nu \left(\frac{\partial^2 u}{\partial y^2}\right)_i^{n+1/2} = \frac{\nu}{2}\left[\frac{u_{i+1}^{n+1} - 2u_i^{n+1} + u_{i-1}^{n+1}}{(\Delta y)^2}\right.$$

$$\left. + \frac{u_{i+1}^n - 2u_i^n + u_{i-1}^n}{(\Delta y)^2}\right] + 0(\Delta y^2) \qquad (11.19b)$$

Thus, Eq. (11.13) becomes:

$$\frac{u_i^{n+1} - u_i^n}{\Delta t} = \frac{\nu}{2}\left[\frac{u_{i+1}^{n+1} - 2u_i^{n+1} + u_{i-1}^{n+1}}{(\Delta y)^2}\right.$$

$$\left. + \frac{u_{i+1}^n - 2u_i^n + u_{i-1}^n}{(\Delta y)^2}\right] + 0(\Delta t^2, \Delta y^2) \qquad (11.20)$$

Note that in order to advance the solution from time level n to time level $n + 1$, there are three unknowns in this equation: u_{i+1}^{n+1}, u_i^{n+1}, and u_{i-1}^{n+1}, as indicated by the filled symbols of Fig. 11.6a. As stated in Ref. 11.2, the accuracy of the method is $0[(\Delta t)^2]$ and $0[(\Delta y)^2]$. Furthermore, the method is unconditionally stable. That is, regardless of the time- or space-step size, the solution will not diverge.

Consider next the implicit formulation of Laasonen, (Ref. 11.2) which is illustrated in Fig. 11.6b. The time derivative of the velocity of the ith node is written as a backward time difference:

$$\left(\frac{\partial u}{\partial t}\right)_i^{n+1} = \frac{u_i^{n+1} - u_i^n}{\Delta t} + 0(\Delta t) \tag{11.21a}$$

The spatial derivative is evaluated using the finite-difference expression at time $(t + \Delta t)$:

$$\nu \left(\frac{\partial^2 u}{\partial y^2}\right)_i^{n+1} = \nu \left[\frac{u_{i+1}^{n+1} - 2u_i^{n+1} + u_{i-1}^{n+1}}{(\Delta y)^2}\right] + 0(\Delta y^2) \tag{11.21b}$$

Thus, Eq. (11.13) becomes

$$\frac{u_i^{n+1} - u_i^n}{\Delta t} = \nu \left[\frac{u_{i+1}^{n+1} - 2u_i^{n+1} + u_{i-1}^{n+1}}{(\Delta y)^2}\right] + 0(\Delta t, \Delta y^2) \tag{11.22}$$

Note that there are again three unknowns in this equation: u_{i+1}^{n+1}, u_i^{n+1}, and u_{i-1}^{n+1}, as indicated by the filled symbols of Fig. 11.6b. As stated in Ref. 11.2, the accuracy of the method is $0[\Delta t]$ and $0[(\Delta y)^2]$. The method is always stable.

Rearranging the terms in Eq. (11.22), we obtain

$$u_{i-1}^{n+1} + \left[-2 - \frac{(\Delta y)^2}{\nu(\Delta t)}\right] u_i^{n+1} + u_{i+1}^{n+1} = \left[-\frac{(\Delta y)^2}{\nu(\Delta t)} u_i^n\right] \tag{11.23}$$

Thus, Eq. (11.22) can be written as a linear finite-difference equation of the general form

$$a_i^n u_{i-1}^{n+1} + b_i^n u_i^{n+1} + c_i^n u_{i+1}^{n+1} = d_i^n \tag{11.24}$$

The coefficients a, b, c, and d contain only constants or terms evaluated at the initial (or known) time step t. Comparing Eqs. (11.23) and (11.24), we see that

$$a_i^n = 1; \quad b_i^n = \left[-2 - \frac{(\Delta y)^2}{\nu(\Delta t)}\right]; \quad c_i^n = 1; \quad d_i^n = \left[-\frac{(\Delta y)^2}{\nu(\Delta t)} u_i^n\right] \tag{11.25}$$

Equation (11.20) can also be written as the general, linear finite-difference equation, Eq. (11.24). This equation leads to a tridiagonal system that can be easily solved by the technique of factorization (Gaussian elimination). Because of its implicit character, Eq. (11.24) is unconditionally stable.

A technique for inverting the tridiagonal system of equations represented by Eq. (11.24) is discussed in Ref. 11.2. Using the Gaussian elimination technique, we can calculate the velocity at the ith node if the velocity at the $(i + 1)$th node is known. Thus,

$$u_i^{n+1} = -h_i^n u_{i+1}^{n+1} + g_i^n \tag{11.26}$$

where

$$h_i^n = \frac{c_i^n}{b_i^n - a_i^n h_{i-1}^n} \tag{11.27}$$

and

$$g_i^n = \frac{d_i^n - a_i^n g_{i-1}^n}{b_i^n - a_i^n h_{i-1}^n} \tag{11.28}$$

Note that the solution procedure would involve first calculating g_i^n and h_i^n from node i = IMAX-1 (the next to last node) to the node $i = 2$. The expressions for a_i^n, b_i^n, c_i^n, and d_i^n are presented for the Laasonen formulation in Eq. (11.25). Similar expressions for the Crank–Nicolson formulation are given in Example 11.3. The values of g_{IMAX}^n and h_{IMAX}^n required to calculate $g_{\text{IMAX}-1}^n$ and $h_{\text{IMAX}-1}^n$ are obtained by applying the boundary condition for the velocity at i = IMAX, which for these numerical solutions represents a point far from the wall, and Eq. (11.26).

Having determined the values of g_i^n and of h_i^n from i = IMAX $-$ 1 to $i = 2$, we can calculate the values of u_i^{n+1} from $i = 2$ to i = IMAX using Eq. (11.26). This can be done, since we know u_1^{n+1} from the wall boundary condition.

Example 11.3

Use the Crank–Nicolson implicit finite-difference representation to obtain solutions to Stokes's first problem. The plate is impulsively started from rest at time $t = 0$ and moves in its plane with a velocity of 10 m/s. The fluid is oil whose kinematic viscosity is 0.000217 m²/s. Compute the velocity as a function of y and t for $\Delta y = 0.001m$, $\Delta t = 0.010s$.

Solution. The Crank–Nicolson finite-difference formulation is given by Eq. (11.20). In order to obtain a solution using Eqs. (11.26) through (11.28), we must first determine the relations for a_i^n, b_i^n, c_i^n, and d_i^n. Rearranging Eq. (11.20) into the general form of Eq. (11.24), it is clear that

$$a_i^n = 1.0 \tag{11.29a}$$

$$b_i^n = -2 - \frac{2}{D} \tag{11.29b}$$

$$c_i^n = 1.0 \tag{11.29c}$$

$$d_i^n = -u_{i+1}^n - u_i^n\left(\frac{2}{D} - 2\right) - u_{i-1}^n \tag{11.29d}$$

Note that for this problem the diffusion number is

$$D = \frac{\nu\,\Delta t}{(\Delta y)^2} = 2.17$$

This value exceeds the stability criterion for explicit solutions. Nevertheless, a stable solution can be obtained using the implicit formulation.

A computer code has been written to generate numerical solutions to this problem. The computed results are given in Table 11.3. Comparing the values at the first node away from the wall, i.e., $y = 0.001m$, we see that there seems to be an error at the early times (i.e., $t = 0.01s$ and $t = 0.02s$), which damps out. It has been shown (Ref. 11.3) that early-time solutions with this implicit method are indeed inaccurate for $D > 0.5$. This emphasizes the distinction between accuracy and stability. A necessary condition for accuracy is numerical stability. On the other hand, stability does not necessarily imply that a method is accurate.

Example 11.4

Repeat Example 11.3 for the following step sizes: $\Delta y = 0.001m$, $\Delta t = 0.002s$.

Solution. The diffusion number for this problem is 0.434. Thus, we have already obtained a solution to this problem using the explicit technique, i.e., Example 11.2. The computed results for the Crank–Nicolson implicit formulation are given in Table 11.4.

TABLE 11.3 VALUES OF u(m/s)

y(m)	t(s)					
	0.000	0.010	0.020	0.040	0.240	1.000
0.0 (wall)	10.000	10.000	10.000	10.000	10.000	10.000
0.001	0.000	7.918	6.853	7.990	9.219	9.616
0.002	0.000	3.135	5.427	6.451	8.446	9.234
0.003	0.000	1.241	3.223	4.709	7.688	8.853
0.004	0.000	0.491	1.701	3.374	6.951	8.474
0.010	0.000	0.002	0.016	0.170	3.272	6.301
0.020	0.000	0.000	0.000	0.000	0.503	3.316
0.030	0.000	0.000	0.000	0.000	0.014	1.286

The velocity fields computed for Examples 11.2, 11.3, and 11.4 at $t = 0.400$ s can be compared in these tables or in Fig. 11.7. The three solutions are in relatively good agreement with each other and with the exact (analytical) solution (ref. 11.1). Thus, one could conclude that the explicit technique provides a valid solution if we stay within the stability critierion. These four sample problems are intended to demonstrate some of the considerations of accuracy and stability that we must consider when using finite-difference representations. We should not extrapolate the results from these solutions for a relatively simple linear equation to significantly different problems. The choice of technique and of difference formulation may depend strongly on the problem to be solved.

LINEARIZATION OF THE NAVIER–STOKES EQUATIONS

Even for a steady, incompressible, two-dimensional laminar boundary layer, the Navier–Stokes equations are nonlinear, partial differential equations. For example, referring to Eq. (7.6), the x component of momentum is

$$\rho u \frac{\partial u}{\partial x} + \rho v \frac{\partial u}{\partial y} = \rho_e u_e \frac{du_e}{dx} + \mu \frac{\partial^2 u}{\partial y^2} \qquad (11.30)$$

Finite-difference approximations for the partial derivatives of the dependent variables are expressed as functions of their values at the streamwise coordinate $i + 1$, where the

TABLE 11.4 VALUES OF u(m/s)

y(m)	t(s)				
	0.000	0.008	0.040	0.240	0.480
0.0 (wall)	10.000	10.000	10.000	10.000	10.000
0.001	0.000	5.911	8.100	9.219	9.448
0.002	0.000	2.859	6.307	8.446	8.898
0.003	0.000	1.136	4.711	7.687	8.353
0.004	0.000	0.380	3.371	6.950	7.816
0.010	0.000	0.000	0.176	3.272	4.884
0.020	0.000	0.000	0.000	0.503	1.659
0.030	0.000	0.000	0.000	0.034	0.369

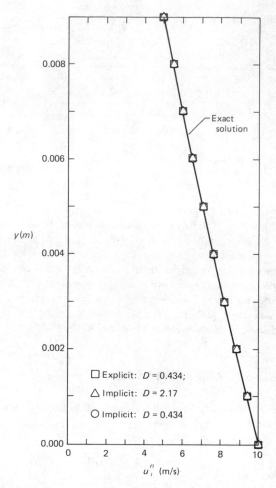

$y(m)$

$\square$ Explicit: $D = 0.434$;

$\triangle$ Implicit: $D = 2.17$

$\bigcirc$ Implicit: $D = 0.434$

u_i^n (m/s)

Figure 11.7 A comparison of the velocity distributions for Examples 11.2 through 11.4 at $t = 0.400$ s.

solutions are to be calculated, and at the upstream station i, where the flow field is already known. The nodal pattern for the finite-difference formulation is shown in Fig. 11.8.

The difference approximations for the partial derivatives involving products are defined so that the dependent variables at the $(i + 1)$ streamwise coordinate appear linearly in the resulting equation. A possible linearized finite-difference representation of Eq. (11.30) is

$$\rho u_{i,j} \frac{u_{i+1,j} - u_{i,j}}{\Delta x} + \rho v_{i,j} \frac{u_{i+1,j+1} - u_{i+1,j-1}}{2\,\Delta y}$$

$$= \rho_e u_e \frac{du_e}{dx} + \mu \frac{u_{i+1,j+1} - 2u_{i+1,j} + u_{i+1,j-1}}{(\Delta y)^2}$$

Note that the term $\rho_e u_e \, (du_e/dx)$ involves only parameters evaluated at the edge of the boundary layer, where the flow is known. Rearranging this equation, we obtain

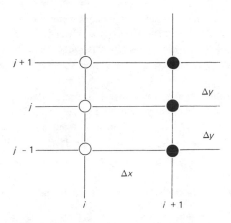

Figure 11.8 Nodal pattern for
Navier–Stokes formulation.

$$u_{i+1,j-1}\left[\frac{\mu}{(\Delta y)^2} + \frac{\rho v_{i,j}}{2(\Delta y)}\right] + u_{i+1,j}\left[-\frac{\rho u_{i,j}}{\Delta x} - \frac{2\mu}{(\Delta y)^2}\right]$$

$$+ u_{i+1,j+1}\left[\frac{\mu}{(\Delta y)^2} - \frac{\rho v_{i,j}}{2(\Delta y)}\right] = \left[-\frac{\rho(u_{i,j})^2}{\Delta x} - \rho_e u_e \frac{du_e}{dx}\right] \qquad (11.31)$$

This may be rewritten as

$$a_{i,j}u_{i+1,j-1} + b_{i,j}u_{i+1,j} + c_{i,j}u_{i+1,j+1} = d_{i,j} \qquad (11.32)$$

Note the similarity between Eqs. (11.32) and (11.24). Again, we have obtained a tri-diagonal system that can be readily solved by the techniques of factorization (i.e., Gaussian elimination).

SUMMARY

The purpose of this chapter is to introduce the reader to the nomenclature and principles of computational fluid dynamics. Examples were worked to demonstrate possible algorithms for representing the finite differences and different techniques for solving the equations. Solution procedures that work very well for one application may fail for another. For the interested reader, there is a rapidly expanding library of journals and texts discussing such problems.

PROBLEMS

11.1. Consider Stokes first problem with water as the bounding fluid medium. The kinematic viscosity of water is 1.078×10^{-5} ft²/s. If $\Delta y = 0.001$ in. and $\Delta t = 0.01s$, would you expect an explicit solution to be stable? The wall moves at a constant speed of 20 ft/s.

11.2. Using the explicit technique, calculate the velocity field for two times steps for the conditions of Prob. 11.1.

11.3. Again, prior to time $t = 0$, the wall and the adjacent water are at rest. After time $t = 0$, the wall moves at 30 ft/s. The kinematic viscosity of water is 1.078×10^{-5} ft²/s. If $\Delta y = 0.001$ ft and $\Delta t = 0.01 s$, would you expect an explicit solution to be stable?

11.4. Using the explicit technique, calculate the velocity field for two time steps for the conditions of Prob. 11.3.

11.5. Consider Stokes first problem for an oil whose kinematic viscosity is 1×10^{-5} m²/s. If you want information about the velocity field with a grid resolution (Δy) of 0.1 cm, what is the maximum time step you can take and still have a stable, explicit solution?

11.6. Repeat Prob. 11.5 for oil whose kinematic viscosity is 2×10^{-4} m²/s.

11.7. Show that, for the Crank–Nicolson implicit finite-difference representation, Eq. (11.29) are the appropriate expressions for a_i^n, b_i^n, c_i^n, and d_i^n.

11.8. Using the implicit Crank–Nicolson formulation, calculate the velocity field for two time steps for the conditions of Prob. 11.3.

11.9. Using a centered difference in time, so that one uses second-order expressions both for the space derivative and for the time derivative, we could write:

$$\frac{u_i^{n+1} - u_i^{n-1}}{2\Delta t} = \nu \frac{u_{i+1}^n - 2u_i^n + u_{i-1}^n}{\Delta y^2}$$

Since the velocities on the left-hand side are evaluated at $t + \Delta t$ and at $t - \Delta t$, whereas they are evaluated at t on the right-hand side, this is known as the *leap-frog* technique. This method is numerically unstable for all $\nu > 0$ and for all time steps $\Delta t > 0$. Using the leap-frog technique, calculate the velocity field for the first three time steps for the conditions of Prob. 11.3.

11.10. Let us replace the center node value of u_i^n in the diffusion term of the equation in Prob. 11.9 by its average value at times $(n - 1)$ and $(n + 1)$, i.e.,

$$u_i^n = 0.5(u_i^{n-1} + u_i^{n+1})$$

Thus,

$$\frac{u_i^{n+1} - u_i^{n-1}}{2\Delta t} = \nu \frac{u_{i+1}^n - u_i^{n+1} - u_i^{n-1} + u_{i-1}^n}{\Delta y^2}$$

Solve this expression to obtain the explicit expression for u_i^{n+1}. The result, which is known as the *DuFort Frankel leap-frog* method, is stable. Use the expression to calculate the velocity field for the first three time steps for the conditions of Prob. 11.3.

REFERENCES

11.1. H. Schlichting, *Boundary Layer Theory*, 7th ed., McGraw-Hill Book Company, New York, 1979.

11.2. R. D. Richtmyer and K. W. Morton, *Difference Methods for Initial Value Problems*, Wiley-Interscience, New York, 1967.

11.3. P. J. Roache, *Computational Fluid Dynamics*, Hermosa Publishers, Albuquerque, N.M., 1976.

CHAPTER TWELVE

Turbomachinery

Turbomachines are devices in which energy is either transferred to or from a continuously moving fluid by the dynamic action of one or more moving blade rows. For a turbomachine, the motion of an unconfined fluid is altered in such a way that a propulsive thrust is produced by the device. As the device moves, power is developed at the device by the fluid motion. For more complex turbomachines, such as turbojets and ramjets, the fluid is made to undergo certain processes that produce the flow patterns that give rise to a propulsive thrust. For these turbomachines, burning fuel supplies the requisite energy for maintaining the necessary flow. Turbomachines differ from reciprocating machines in that the fluid in a turbomachine is at no time trapped or confined by the device, whereas for reciprocating machines or positive-displacement machines (such as the diesel engine), the fluid is confined in cylinders during most of the process.

At this point, let us consider further those pumps and turbines that can be classified as turbomachines. Turbines extract useful work from the fluid energy. Pumps add energy to the fluids. These processes are accomplished by directing the fluid motion with vanes fixed rigidly to a shaft. The assembly of blades that is attached to the shaft of a turbine is often called a runner, while in pumps this assembly is called an impeller. Turbines are generally classified either as impulse turbines or as reaction turbines.

IMPULSE TURBINES

Impulse turbines are driven by one or more high-speed free jets of fluid, much like the simple device of Example 4.6. The fluid is accelerated as it flows through a nozzle, that is, undergoes a process in which the pressure decreases, to obtain the required kinetic energy. The impinging jet is turned by a vane (or bucket) producing a force to turn the

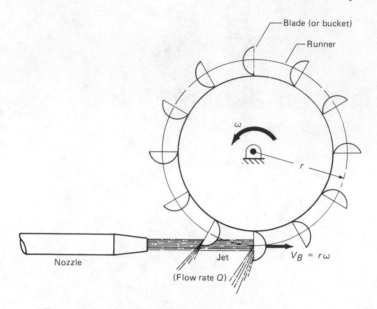

Figure 12.1 Impulse turbine, for example, a Pelton water wheel.

device. The Pelton water wheel, which is illustrated in Fig. 12.1, is an example of an impulse turbine wherein a single jet of water from a nozzle impinges on the system of buckets attached to a wheel. The runner is the assembly of buckets located at the periphery of the wheel at a distance r from the axis to the center of the buckets. The horizontal cross section of a bucket is shown in Fig. 12.2. Note that the jet is split into two parts by the bucket and is turned in a horizontal plane, with half discharged from each side to avoid unbalanced forces on the shaft. The flow is turned almost 180° from its original direction. If we neglect the effects of gravity and friction, the liquid undergoes no change in speed relative to the vane in the runner over which it moves. Atmospheric pressure

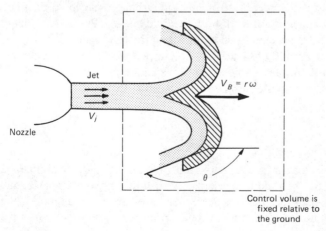

Control volume is
fixed relative to
the ground

Figure 12.2 Water jet impinging on the moving bucket of a Pelton water wheel.

surrounds both the jet issuing from the nozzle and the runner. Furthermore, the static pressure of the fluid as it leaves the runner is the same as that at entry. Hence, a fundamental characteristic of an impulse turbine is that the expansion (or acceleration of the flow) takes place in the nozzle and not on the vanes of the turbine.

Impulse-type turbines are of relatively low specific speed, suitable for the relatively high heads. Impulse turbines often employ a horizontal shaft.

REACTION TURBINES

For a radial-flow reaction turbine, such as shown in Fig. 12.3, the fluid enters at A and is directed by stationary blades (also called guide vanes or wicket gates) that are located outside the runner. The flow moves along the runner blades toward the central region B,

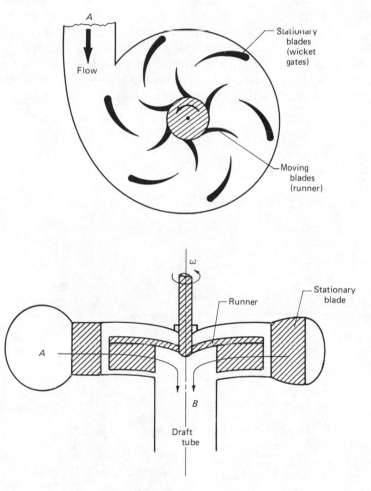

Figure 12.3   Reaction-type turbine.

where it is removed through the draft tube. In a reaction turbine, a portion of the fluid's energy is converted into kinetic energy as it flows through the wicket gates. Additional conversion takes place through the runner. Note that, since the velocity components of the flow passing through the impeller are in a plane perpendicular to the axis of the runner, the device is known as a radial-flow reaction turbine. For other types of reaction turbines, the impeller may produce an axial flow or a mixed flow.

It is a characteristic of a reaction turbine (whether it is radial-flow or axial-flow type) that all passages are filled with liquid and that the flow moves at all times through the entire runner. In contrast to the impulse turbines of previous examples, the pressure is reduced as the fluid flows through the runner. Thus, even if the effects of friction and gravity are neglected, the speed of the fluid relative to the runner vanes is not constant, as was the case for impulse turbines. Instead the speed will increase along the runner vanes. In effect, the impeller acts partly as a nozzle through which the fluid accelerates. The energy is converted to useful work by changing the moment of momentum.

Reaction turbines are often divided into one of two classes: the Francis reaction type, shown in Fig. 12.4, and the propellor reaction type. Both reaction types generally employ a vertical shaft, although small reaction turbines have horizontal shafts for accessibility of parts and ease of erection and repair. Vertical shaft installations are ordinarily more suitable (1) where the most efficient setting of the runner vanes is desired and (2)

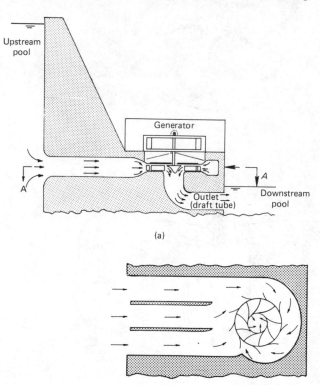

Figure 12.4 Reaction turbine, for example, a Francis-type runner: (a) elevation view; (b) plan view, section AA.

with direct-connected hydroelectric units where a large fluctuation of water levels requires the electric generator to be located above the extreme high-water level while avoiding an excessively long draft tube.

APPLICATION OF THE MOMENT OF MOMENTUM EQUATION TO IMPULSE TURBINES

In Example 4.6, we considered flow over a curved trough that was moving at a constant speed (V_0) relative to the ground. The trough of that example may be considered as an element of an impulse turbine.

Example 12.1

A jet of water issues from the nozzle at a speed V_j with a volumetric flow rate of Q, as shown in Fig. 12.1. If the runner is loaded by a generator so as to rotate at a constant angular speed of ω rad/s, what is the torque developed by the wheel due to the water flow?

Solution. Rigorously speaking, the flow is not steady, since the orientation of the bucket that is in contact with the jet of water changes continuously relative to the impinging jet. Furthermore, there may be differing numbers of buckets in varying degrees of contact with the jet at any instant of time. However, the variation in torque due to the unsteady nature of the flow is small. To compute the average torque, we shall assume that there is an "average" steady flow and that this steady flow corresponds to the instantaneous flow of a full jet when it impinges on a bucket in its lowermost position, that is, when the bucket is moving horizontally with a constant speed of $r\omega$. We can solve for the torque developed by this "steady" impingement process in either of two ways: (a) using the linear momentum equation as applied to the impinging jet or (b) applying the moment of momentum equation to the flow.

   (a) Solution using the linear momentum equation: To compute the average torque, let us apply the linear momentum equation to the bucket moving horizontally at a constant speed $r\omega$, as shown in Fig. 12.2. The control volume is fixed relative to the ground. Thus, the volumetric flow rate for the jet is Q and the velocity of the fluid entering the control volume is V_j. Since atmospheric pressure acts uniformly over the surface of the control volume, the force of the bucket on the fluid is

$$F_{BFX} = -\rho Q V_j - \rho Q V_{2x} \tag{12.1}$$

The negative sign for the V_{2x} term assumes that the resultant exit velocity relative to the ground is to the left, as shown in Fig. 12.2. To determine the exit velocity of the flow over the moving bucket relative to the ground, we will add the exit velocity of the water relative to the bucket and the velocity of the bucket relative to the ground. These velocities are shown in the sketch of Fig. 12.5. As was discussed in Example 4.6, the velocity of the impinging jet from a fixed nozzle relative to a moving vane is $V_j - r\omega$. In the absence of friction and gravity, the relative velocity is unchanged in magnitude. Thus, the exit velocity of the water relative to the bucket is $V_j - r\omega$, designated as (1) in Fig. 12.5. The x component of the resultant velocity of the water leaving the control volume relative to the ground (V_{2x}) is

$$V_{2x} = -(V_j - r\omega)\cos\theta - r\omega \tag{12.2}$$

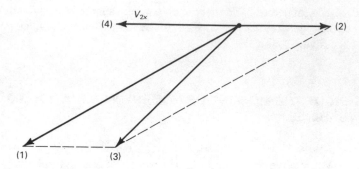

Figure 12.5   Velocity components for Example 12.1a: (1) velocity of the water relative to the bucket ($V_j - r\omega$); (2) velocity of the bucket relative to the ground ($r\omega$); (3) velocity of the fluid leaving the control volume relative to the ground; (4) x component of 3, given by Eq. (12.2).

As before, the sign convention is such that V_{2x} is to the left. Thus, for the obtuse angle θ of Fig. 12.5, $\cos \theta$ is negative. Substituting Eq. (12.2) into Eq. (12.1),

$$F_{BFx} = -\rho Q(V_j - r\omega) + \rho Q(V_j - r\omega) \cos \theta = \rho Q(V_j - r\omega)(\cos \theta - 1)$$

The force of the fluid on the bucket is the negative of this force:

$$F_{FBx} = \rho Q(V_j - r\omega)(1 - \cos \theta) \tag{12.3}$$

The average torque on the water wheel is r times this force:

$$\text{Torque} = \rho Q r(V_j - r\omega)(1 - \cos \theta) \tag{12.4}$$

and the power developed by the wheel is the product of the linear velocity ($r\omega$) times the force:

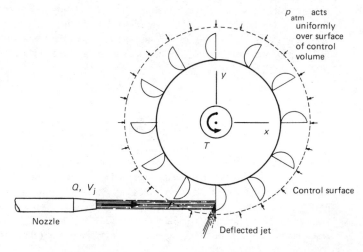

Figure 12.6   Control volume for Example 12.1b.

$$\text{Power} = \rho Q r \omega (V_j - r\omega)(1 - \cos \theta) \tag{12.5}$$

(b) Solution using the moment of momentum equation: We shall analyze this flow by applying the moment of momentum equation to a stationary control volume that completely encloses the water wheel, as shown in Fig. 12.6. For Eq. (4.46), we see that, since the shaft of the water wheel crosses the control volume, it transmits the torque generated by the buckets as they deflect the flow. We shall call this torque, T_{buckets}. For a balanced wheel, T_{body} is zero. Since the flow is "steady," Eq. (4.46) becomes

$$T_{\text{buckets}} = \oiint r V_\theta (\rho \vec{V} \cdot \vec{dA}) \tag{12.6}$$

For the fluid entering the control volume, the moment of momentum is

$$- r V_j \rho Q$$

The moment of momentum of the fluid leaving the control volume is

$$r \left[(V_j - r\omega) \cos \theta + r\omega \right] \rho Q$$

Combining these relations,

$$T_{\text{buckets}} = \rho Q r \left[(V_j - r\omega) \cos \theta - (V_j - r\omega) \right]$$

The torque developed by the buckets as they deflect the jet of water is the negative of the torque transmitted to the shaft through the wheel. Thus,

$$\text{Torque} = \rho Q r (V_j - r\omega)(1 - \cos \theta)$$

where the geometric convention assumes that $\cos \theta$ is negative. Note that this is identical to the equation obtained using the linear momentum formulation. However, there are many problems for which the moment of momentum approach provides a more suitable means of modeling the flow.

Example 12.2

A Pelton water wheel is to be used to drive a generator at 600 rpm. The volumetric flow rate and the initial velocity for the jet of water are 0.4 m³/s and 100 m/s, respectively. The ratio of the bucket (or vane) speed to the initial jet speed is 0.47. If the blade angle is 170°, (a) what is the diameter of the wheel to the centerline of the buckets, (b) what is the power developed, and (c) what is the kinetic energy per newton remaining in the fluid?

Solution.   The ratio of the vane speed to the initial jet speed is given as 0.47. Thus, for part (a)

$$\frac{r\omega}{V_j} = 0.47$$

$$r = 0.47 \, \frac{100 \text{ m/s}}{(600/60) \, 2\pi \text{ rad/s}} = 0.748 \text{ m}$$

Thus,

$$d = 1.496 \text{ m}$$

Using Eq. (12.5) for part (b), the power developed is

$$P = \rho Q r \omega (V_j - r\omega)(1 - \cos \theta)$$

$$= 1000 \text{ kg/m}^3 \ (0.4 \text{ m}^3/\text{s})(0.748 \text{ m})(20\pi \text{ rad/s})(53 \text{ m/s})(1.9848)$$

$$= 1.9775 \times 10^6 \text{ N} \cdot \text{m/s} = 1.9775 \times 10^6 \text{ W} = 1977.5 \text{ kW}$$

To determine the kinetic energy remaining in the jet for part (c), let us calculate the components of the absolute velocity of the water as it leaves the bucket. Using Eq. (12.2) to calculate V_{2x},

$$V_{2x} = -(V_j - r\omega) \cos \theta - r\omega = -53 \ (-0.9848) - 47 = +5.194 \text{ m/s}$$

Recall that the plus sign indicates that the flow is to the left. Similarly,

$$V_{2y} = (V_j - r\omega) \sin \theta = 9.203 \text{ m/s}$$

Thus, the kinetic energy per newton is

$$\text{k.e.} = \left(\frac{V_{2x}^2 + V_{2y}^2}{2} \right) \frac{1}{9.8066} = 5.694 \text{ N} \cdot \text{m/N}$$

In practical applications, Pelton wheels are employed where high heads (i.e., changes in elevation from the headwater to the tailwater of 200 m to more than 1 km) are available. Usually one jet is used, and it discharges horizontally against buckets located on the lower periphery of the wheel, as shown in Fig. 12.7. The speed of the wheel is regulated for the generation of electric power.

Example 12.3

Consider the impulse turbine shown in Fig. 12.7. The elevation of the free surface of the headwater is 1400 m; that of the nozzle is 1100 m. The effective resistance coefficient of the pipe, control valves, elbows, and the like, of the penstock is 0.0225. The pipe is 75 cm in diameter and 1.0 km long. The diameter of the jet is 15 cm in diameter. The water

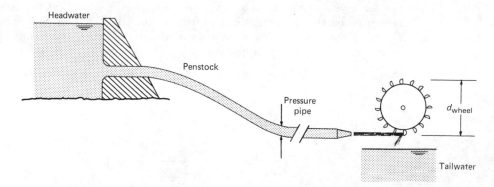

Figure 12.7   Impulse turbine system. Elevation change between headwater and tailwater is typically several hundred meters.

temperature is 10°C. If $V_{bucket} = r\omega = \frac{1}{2} V_j$, $\theta = 173°$, and the efficiency of the turbine is 85%, what is the power output in kilowatts?

Solution. Using Eqs. (6.1) and (6.2),

$$\frac{V_1^2}{2g} + z_1 + \frac{p_1}{\rho g} = \frac{V_j^2}{2g} + z_j + \frac{p_j}{2g} + h_f$$

where

$$h_f = \frac{V_2^2}{2g} \frac{L}{D} f$$

where 1 denotes conditions at the headwater, j at the jet, and 2 in the penstock pipe. By continuity,

$$V_2^2 = V_j^2 \left(\frac{A_j}{A_2}\right)^2 = V_j^2 \frac{D_j^4}{D_2^4} = 0.0016 V_j^2$$

Furthermore, $V_1 \approx 0$, $z_1 - z_j = 300$ m, and $p_1 = p_j = p_{atm}$. Thus,

$$V_j^2 = \frac{(z_1 - z_j)2g}{1 + 0.0016 \, (L/D)f} = \frac{(300)(2)(9.8066)}{1 + 0.0016(1333.3)(0.0225)}$$

$$V_j = 74.93 \text{ m/s}$$

Using Eq. (12.5) to calculate the power and noting that $r\omega = \frac{1}{2} V_j$,

$$P = \rho Q r\omega (V_j - r\omega)(1 - \cos \theta) = \rho Q \frac{V_j^2}{4} (1 - \cos \theta)$$

Using Table 1.3 to calculate the density of water at 10°C, $\sigma = 0.9993$. Thus, the gross power is

$$P = 999.3 \text{ kg/m}^3 \frac{1}{4} \left[\frac{\pi}{4} (0.15)^2 \text{ m}^2\right] [74.93 \text{ m/s}]^3 (1.9925)$$

$$P = 3701 \text{ kW}$$

The power output of the turbine is

$$\text{Output} = P \times \text{efficiency} = 3146 \text{ kW}$$

APPLICATION OF THE MOMENT OF MOMENTUM EQUATION TO REACTION TURBINES

Consider a system of fixed vanes that are arranged symmetrically around the periphery of a circle, as shown in Fig. 12.8. In this figure, the fluid approaches the cascade radially, similar to the flow approaching a two-dimensional sink. As the fluid moves through the fixed vanes, it is turned so that its moment of momentum is changed from zero to a value dependent upon the mass flow rate, the tangential component of velocity of the fluid

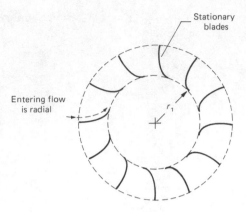

Figure 12.8 Stationary blades arranged symmetrically around the periphery of a circle.

leaving the guide vanes, and the radius. However, no work is done by this flow, since the vanes do not move.

Consider next a system containing not only the fixed vanes that are shown in Fig. 12.8 but also a series of vanes that are located within the fixed vane assembly and that are rotating at a speed ω, such as shown in Fig. 12.9. For efficient operation of the complete system, the fluid particles should move from the guide vanes onto the runner vanes with the least disturbance. That is, the flow should enter the runner with a direction tangent to the runner vanes. If the flow approaches the vane of the runner at too large an angle of attack, flow separation, or *shock,* occurs.

Thus, as shown in Fig. 12.10, the fluid enters the runner of a Francis-type turbine so that the relative velocity leaving the wicket gates is tangent to the leading edge of the vanes. The tangential component is gradually reduced as the fluid traverses the vane, so the flow is mostly radial with relatively little whirl (tangential component of velocity) remaining. The pressure decreases significantly during this flow process.

It should be apparent that the losses in a turbine will be greater if the flow approaches the vane of the runner at an angle of attack such that separation will occur. Thus, the vanes of an impeller designed for a given speed and flow rate will have a particular optimum blade angle, β_1. However, if the flow rate is changed from the nominal design conditions, the guide vanes and impeller vane angles will not "match" for the new flow

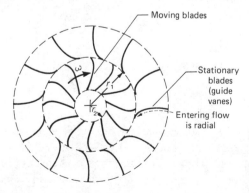

Figure 12.9 System of blades for a radial-flow rection turbine.

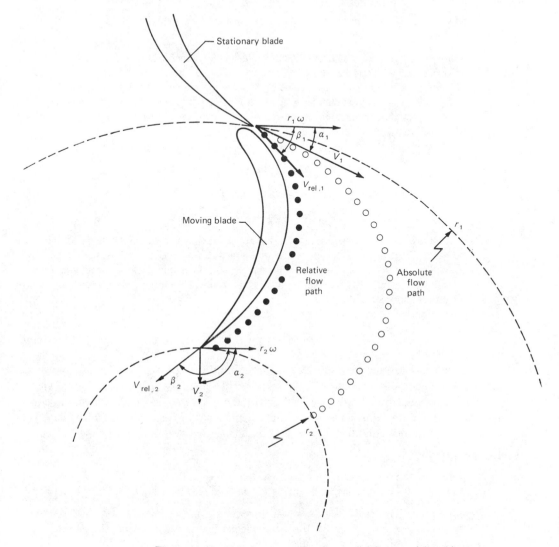

Figure 12.10 Velocity components for a radial-flow reaction turbine.

conditions. Most turbines used in hydroelectric installations are made with movable guide vanes to provide a better match at the inlet over a range of flow rates. Thus, α_1 is increased or decreased automatically to accommodate fluctuating power demands on the turbine.

Example 12.4

Fluid enters the runner of a radial impulse turbine at $r = r_1$ with a velocity of V_1 at an angle α_1 with respect to a tangent to the outer radius of the runner, as shown in Fig. 12.10. The fluid leaves the runner at $r = r_2$ with a velocity of V_2 at an angle of α_2. The density of the fluid is ρ; the volumetric flow rate is Q. Neglecting viscous effects and assuming that the flow is steady, one-dimensional, and incompressible, develop expressions for the torque and the power.

Solution. The guide vanes cause the fluid outside the runner to have a tangential component of velocity as it enters the runner. Thus, the fluid will have an initial amount of angular momentum with respect to the turbine as it enters the runner. The magnitude and direction of the velocity change continuously as the fluid flows through the passages of the runner. Thus, the angular momentum of the fluid is changed, producing a torque on the runner, which delivers power.

Applying Eq. (4.46) to the flow, the torque of the runner on the fluid is

$$T_{RFx} = -\rho Q r_1 V_1 \cos \alpha_1 + \rho Q r_2 V_2 \cos \alpha_2$$

The torque of the turbine is the negative of this. Thus,

$$T = \rho Q (r_1 V_1 \cos \alpha_1 - r_2 V_2 \cos \alpha_2) \tag{12.7}$$

It is interesting to note that, even though the pressure changes as the fluid goes through the runner, it does not enter into the expression that we have derived for the torque. The reason that it does not appear is because the pressure forces that act on the outer and inner control surfaces all pass through the axis of the runner. Therefore, the pressure forces do not produce moments about the given axis.

The power generated by the torque is ωT:

$$P = \rho Q \omega (r_1 V_1 \cos \alpha_1 - r_2 V_2 \cos \alpha_2) \tag{12.8}$$

Recall that turbines extract work from the fluid energy, whereas pumps, blowers, and turbo compressors add energy to the fluid. Since the only displacement of the vanes is in the tangential direction, work is done by the displacement of the tangential components of force on the runner. The radial components of force on the runner have no displacement in the radial direction and, thus, they do not work.

Example 12.5

Water flows through a reaction turbine, such that $r_1 = 5$ ft and $\omega = 100$ rpm. If the angle at the end of the stationary blade (α_1) is 20° and if β_1 is 60°, what is V_1 for matched flow?

Solution. Consider the velocities at the interface of the stationary blade and the moving blade, that is, $r = r_1$ of Fig. 12.10. Examining the detailed sketch of the relevant velocities, as shown in Fig. 12.11, we see that

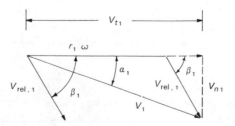

Figure 12.11 Velocities for Example 12.5.

$$V_{n1} = V_1 \sin \alpha_1 = V_{\text{rel},1} \sin \beta_1$$

and

$$V_{t1} = V_1 \cos \alpha_1 = r_1 \omega + V_{\text{rel},1} \cos \beta_1$$

Rearranging the terms in these two equations to eliminate $V_{\text{rel},1}$ and solving for V_1,

$$V_1 = \frac{r_1 \omega}{\cos \alpha_1 - \sin \alpha_1 \cot \beta_1} = \frac{5 \text{ ft} \times (200\pi)/60 \text{ rad/s}}{\cos(20) - \sin(20) \cot(60)} = 70.54 \text{ ft/s}$$

HEAD AND ENERGY RELATIONS FOR A PUMP

Assuming that the flow is steady, the pump increases the Bernoulli head of the flow between the inlet of the impeller at r_2 and the exit at r_1 (see Fig. 12.9). For incompressible flow, the net head is

$$H = \left(\frac{p_1}{\rho g} + \frac{V_1^2}{2g} + z_1 \right) - \left(\frac{p_2}{\rho g} + \frac{V_2^2}{2g} + z_2 \right) = h_s - h_f \qquad (12.9)$$

where h_s is the head supplied by the pump and h_f represents the losses.

The power delivered to the fluid equals the product of the specific weight, discharge, and net head change:

$$P_w = \gamma Q H \qquad (12.10)$$

where P_w is known as the water horsepower. The power required to drive the pump is the brake horsepower:

$$bhp = \omega T \qquad (12.11)$$

where ω is the angular velocity of the shaft and T is the shaft torque. If there were no losses, P_w and bhp would be equal. When one accounts for the losses, the efficiency of the pump (η) is defined as the power delivered to the fluid divided by the brake horsepower. Thus,

$$\eta = \frac{P_w}{bhp} = \frac{\gamma Q H}{\omega T} \qquad (12.12)$$

Recall that h_s is the head supplied by the pump and h_f represents the losses, as stated in Eq. (12.9). Thus, the hydraulic efficiency is

$$\eta = \frac{h_s - h_f}{h_s} = 1 - \frac{h_f}{h_s} \qquad (12.13)$$

where h_f has three components: (1) the shock losses at the inlet due to an imperfect match between the inlet flow and the blade entrances, (2) the friction losses in the blade passages, and (3) the circulation loss due to an imperfect match at the exit of the impeller blades.

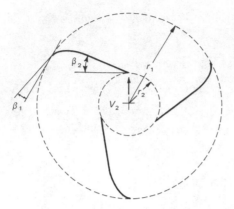

Figure 12.12 Geometry of typical runner blades of the impeller of a centrifugal water pump (Example 12.6).

Example 12.6

The geometry of the impeller of a centrifugal water pump, as shown in Fig. 12.12, is such that $r_1 = 30$ cm, $\beta_1 = 10°$, $r_2 = 10$ cm, and $\beta_2 = 20°$. The impeller is 5 cm wide (w_2) at the inlet ($r = r_2$) and 2 cm wide (w_1) at the exit ($r = r_1$). The impeller rotates at 1800 rpm. If the losses are neglected, (a) calculate the volumetric flow rate if the entering flow is shockless for $\alpha_2 = 90°$, (b) calculate the theoretical head, (c) calculate the pressure rise through the impeller, and (d) calculate the water power.

Solution. Note that $\omega = \dfrac{2\pi(1800)}{60} = 60\pi$ rad/s

(a) To calculate the shockless flow at the entrance, let us refer to the velocities in Fig. 12.13:

$$V_{rel,2} \cos \beta_2 = r_2\omega \quad \text{and} \quad V_{rel,2} \sin \beta_2 = V_2$$

since $\alpha_2 = 90°$. Eliminating $V_{rel,2}$ in these two equations,

$$V_2 = r_2\omega \tan \beta_2 = 0.10(60\pi) \tan20° = 6.861 \text{ m/s}$$

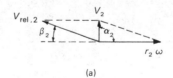

(a)

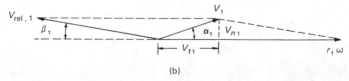

(b)

Figure 12.13 Velocity components for Example 12.6: (a) sketch of the relevant velocities at the inlet; (b) sketch of the relevant velocities at the exit.

Hence, since V_2 is perpendicular to the entrance cylinder whose radius is r_2, the volumetric flow rate is

$$Q = V_2 2\pi r_2 w_2 = 6.861(2\pi 0.1)(0.05) = 0.2155 \text{ m}^3/\text{s}$$

(b) To calculate the theoretical head, we need to determine the flow at the exit plane. Using the volumetric flow rate (or discharge), we can calculate the component of V_1 normal to the exit cylinder (V_{n1}):

$$Q = V_{n1} 2\pi r_1 w_1$$

Thus,

$$V_{n1} = \frac{0.2155}{(2\pi 0.3)(0.02)} = 5.716 \text{ m/s}$$

Referring to Fig. 12.13b,

$$V_{n1} = V_1 \sin \alpha_1 = V_{\text{rel},1} \sin \beta_1$$

and

$$V_{t1} = V_1 \cos \alpha_1 = r_1 \omega - V_{\text{rel},1} \cos \beta_1 = r_1 \omega - V_{n1} \cot \beta_1$$

$$= 0.3(60\pi) - 5.716 \cot 10° = 24.132 \text{ m/s}$$

Thus,

$$\alpha_1 = \tan^{-1} \frac{V_{n1}}{V_{t1}} = 13.33° \quad \text{and} \quad V_1 = 24.800 \text{ m/s}$$

Note that for $\eta = 1$ we can use Eq. (12.12) to calculate the net head:

$$H = \frac{\omega T}{\gamma Q} = \frac{\omega T}{\rho g Q}$$

And from Eq. (12.7),

$$T = \rho Q (r_1 V_1 \cos \alpha_1 - r_2 V_2 \cos \alpha_2)$$

Thus,

$$H = \frac{\omega}{g} (r_1 V_1 \cos \alpha_1 - r_2 V_2 \cos \alpha_2)$$

Since $\alpha_2 = 90°$,

$$H = \frac{60\pi \text{ 1/s}}{9.8066 \text{ m/s}^2} (0.3 \text{ m})(24.800 \text{ m/s}) \cos(13.33°) = 139.15 \text{ m}$$

(c) To determine the pressure rise, we use Eq. (12.9) and note that $z_1 = z_2$. The governing equation is

$$p_1 - p_2 = \rho g \left(H + \frac{V_2^2}{2g} - \frac{V_1^2}{2g} \right)$$

Assume that the water temperature is 20°C so that:

$$\rho g = \gamma = 9.7889 \times 10^3 \text{ N/m}^3$$

Thus,

$$p_1 - p_2 = 9.7889 \times 10^3 \left[139.15 + \frac{(6.861)^2 - (24.800)^2}{2(9.8066)} \right]$$

$$= 1.0787 \times 10^6 \text{ N/m}^2 = 10.65 \text{ atm}$$

(d) The water power (P_w) is

$$P_w = \gamma Q H = 9.7889 \times 10^3 \text{ N/m}^3 \, (0.2155 \text{ m}^3/\text{s})(139.15 \text{ m}) = 293.5 \text{ kW}$$

PUMP PERFORMANCE AND SIMILARITY RELATIONS

The performance of a centrifugal pump is described by the volumetric flow rate, or discharge (Q), the head (H), the power input (bhp), and the speed of rotation (n). Because of the existence of open passages between the inlet and the exit, the pressure increase through the pump is a function of the velocities inside the pump and is, therefore, a function of the capacity and the speed of rotation. Typical variations in the head, the power input, and the efficiency are presented in Fig. 12.14 as a function of the volumetric flow rate for a given speed. These curves are called the characteristic curves of pump performance and are determined experimentally.

If the effects of viscosity are neglected, all forces and pressure differences in the pump change proportionally to the square of the velocities, provided that the form of the flow remains similar. The fluid velocities are proportional to Q/D^2, where D is a characteristic dimension of the pump, such as the impeller diameter. The velocities of the rotating parts are proportional to nD. As discussed in Ref. 12.1, the operating conditions of a turbomachine will be dynamically similar at two different rotational speeds if all the

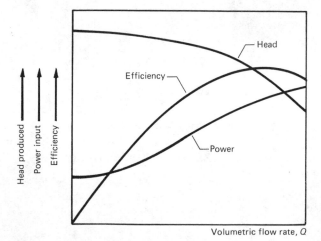

Figure 12.14   Typical characteristic curves for a given speed. (From *Marks' Mechanical Engineers Handbook*, 6th ed., edited by T. Baumeister. Copyright © 1958 by McGraw-Hill Book Company. Used with the permission of McGraw-Hill Book Company.)

fluid velocities at corresponding points within the machine are in the same direction and are proportional to the blade speed. Thus, similar flow conditions occur if the ratio of fluid velocities to the velocities of the rotating parts is the same. That is, flows are similar if

$$\frac{Q_1/D_1^2}{n_1 D_1} = \frac{Q_2/D_2^2}{n_2 D_1} \qquad (12.14a)$$

This grouping is known as the capacity coefficient,

$$C_Q = \frac{Q}{nD^3} \qquad (12.15a)$$

Since the head is proportional to the square of the flow velocities, it follows that

$$\frac{H_1}{(Q_1/D_1^2)^2} = \frac{H_2}{(Q_2/D_2^2)^2} \qquad (12.14b)$$

Rearranging and multiplying by g so that we obtain a dimensionless grouping,

$$C_H = \frac{gH}{n^2 D^2} \qquad (12.15b)$$

which is known as the head coefficient.

Combining these relations with the definitions for power given in Eqs. (12.10) and (12.11), we find that for the same fluid

$$\frac{P_1}{Q_1 H_1} = \frac{P_2}{Q_2 H_2}$$

or

$$\frac{P_1}{n_1^3 D_1^5} = \frac{P_2}{n_2^3 D_2^5} \qquad (12.14c)$$

Similarly, we obtain the definition for the dimensionless power coefficient:

$$C_p = \frac{bhp}{\rho n^3 D^5} \qquad (12.15c)$$

As discussed in Ref. 12.2, these similarity relations have been found to be accurately satisfied for fluids of low viscosity, such as water and thin oils, and pumps of reasonably large dimensions and fluid velocities. Note that these conditions imply that the similarity relations are relatively valid for large Reynolds numbers.

Example 12.7

A fan operating at 1800 rpm develops a head of 6 in. of water at a capacity of 160 ft³/s. It is desired to build a larger, but geometrically similar, fan that will deliver the same head of 6 in. of water at the same efficiency, but at a lower speed of 1500 rpm. What is the capacity of the larger fan?

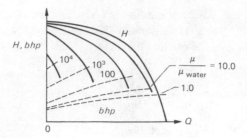

Figure 12.15 Effect of viscosity on centrifugal-pump performance. (From *Fluid Mechanics* by F. M. White. Copyright © 1979 by McGraw-Hill Book Company. Used with the permission of McGraw-Hill Book Company.)

Solution. Since we are to match dimensionless groupings,

$$C_{H_1} = C_{H_2} \quad \text{and} \quad C_{Q_1} = C_{Q_2}$$

Applying Eq. (12.15b) with the first condition,

$$\frac{D_2}{D_1} = \sqrt{\frac{n_1^2 H_2}{n_2^2 H_1}} = \frac{n_1}{n_2}$$

since $H_2 = H_1$. Applying Eq. (12.15a) with the second condition,

$$\frac{Q_2}{Q_1} = \frac{n_2 D_2^3}{n_1 D_1^3}$$

Thus,

$$\frac{Q_2}{Q_1} = \left(\frac{n_1}{n_2}\right)^2 = 1.440$$

and $Q_2 = 1.440(160) = 230.4 \text{ ft}^3/\text{s}$

For small- or medium-sized pumps, pumping viscous fluids, the similarity relations of Eqs. (12.14) and (12.15) become inaccurate. Furthermore, White (Ref. 12.3) notes that when centrifugal pumps are used to pump very viscous liquids there is a strong effect on performance. Typical test curves of head and brake horsepower are presented as a function of discharge in Fig. 12.15. There is a dramatic decrease in head and discharge as viscosity increases. Furthermore, the power requirements increase as viscosity increases.

SPECIFIC SPEED

We have seen that a pump's performance may be given in terms of its power coefficient and its head coefficient for a range of values of the discharge coefficient. The type of machine that is best suited for a given application depends on the head and discharge. For example, axial-flow machines are best suited for low heads with high discharges, while radial-flow machines are best suited for higher heads with lower discharges. The parameter used in the determination of which type is best suited for a given application is the specific speed, n_s. The specific speed characterizes the operating conditions with respect to hydraulic design without reference to size. Thus, the specific speed is obtained by combining C_H and C_Q in such a manner that D is eliminated. The resultant equation for n_s is

$$n_s = \frac{(C_Q)^{0.5}}{(C_H)^{0.75}} = \frac{nQ^{0.5}}{g^{0.75}H^{0.75}}$$

(12.16a)

It should be noted that, traditionally in the United States, the specific speed used for pumps is defined as

$$N_s = \frac{NQ^{0.5}}{H^{0.75}}$$

(12.16b)

where N is the speed in revolutions per minute, Q is the volumetric flow rate in gallons per minute, and H is the head in feet. Since metric units are not yet fully in use in the United States, many references published in this country use Eq. (12.16b) as the definition for specific speed.

Centrifugal pumps have relatively low specific speeds; mixed-flow pumps have medium specific speeds; and axial-flow pumps have high specific speeds.

CAVITATION

The static pressure in a closed stream of fluid decreases as the velocity of the flow increases. Fluid velocities in a closed stream reach a definite upper limit that corresponds to the condition when the absolute pressure becomes equal to the vapor pressure of the fluid. When this limit is reached, the fluid vaporizes, forming vapor pockets in the stream. This form of vaporization in a fluid stream is known as cavitation. The formation of vapor cavities decreases the useful channel space for the liquid and, thus, decreases the efficiency of the machine. Cavitation causes three undesirable conditions: (1) reduced efficiency, (2) damage to the impeller surface and nearby casing walls, and (3) noise and vibrations.

Since cavitation is caused by the reduction of the absolute pressure below the vapor pressure, it will usually begin in the suction passages of the pump, in particular in those of the impeller. For a given pump head and discharge, the relative velocity in the inlet passages of the impeller will increase with the speed of rotation.

The *net positive-suction head* (NPSH) is defined as the head required at the pump inlet to keep the liquid from cavitating. The pump inlet or suction side is the low-pressure point where cavitation will first occur. The NPSH is

$$\text{NPSH} = \frac{p_i}{\rho g} + \frac{V_i^2}{2g} - \frac{p_v}{\rho g}$$

(12.17)

where p_i and V_i are the pressure and velocity at the pump inlet and p_v is the vapor pressure of the liquid. The value of NPSH is given from the pump performance curve. We must ensure that the right-hand side of Eq. (12.17) is equal to or greater than NPSH to avoid cavitation.

If the pump inlet is placed at a height z_i above a reservoir whose free surface is at pressure p_a, we can use Bernoulli's equation to rewrite Eq. (12.17) as

$$\text{NPSH} = \frac{p_a}{\rho g} - z_i - h_{fi} - \frac{p_v}{\rho g} \tag{12.18}$$

where h_{fi} is the friction-head loss between the reservoir and pump inlet. Knowing p_a and h_{fi}, we can calculate the value of z_i that will keep the right-hand side greater than the required NPSH.

Example 12.8

The performance curves of a centrifugal water pump require that NPSH be 21 ft. Water at 68°F is taken from a reservoir whose surface is at standard atmospheric pressure (i.e., 14.696 lbf/in.², absolute). The head loss from the reservoir to the pump inlet is 6 ft. If $p_v = 0.26$ lbf/in.², absolute, where should the pump be placed to avoid cavitation.

Solution.   For water at 68°F, $\sigma = 0.9982$. Thus, $\rho = 1.937$ slugs/ft³.

$$\text{NPSH} \leq \frac{p_a - p_v}{\rho g} - z_i - h_{fi}$$

$$21 \leq \frac{(14.696 - 0.26)144}{1.937(32.174)} - z_i - 6.0$$

$$z_i \leq 33.36 - 6.0 - 21.0 = 6.36 \text{ ft}$$

The pump inlet should be no more than 6.36 ft above the surface of the reservoir.

SUMMARY

The fluid dynamics of turbomachines has been developed in this chapter. The general characteristics of impulse turbines and reaction turbines have been discussed. The theory presented in this chapter represents idealized flows of single-unit installations. In order to account for viscous effects and to design multistage pumps, the reader will need to refer to more extensive treatments of the subject.

PROBLEMS

12.1. Using Eq. (12.5), show that a Pelton water wheel develops its maximum power when $\theta = 180°$ and the linear velocity of the buckets $(r\omega)$ is $0.5V_j$.

12.2. A Pelton water wheel has a mean radius of 4 ft. If the angle θ of the bucket is 172° and the bucket velocity is $0.48V_j$, what is the torque developed by the wheel if a 3-in.-diameter jet having a speed of 100 fps is used? The water temperature is 68°F.

12.3. A Pelton water wheel is used to drive a generator at 600 rpm. The water jet is 7 cm in diameter and has a velocity of 100 m/s. If the angle θ of the bucket is 170° and the ratio of the vane speed to the initial jet speed is 0.45, what is the diameter of the wheel to the centerline of the buckets? Neglecting losses, what is the power developed and the kinetic energy remaining in the fluid?

12.4. A penstock that is 75 cm in diameter and 10 km long carries water from a reservoir to an impulse turbine. If the turbine is 86% efficient, what power can be produced by the system if the upstream reservoir elevation is 650 m above the turbine jet? Assume that the effective resistance coefficient of the penstock is 0.025. If the jet is 20 cm in diameter, $V_{bucket} = 0.5 \, V_j$, and the wheel rotates at 360 rpm, what is the diameter of the turbine wheel? $\theta = 173°$.

12.5. Show that the torque developed by a reaction turbine may be written as

$$T = \rho Q [r_1 V_1 \cos \alpha_1 - r_2(V_{2,rel} \cos \beta_{2\rho} + \omega r_2)]$$

where $V_{2,rel}$ is the relative velocity at the exit (inner radius) of the impeller and where β_2 is the obtuse angle shown in Fig. 12.10.

12.6. Show that the power generated by the torque of a turbine can be written as

$$P = -\rho Q n (\Gamma_1 - \Gamma_2)$$

where n is number of revolutions per unit time, and Γ_1 and Γ_2 represent the circulation $\oint \vec{V} \cdot \vec{dr}$ around the outer radius r_1 and the inner radius r_2, respectively.

12.7. A radial-flow reaction turbine rotates at a speed of 100 rpm and discharges 200 ft³/s. Flow at the inlet station is matched, and $\alpha_1 = 20°$, $\beta_1 = 60°$, and $r_1 = 5$ ft. If β_2 is 120°, $r_2 = 2$ ft., and $\alpha_2 = 90°$, determine the torque and the power developed for incompressible, frictionless flow of water at 68°F. Assume that $w_1 = w_2$.

12.8. Water at 68°F flows through a reaction turbine at a volumetric flow rate of 400 ft³/s. It enters the impeller with a tangential velocity component of 82 ft/s at a radius of 4 ft. The height of the turbine blades is 6 in., i.e., $w_1 = w_2 = 6$ in. It is discharged in the axial direction where $r_2 = 1$ ft. What is the torque exerted on the impeller?

12.9. Neglecting losses, what is the head developed by the turbine of Prob. 12.8?

12.10. Water flows through a reaction turbine at a rate of 5000 gal/min when $\omega = 1200$ rpm. At the inlet radius $r_1 = 1.0$ ft, $w_1 = 3.0$ in., and $\beta_1 = 40°$. If the flow is matched, what are V_1 and α_1?

12.11. For the flow conditions of Prob. 12.10, $\alpha_2 = 90°$, $r_2 = 4.0$ in., and $w_2 = 2.0$ in. Neglecting losses, calculate (a) the theoretical head, (b) the pressure change through the impeller, and (c) the water power.

12.12. What should be the angle of the wicket gates of a reaction turbine if the turbine is to develop 12,000 hp from a discharge of 400,000 gal/min? The diameter of the opening just inside the wicket gates is 12 ft and the height is 3 ft. The turbine turns at 200 rpm. Flow leaves the runner in the radial direction.

12.13. The discharge of a centrifugal pump is 2500 gal/min when rotating at 1500 rpm. The dimensions of the outlet of the impeller are $r_1 = 8$ in., $w_1 = 2$ in., and $\beta_1 = 30°$. Neglecting any possible losses, what are (a) the brake horsepower developed and (b) the theoretical head rise, when $\alpha_2 = 90°$?

12.14. A centrifugal pump rotates at 1200 rpm. Its characteristic dimensions are $r_2 = 15$ cm, $w_2 = 7$ cm, $\beta_2 = 20°$ at the inlet radius and $r_1 = 30$ cm, $w_1 = 5$ cm, and $\beta_1 = 10°$ at the exit radius. For the inviscid flow of water at 20°C, calculate the volumetric flow rate Q, the power delivered to the fluid P_w, and the change in head H.

12.15. A pump delivers gasoline at 60°F at a volumetric flow rate of 15 gal/min. The inlet conditions are such that $p_1 = 15$ psia, $z_1 = 2$ ft, and $V_1 = 5$ ft/s. At the exit, $p_2 = 80$ psia, $z_2 = 4$ ft, and $V_2 = 10$ ft/s. If the pump is 85% efficient, how much motor horsepower is required?

12.16. Calculate C_Q, C_H, and C_P for the pump of Prob. 12.13.

12.17. A pump geometrically similar to that of Prob. 12.13, but larger, is to be built. If the pump is to deliver the same bhp at the same head H, what is the ratio of speed and flow rates if the larger pump is to be four times as large as that of Prob. 12.13?

12.18. Calculate C_Q, C_H, and C_P for the pump of Prob. 12.14.

12.19. If the net head (H) is varied for a turbine operating at a given valve opening and efficiency, show that the speed will vary as $H^{0.5}$ and the output power as $H^{1.5}$.

12.20. What is the specific speed for the pump of Prob. 12.13?

12.21. What is the specific speed for the pump of Prob. 12.14?

REFERENCES

12.1. S. L. Dixon, *Fluid Mechanics, Thermodynamics of Turbomachinery*, Pergamon Press, Elmsford, N.Y., 1966.

12.2. Theodore Baumeister, editor-in-chief, *Marks' Mechanical Engineers Handbook*, 6th ed., McGraw-Hill Book Company, New York, 1958.

12.3. F. M. White, *Fluid Mechanics*, McGraw-Hill Book Company, New York, 1979.

APPENDIX

Conversion Factors

Density:

$$1.00 \text{ kg/m}^3 = 1.9404 \times 10^{-3} \text{ slug/ft}^3 = 6.2430 \times 10^{-2} \text{ lbm/ft}^3$$

$$1.00 \text{ lbm/ft}^3 = 3.1081 \times 10^{-2} \text{ slug/ft}^3 = 16.0178 \text{ kg/m}^3$$

Energy or work:

$$1.00 \text{ cal} = 4.187 \text{ J} = 4.187 \text{ N} \cdot \text{m}$$

$$1.00 \text{ Btu} = 778.2 \text{ ft lbf} = 0.2520 \text{ kcal} = 1055 \text{ J}$$

Flow rates:

$$1.00 \text{ gal/min} = 6.309 \times 10^{-5} \text{ m}^3/\text{s} = 2.228 \times 10^{-3} \text{ ft}^3/\text{s}$$

Force:

$$1.00 \text{ N} = 10^5 \text{ dyne} = 0.2248 \text{ lbf}$$

$$1.00 \text{ lbf} = 4.4482 \text{ N}$$

$$1.00 \text{ lbf} = 16.0 \text{ oz}$$

$$1.00 \text{ U.S. ton} = 2000 \text{ lbf}$$

Heat flux:

$$1.00 \text{ W/cm}^2 = 0.2388 \text{ cal/s} \cdot \text{cm}^2 = 0.8806 \text{ Btu/ft}^2 \cdot \text{s}$$
$$= 3.170 \times 10^3 \text{ Btu/ft}^2 \cdot \text{h}$$

Length:

$$1.00 \text{ m} \quad = 3.2808 \text{ ft} = 39.37 \text{ in.}$$
$$1.00 \text{ km} \quad = 0.6214 \text{ mile} = 1093.6 \text{ yd}$$
$$1.00 \text{ ft} \quad = 0.3048 \text{ m} = 30.48 \text{ cm}$$
$$1.00 \text{ ft} \quad = 12 \text{ in.} = 0.3333 \text{ yd}$$
$$1.00 \text{ mile} = 5280 \text{ ft} = 1760 \text{ yd} = 1609.344 \text{ m}$$

Mass:

$$1.00 \text{ kg} \quad = 1000 \text{ g} = 2.2047 \text{ lbm}$$
$$1.00 \text{ slug} = 32.174 \text{ lbm} = 14.593 \text{ kg}$$

Power:

$$1.00 \text{ kW} \quad = 1000.0 \text{ W} = 1000.0 \text{ N} \cdot \text{m/s} = 0.2388 \text{ kcal/s}$$
$$1.00 \text{ kW} \quad = 1.341 \text{ hp}$$
$$1.00 \text{ hp} \quad = 550 \text{ ft} \cdot \text{lbf/s} = 0.7457 \text{ kW}$$
$$1.00 \text{ Btu/s} = 1.415 \text{ hp}$$

Pressure:

$$100 \text{ N/m}^2 \quad = 1.4504 \times 10^{-4} \text{ lbf/in.}^2 = 2.0886 \times 10^{-2} \text{ lbf/ft}^2$$
$$1.00 \text{ bar} \quad = 10^5 \text{ N/m}^2 = 10^5 \text{ Pa}$$
$$1.00 \text{ lbf/in}^2 \quad = 6.8947 \times 10^3 \text{ N/m}^2$$
$$1.00 \text{ lbf/in.}^2 \quad = 144.00 \text{ lbf/ft}^2$$

Specific enthalpy:

$$1.00 \text{ N} \cdot \text{m/kg} = 1.00 \text{ J/kg} = 1.00 \text{ m}^2/\text{s}^2$$
$$1.00 \text{ N} \cdot \text{m/kg} = 4.3069 \times 10^{-4} \text{ Btu/lbm} = 1.0781 \text{ ft lbf/slug}$$
$$1.00 \text{ Btu/lbm} \quad = 2.3218 \times 10^3 \text{ N} \cdot \text{m/kg}$$

Specific heat:

$$1.00 \text{ N} \cdot \text{m/kg} \cdot \text{K} = 1.00 \text{ J/kg} \cdot \text{K} = 2.3928 \times 10^{-4} \text{ Btu/lbm} \cdot {}^\circ\text{R}$$
$$= 5.9895 \text{ ft} \cdot \text{lbf/slug} \cdot {}^\circ\text{R}$$
$$1.00 \text{ Btu/lbm} \cdot {}^\circ\text{R} = 32.174 \text{ Btu/slug} \cdot {}^\circ\text{R} = 4.1793 \times 10^3 \text{ N} \cdot \text{m/kg} \cdot \text{K}$$
$$= 4.1793 \times 10^3 \text{ J/kg} \cdot \text{K}$$

Temperature:

The temperature of the ice point is 273.15 K (491.67°R)

$$1.00 \text{ K} = 1.80{}^\circ\text{R}$$
$$\text{K} = {}^\circ\text{C} + 273.15$$
$${}^\circ\text{R} = {}^\circ\text{F} + 459.67$$
$$T{}^\circ\text{F} = 1.8 \, (T{}^\circ\text{C}) + 32$$

Velocity:

$$1.00 \text{ m/s} = 3.60 \text{ km/h}$$
$$1.00 \text{ km/h} = 0.2778 \text{ m/s} = 0.6214 \text{ mile/h} = 0.9113 \text{ ft/s}$$
$$1.00 \text{ ft/s} = 0.6818 \text{ mile/h} = 0.59209 \text{ knot}$$
$$1.00 \text{ mile/h} = 1.467 \text{ ft/s} = 1.609 \text{ km/h} = 0.4470 \text{ m/s}$$
$$1.00 \text{ knot} = 1.15155 \text{ mile/h}$$

Viscosity:

$$1.00 \text{ kg/m} \cdot \text{s} = 0.67197 \text{ lbm/ft} \cdot \text{s} = 2.0886 \times 10^{-2} \text{ lbf} \cdot \text{s/ft}^2$$
$$1.00 \text{ lbm/ft} \cdot \text{s} = 3.1081 \times 10^{-2} \text{ lbf} \cdot \text{s/ft}^2 = 1.4882 \text{ kg/m} \cdot \text{s}$$
$$1.00 \text{ lbf} \cdot \text{s/ft}^2 = 47.88 \text{ N} \cdot \text{s/m}^2 = 47.88 \text{ Pa} \cdot \text{s}$$
$$1.00 \text{ centipoise} = 0.001 \text{ kg/m} \cdot \text{s} = 6.7197 \times 10^{-4} \text{ lbm/ft} \cdot \text{s}$$

Volume:

$$1.00 \text{ liter} = 1000.0 \text{ cm}^3$$
$$1.00 \text{ barrel} = 5.6146 \text{ ft}^3$$
$$1.00 \text{ ft}^3 = 1728 \text{ in.}^3 = 0.03704 \text{ yd}^3 = 7.481 \text{ gal}$$
$$= 28.32 \text{ liters}$$
$$1.00 \text{ gal} = 3.785 \text{ liters} = 3.785 \times 10^{-3} \text{ m}^3$$

Index